POPULATION

W9-CES-555

POPULATION

POPULATION
An Introduction to Concepts and Issues
Thirteenth Edition

John R. Weeks

San Diego State University

CENGAGE

Australia • Brazil • Mexico • Singapore • United Kingdom • United States

CENGAGE

Population: An Introduction to Concepts and Issues, **Thirteenth Edition**

John R. Weeks

Product Director: Laura Ross

Associate Product Manager: Kori Alexander

Production Assistant: Hannah Ells

Learning Designer: Emma Guiton

Senior Content Manager: Kathy Sands-Boehmer

Digital Design Lead: Matt Altieri

IP Analyst: Deanna Ettinger

Marketing Manager: Tricia L. Salata

Senior Marketing Development Manager: Nicole Hurst

Art Director: Nadine Ballard

Manufacturing Buyer: Karen Hunt

Manuscript Editor: Deanna Weeks

Production Service: MPS Limited

Cover Designer: Nadine Ballard

© 2021 Cengage Learning, Inc.

ALL RIGHTS RESERVED. No part of this work covered by the copyright herein may be reproduced or distributed in any form or by any means except as permitted by U.S. copyright law, without the prior written permission of the publisher.

For product information and technology assistance, contact us at **Cengage Customer & Sales Support, 1-800-354-9706** or **support.cengage.com.**

For permission to use material from this text or product, submit all requests online at **www.cengage.com/permissions.**

Library of Congress Control Number: 2019913245

Student Edition:
ISBN-13: 978-0-357-36057-6
ISBN-10: 0-357-36057-5

Loose-leaf Edition:
ISBN: 978-0-357-03631-0

Cengage
200 Pier 4 Boulevard
Boston, MA 02210
USA

Cengage is a leading provider of customized learning solutions with employees residing in nearly 40 different countries and sales in more than 125 countries around the world. Find your local representative at **www.cengage.com.**

Cengage products are represented in Canada by Nelson Education, Ltd.

To learn more about Cengage platforms and services, register or access your online learning solution, or purchase materials for your course, visit **www.cengage.com.**

Printed at CLDPC, USA, 09-19

To Deanna

BRIEF TABLE OF CONTENTS

PART ONE   **A DEMOGRAPHIC PERSPECTIVE**
CHAPTER 1   Introduction to Demography   3
CHAPTER 2   Demographic Data and Applied Demography   43
CHAPTER 3   Demographic Perspectives and Theories   91

PART TWO   **POPULATION PROCESSES**
CHAPTER 4   The Health and Mortality Transition   139
CHAPTER 5   The Fertility Transition   187
CHAPTER 6   The Migration Transition   241
CHAPTER 7   The Urban Transition   287

PART THREE   **USING THE DEMOGRAPHIC PERSPECTIVE**
CHAPTER 8   The Age Transition and the Life Course   329
CHAPTER 9   Family Demography and Life Chances   367
CHAPTER 10   Population, the Environment, and Global Sustainability   414

GLOSSARY   456
BIBLIOGRAPHY   467
GEOGRAPHIC INDEX   496
SUBJECT INDEX   505

DETAILED TABLE OF CONTENTS

PREFACE   xix

PART ONE
A DEMOGRAPHIC PERSPECTIVE

CHAPTER 1
INTRODUCTION TO DEMOGRAPHY   3

WHAT IS DEMOGRAPHY?   5

HOW DOES DEMOGRAPHY CONNECT THE DOTS?   5
    The Relationship of Population to Resources   7
    The Relationship of Population to Social and Political Dynamics   8
    The Relationship of Population to the Rights of Women   10

WORLD POPULATION GROWTH   11
    A Brief History   11
    How Fast Is the World's Population Growing Now?   14
    The Power of Doubling—How Fast Can Populations Grow?   16
    Why Was Early Growth So Slow?   17
    Why Are More Recent Increases So Rapid?   18
    How Many People Have Ever Lived?   18
    Redistribution of the World's Population Through Migration   19

GEOGRAPHIC DISTRIBUTION OF THE WORLD'S POPULATION   21

GLOBAL VARIATION IN POPULATION SIZE AND GROWTH   23
    North America   24
    Mexico and Central America   27
    South America   28
    Europe   29

North Africa and Western Asia   30
Sub-Saharan Africa   31
ESSAY: *Connecting the Demographic Dots in the Middle East*   32
South and Southeast Asia   35
East Asia   37
Oceania   39

SUMMARY AND CONCLUSION   40

MAIN POINTS   41

QUESTIONS FOR REVIEW   42

CHAPTER 2
DEMOGRAPHIC DATA AND APPLIED DEMOGRAPHY   43

POPULATION CENSUSES   44
The Census of the United States   48
ESSAY: *Demographics of Politics: Why the Census Matters*   52
The Census of Canada   63
The Census of Mexico   64
IPUMS—Warehouse of Global Census Data   66

REGISTRATION OF VITAL EVENTS   66

COMBINING THE CENSUS AND VITAL STATISTICS   71

ADMINISTRATIVE DATA   71

SAMPLE SURVEYS   72
Demographic Surveys in the United States   72
Canadian Surveys   73
Mexican Surveys   73
European Surveys   74
Demographic and Health Surveys   74
Demographic Surveillance Systems   75

HISTORICAL SOURCES   75

SPATIAL DEMOGRAPHY   76
Mapping Demographic Data   78
GIS and the Census   80

APPLIED DEMOGRAPHY   81
Political Planning   81
Social Planning   82
Business Planning/Marketing   83

SHOULD YOU PURSUE A CAREER IN DEMOGRAPHICS?   87

SUMMARY AND CONCLUSION   88

MAIN POINTS   89

QUESTIONS FOR REVIEW   90

CHAPTER 3
DEMOGRAPHIC PERSPECTIVES AND THEORIES   91

PREMODERN POPULATION DOCTRINES   95

THE PRELUDE TO MALTHUS   100

THE MALTHUSIAN PERSPECTIVE   101
    Causes of Population Growth   102
    Consequences of Population Growth   103
    Avoiding the Consequences   104
    Critique of Malthus   105
    Neo-Malthusians   107

THE MARXIAN PERSPECTIVE   107
    ESSAY: *Who Are the Neo-Malthusians and Why Do We Care?*   108
    Causes of Population Growth   110
    Consequences of Population Growth   110
    Critique of Marx   111

THE PRELUDE TO THE DEMOGRAPHIC TRANSITION THEORY   112
    Mill   113
    Dumont   114
    Durkheim   115

THE THEORY OF THE DEMOGRAPHIC TRANSITION   115
    Critique of the Demographic Transition Theory   119
    Reformulation of the Demographic Transition Theory   119
    The Theory of Demographic Change and Response   122
    Cohort Size Effects   124

THE THEORY OF THE SECOND DEMOGRAPHIC TRANSITION   125

THE DEMOGRAPHIC TRANSITION IS REALLY A SET OF TRANSITIONS   126
    The Health and Mortality Transition   126
    The Fertility Transition   127
    The Age Transition   129
    The Migration Transition   130
    The Urban Transition   130
    The Family and Household Transition   131
    Impact on Local and Global Society   132

SUMMARY AND CONCLUSION   133

MAIN POINTS   134

QUESTIONS FOR REVIEW   135

PART TWO
POPULATION PROCESSES

CHAPTER 4
THE HEALTH AND MORTALITY TRANSITION   139

DEFINING THE HEALTH AND MORTALITY TRANSITION   140

HEALTH AND MORTALITY CHANGES OVER TIME   141
 The Roman Empire to the Industrial Revolution   142
 Industrial Revolution to the Twentieth Century   143
 World War II as a Modern Turning Point   146
 Postponing Death by Preventing and Curing Disease   147
 The Nutrition Transition   149

LIFE SPAN AND LONGEVITY   150
 Life Span   150
 Longevity   151

DISEASE AND DEATH OVER THE LIFE CYCLE   152
 Age Differentials in Mortality   152
 Infant Mortality   153
 Mortality at Older Ages   155
 Sex and Gender Differentials in Mortality   157

CAUSES OF POOR HEALTH AND DEATH   159
 Communicable Diseases   159
 Emerging Infectious Diseases   161
 Maternal Mortality   162
 Noncommunicable Diseases   163
 ESSAY: *Mortality Control and the Environment*   164
 Injuries   166
 The "Real" Causes of Death   167

MEASURING MORTALITY   169
 Crude Death Rate   169
 Age/Sex-Specific Death Rates   170
 Age-Adjusted Death Rates   170
 Life Tables   171
 Life Table Calculations   176
 Disability-Adjusted Life Years   178

HEALTH AND MORTALITY INEQUALITIES   179
 Educational and Socioeconomic Differentials in Mortality   179
 Inequalities by Race and Ethnicity   180
 Marital Status and Mortality   182
 Urban and Rural Differentials   182
 Neighborhood Differences in Mortality   183

SUMMARY AND CONCLUSION   184

MAIN POINTS   185

QUESTIONS FOR REVIEW   186

CHAPTER 5
THE FERTILITY TRANSITION   187

WHAT IS THE FERTILITY TRANSITION?   188

HOW HIGH COULD FERTILITY LEVELS BE?   189
    The Biological Component   189
    The Social Component   191

WHY WAS FERTILITY HIGH FOR MOST OF HUMAN HISTORY?   193
    Need to Replenish Society   194
    Children as Security and Labor   195

THE PRECONDITIONS FOR A DECLINE IN FERTILITY   196

IDEATIONAL CHANGES THAT MUST TAKE PLACE   197

MOTIVATIONS FOR LOWER FERTILITY LEVELS   198
    The Supply-Demand Framework   198
    ESSAY: *Reproductive Rights, Reproductive Health, and the*
    Fertility Transition   200
    The Innovation-Diffusion and "Cultural" Perspective   205

HOW CAN FERTILITY BE CONTROLLED?   207
    Proximate Determinants of Fertility   207
    Proportion Married—Limiting Exposure to Intercourse   209
    Use of Contraceptives   209
    Induced Abortion   213
    Involuntary Infecundity from Breastfeeding   213
    The Relative Importance of the Proximate Determinants   214

HOW DO WE MEASURE CHANGES IN FERTILITY?   215
    Period Measures of Fertility   216
    Cohort Measures of Fertility   221
    Fertility Intentions   222

HOW IS THE FERTILITY TRANSITION ACCOMPLISHED?   223

GEOGRAPHIC VARIABILITY IN THE FERTILITY TRANSITION   224

CASE STUDIES IN THE FERTILITY TRANSITION   225
    United Kingdom and Other European Nations   226
    China   229
    The United States   232

SUMMARY AND CONCLUSION   238

MAIN POINTS   239

QUESTIONS FOR REVIEW   240

CHAPTER 6
THE MIGRATION TRANSITION   241

WHAT IS THE MIGRATION TRANSITION?   242

DEFINING MIGRATION   243
    Internal Migrants   245
    International Migrants   245
    Stocks Versus Flows   246

MEASURING MIGRATION   250

WHY DO PEOPLE MIGRATE?   253
    Migration Selectivity   253
    The Push-Pull Theory   255
    A Conceptual Model of Migration Decision Making   255
    Explaining International Migration   258

MIGRATION WITHIN THE UNITED STATES   262

GLOBAL PATTERNS OF MIGRATION   265
    The Current Situation   265
    How Did We Get to This Point?   268

AMERICA'S IMMIGRATION TRENDS   295
    Historical Background of Migration and Immigration Laws   270
    ESSAY: *Is Migration a Crime? Illegal Immigration in Global Context*   274
    Current Immigration Trends   278

CANADA'S IMMIGRATION TRENDS   279

FORCED MIGRATION   279
    Refugees and Internally Displaced Persons   279
    Slavery   280

IMPACT OF MIGRATION ON SOCIETY   281

SUMMARY AND CONCLUSION   284

MAIN POINTS   285

QUESTIONS FOR REVIEW   286

CHAPTER 7
THE URBAN TRANSITION   287

WHAT IS THE URBAN TRANSITION?   288

DEFINING URBAN PLACES   289

THE HISTORICAL PATTERN OF THE URBAN TRANSITION   291

THE PROXIMATE DETERMINANTS OF THE URBAN TRANSITION   296
Internal Rural-to-Urban Migration   296
Natural Increase   297
Mortality   297
Fertility   299
International Urbanward Migration   301
Reclassification   301
An Illustration from Mexico   302
An Illustration from China   303

THE URBAN HIERARCHY   304
Defining the Metropolis   304
City Systems   308
ESSAY: *Cities as Sustainable Environments*   310

THE URBAN EVOLUTION THAT ACCOMPANIES THE
URBAN TRANSITION   312
Urban Crowding   313
Slums   316
Suburbanization   318
Residential Segregation   320
Urban Sprawl   322
Gentrification   324

SUMMARY AND CONCLUSION   324

MAIN POINTS   325

QUESTIONS FOR REVIEW   326

PART THREE
USING THE DEMOGRAPHIC PERSPECTIVE

CHAPTER 8
THE AGE TRANSITION AND THE LIFE COURSE   329

WHAT IS THE AGE TRANSITION?   330

THE CONCEPTS OF AGE AND SEX   330
Age Stratification   331
Age Cohorts and Cohort Flow   333
Gender and Sex Ratios   335
The Feminization of Old Age   336

DEMOGRAPHIC DRIVERS OF THE AGE TRANSITION   338
The Impact of Declining Mortality   340

The Impact of Declining Fertility   342
Where Does Migration Fit In?   344

DEMOGRAPHIC DIVIDENDS—AGE TRANSITIONS AT WORK   345
Measuring the Age Structure   345
The Progression from a Young to an Old Age Structure   346
Youth Bulge—Dead End or Dividend?   346
China's Demographic Dividend   347
What Happened to India's Demographic Dividend?   349
Demographic Dividends in the United States and Mexico   350

THE LIFE COURSE AND POPULATION AGING   351
What Is Old?   352
The Third Age (Young-Old) and Fourth Age (Old-Old)   353
ESSAY: *The Age Transition Force Is with Us*   354
Centenarians—The Oldest of the Old-Old   358

READING THE FUTURE FROM THE AGE STRUCTURE   358
Population Projections   358
Backward or Inverse Projection   363
Population Momentum   363

SUMMARY AND CONCLUSION   364

MAIN POINTS   365

QUESTIONS FOR REVIEW   366

CHAPTER 9
FAMILY DEMOGRAPHY AND LIFE CHANCES   367

DEFINING FAMILY DEMOGRAPHY AND LIFE CHANCES   368
The Growing Diversity in Family Structure and Household Composition   371
Gender Equity and the Empowerment of Women   374

PROXIMATE DETERMINANTS OF FAMILY AND HOUSEHOLD
CHANGES   375
Delayed Marriage Accompanied by Leaving the Parental Nest   376
Cohabitation   379
Nonmarital Childbearing   379
Childlessness   381
Divorce   382
Widowhood   383
The Combination of These Determinants   383

CHANGING LIFE CHANCES   383
Education   384
Labor Force Participation   388

Occupation   390
Income   392
Poverty   396
Wealth   398
Race and Ethnicity   401
ESSAY: *Show Me the Money!*   402
Religion   408

SUMMARY AND CONCLUSION   410

MAIN POINTS   412

QUESTIONS FOR REVIEW   413

CHAPTER 10
POPULATION, THE ENVIRONMENT, AND GLOBAL SUSTAINABILITY   414

THE USE AND ABUSE OF THE EARTH'S RESOURCES   416
Economic Growth and Development   417
Measuring GNI and Purchasing Power Parity   417

HOW IS POPULATION RELATED TO ECONOMIC DEVELOPMENT?   419
Is Population Growth a Stimulus to Economic Development?   420
Does Demographic Overhead Explain the Relationship?   422
Are Demographic Dividends the Key to Economic Development?   423

CAN BILLIONS MORE BE FED, GIVEN OUR ENVIRONMENTAL
ISSUES?   424
The History of Economic Development and Food   425
We Are at the Limit of Land to Be Used for Growing Food   427
Moving to a More Plant-Based Diet   428
Our History of Getting More Food from the Land   429

THE DEMAND FOR FOOD IS GROWING FASTER THAN THE
POPULATION   431

THE ENVIRONMENTAL CONSTRAINTS TO GROWING MORE FOOD   433
Water Supply Issues   433
Polluting the Ground   435
ESSAY: *How Big Is Your Ecological Footprint?*   436
Air Pollution and Climate Change   440

HUMAN DIMENSIONS OF ENVIRONMENTAL CHANGE   443
Assessing the Damage Attributable to Population Growth   443
Environmental Disasters Lead to Death and Dispersion   444

SUSTAINABLE DEVELOPMENT—POSSIBILITY OR OXYMORON?   447

POLICIES AIMED AT SLOWING POPULATION GROWTH   451

SUMMARY AND CONCLUSION   453

MAIN POINTS   454

QUESTIONS FOR REVIEW   455

GLOSSARY   456
BIBLIOGRAPHY   467
GEOGRAPHIC INDEX   496
SUBJECT INDEX   505

PREFACE

I wrote this book with a wide audience in mind because I find that students in my classes come from a wide range of academic disciplines and bring with them an incredible variety of viewpoints and backgrounds. No matter who you are, demographic events are influencing your life, and the more you know about them, the better able you will be to navigate through life.

When I think about population growth in the world, I conjure up an image of a bus hurtling down the highway toward what appears to be a cliff. The bus is semi-automatic and has no driver in charge of its progress. Some of the passengers on the bus are ignorant of what seems to lie ahead and are more worried about whether the air conditioning is turned up high enough or wondering how many snacks they have left for the journey. Other, more alert, passengers are looking down the road, but some of them think that what seems like a cliff is really just an optical illusion and is nothing to worry about; some think it may just be a dip, not really a cliff. Those who think it is a cliff are trying to figure out how to apply the brakes, knowing that a big bus takes a long time to slow down even after the brakes are put on.

Are we headed toward a disastrous scenario? We don't really know for sure, but we simply can't afford the luxury of hoping for the best. The population bus is causing damage and creating vortexes of social, economic, political, and environmental change as it charges down the highway, whether or not we are heading for the cliff. The better we understand its speed and direction, the better we will be at steering it and managing it successfully. No matter how many stories you have heard about the rate of population growth coming down or about the end of the population explosion, the world is projected by demographers at the United Nations and other organizations to add two or three billion more to the current count of almost eight billion before it stops growing. Huge implications for the future lie in that growth in numbers.

The world's population is growing because death rates have declined over the past several decades at a much faster pace than birth rates have, and as we go from the historical pattern of high birth and death rates to the increasingly common pattern of low (or even very low) birth and death rates, we pass through the demographic transition. This is actually a whole set of transitions relating to changes in health and mortality, fertility, migration, age structure, urbanization, and family and household structure. Each of these separate, but interrelated, changes has serious consequences for the way societies and economies work, and for that reason they have big implications for you personally. Over time, these transitions have evolved in ways that vary from one part of the world to another, so their path and progress are less predictable than we once thought, but we have good analytical tools for keeping track of them and potentially influencing them. My goal in this book is to provide you with those tools so that you have a better understanding of how the world works.

The growth in numbers (the bus hurtling toward what we hope is not a cliff) and the transitions and evolutions created in the process (the vortex created by the passing bus) have to be dealt with simultaneously, and our success as a human civilization depends on how well we do in this project. A lot is at stake here, so another of my aims is to provide you with as much insight as possible into the ways in which these demographic trends of growth, transition, and evolution affect your life in large and small ways.

Over the years, I have found that most people are either blissfully unaware of the enormous impact of population growth and change on their lives, or they are nearly overwhelmed whenever they think of population growth because they have heard so many horror stories about impending doom, or, increasingly, they have heard that population growth is ending and thus assume that the story has a happy ending. This latter belief is in many ways the scariest, because the lethargy that develops from thinking that the impact of population growth is a thing of the past is exactly what will lead us to doom. My purpose in this book is to shake you out of your lethargy (if you are one of those types), without necessarily scaring you in the process. I will introduce you to the basic concepts of population studies and help you develop your own demographic perspective, enabling you to understand some of the most important issues confronting the world. My intention is to sharpen your perception of population growth and change, to increase your awareness of what is happening and why, and to prepare you to cope with (and help shape) a future that will be shared with billions more people than there are today.

How Is the Book Organized?

In order to help you understand how the world works demographically in more detail, the book is organized into three parts, each building on the previous one. There is a story to tell here, and though each chapter can stand on its own, you'll understand its meaning much more if you've absorbed the previous chapters. The first part of the book is called "A Demographic Perspective." The first chapter is designed to introduce you to the field of population studies and illustrate why this is such an important topic. The term "demographics" is widely used, but most people using the term have only a limited understanding of the scope and depth of demography. This chapter reviews world population trends, so that you have a good idea of what is happening in the world demographically, how we got to this point, and where we seem to be heading. The second chapter provides you with a background on the kinds of demographic data that we use in order to build our understanding of the world. These data can also be applied to a variety of practical uses in political, social, and business planning, and I show you how that is done. The third chapter introduces you to the major perspectives and theories about population growth and change, so that you have a clear idea of how to use demographic data to test theories about what is happening in the world.

In Part Two, "Population Processes," I discuss four of the basic demographic processes whose transitions are transforming the world—the health and mortality transition (Chapter 4), the fertility transition (Chapter 5), the migration transition (Chapter 6), and the closely related urban transition (Chapter 7). Knowledge of these population processes and transitions provides you with the foundation you need to understand why changes occur and what might be done about them.

Part Three, "Using the Demographic Perspective," is devoted to studying the interaction of the population processes and societal changes that occur as fertility, mortality, migration, and urbanization change the structure of society. All of the transitions discussed in Part Two come together under what I call the "master transition"—the age transition and its associated alterations in our life course (Chapter 8). On an everyday basis, most of us encounter demographic change in the context of what is going on in our families and our household, and Chapter 9 is devoted to family demography and life chances. The final chapter (Chapter 10) explores the relationships between population, the environment, and sustainability. Can economic growth and development be sustained in the face of continued population growth? Can we avoid environmental catastrophe as we try to feed billions more people? There are no simple answers to these questions, but we are facing a future in which we will have to deal with the global and local consequences of a larger and constantly changing population. I conclude with a review of the ways in which the global community is trying to cope politically with these changes as they alter the fabric of human society.

What Is New in This Thirteenth Edition

Populations are constantly changing and evolving, and each successive edition of this book has aimed to keep up with demographic trends and the explanations for them. Thus, every chapter of this current edition has been revised for recency, relevancy, reliability, and readability. At the same time, the teaching and learning environment has changed substantially over the years, and in this edition, I have responded to calls from users of the book to reorganize material and reduce the number of chapters so that everything of vital importance can be readily covered in one academic term. This edition has only 10 chapters, rather than the 12 chapters in the previous edition, but all of the really good stuff is still in here.

- Chapter 1, "Introduction to Demography," updates the way in which demography connects the dots in the world, including a substantially revised essay on "Connecting the Demographic Dots in the Middle East." Most important, I have moved the discussion of global population trends into this introductory chapter, and of course, I have used the latest numbers available at the time.

- Chapter 2, "Demographic Data and Applied Demography," is now moved up in the chapter order so that readers know early on the sources of information informing the entire book. It brings you the latest information about censuses and surveys throughout the world, with a special focus on the United States, Canada, and Mexico. There is also an expanded section on applied demography, including a discussion of spatial demography, along with a revised essay, "Demographics of Politics: Why the Census Matters."

- Chapter 3, "Demographic Perspectives and Theories," brings in the latest thinking on demographic theories, while at the same time emphasizing that the demographic transition is a whole suite of transitions, the discussion of which is really what the book is all about. I have expanded the discussion about the second demographic transition and revised the essay "Who Are the Neo-Malthusians and Why Do We Care?"

- Chapter 4, "The Health and Mortality Transition," has all the latest numbers on disease and mortality, as well as the latest thinking on the changing scope of health as populations age. Also included in this chapter, of course, is a discussion about the various ways in which we measure mortality. The essay in the chapter focuses on "Mortality Control and the Environment."

- Chapter 5, "The Fertility Transition," discusses the latest data and theories about fertility change over time and across regions, with a special emphasis on how the roles and status of women in society influence fertility levels. The chapter also includes updated discussions of how to measure fertility. The essay is "Reproductive Rights, Reproductive Health, and the Fertility Transition."

- Chapter 6, "The Migration Transition," updates the trends throughout the world in the movement of people between and within countries, with renewed discussion of the ways in societies and migrants adapt to each other. The essay updates the topic still bedeviling the United States and other rich countries: "Is Migration a Crime? Illegal Immigration in Global Context."

- Chapter 7, "The Urban Transition," is now placed right after the chapter on migration, since most modern migration is toward or between urban places. The focus is on the history of urbanization, and then how urban places are evolving into the diverse homes of a majority of humans. The essay looks at one of the most pressing issues facing the future: "Cities as Sustainable Environments."

- Chapter 8, "The Age Transition and the Life Course," reviews the latest literature on the drivers of changing age structures around the world, with a special emphasis on demographic dividends as examples of how important the age transition is. The latter part of the chapter looks at the more personal part of aging as the human life course undergoes dramatic shifts. Methods of projecting populations using age-specific death, fertility, and migration data are also covered. The goal of the essay is to capture the big issue: "The Age Transition Force Is with Us."

- Chapter 9, "Family Demography and Life Chances," explores the immense changes taking place in family and household life as all of the other transitions have genuinely revolutionized human society. These changes affect every individual's life chances, and the chapter updates those perspectives and data. The essay looks at what many people in the world are particularly interested in: "Show Me the Money!"

- Chapter 10, "Population, the Environment, and Global Sustainability," examines the global links between population growth and change, economic growth and change, and the tremendous human impact on our environment. We are at a critical point globally in our need to focus on what is required to sustain the additional billions projected to be joining us over the course of this century. There is also an updated version of the very popular essay: "How Big Is Your Ecological Footprint?"

Special Features of the Book

To help increase your understanding of the basic concepts and issues of population studies, the book contains the following special features.

Short Essays As noted above in the chapter descriptions, each chapter contains a short essay on a particular population concept, designed to help you better understand current demographic issues covered in that chapter. Each essay ends with two discussion questions to encourage you to think about the topic in greater depth.

Main Points A list of 10 main points appears at the end of each chapter to help you review chapter highlights.

Questions for Review A set of five questions are provided at the end of each chapter, designed to stimulate thinking and class discussion on topics covered in the text.

Glossary A glossary in the back of the book defines key population terms. These terms are in boldface type when introduced in the text to signal that they also appear in the glossary.

Complete Bibliography This is a fully referenced book, and all of the publications and data sources I have used are included in a bibliography at the end of the book.

A Thorough Index To help you find what you need in the book, I have built as complete an index as possible, divided into a Subject Index and a Geographic Index.

Digital Resources

New to this edition, the MindTap digital platform offers:

- An interactive eBook, in which students can highlight key text, add notes, and create custom flashcards

- Video resources, practice activities, and application activities that empower students toward authentic and thoughtful learning experiences
- A capstone project for the course
- A digital test bank, which includes multiple choice, true/false, and essay questions for each chapter
- A fully mobile experience via the MindTap mobile app, so students can read or listen to textbooks and study with the aid of instructor notifications and flashcards

Ancillary Course Material

An Instructor's Manual and other ancillary materials are available through the book's home page on the publisher's website: *https://www.cengage.com/c/population -an-introduction-to-concepts-and-issues-13e-weeks/*

I regularly update my blog, providing resources for instructors and students: *http://weekspopulation.blogspot.com/.*

Personal Acknowledgments

Like most authors, I have an intellectual lineage that I feel is worth tracing. In particular, I would like to acknowledge my principal mentor, Kingsley Davis, whose standards as a teacher and scholar will always keep me reaching; Eduardo Arriaga; Judith Blake; Thomas Burch; Carlo Cipolla; Murray Gendell; Nathan Keyfitz; and Samuel Preston. Individually and collectively, they have guided me in my quest to unravel the mysteries of how the world operates demographically. Thanks are due also to Steve Rutter, formerly of Wadsworth Publishing Company, who first suggested that I write this book, and to Kathy Sands-Boehmer at Cengage who very skillfully and patiently managed the production of this thirteenth edition of the book.

Special thanks go to John, Gregory, Jennifer, Amy, and Jim for teaching me the costs and benefits of children and children-in-law. They have instructed me, in their various ways, in the advantages of being first-born, the coziness of the middle child, and the joys that immigration can bring to a family. They have also brought me seven wonderful grandchildren: Andrew, Sophie, Benjamin, Julia, Elizabeth, Kayla, and James. I have the best possible family demography!

However, the one person who is directly responsible for the fact that the first, second, third, fourth, fifth, updated fifth, sixth, seventh, eighth, ninth, tenth, eleventh, twelfth, and now the thirteen editions were written, and who deserves credit for the book's strengths, is my wife, Deanna. Her creativity, good judgment, and hard work in reviewing and editing the manuscript benefited virtually every page, and the book, like my life, is dedicated to her.

Other Acknowledgments

I would also like to thank the users of the earlier editions, including professors, their students (many of whom are now professors), and my own students, for their comments and suggestions. Many, many other people have helped since the first edition came out more than 40 years ago, and I am naturally very grateful for all of their assistance. Thanks also for the many useful reviews of the twelfth edition that helped to inspire changes in this edition.

Other Acknowledgments

I would also like to thank the users of the earlier editions, including professors, their students (many of whom are now professors), and my own students, for their comments and suggestions. Many, many other people have helped since the first edition came out more than 40 years ago, and I am naturally very grateful for all of their assistance. Thanks also for the many useful reviews of the twelfth edition that helped to inspire changes in this edition.

PART ONE

A DEMOGRAPHIC PERSPECTIVE

CHAPTER 1
Introduction to Demography

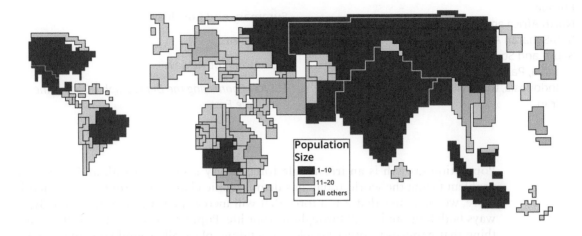

Figure 1.1   Cartogram of Countries of the World by Population Size

Note: The map shows the size of each country of the world according to its population. Each square represents approximately 2 million persons.

Source: Prepared by John Weeks and Sean Taugher using data from the United Nations Population Division World Population Prospects: The 2019 Revision; data refer to estimates for 2020.

What Is Demography?

How Does Demography Connect the Dots?
The Relationship of Population to Resources
    Food
    Water
    Energy
    Housing and Infrastructure
    Environmental Degradation
The Relationship of Population to Social and
    Political Dynamics
    Regional Conflict
    Globalization
    Global Migration
The Relationship of Population to the Rights
    of Women

World Population Growth
A Brief History

How Fast Is the World's Population Growing
    Now?
The Power of Doubling—How Fast Can
    Populations Grow?
Why Was Early Growth So Slow?
Why Are More Recent Increases So Rapid?
How Many People Have Ever Lived?
Redistribution of the World's Population through
    Migration
    European Expansion
    "South" to "North" Migration
    The Urban Revolution

**Geographic Distribution of the World's
    Population**

**Global Variation in Population Size
    and Growth**
North America

United States
Canada
Mexico and Central America
South America
Europe
North Africa and Western Asia
Sub-Saharan Africa
South and Southeast Asia
  India, Pakistan and Bangladesh
  Indonesia, the Philippines and Vietnam
  Iran

East Asia
  China
  Japan
Oceania

Summary and Conclusion

Main Points

Questions for Review

ESSAY: *Connecting the Demographic Dots in the Middle East*

Population growth is an irresistible force. Every social, political, and economic problem facing the world today has demographic change as a root cause. What is more, we guarantee that it is a force that will increasingly affect you, personally, in ways both large and small throughout your life. Population change is not just something that happens to other people—it is taking place all around you, and you are making your own contribution to it.

Our story begins with what is arguably the most important phenomenon in human history: the rise of life expectancy over the past two centuries, most dramatically since the end of World War II. Medical and public health advancements are rightfully heralded and celebrated, but there have been consequences. More people living longer has produced unprecedented population growth and previously unthinkable transformations in human society. What is perhaps most interesting to you, personally, is that this past is definitely prologue to your own future since the world's population will almost certainly continue to increase for the rest of your life. Though most of this growth will take place in developing countries (more specifically, in the cities of those countries), we will all experience the consequences.

Despite declining birth rates in most parts of the world, it is a fact that the number of people added to the world each day is higher today than at any time in history. Demographic change can be both good and bad news, but there is no question that population growth makes implacable demands on natural and societal resources. A baby born this year won't create much of a stir outside her immediate family, but in a few years she will be eating more and needing clothes, an education, then a job and a place of her own. And, then, most likely she will have babies of her own and the cycle continues.

Understanding these and a wide range of related issues is the business of demography. Whether your concern with demography is personal or global or a combination, unraveling the "whys" of population growth and change will provide you with a better perspective on the world and how it works. This book is an odyssey to understand the component parts of this powerful force, how they operate, and how they can be influenced to change the course of human history.

What Is Demography?

The term *demography* comes from the Greek root *demos*, which means "ordinary citizens," and the Greek word *graphia*, which means "study of." It was coined in 1855 by Achille Guillard who used it in the title of his book "Elements de Statistique Humaine ou Démographie Comparée." Guillard defined demography as "the mathematical knowledge of populations, their general movements, and their physical, civil, intellectual and moral state" (Guillard 1855:xxvi). This is generally in tune with how we use the term today in that modern demography is the study of the determinants and consequences of population change and is concerned with effectively everything that influences and can be influenced by:

- **population size** (how many people there are in a given place)
- **population growth or decline** (how the number of people in that place is changing over time)
- **population processes** (the levels and trends in fertility, mortality, migration and urbanization that are determining population size and change)
- **population spatial distribution** (where people are located and why)
- **population structure** (how many males and females there are of each age)
- **population characteristics—popularly known these days as "demographics"** (what people are like in a given place, in terms of variables such as education, income, occupation, family and household relationships, immigrant and refugee status, and the many other characteristics that add up to who we are as individuals or groups).

How Does Demography Connect the Dots?

It may sound presumptuous, even preposterous, to suggest that nearly everything is connected to demography, but it really is true. The demographic foundation of our lives is deep and broad. As you will see in this book, demography affects nearly every facet of your life in some way or another. Population change is one of the prime forces behind social and technological change all over the world. As population size and composition change in an area—whether it be growth or decline— people have to adjust, and from those adjustments radiate innumerable alterations to the way society operates. We see the adjustments, but the demographic changes behind those adjustments are not always so obvious. As Paul Taylor (2017) very nicely put it, "Demography is a drama in slow motion."

Demography is a force associated with every improvement in human well-being that the world has witnessed over the past few hundred years. Children survive as never before, adults are healthier than ever before, women can limit their exposure to the health risks involved with pregnancy and still be nearly guaranteed that the one or two or three of their babies will not just survive, but will thrive to adulthood. Having fewer pregnancies and babies in a world where most adults now reach old age means that men and women have more "scope" in life, more time to develop their personal capacities and more time and incentive to build a future for themselves, their children, and everyone else. Longer lives and the societal need for less childbearing by women mean that the composition of families and households becomes more diverse, and women have more choices and control in life. The changes taking place all over the world in family structure are not the result of a breakdown of social norms so much as they are the natural consequence of societies adapting to the demographic changes of people living longer with fewer children in a world where urban living and migration are vastly more common than ever before. These are all facets of demography affecting your life in important ways.

You may have heard the phrase "demography is destiny," which was coined in the 1970 book "The Real Majority," by Richard Scammon (a former director of the U.S. Census Bureau) and Ben Wattenberg (Scammon and Wattenberg 1970). They were focusing especially on the way in which political views are influenced by demographic characteristics such as age, sex, income, education and race/ethnicity. As the numbers of people with differing "demographics" increase or decrease, voting patterns may well change. This does not necessarily mean, however, that you can easily predict the future based on demographic trends. To be sure, demographic change *does* demand a societal response, but different societies will respond differently, sometimes for the better, sometimes not. Either way, it turns out that population structures are sufficiently predictable that we can at least suggest the kinds of responses from which societies are going to have to choose.

It is a fact that the population of the world is increasing by more than 200,000 people per day, as we discuss in more detail below, but it is also a fact that this growth is much more intense in some areas of the world than in others. In those places where societies have been unable to cope adequately, especially with increasing numbers of younger people, the fairly predictable result has been social, economic, and political instability. At the other end of the spectrum, there is considerable angst in some of the richer countries where very low fertility has pushed the population to the edge of, or actually into, a decline.

Population change is obviously not the only source of trouble (or opportunity) in the world, but its impact is often incendiary, igniting other dilemmas that face human society. Without understanding population dynamics, for example, we cannot fully grasp why the world is globalizing at such a rapid pace, nor can we understand the roots of conflict from the Middle East to Southeast Asia, nor why there is a simultaneous acceptance of and backlash against immigrants in the United States and Europe. And we cannot begin to imagine our future without taking into account the fact that the population of the world at the middle of this century is projected to include two billion more people than it does now (and there may be an additional billion by the end of the century), since the health of the planet depends upon being able to sustain a much larger number of people than are currently alive. Because so much that happens in your life will be influenced by the consequences of population change, it behooves you to understand the causes and mechanisms of those changes. Let's look at some examples.

The Relationship of Population to Resources

Food   The precipitous spike in world population growth over the past two centuries has awakened us to the recognition that the global resources upon which we are dependent for survival are not limitless. Indeed, none of the basic resources required to expand food output—land, water, energy—can be considered abundant today, as we detail in Chapter 10. This especially impacts less developed countries with rapidly rising food demands and small energy reserves. Even now in sub-Saharan Africa, food production is not keeping pace with population growth, and this raises the fear that the world may have surpassed its ability to sustain even current levels of food production, much less meet the demands of the three billion additional people who are projected to be in line for a seat at the dinner table by the end of this century (United Nations Population Division 2019). And the problem is not just on land. The annual catch of wild fish leveled off in the 1990s and has been declining since then, with an increasing fraction of fish coming from farms harvesting the few species amenable to aquaculture. Will a diet that is more plant-based, rather than increasingly meat-based (which uses a lot of land to feed animals rather people), be the solution?

Water   An estimated one in three humans already faces water scarcity, as demand for fresh water increases faster than the available supply. For example, the world's most populous country, China, is facing a water shortage that could threaten its economic well-being (Lou et al. 2019; Parton 2018), and Africa's largest reservoir of fresh water, Lake Chad, has shrunk by 90 percent over the past several decades, threatening the health of people and crops in sub-Saharan Africa (Ross 2018). Despite the fact that there are oceans of water all over the earth, we humans and other animals, along with the plants that we grow to eat, need fresh water, not salt water. We know how to convert salt water into fresh water, but the process requires a lot of energy. The oil-rich countries of the Middle East may be able to "change oil into water" but most countries cannot afford to do that.

Energy   Every person added to the world's population requires energy to prepare food, acquire clothing and shelter, and to fuel economic life in general. Our rising standard of living is directly tied to our increasing use of energy, and every increment in demand is another claim on those resources. We know that petroleum reserves are limited, but can we transition quickly enough to solar and/or wind energy to meet the needs of a growing population? No one knows for sure, but we have to hope so. Will biofuels be the answer? Not likely, because they come from valuable crop land that we need for growing food. Will damming up more rivers to create hydroelectric power be the answer? Experience suggests that damming rivers creates widespread, long-term environmental problems.

Housing and Infrastructure   All future population growth in the world is expected to show up in the cities, especially those in developing countries, and not just mega-cities, but smaller cities that most of us have never heard of. The irony of growing more food is that it requires mechanization rather than more laborers, so as the number of babies born in rural areas continues to exceed deaths, the "excess" population is forced to move to cities in hopes of finding a job there. This means building homes (which requires lumber, concrete, and a lot of other resources) and providing urban infrastructure (water, sewerage, electricity, roads, telecommunications, etc.) for the estimated three billion newcomers. This increasing "demographic overhead" is burdensome, particularly for those countries that cannot provide adequately for their existing urban populations.

Environmental Degradation   As the human population has increased, so has its potential for disrupting the earth's biosphere. The very same explosion in scientific knowledge that has allowed us to push death back to ever older ages, thus unleashing population growth, has also taught us how to convert the earth's natural resources into those things that comprise our higher standard of living. And it is not just that we are using up resources—waste accompanies use. The use of fossil fuel releases carbon dioxide into the atmosphere, generating deleterious effects on global climate conditions, evidenced perhaps most dramatically by the melting glaciers and Arctic ice. We are also damaging the hydrosphere (the world of water) by contaminating the fresh water supply, destroying coral reefs and fishing out the ocean, while also wreaking havoc on the lithosphere (the thin layer of the earth's crust upon which we live) by degrading the land with toxic waste and permitting top soil loss, desertification, and deforestation.

The Relationship of Population to Social and Political Dynamics

Regional Conflict   Back in 1967, even before the publication of Paul Ehrlich's "Population Bomb" (Ehrlich 1968), Harry Harrison (1967) wrote a widely read book called "Make Room/Make Room," which in 1973 was made into a popular movie called "Soylent Green." This was a work of science fiction starring Charlton Heston and Edward G. Robinson in which they confront life way in the future in 2022 (oops, that's like right now!). This is a world suffering from overpopulation, depleted resources, poverty, dying oceans, and a hot climate due to the greenhouse effect, where much of the population survives on processed food rations, including "soylent green" which turns out to be "recycled" humans. This certainly is a dystopian view of the world. The term "dystopia" (Hell on Earth) is of course the opposite of "utopia" (Heaven on Earth) and the role of demography in dystopias has been captured in "Demodystopias" by Andreu Domingo (2008), an article published in the major demography journal "Population and Development Review."

A lot of similarly themed books and movies have come along since "Make Room/Make Room," but the world has not collapsed. So, having escaped these frightening scenarios thus far, it is tempting to think that population growth has not really had much of an impact on civil society. That's because the real impact is harder to see, even if *very* real—the "drama in slow motion," we spoke of earlier. Demographic change creeps up on us one age group at a time, forcing families, communities, and then societies to adjust in some way or another. One reaction to population growth is to accept or even embrace the change and then seek positive solutions to the dilemmas presented by an increasingly larger (or smaller, for that matter) younger population (or older population)—you get the idea. Another reaction, of course, is to reject change. This is what the Taliban have been trying to do for decades in parts of Afghanistan and Pakistan—to forcibly prevent a society from modernizing and, in the process, keeping death rates higher than they might otherwise be (Afghanistan has one of the highest rates of maternal mortality in the world, not to mention the deaths from the violence there), and maintaining women in an inferior status by withholding access to education, paid employment, health care and the means of preventing pregnancy. The difficulty the Taliban (or any similar group such as al-Qaeda, the Islamic State or Boko Haram) face (besides active military intervention to stop them) is that it is very hard, if not impossible, to put the genie back in the bottle once people have been made aware of the freedoms that are inherently associated with modernization. Very few people in the world prefer to go back to the "traditional" life of harsh exposure to disease, oppression, and death.

Globalization   Regional conflict of the kind discussed in the essay later in this chapter is one response to population growth. Another less violent, albeit still controversial, response has been globalization. Most broadly, globalization can be thought of as an increasing level of connectedness among and between people and places all over the world, although the term has taken on a more politically charged dimension since many people interpret it to mean a penetration of less developed nations by multinational companies from the more developed nations. This trend is promoted by the removal of trade barriers that protect local industries and by the integration of local and regional economies into a larger world arena. The pros and cons of this process invite heated debate, but an important element of globalization is that it is closely related to, indeed is a response to, the enormous increase in worldwide population growth that has taken place since the end of World War II.

Control over mortality, which has permitted the growth of population, occurred first in the countries of Europe and North America, and it was there that population first began to grow rapidly in the modern world, gaining steam in the late nineteenth and early twentieth centuries. However, after World War II, death control technology was spread globally, especially through the work of various United Nations agencies, funded by the governments of the richer countries. Since declines in mortality initially affect infants more than any other age group, there tends to be a somewhat delayed reaction to the effects of a mortality decline until those children who would otherwise have died reach an age where they must be educated, clothed, fed, and jobs and homes must be created for them on a scale never before imagined.

As huge new cohorts of young people came of age and needed jobs in developing countries (especially China), their willingness to work for relatively low wages did not go unnoticed by manufacturers in North America, Europe, and Japan. Nor have big companies failed to notice the growing number of potential consumers for products, especially those aimed at younger people, who represent the bulk of the population in developing countries. Given the demographics, it should not be surprising to us that jobs have moved to the developing countries and that younger consumers in those countries have been encouraged to spend their new wages on products that are popular with younger people in the richer countries, including music, fast food, cars, mobile phones, and electronic games.

Globalization of the labor market exists in large part because of the nature of world demographic trends. However, the sheer volume of population growth in less developed countries is not a guarantee that jobs will automatically head their way from richer countries. The likelihood goes up with two other demographically related factors in the less developed nations: (1) declining fertility; and (2) increasing education. If fertility falls swiftly after mortality has gone down, the age structure goes through a transition in which there is a bulge of young adults ready to work, who are burdened neither by a lot of dependent younger siblings nor yet by a lot of dependent older people. As we will discuss in more detail in Chapter 8, this demographic dividend can be used to good advantage, especially if a country (think China) has also spent societal resources educating its children so that the young people can readily step up to jobs that might be moved there from richer countries in addition to the jobs they create themselves.

Global Migration   Globalization of the labor force has significantly broadened the ancient relationship between jobs and geography by bringing jobs to people in developing countries. For most of human history a lack of jobs meant that young people moved to where the jobs were (or, at least, where they thought they were). That still happens. Even as some jobs are heading to developing countries, many young people in those countries are headed to the richer countries, facilitated by the demographic fit between the young age structures of developing countries and the aging populations in richer countries (Weeks and Weeks 2010). Problems arise, however, because immigrants tend to be different. They may look different, have a different language, a different religion, and differ in their expectations about how society operates. Furthermore, since the immigrants tend to be young adults, they will wind up contributing disproportionately to the birth rate in their new countries, leading to a rapid and profound shift in the ethnic composition of the younger population in their adopted community. As we discuss in Chapter 6, these differences create problems for all societies and create situations of backlash against immigrants that we can see very clearly today in Europe, the United States, and Australia.

The Relationship of Population to the Rights of Women

There is probably no more important demographic issue than the rights of women. As we discuss in Chapter 4, women inherently have a higher life expectancy than men, unless society intervenes to undermine that biological advantage. The other biological issue—reproduction—rears its head when society seeks to prevent women from controlling their own reproductive behavior, as we discuss in Chapter 5. In social terms, all evidence shows that men and women are equally able to be good or bad parents, equally able to become educated and succeed (or not) occupationally and economically, equally able to lead societies politically. Any group that oppresses women and suppresses their contributions will have a distinctively unfavorable demographic profile and will almost certainly suffer in terms of overall well-being. This theme will emerge regularly in subsequent chapters.

Let us now trace the history of population growth in the world, to give you more background on how we got ourselves into the current situation. Then we will go on a brief guided tour through each of the world's major regions, highlighting current patterns of population size and rates of growth, with a special emphasis on the world's 10 most populous countries.

World Population Growth

A Brief History

Let's start at the beginning, or at least our best (educated) guess about the beginning. Modern human beings (*homo sapiens*) have been around for about 200,000 years (Cann and Wilson 2003; McHenry 2009; Harari 2015), although only in the past 50,000 years or so have *homo sapiens* been the only human group alive. That's still a long time, yet our presence on the earth was scarcely noticeable until very recently. For almost all of that time, humans were hunter-gatherers (foragers) living a primitive existence marked by high fertility, high mortality, and at best only very slow population growth. Given the very difficult exigencies for survival in these early societies, it is no surprise that the population of the world on the eve of the Neolithic Agrarian Revolution (also known as the Agricultural Revolution or simply the Neolithic Revolution) about 10,000 years ago is estimated to have been only 4 million people (see Figure 1.2).

Many people argue that the Neolithic Revolution occurred slowly but pervasively across the face of the earth precisely because the hunting-gathering populations were growing just enough to push the limit of the carrying capacity of their way of life (Boserup 1965; Cohen 1977; Harris and Ross 1987; Sanderson 1995). Carrying capacity refers to the number of people that can be supported indefinitely in an area given the available physical resources and the way in which people use those resources (Miller and Spoolman 2012). Since hunting and gathering use resources *extensively* rather than *intensively*, it was natural that over tens of thousands of years humans would move inexorably into the remote corners of the earth in search of sustenance. Eventually, people in most of those corners began to use the environment more intensively, leading to the more sedentary, agricultural way of life that characterized most of human society for the past 10,000 years, starting first in what is now the Middle East, and then in what is now the eastern part of China.

The population began to grow more noticeably after the Neolithic Revolution (Livi-Bacci 2017). Between 8000 and 5000 BCE, about 333 people on average (births minus deaths) were being added to the world's total population each year, but by 500 BCE, as major civilizations were being established in China, India, and Greece, the world was adding 100,000 people each year to the total.

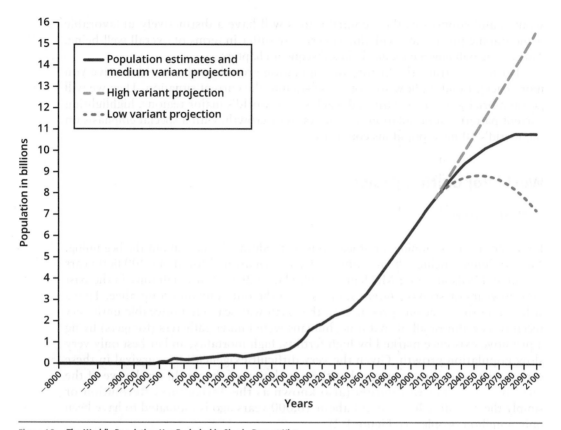

Figure 1.2   The World's Population Has Exploded in Size in Recent History

Note: Time is not to scale.

Sources: The population data through 1940 are drawn from the U.S. Census Bureau, International Programs Center "Historical Estimates of the World Population," (https://www.census.gov/data/tables/time-series/demo/international-programs/historical-est-worldpop.html), accessed 2018. The numbers reflect the average of the estimates shown in that table. Population figures for 1950 through 2100 are from the United Nations Population Division, 2019, World Population Prospects 2019.

By the time of Christ (the Roman Period, 1 CE) there may well have been more than 200 million people on the planet, and the number was increasing by nearly 300,000 each year.

There was some backsliding in the third through fifth centuries CE when increases in mortality, probably due to the plague, led to declining population size in the Mediterranean area as the Roman empire crumbled, and in China as the Han empire collapsed from a combination of flood, famine, and rebellion (McEvedy and Jones 1978). Population growth recovered its momentum only to be swatted down by yet another plague, the Black Death, that arrived in Europe in the middle of the fourteenth century and didn't leave until the middle of the seventeenth century (Cantor 2001; Livi-Bacci 2017).

After that, during the period from about 1650 to 1850, Europe as a whole experienced rather dramatic population growth as a result of the disappearance of the plague, the introduction of the potato from the Americas, and evolutionary (although not revolutionary) changes in agricultural practice—probably a response to the receding of the Little Ice Age (Fagan 2000)—that preceded (and almost certainly helped to stimulate) the Industrial Revolution (Cohen 1995). The potato was in many ways a game-changer for Europe, because potatoes have more calories, vitamins, and nutrients per acre of food grown than any other crop previously grown in Europe. Consuming potatoes improved health and thus lowered the death rate. So much so, in fact, that Nathan Nunn and Nancy Qian (2011:643) estimate that "the introduction of the potato explains 25–26 percent of the increase in Old World population between 1700 and 1900 [largely through a reduction in the death rate] and 27–34 percent of the increase in urbanization [because fewer people were needed on the land to grow potatoes than other staple crops]." Thus, on the eve of the Industrial Revolution in the middle of the eighteenth century (about 1750), the population of the world was approaching one billion people and was increasing by more than two million every year.

It is quite likely that the Industrial Revolution occurred in part because of this population growth. It is theorized that the Europe of 300 or 400 years ago was reaching the carrying capacity of its agricultural society, so Europeans first spread out looking for more room and then began to invent more intensive uses of their resources to meet the needs of a growing population (Harrison 1993), building on the scientific discoveries inspired by the European Enlightenment. The major resource was energy which, with the discovery of fossil fuels (first coal, then oil and natural gas), helped to light the fire under industrialization.

Since the beginning of the Industrial Revolution approximately 250 years ago, the size of the world's population has increased even more dramatically, as you can visualize in Figure 1.2. For tens of thousands of years, the population of the world grew slowly, and then within scarcely more than 200 years, the number of people has mushroomed to nearly eight billion and is still going strong. There can be little question why the term population explosion was coined to describe these historically recent demographic events. As you can see in Table 1.1, the world's population did not reach one billion until after the American Revolution—the United Nations fixes the year at 1804 (United Nations Population Division 1999)—but since then we have been adding each additional billion people at an accelerating pace. The two billion mark was hit in 1927, just before the Great Depression and 123 years after the first billion. In 1960, only 33 years later, came three billion; and four billion came along only 14 years after that, in 1974. We then hit five billion 13 years later, in 1987; we passed the six billion milestone 12 years later, in 1999; and in another 12 years, in 2011, we reached the seventh billion. Demographers at the United Nations project that we could reach eight billion in 2023, nine billion in 2037, and 10 billion in 2056—an incredible 10-fold increase in only two and a half centuries (United Nations Population Division 2019).

We will discuss the methods of population projections in Chapter 8, but let us note that nearly everyone agrees that global population growth is likely to come to an end sometime late in this century or early in the next century when fertility

Table 1.1   The Billion People Progression

Year	Population in billions	Annual rate of population growth (%)	Annual Increase in millions
1804	1	0.4	4
1927	2	1.1	22
1960	3	1.3	39
1974	4	2.0	80
1987	5	1.6	80
2000	6	1.4	84
2011	7	1.2	84
2023	8	1.0	80
2037	9	0.7	63
2056	10	0.5	50

Sources: The population data through 1940 are drawn from the U.S. Census Bureau, International Programs Center "Historical Estimates of the World Population," (https://www.census.gov/data/tables/time-series/demo/international-programs/historical-est-worldpop.html), accessed 2018. The numbers reflect the average of the estimates shown in that table. Population figures for 1950 through 2100 are from the United Nations Population Division, 2019, World Population Prospects 2019.

eventually—and hopefully sooner rather than later—drops to low levels everywhere on the planet. We are not sure exactly when this will happen, nor exactly how many of us there will be when that time comes. The right side of Figure 1.2 shows the spread of options as calculated by the United Nations Population Division out to the end of this century. The middle projection, which the UN demographers think is the most likely, levels off just shy of 11 billion by the end of the century, and assumes that the average number of births per woman in the world will eventually reach replacement level of just slightly more than two. The high projection of 15.6 billion in 2100 assumes that fertility levels decline but will not drop to replacement, and so the world population keeps growing; whereas the low projection of 7.3 billion in 2100 assumes that fertility drops well below replacement, which, of course, would lead to eventual extinction if nothing changed.

How Fast Is the World's Population Growing Now?

The *rate* of population growth is obviously important (it's the "explosive" part), yet the *numbers* are what we actually cope with. You get a glimpse of the different patterns over time in Table 1.1, but Figure 1.3 provides more detail. You can see that the average annual rate of population growth peaked around 1970 (probably 1968) and has been declining since then, except for a little backsliding in the 1980s. This is good news, of course, but is tempered by the fact that as we continue to build on an ever larger base of people, the lower rates of growth are still producing very large absolute increases in the human population. When you have a base of nearly eight billion (our current population), the seemingly slow rate of growth of just above 1.1 percent per year for the world as a whole still translates into the annual addition of 81 million people; whereas "only" 73 million were being added annually when the rate of growth peaked in 1968, and there were only 23 million per year being added when the world was last growing at about 1.0 percent per year, just as World War II was ending. Put another way, during the next 12 months, approximately 140 million babies will be born in the world, while 59 million people of all ages will die, resulting in that net addition of 81 million people. In the two seconds it took you to read that sentence, nine babies were born while four people died, and so the world's population increased by five.

Figure 1.3 shows a drop in the rate of population growth in the 1930–60 period. The Great Depression lowered the birth rate, especially in Europe and

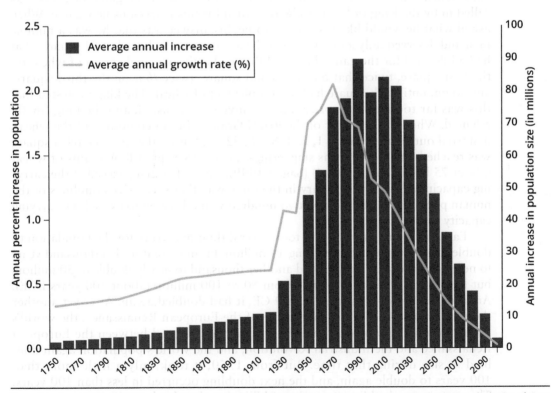

Figure 1.3   Tens of Millions of People Are Still Being Added to the World's Total Population Each Year, Despite the Drop in the Growth Rate

Source: The population data through 1940 are drawn from the U.S. Census Bureau, International Programs Center "Historical Estimates of the World Population," (https://www.census.gov/data/tables/time-series/demo/international-programs/historical-est-worldpop.html), accessed 2018. The numbers reflect the average of the estimates shown in that table. Population figures for 1950 through 2100 are from the United Nations Population Division, 2019, World Population Prospects 2019.

North America, whereas World War II increased the death rate. There was also a terrible famine in China in 1959–60, which was produced by Mao Zedong's Great Leap Forward program of 1958, in which the Chinese government "leapt forward" into industrialization by selling "surplus" grain to finance industrial growth. Unfortunately, the grain was not surplus, and the confiscation of food amounted to a self-imposed disaster that led to the deaths of 30 million Chinese in the following two years (1959 and 1960) (Becker 1997). Yet even though the Chinese famine was undoubtedly one of the largest disasters in human history, world population growth quickly rebounded, and the growth rate hit its record high shortly after that.

The Power of Doubling—How Fast Can Populations Grow?

Human populations, like all living things, have the capacity for exponential increase, which can be expressed neatly by the time it takes to double in population size. The incredible power of doubling is illustrated by the tale of the Persian chessboard. The story is told that the clever inventor of the game of chess was called in by the King of Persia to be rewarded for this marvelous new game. When asked what he would like his reward to be, his answer was that he was a humble man and deserved only a humble reward. Gesturing to the board of 64 squares that he had devised for the game, he asked that he be given a single grain of wheat on the first square, twice that on the second square, twice *that* on the third square, and so on, until each square had its complement of wheat. The king protested that this was far too modest a prize, but the inventor persisted, and the king finally relented. When the Overseer of the Royal Granary began counting out the wheat, it started out small enough: 1, 2, 4, 8, 16, 32 . . . but by the time the 64th square was reached, the number was staggering—nearly 18.5 quintillion grains of wheat (about 75 billion metric tons!) (Sagan 1989). This, of course, exceeded the carrying capacity of the royal granary in the same way that successive doublings of the human population over the past two hundred years threaten to exceed the carrying capacity of the planet.

Early on in human history it took several thousand years for the population to double to a size eventually reaching 14 million. From there it took a thousand years to nearly double to 27 million and another thousand to nearly double to 50 million, but less than 500 years to double from 50 to 100 million (about 500 years BCE). Another thousand years later, in 500 CE, it had doubled again. After yet another thousand years, in 1500, in the middle of the European Renaissance, the world's population had doubled again. About 400 years elapsed between the European Renaissance and the Industrial Revolution, and the world's population again doubled in size during that time. But from 1750, it took only a little more than 100 years to double again, and the next doubling occurred in less than 100 years. The most recent doubling (from 3 to 6 billion) took only about 40 years.

Will we double again in the future? Probably not. Indeed, we should hope not, because we don't really know at this point how we will feed, clothe, educate and find jobs for the nearly eight billion alive now, much less the additional three billion who are expected between now and the end of this century. Once you realize how rapidly a population can grow, it is reasonable to wonder why early growth of the human population was so slow.

Why Was Early Growth So Slow?

The reason the population grew so slowly during the first 99 percent of human history was simple: death rates were very high. During the hunting-gathering phase of human history (tens of thousands of years), it is likely that life expectancy at birth averaged about 20 years (Petersen 1975; Livi-Bacci 2017). At this level of mortality, more than half of all children born will die before age five, and the average woman who survives to the reproductive years will have to bear nearly seven children in order to assure that two will survive to adulthood.

Research in the twentieth century on the last of the hunting-gathering populations in sub-Saharan Africa suggested that a premodern woman might have deliberately limited the number of children born by spacing them a few years apart to make it easier to nurse and carry her youngest child and to permit her to do her work (Dumond 1975). She may have accomplished this by abstinence, abortion, or possibly even infanticide (Howell 1979; Lee 1972). Similarly, sick and infirm members of society were at risk of abandonment once they were no longer able to fend for themselves. Not everyone agrees that there was any deliberate population control among early human populations, believing more simply that societies struggled to give birth to enough children to overcome the obstacle faced by the routinely high death rates among children (Caldwell and Caldwell 2003).

As humans settled into agricultural communities, population began to increase at a slightly higher rate than during the hunting-gathering era, and Jean-Pierre Bocquet-Appel (2008) has called this the Neolithic Demographic Transition. Initially it was thought that birth rates remained high, but death rates declined slightly because of the steadier supply of food, and thus the population grew. However, archaeological evidence combined with studies of extant hunter-gatherer groups has offered a somewhat more complicated explanation for growth during this period (Spooner 1972). Fertility rates did, indeed, rise as new diets improved the ability of women to conceive and bear children. Also, it became easier to wean children from the breast earlier because of the greater availability of soft foods, which are easily eaten by babies. This would have shortened the birth intervals, and the birth rate could have risen on that account alone, and to a level higher than the death rate, thus promoting population growth. However, the sedentary life and the higher-density living associated with farming probably also *raised* death rates by creating sanitation problems and heightening exposure to communicable diseases. Nonetheless, growth rates increased even in the face of higher mortality as fertility rates rose to a level slightly higher than the death rate.

It should be kept in mind, of course, that only a small difference between birth and death rates is required to account for the slow growth achieved after the Agricultural Revolution. Between 8000 BCE and 1750 CE, the world was adding an average of only 67,000 people each year to the population. Right now, as you read this, that many people are being added every seven hours.

Why Are More Recent Increases So Rapid?

The acceleration in population growth after 1750 was due largely to the declines in the death rate that came about as part of the scientific revolution that accompanied the Industrial Revolution. First in Europe and North America and more recently in the rest of the world, death rates have decreased sooner and much more rapidly than have fertility rates. The obvious result has been that many fewer people die than are born each year. In the more developed countries, declines in mortality at first were due to the effects of economic development and a rising standard of living—people were eating better, wearing warmer clothes, living in better houses, bathing more often, drinking cleaner water, and so on (McKeown 1976). These improvements in the human condition helped to lower exposure to disease and also to build up resistance to illness. Later, especially after 1900, much of the decline in mortality was due to improvements in public health and medical technology, including sanitation and especially vaccination against infectious diseases (Preston and Haines 1991).

Declines in the death rates first occurred only in those countries experiencing economic development. In each of these areas, primarily Europe and North America, fertility also began to decline within at least one or two generations after the death rate began its drop. However, since World War II, medical and public health technology has been available to virtually all countries of the world regardless of their level of economic development. In the less developed countries, although the risk of death has been lowered dramatically, birth rates have gone down less quickly, and the result is continuing population growth. Almost all the current growth of the world's population is originating in less developed nations. We say "originating" because some of that growth then spills into the more developed countries through migration. Between 2020 and 2050, the medium projections of the United Nations suggest that the world will add 1.94 billion people. Only 2 percent of this increase is expected to occur in the more developed nations.

How Many People Have Ever Lived?

The fact that we have gone from 1 billion to almost 8 billion in little more than 200 years has led some people to speculate that a majority of people ever born must surely still be alive. Let us burst that idea before it can take root in your mind. In fact, our current contribution to history's total represents only a relatively small fraction of all people who have ever lived. The first set of analyses was by Nathan Keyfitz (Keyfitz 1966; Keyfitz and Caswell 2005), and we have used his formulas to estimate the number of people who have ever lived, assuming conservatively that we started with two people (call them Adam and Eve if you'd like) 200,000 years ago. The results of these calculations suggest that as of 2020 a total of 77.8 billion people have ever been born, of whom the 7.8 billion estimated to be alive in 2020 constitute 10.0 percent. Another popular set of estimations are those by Carl Haub of the Population Reference Bureau (Haub 2011; Kaneda and Haub 2018). Those calculations assume that humans have been around for only the past 50,000 years (as we noted above with respect to *homo sapiens*), and that 108 billion humans have been born in that time, of which the current population represents 6.9 percent of the total.

You can appreciate that the number of people ever born is influenced by the length of time you believe humans have been around and, especially, by the estimate of the birth rate. There is no reasonable calculation, however, that generates a value much higher than 10 percent, so we can safely assume that only a small fraction of humans ever born are now alive, although the percentage is constantly getting (slightly) higher because of our ever larger population size. Furthermore, no matter how you calculate it, the dramatic drop in infant and childhood mortality over the last two centuries means that babies are now far more likely than ever to grow up to be adults. Thus the adults alive today actually do represent a considerable fraction of all people who have ever lived to *adulthood*.

Redistribution of the World's Population through Migration

The vast increase in numbers is not the only important demographic change to occur in the past few hundred years. There has also been a massive redistribution of the population. As populations have grown unevenly in different areas of the world, the pressures or desires to migrate have also grown. This pattern is predictable enough that we label it the migration transition component of the overall demographic transition (which we will discuss first in Chapter 3 and then more thoroughly in Chapter 6). Migration streams generally flow from areas where there are too few jobs to areas where there is more opportunity. Thus we have migration from Latin America and Asia to the United States, from Asia to Canada, from Africa and Asia to Europe, and within Europe from the east to the west.

In earlier decades, the shortage of jobs generally occurred when the population grew dense in a particular region, and people then felt pressured to migrate to some other less populated area, much as high-pressure storm fronts move into low-pressure weather systems. This is precisely the pattern of migration that characterized the expansion of European populations into other parts of the world, as European farmers sought land that they could work in less densely settled areas. This phenomenon of European expansion is, of course, critically important because as Europeans moved around the world, they altered patterns of life, including their own, wherever they went.

European Expansion   Beginning in the fourteenth century, migration out of Europe began gaining momentum, revolutionizing the entire human population in the process. With their gun (and germ)-laden sailboats, Europeans began to stake out the less developed areas of the world in the fifteenth and sixteenth centuries—and this was only the beginning. Migration of Europeans to other parts of the world on a massive scale took hold in the nineteenth century, when the European nations began both to industrialize and to swell in numbers due to the decline in mortality. As Kingsley Davis has put it:

> Although the continent was already crowded, the death rate began to drop and the population began to expand rapidly. Simultaneous urbanization, new occupations, financial panics, and unrestrained competition gave rise to status instability on a scale never known before. Many a bruised or disappointed European was ready to seek his fortune abroad, particularly since the new lands, tamed by the pioneers, no longer seemed wild and remote but rather like paradises where one could own land and start a new life. The invention of the steamship (the first one crossed the Atlantic in 1827) made the decision less irrevocable (Davis 1974:98).

Before the great expansion of European people and culture, Europeans represented about 18 percent of the world's population, with almost 90 percent of them living in Europe itself. By the 1930s, at the peak of European dominance in the world, people of European origin in Europe, North America, and Oceania accounted for 35 percent of the world's population (Durand 1967). By the beginning of the twenty-first century, the percentage had declined to 16, and it is projected to drop to 12 percent by the middle of the century (United Nations Population Division 2019). However, even that may be a bit of an exaggeration, since the rate of growth in North American and European countries is increasingly influenced by immigrants and births to immigrants from developing nations.

"South" to "North" Migration   Since the 1930s, the outward expansion of Europeans has ceased. Until then, European populations had been growing more rapidly than the populations in Africa, Asia, and Latin America, but since World War II that trend has been reversed. The less developed areas now have by far the most rapidly growing populations. It has been said that "population growth used to be a reward for doing well; now it's a scourge for doing badly" (Blake 1979). This change in the pattern of population growth has resulted in a shift in the direction of migration. For the past several decades there has been far more migration from less developed countries (the "South") to developed areas (the "North") than the reverse. Furthermore, since migrants are generally young adults of reproductive age, and since migrants from less developed areas generally have higher family size expectations than natives of the developed regions, their migration makes a disproportionate contribution over time to the overall population increase in the developed area to which they have migrated. As a result, the proportion of the population whose origin is one of the modern world's less developed nations tends to be on the rise in nearly every developed country. Within the United States, for example, non-Hispanic whites (the European-origin population) are no longer the majority in the state of California, and it is likely that the Hispanic-origin population (largely of Mexican ancestry) will represent the majority of Californians by the middle of this century since the majority of all births in California (as in all Southwestern states) are now to Hispanic mothers. Note that we use "Hispanic" rather than the often-used "Latino" or "Latinx" only because the term Hispanic is most often found in government statistics.

When Europeans migrated, they were generally filling up territory that had very few people, because they tended to be moving in on land used by hunter-gatherers who, as noted above, use land extensively rather than intensively. Those seemingly empty lands or frontiers have essentially disappeared today, and as a consequence migration into a country now results in more noticeable increases in population density. And, just as the migration of Europeans was typically greeted with violence from the indigenous population upon whose land they were encroaching, migrants today routinely meet prejudice, discrimination, and violence in the places to which they have moved. These days migrants are most likely to be moving to cities, because that's where the jobs are.

The Urban Revolution   Until very recently in world history, almost everyone lived in basically rural areas. Large cities were few and far between. For example, Rome's population of 650,000 in 100 CE was probably the largest in the ancient world (Chandler and Fox 1974). It is estimated that as recently as 1800, less than one percent of the world's population lived in cities of 100,000 or more. Nearly half of all humans now live in cities of that size.

The redistribution of people from rural to urban areas occurred earliest and most markedly in the industrialized nations. For example, in 1800 about 10 percent of the English population lived in urban areas, primarily London. Now, 90 percent of the British live in cities. Similar patterns of urbanization have been experienced in other European countries, the United States, Canada, and Japan as they have industrialized. In the less developed areas of the world, urbanization was initially associated with a commercial response to industrialization in these three places. In other words, in many areas where industrialization was not occurring, Europeans had established colonies or trade relationships. The principal economic activities in these areas were not industrial but commercial in nature, associated with buying and selling. The wealth acquired by people engaged in these activities naturally attracted attention and urban centers sprang up all over the world.

During the second half of the twentieth century, when the world began to urbanize in earnest, the underlying cause was the rapid growth of the rural population (we discuss this in more detail in Chapter 7). The rural population in every less developed nation has outstripped the ability of the agricultural economy to absorb it. As we noted above, it is a paradox that in order to grow enough food for an increasing population, people have had to be replaced by machines in agriculture, and that has sent the redundant rural population off to the cities in search of work. Herein lie the roots of many of the social problems confronting the world in the twenty-first century.

Geographic Distribution of the World's Population

The five most populous countries in the world account for nearly half the world's population (an estimated 47 percent in 2020) but only 21 percent of the world's land surface. These countries include China, India, the United States, Indonesia, and Brazil, as you can see in Table 1.2. Rounding out the top 10 are Pakistan, Nigeria, Bangladesh, Russia, and Mexico. Within these 10 most populous nations reside 58 percent of all people. You can see that you have to visit only the top 20 countries

Table 1.2   The Twenty Most Populous Countries in the World, 1950, 2020, and Projected to 2050

Rank	1950 Country	Population (in millions)	Area (000 sq miles)	2020 Country	Population (in millions)	Area (000 sq miles)	2050 Country	Population (in millions)	Area (000 sq miles)
1	China	563	3,601	China	1,425	3,601	India	1,639	1,148
2	India	370	1,148	India	1,383	1,148	China	1,402	3,601
3	Soviet Union	180	8,650	United States	331	3,536	Nigeria	401	352
4	United States	152	3,536	Indonesia	272	705	United States	379	3,536
5	Japan	84	145	Brazil	214	3,265	Pakistan	338	298
6	Indonesia	83	705	Pakistan	208	298	Indonesia	331	705
7	Germany	68	135	Nigeria	206	352	Brazil	229	3,265
8	Brazil	53	3,265	Bangladesh	170	50	Ethiopia	205	426
9	United Kingdom	50	93	Russia	144	6,521	Congo (Kinshasa)	194	905
10	Italy	47	114	Mexico	134	737	Bangladesh	193	50
11	Bangladesh	46	50	Japan	126	145	Egypt	160	384
12	France	42	212	Ethiopia	113	426	Mexico	155	737
13	Pakistan	39	298	Philippines	110	115	Philippines	144	115
14	Nigeria	32	352	Egypt	103	384	Russia	136	6,521
15	Mexico	28	737	Vietnam	98	126	Tanzania	129	365
16	Spain	28	193	Congo (Kinshasa)	90	905	Vietnam	110	126
17	Vietnam	26	126	Turkey	84	297	Japan	106	145
18	Poland	25	118	Iran	84	632	Iran	103	632
19	Egypt	21	384	Germany	83	93	Turkey	97	297
20	Philippines	21	115	Thailand	69	197	Kenya	92	224
Top 20		1,958	23,977		5,447	23,533		6,543	23,832
World		2,556	57,900		7,795	57,900		9,735	57,900
% top 5		53%	29%		47%	21%		43%	15%
% top 10		65%	37%		58%	35%		55%	25%
% top 20		77%	41%		70%	41%		67%	41%

Source: Adapted by John R. Weeks from Population Division of the Department of Economic and Social Affairs of the United Nations Secretariat, World Population Prospects 2019. Projections to 2050 are based on the medium fertility variant.

in order to shake hands with seven out of every ten people (70 percent) in the world. In doing so, you would travel across 41 percent of the earth's land surface. The rest of the population is spread out among 214 other countries that account for the remaining 59 percent of the earth's terrain.

If you set a goal to be as efficient as possible in maximizing the number of people you visit while minimizing the distance you travel, your best bet would be to schedule a trip to China and the Indian subcontinent. Four out of every ten people live in those two contiguous regions of Asia, and in Figure 1.1, at the beginning of this chapter, you can see how these areas stand out in the map of the world drawn with country size proportionate to population. Population growth in Asia is not a new story. In 1500, as Europeans were venturing beyond their shores, China and India (or more technically the Indian subcontinent, including the modern nations of India, Pakistan, and Bangladesh) were already the most populous places on earth, and all of Asia accounted for 53 percent of the world's 461 million people. Five centuries later, the population in Asian countries accounts for 61 percent of all the people on earth, although it is projected to drop back to 58 percent by the year 2050 because of the recent dramatic drop in fertility throughout most of Asia.

Sub-Saharan Africa, on the other hand, had about as many people as Europe did in 1500, comprising 17 percent of the world's population at that time. However, contact with Europeans tended to be deadly for Africans because of disease, violence and, especially, slavery. It has been estimated that the export slave trade actually reversed African population growth from 1730 to 1850 (Manning and Griffith 1988). By the twentieth century, however, sub-Saharan Africa had rebounded in population size, comprising 14 percent of the total world population in 2020, and projected to be 26 percent of the total by 2050—well beyond where it had been in percentage terms in the year 1500, and with four times as many people as are projected to be in Europe in that year. In Table 1.2 you can see that in 1950 there were four European nations in the top 10 with respect to population (the former Soviet Union, West Germany, United Kingdom, and Italy) and no countries from Africa in that group. A century later, in 2050, it is projected that there will be no European countries in the top 10, whereas there will be three from Africa (Nigeria, Democratic Republic of Congo, and Ethiopia).

Global Variation in Population Size and Growth

World population is currently growing at a rate of 1.1 percent annually, implying a net addition of 81 million people per year (see Figure 1.3), but there is a lot of variability underlying those global numbers. Germany and Russia, along with most countries in Southern and Eastern Europe, are expected to have fewer people in 2050 than in 2020. That is also the expectation for both China and Japan. Growth will take place largely in the less developed nations, and in Figure 1.4 you can see where countries with the highest and lowest rates of growth are geographically. The most rapidly growing regions in the world tend to be in the mid-latitudes, and these are nations that are least developed economically—the "Global South;" whereas the slowest growing are the richer nations, which tend to be more northerly and

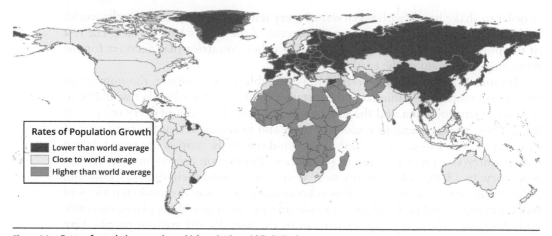

Figure 1.4   Rates of population growth are highest in the middle latitudes

Note: The average rate of growth at the country level between 2015 and 2020 was 1.1 percent per year. Close to world average is defined as between 0.6 to 1.6 percent per year; lower than world average is less than 0.6, and higher than world average is above 1.6.

Source: Adapted by John R. Weeks from Population Division of the Department of Economic and Social Affairs of the United Nations Secretariat, World Population Prospects 2019.

southerly (even though we label them as the "Global North"). It has not always been that way, however.

Before the Great Depression of the 1930s, the populations of Europe and, especially, North America were the most rapidly growing in the world. During the decade of the 1930s, however, growth rates declined in those two areas to match approximately those of most of the rest of the world, which was about 0.75 percent per year—a doubling time of 93 years. After World War II, rates of growth took off in Africa, Asia, and Latin America, but as we moved into the twenty-first century, the situation has changed again, and now Europe and much of East Asia are on the verge of depopulation while rapid growth is occurring predominantly in Africa and Western Asia, along with Central America—the last holdout of rapid population growth in Latin America.

Let's examine these trends in more detail, focusing particular attention on the ten most populous nations, with a few other countries included to help illustrate the variability of demographic situations in which countries find themselves.

North America

The United States and Canada—North America—have a combined population of 369 million as of 2020, representing just under 5 percent of the world's total. The United States, with 331 million (third largest in the world), has 90 percent of North America's population, with Canada's 38 million people accounting for the remaining 10 percent. The demographic trajectories of the two countries are intertwined but are not identical.

United States   It does not take a demographer to notice that the population of the United States has undergone a total transformation since John Cabot (an Italian hired by the British to search the New World) landed in Newfoundland in 1497 and claimed North America for the British. As was true throughout the western hemisphere, European guns and diseases rather quickly decimated the native American Indian population, making it easier to establish a new culture. Europeans had diseases and weapons that had never been seen by the indigenous populations, but the indigenous population had nothing that was new and dangerous to the Europeans, save perhaps for syphilis (Crosby 1972).

No one knows the size of the indigenous population in North America when the Europeans arrived, which of course leads to a lot of speculation (Mann 2011). After reviewing the evidence, Matthew Snipp (1989) concluded that in 1492 the number might have been anywhere between two and five million (keep in mind that Central and South America had much larger populations). We are more certain that by 1850, disease and warfare had reduced the native population to perhaps as few as 250,000, while the European population had increased to 25 million. Indeed, it was widely assumed that the American Indian population was on the verge of disappearing (Snipp 1989).

Early America was a model of demographic decimation for the indigenous population, while being a model of rapid population growth for the European-origin population. Yet even among the latter it was a land of substantial demographic contrasts. Among the colonies existing in the seventeenth century, for example, those in New England seem to have been characterized by very high birth rates (women had an average of seven to nine children) yet relatively low mortality rates (infant mortality rates in Plymouth Colony may have been as low as in some of today's less developed nations, apparently a result of the fairly good health of Americans even during that era) (Demos 1965; Wells 1971, 1982). Demos notes that "the popular impression today that colonial families were extremely large finds the strongest possible confirmation in the case of Plymouth. A sample of some ninety families, about whom there is fairly reliable information, suggests that there was an average of seven to eight children per family who actually grew to adulthood" (1965:270). In the southern colonies during the same time period, however, life was apparently much harsher, probably because the environment was more amenable to the spread of disease, including yellow fever and malaria. In the Chesapeake Bay colony of Charles Parish, higher mortality meant that few parents had more than two or three living children at the time of their death (Smith 1978).

Despite the regional diversity, the American population grew rather steadily during the seventeenth and eighteenth centuries, and though some of the increase in the number of Europeans in America was attributable to in-migration, the greater percentage actually was due to natural increase (the excess of births over deaths). The nation's first census, taken in 1790, shortly after the American Revolution, counted 3.9 million Americans, and although the population was increasing by nearly 120,000 a year, only about three percent of the increase was a result of immigration. With a crude birth rate of about 55 births per thousand population (higher than any country in the world today) and a crude death rate of about 28 deaths per thousand (also higher than any country in the world today), there were twice as many people being born each year as were dying. At this rate, the population was doubling in size every 25 years.

Though Americans may picture foreigners pouring in seeking freedom or fortune, it was not until the last third of the nineteenth century that migration became a substantial factor in American population growth. In fact, during the first half of the nineteenth century, immigrants accounted for less than five percent of the population increase in each decade, whereas in every decade from the 1850s through the 1920s immigrants accounted for at least 20 percent of the growth of population.

Throughout the late nineteenth and early twentieth centuries, the birth rate in the United States was falling. There is evidence that fertility among American Quakers began to be limited at about the time of the American Revolution (Wells 1971; Leasure 1989), and the rest of the nation was only a few decades behind their pace. By the 1930s, fertility actually dropped below replacement level (as we discuss in Chapter 5). Furthermore, since restrictions on immigration (discussed in Chapter 6) had all but halted the influx of foreigners during the Great Depression, Americans were facing the prospect of potential depopulation.

Then, in the early post–World War II era, forecasts of population decline were upset and replaced by the realities of a population explosion. The result was the period from 1946 to 1964 generally known as the "baby boom" era. It was a time when the United States experienced a rapid rate of increase in population accomplished almost entirely by increases in fertility. The baby boom, in turn, was followed in the late 1960s and early 1970s by a "baby bust" (now widely known as Generation X, as we discuss in the next chapter). Fertility bounced back up a bit in the 1990s, but since 2005 it has been declining, dropping again to below-replacement level.

Despite this low fertility, however, population growth has continued to be the order of the day largely because in the 1960s and then again in the 1990s adjustments in the nation's immigration laws opened the doors wider. Indeed, the one million immigrants (legal and estimated undocumented) being added each year account for nearly 40 percent of the annual increase in population. More importantly, from a demographic perspective, immigrants are primarily people of reproductive age and they are having children at a rate that is above replacement level. Indeed, variations in fertility levels in the United States are increasingly determined by fertility differences among the various racial and ethnic groups.

Canada   The French were the first Europeans to settle the area that has become Canada, but in 1763 the French government ceded control of the region to the British. A century later the British North America Act of 1867 united all of the provinces of Canada into the Dominion of Canada, and every census since then has asked about "origins" as a way of keeping track of the numerical balance between the historically rival French-speaking and English-speaking groups (Boyd, Goldmann, and White 2000).

In the seventeenth and eighteenth centuries, the high fertility of French speakers in Canada was legendary, and they maintained higher-than-average levels of fertility until the 1960s (Beaujot 1978), probably due to the strong influence of the Catholic Church in Québec (McQuillan 2004). In the rest of Canada, fertility began to drop in the nineteenth century and, as in the United States, reached very low levels in the 1930s before rebounding after World War II in a baby boom that was similar in its impact on Canadian society to that experienced in the United States. This boom was similarly followed by a baby bust and then a small echo of the baby boom. Canada (including the province of Quebec) now has a fertility level that is well below replacement (1.6 children per woman).

Just as fertility is lower in Canada than in the United States, so is mortality, with life expectancy in Canada about two years longer than in the United States. In both of these respects the demographic profile of Canada is more like that of Europe than of the United States. However, when it comes to immigration, Canada more closely reflects the Northern American history of being a receiving ground for people from other nations. Despite its lower fertility, Canada's overall rate of population growth exceeds that of the United States because it accepts more immigrants per person than the United States does (though the United States accepts a higher total number).

Mexico and Central America

Mexico (which the United Nations includes in Central America, although some people put Mexico in North America) and the other countries of Central America have also been growing since the end of World War II as a result of rapidly dropping death rates and birth rates that have only more recently begun to drop. With an estimated population in 2020 of 134 million (tenth most populous in the world, as shown in Table 1.2), Mexico accounts for about three-fourths of the population of the region, with the remainder distributed among (in order of size) Guatemala, Honduras, El Salvador, Nicaragua, Costa Rica, Panama, and Belize. The combined regional population of 184 million as estimated for the year 2020 is a little more than 2 percent of the world's total.

Indigenous populations in Mexico and Central America had developed more advanced agricultural societies than had those in North America at the time of European contact. The Aztec civilization in central Mexico and the remnants of the Mayan civilization farther south centered near Guatemala encompassed many millions more people than lived on the northern side of what is now the United States–Mexico border. This fact, combined with the Spanish goal of extracting resources (a polite term for plundering) from the New World rather than colonizing it, produced a very different demographic legacy from what we find in Canada and the United States.

Mexico was the site of a series of agricultural civilizations as far back as 2,500 years before the invasion by the Spanish in 1519. Within a relatively short time after Europeans arrived, however, the population of several million was cut by as much as 80 percent due to disease and violence. This population collapse (a true implosion) was precipitated especially by contact with European diseases, but it reflects the fact that mortality was already very high before the arrival of the Europeans, and it did not take much to upset the demographic balance (Alchon 1997). By the beginning of the twentieth century, life expectancy was still very low in Mexico, less than 30 years (Morelos 1994), and fertility was very high in response to the high death rate. However, since the 1930s the death rate has dropped dramatically, and life expectancy in Mexico is now 80 years for women, six years above the world average and only two years less than in the United States.

For several decades, this decline in mortality was not accompanied by a change in the birth rate, and the result was a massive explosion in the size of the Mexican population. In 1920, before the death rate began to drop, there were 14 million people in Mexico (Mier y Terán 1991). By 1950 that had nearly doubled to 26 million, and by 1970, it had nearly doubled again to 49 million. In the 1970s, the birth rate finally began to decline in Mexico, encouraged by a change in government policy that began promoting small families and the provision of family planning. Mexican women had been bearing an average of six children each for many decades (if not centuries), but by 2020 this figure is estimated to have dropped to 2.1 children per woman for the country, and in the capital of Mexico City fertility had dropped below replacement level as long ago as the year 2000 (INEGI 2013). Nonetheless, until very recently the massive buildup of young people had been straining every ounce of the Mexican economy, encouraging out-migration, especially to the United States.

Most of the other countries of Central America have experienced similar patterns of rapidly declining mortality, leading to population growth and its attendant pressures for migration to other countries where the opportunities might be better. Not every country in the region has experienced the same fertility decline as Mexico, however. In particular, Guatemala, Honduras and El Salvador—the so-called "Northern Triangle"—are countries in which a high proportion of the population is indigenous (rather than being of mixed native and European origin), and Guatemala and Honduras, in particular, have birth rates that are above the world average, partly as a result of their very high rates of adolescent fertility (Shakya, Weeks, and Christakis 2019). These demographic factors compound the political and economic corruption in those countries and have encouraged entire families to migrate north to seek asylum in the United States, abetted by North American nonprofit organizations and, more importantly, human traffickers.

South America

The 436 million inhabitants of South America as of 2020 represent about six percent of the world's total population, with Brazil—the world's fifth most populous country—accounting for half of that. The modern history of Brazil began when Portuguese explorers found an indigenous hunter-gatherer population in that region and tried to enslave them to work on plantations. These attempts were unsuccessful, and the Portuguese wound up populating the colony largely with African slaves. The four million slaves taken to Brazil represent more than one-third of all enslaved persons transported from Africa to the western hemisphere between the sixteenth and nineteenth centuries (Thomas 1997). The Napoleonic Wars in Europe in the early part of the nineteenth century allowed Brazil, like most Latin American countries, to gain independence from Europe, and the economic development that followed ultimately led to substantial migration into Brazil from Europe during the latter part of the nineteenth century. At the same time, Brazil was the last country in the Western Hemisphere to outlaw slavery, doing so in 1888. Brazil is a society that is now about half European-origin and half African-origin or mixed race. The country also attracted Japanese immigrants early in the twentieth century and again after World War II.

Brazil boasts a land area nearly equal in size to the United States, upon which an estimated 214 million people currently reside. Between the 1960s and the 1990s, Brazil experienced a reduction in fertility described as "nothing short of spectacular" (Martine 1996:47). In 1960, the average Brazilian woman was giving birth to more than 6 children, but it had dropped to 2.5 by 1995 and it has since declined even further to 1.7—well below replacement level. For many years, the influence of the Catholic Church was strong enough to cause the government to forbid the dissemination of contraceptive information or devices. However, economic development beginning in the1960s seems clearly to have overridden the Church's influence and encouraged a decline in fertility, even if that drop was spatially uneven—starting first in the south and southeast and then spreading north and northeast from there (Schmertmann, Potter, and Cavenaghi 2008). The infant mortality rate of 13 deaths per 1,000 live births in Brazil is half the world average, and female life expectancy of 79 years is well above the world average.

The other countries of South America can be loosely divided into those three most southerly nations (including Argentina, Chile, and Uruguay) in which the populations are predominantly of European origin, and the remaining countries with higher proportions of indigenous and mixed (mestizo) populations. The former tend to have lower fertility and higher life expectancy—levels very similar to Brazil's. The other countries tend to have higher fertility, somewhat higher mortality, and higher rates of population growth.

Europe

The combined population of Western, Northern (including Scandinavia), Southern, and Eastern Europe (including Russia) is about 743 million, or about 10 percent of the world's total. Russia is currently the most populous, accounting for 19 percent of Europe's total. With 144 million, it is the ninth most populous country in the world. The next most populous countries in Europe are, in order, Germany (nineteenth most populous in the world), the United Kingdom, France, and Italy and they, along with Russia, comprise more than half of all Europeans.

Europe as a region is on the verge of depopulating. This is because several European countries, including its two largest nations, Russia and Germany, currently have more deaths than births and they are not taking in enough immigrants to compensate for that fact. Not a single country in Eastern or Southern Europe is projected by the United Nations demographers to have more people in 2050 than they currently have, whereas nearly every one of the Northern and Western European countries—except Germany—is expected to have the same number or slightly more people by mid-century.

It is not a coincidence that German demographics look more like eastern than Western Europe. When East Germany was reunited with West Germany in 1990, the combined Germany inherited the East's dismal demographics and that largely explains why Germany teeters on depopulation. Russia's situation is especially noteworthy because depopulation is not just a result of below replacement fertility. Until very recently, life expectancy for males was actually declining, signaling major societal stresses. In fact, researchers have argued that the breakup of the Soviet Union was foreshadowed by its rise in death rates (Feshbach and Friendly 1992; Shkolnikov, Meslé, and Vallin 1996). The birth rate was already low in Russia before the breakup, and since then the average number of children being born per woman has remained well below replacement level.

The rest of Europe has experienced very low birth rates without the drop in life expectancy that has plagued Russia. Where population growth is occurring, such as in France, the United Kingdom, and Ireland, it is largely attributable to the immigration of people from less developed nations as well as from Eastern Europe.

It should not be a surprise that fertility and mortality are both low in Europe, since that is the part of the world where mortality first began its worldwide decline approximately 250 years ago and where fertility began *its* worldwide decline about 150 years ago. What is surprising, however, is how low the birth rate has fallen. It is especially low in the Mediterranean countries of Italy and Spain, where fertility has dropped well below replacement level—in predominantly Catholic societies where fertility for most of history has been higher than in the rest of Europe. France, Sweden, and Norway—countries that were among the earliest to experience declines in fertility—have emerged with fertility rates that are now among the highest in Europe, although still below the replacement level. As we discuss in both Chapters 5 and 9, it is likely that an improvement in the status of women may be required to push fertility levels in Europe back up to the replacement level. Throughout Eastern and Southern Europe women have been given the opportunity for education and a career, but traditional attitudes remain in terms of their domestic role. Combining a career with family-building is generally frowned upon and, in response, women have tended to choose a career and either a small family or no family at all.

We have already mentioned that a major consequence of the low birth rate is an aging of the population that has left Europe with too few young people to take jobs and pay taxes. Into this void have swept millions of immigrants, many of them illegal, and Europeans are very divided in their reaction to this phenomenon. Some see the immigrants as the necessary resource that will keep the economy running and pension checks flowing for aging Europeans. Others see the immigrants as a very real threat to the European way of life, coming as they mainly do from Africa and Asia.

North Africa and Western Asia

The areas of the world usually described as North Africa and Western Asia are very similar to what is often called the MENA (Middle East and North Africa) region—which we discuss in more detail in the essay in this chapter. However, though Iran is part of MENA it is technically in South Asia, not Western Asia, and there are a few countries north of MENA that were once part of the former Soviet Union, but are technically in Western Asia. Overall, North Africa and Western Asia have a combined estimated population of 527 million as of 2020, which is projected to increase to 754 million by 2050. The region is characterized especially by the presence of Islam (with the obvious notable exception of Israel), and by being one of the more rapidly growing areas of the world, in which violence and conflict have all too often gone hand-in-hand with population growth and youth bulges.

Egypt is the most populous of the countries in North Africa and Western Asia, with 103 million people (fourteenth most populous in the world), followed by Turkey with 84 million (seventeenth most populous). Together they account for three-fourths of the region's total population. Keep in mind that right next door to Turkey is Iran, also with 84 million (eighteenth most populous in the world), even though the UN definitions put Iran in South Asia, not Western Asia, as we noted above.

Egyptians are crowded into the narrow Nile Valley. With its rate of growth of 2.1 percent per year, Egypt's population would double in 33 years without a significant drop in the birth rate, and this rapid growth constantly hampers even the most ambitious strategies for economic growth and development. Indeed, this is almost certainly a key reason for the political turmoil in Egypt. As is true for nearly all countries in this region of the world, the explosive growth in numbers is due to the dramatic drop in mortality since the end of World War II. In 1937, life expectancy at birth in Egypt was less than 40 years (Omran and Roudi 1993), whereas by now it has risen to 72. Even with such an improvement in mortality, however, death rates are just at the world average, while the number of children born to women (3.4) is well above the world average (2.4). Because of this high fertility, a very high proportion (34 percent) of the population is under age 15, and that is part of the recipe for the problems that beset Egypt.

Turkey has fared better demographically than most of the Arab nations that were once in its orbit when Turkey was the political center of the Ottoman Empire. Its fertility has recently dropped to replacement level and life expectancy is five years above the global average. The percentage of the population under age 15 is steadily declining, and the overall rate of growth is lower than its neighbors. Its demography is edging closer to a European pattern, consistent with its push to join the European Union. Note that the western part of Turkey (closer to Europe) is demographically more European than the eastern part of the country, where fertility is much higher and female literacy much lower (Isik and Pinarcioglu 2006; Courbage and Todd 2011). It is notable that Turkey's southeastern neighbors—Iraq and Syria—have high birth rates, high growth rates, high fractions under age 15, and high levels of conflict and violence. Unfortunately, these countries seem more typical of the region than does Turkey.

Sub-Saharan Africa

According to most evidence, sub-Saharan Africa is the place from which all human life originated (see, for example, Wilson and Cann 1992; Harari 2015), and the more than one billion people living there now comprise 14 percent of the world's

Connecting the Demographic Dots in the Middle East

The population of the Middle East and North Africa (MENA) is mostly, although not entirely, Arab and has been in demographic and political flux for a very long time. As we discuss in this chapter, it is comprised of all North African countries and several Western Asian nations (you can see the list in the table accompanying this essay). It is especially the size and rate of increase in the youthful population that has been explosive throughout MENA. Somewhat presciently prior to the Arab Spring that erupted in 2010, *The Economist* (2009:8) put it succinctly: "By far the biggest difficulty facing the Arabs—and the main item in the catalogue of socio-economic woes submitted as evidence of looming upheaval—is demography." The rapid drop in mortality after World War II, followed by a long delay in the start of fertility decline, produced a very large population of young people in need of jobs. They have spread throughout the region looking for work, and many have gone to Europe and North and South America. The economies within the region have not been able to keep up with the demand for jobs, and this has produced a generation of young people who, despite being better educated than their parents, face an uncertain future in an increasingly crowded world. The demographic situation has fueled discontent and has almost certainly contributed to the rise of radical Islam and terrorism, while helping to bring down the governments of Tunisia, Libya, and Egypt, and sparking long civil wars in Syria and Yemen.

The politics underpinning the uprising stretch back decades, with the region especially roiled by the creation of the state of Israel in the late 1940s. To put that decision into historical context you need to understand that at the end of World War I, the British took control of Palestine, which included the territory of what is now modern Israel and Jordan, from the remnants of the Ottoman Empire. As early as 1917, under the Balfour Declaration, the British had already agreed to help establish a Jewish national home in Palestine. Then, in the 1930s and 1940s, when European anti-Semitism encouraged the mass migration of Jews to Palestine, the resulting change in the demographics of the region led inexorably in the direction of a Jewish state. Not unexpectedly, this influx of European Jews was resisted, first by Palestinian Arabs and subsequently by virtually all Arab states.

In 1946, at the end of World War II, the modern state of Jordan was granted full independence, and Britain handed the decision about Palestine to the United Nations. In 1947 the United Nations passed General Assembly Resolution 181, which ". . . provided for the creation of two states, one Arab and the other Jewish, in Palestine, and an international regime for Jerusalem. The Zionists (those in support of a Jewish state) approved of the plan but the Arabs, having already rejected an earlier, more favorable (for them) partition offer from Britain, stood firm in their demand for sovereignty over Palestine in full" (Oren 2002:4). The stage was thus set for the continuing struggle for control of the region. The nascent state of Israel was immediately attacked by armies from all surrounding Arab nations but managed to prevail, and when hostilities ended in 1949 Israel had claimed more territory than originally allotted to it by the United Nations. Because as many as 750,000 of Palestine's Arabs (who came to be known simply as Palestinians) had fled the area when fighting broke out, the Jewish population emerged as the demographic majority. The Palestinian population was effectively cordoned into the Gaza Strip and the West Bank.

During the more than half century since the creation of Israel, its continued existence has been a political issue on the world stage, and the entire MENA region has been increasing dramatically in population size—always a powerful underlying force for change. In 1950 MENA had a population of 81 million (see the table accompanying this essay)—almost exactly the same as the population of Japan in that year. But the estimated MENA population in 2020 is 465 million—nearly a 500 percent increase!! By comparison, Japan had increased to only 126 million in 2020, a 56 percent increase. The United Nations Population Division projects the MENA region to add nearly 200 million more people by 2050, to a whopping 658 million, while Japan is projected to decline down to 106 million. In 1950 the region was dominated demographically by Egypt and Iran, and although they are still the two *most* populous countries, they are no longer the *only* populous countries.

Countries of the MENA Region by Population Size, Total Fertility Rate, and Percent of the Population Under the Age of 15

Country	Population (millions) in:			% < 15 in 2020	TFR 2020
	1950	2020	2050		
Iraq	6	42	71	40	4.27
Yemen	5	30	48	39	3.84
West Bank and Gaza (Palestine)	1	5	9	39	3.91
Jordan	1	10	13	34	3.26
Syria	3	19	33	34	2.84
Egypt	21	103	160	33	3.15
Algeria	9	43	61	30	2.65
Israel	1	9	13	28	2.92
Libya	1	7	8	27	2.21
Morocco	9	37	46	27	2.42
Saudi Arabia	3	35	45	24	2.48
Tunisia	3	12	14	24	2.15
Iran	17	84	103	23	1.62
Lebanon	1	6	6	22	1.97
Kuwait	0	4	5	21	1.00
Oman	1	5	7	21	2.54
Bahrain	0	2	2	18	2.12
Qatar	0	3	4	14	1.88
United Arab Emirates	0	10	10	14	1.72
MENA Region	81	465	658	30	

Note: Projections are based on the medium fertility assumptions; not also that Turkey is not included in most definitions of MENA.
Source: Adapted by John R. Weeks using data from United Nations Population Division (2019).

It is not a coincidence that the countries with the highest levels of volatility are those with the highest birth rates (expressed here as the total fertility rate—the average number of children per woman of reproductive age—which we discuss in detail in Chapter 5), and the highest percentages of the population that are under the age of 15. These are good indicators of a youth bulge that can portend disaster if not handled well (Weeks and Fugate 2012).

As both populations and political tensions have exploded, the region has also been pushing hard against its environmental constraints—especially water. Thomas Friedman, writing in the *New York Times*, produced a very cogent analysis of the situation: "All these tensions over land, water and food are telling us something: The Arab awakening was driven not only by political and economic stresses, but, less visibly, by environmental, population and climate stresses as well. If we focus

(continued)

Connecting the Demographic Dots in the Middle East (*Continued*)

only on the former and not the latter, we will never be able to help stabilize these societies" (Friedman 2012). The World Bank (2008) noted that MENA is the most water scarce region in the world, and it is getting worse as the population grows.

The implosion of Syria into civil war also had demographic, environmental, and political roots, and the consequence of the war has been a huge displacement of people. The flood of refugees out of the country has been an enormous problem for Syria's neighbors and for Europe, to where many of the refugees tried to escape, as we discuss in Chapter 6. There have also been millions of people internally displaced as warring factions in Syria bombed neighborhoods in one city after another, forcing people to flee for their lives (keeping in mind that tens of thousands have been killed).

The Humanitarian Information Unit of the U.S. Department of State tries to monitor these kinds of population movements, and in the accompanying infographic you get a sense of the demographic impact of the Syrian conflict. The bottom line is that this region is on course to continue its extreme rate of population growth even in the face of political turmoil and serious environmental constraints. This suggests that regional stability may be a long way away, and the effects will ripple throughout the world.

Discussion Questions: (1) Do you think there is a causal relationship between population growth in the MENA region and armed conflict? Why or why not? **(2)** How do you think the status of women in the Middle East might be influencing both demographic and political trends?

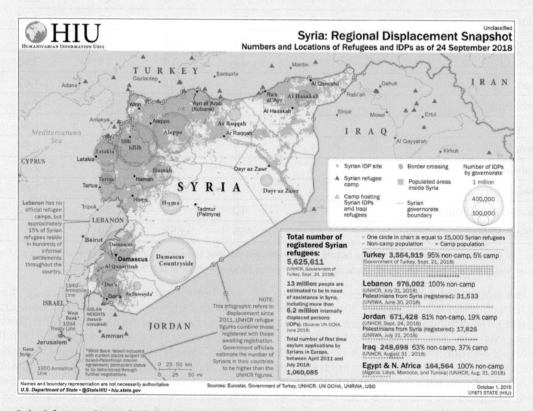

Syrian Refugees and Internally Displaced Persons as of 2018

Source: U.S. Department of State Humanitarian Information Unit: https://hiu.state.gov/hiu-products/Syria _DisplacementSnapshot_2018Oct01_HIU_U1873.pdf (accessed 2019).

total. Nigeria, with 206 million (seventh most populous in the world) accounts for one in five of those billion people, followed by Ethiopia (twelfth most populous) and the Democratic Republic of the Congo (sixteenth most populous in the world). Note that there are two countries with Congo in the name: the most populous (the Democratic Republic) has Kinshasa as its capital; and the other less populous Republic of Congo has Brazzaville as its capital.

All three of these populous sub-Saharan African countries (as well as their neighbors) have incredibly high levels of fertility, especially considering the fact that death rates are much lower than they used to be. In the Congo the average woman is currently having 6.3 children each, in Nigeria she is having 5.5, and in Ethiopia she is having 4.4 children. Not surprisingly, these high birth rates, in combination with declining infant and child mortality, produce young populations. All three of these countries have more than 40 percent of the population under age 15. This means rapid population growth, and Nigeria is projected to vault over the United States as the third most populous country by the middle of this century. The Congo and Ethiopia are both projected to move into the top 10, and their neighbors, Tanzania, and Kenya, are projected to move into the top 20 by 2050, as you can see in Table 1.2.

Given the high rates of population growth of these already populous sub-Saharan African countries, it is not surprising that they are beset by internal violence and conflict. Nigeria is home to Boko Haram, one of the world's most notorious terrorist groups. In 2019 the Ethiopian government announced that it was delaying the population census count because of political instability. More than one million people have fled their homes largely because of ethnic-driven conflict in the country (Hailu 2019). The Congo has more than four million internally displaced persons, according to data from the United Nations High Commissioner for Refugees, most of whom are also victims of inter-ethnic conflict.

South and Southeast Asia

South and Southeast Asia as a region is home to 2.6 billion people, one-third of the world's total. The Indian subcontinent dominates this area demographically—India (the world's second most populous nation), Pakistan (sixth), and Bangladesh (eighth) encompass two-thirds of the region's population. But Indonesia, the world's fourth most populous nation (and the one with the largest Muslim population in the world), is also part of Southeast Asia, as are two other countries on the top 20 list—the Philippines (thirteenth) and Vietnam (fifteenth). And we cannot forget that Iran, the world's nineteenth most populous nation, is technically in South Asia, even though also in MENA, as we noted previously.

India, Pakistan, and Bangladesh   Second to China in population size, at least for the moment, is India, with the current population estimated to be almost 1.4 billion, but projected to be almost 1.6 billion (more populous than China) by the middle of this century (see Table 1.2). Mortality is somewhat higher in India than in China, and the birth rate is quite a bit higher. Indian females have a life expectancy at birth of 70 years—four years below the world average, but a substantial improvement over the 27 years that prevailed back in the 1920s (Adlahka and Banister 1995). The infant mortality rate of 34 per 1,000 is higher than the world average, but it is also far lower than it was just a few decades ago. Women are bearing children at a rate of 2.3 each, although in urban areas it has dropped to below replacement level, as we discuss in Chapter 7, and most children in India now survive to adulthood. With an annual growth rate of 1.4 percent, the Indian population is increasing by 19 million people each year. Thus, nearly one in four people being added to the world's population annually is from India. The population of the Indian subcontinent is already more populous than mainland China, and that does not take into account the millions of people of Indian and Pakistani origin who are living elsewhere in the world.

India's population is culturally diverse, and this is reflected in rather dramatic geographic differences in fertility and rates of population growth within the country. In the southern states of Kerala and Tamil Nadu, fertility had dropped below the replacement level by the mid-1990s and has stayed there since. However, in the four most populous states in the north (Bihar, Madhya Pradesh, Rajasthan, and Uttar Pradesh), where 40 percent of the Indian population lives, the average woman was bearing more than three children, according to the most recent fertility survey data (2015–16) as of this writing (DHS Program 2019).

At the end of World War II, when India was granted its independence from British rule, the country was divided into predominantly Hindu India and predominantly Muslim Pakistan, with the latter having territory divided between West Pakistan and East Pakistan. In 1971, a civil war erupted between the two disconnected Pakistans and, with the help of India, East Pakistan won the war and became Bangladesh. Although Pakistan and Bangladesh are both Muslim, Bangladesh has a demographic profile that now looks more like India than Pakistan. The average woman in Bangladesh now gives birth to 2.1 children (slightly fewer than in India), whereas fertility in Pakistan has remained much higher (currently 3.1 children per woman). The overall rate of population growth in Bangladesh is 1.4 percent per year (exactly the same as India's), but it is 1.9 percent per year in Pakistan. Still, both Pakistan and Bangladesh have grown so much since independence in 1947 that, were they still one country, they would be the third most populous nation in the world.

Indonesia, the Philippines and Vietnam Indonesia is a string of nearly 18,000 islands in Southeast Asia, with an estimated 265 million people spread out among nearly 1,000 of those islands. A former Dutch colony, it has experienced a substantial decline in fertility in recent years, but Indonesian women nonetheless are bearing 2.4 children each, which puts them right at the world average. Given the increasing life expectancy, now just three years below the world average, the population is growing at 1.2 percent per year—right at the world average. For several decades, Indonesia has dealt with population growth through a program of transmigration in which people have been sent from the more populous to the less populous islands. These largely forested outer islands have suffered environmentally from the human encroachment, without necessarily dealing successfully with

Indonesia's basic dilemma, which is how to raise its burgeoning young adult population out of poverty. This dilemma has contributed to increased political instability, as well as a rise in the level of Islamic fundamentalism and terrorism.

The Philippines is a set of more than 7,000 islands to the north of Indonesia. About 2,000 of those islands are inhabited. It has even higher fertility than Indonesia (an average of 2.7 children per woman), but also experiences more out-migration than Indonesia does. Although the country is predominantly Catholic, concentrated especially in the northern Luzon islands, there have long been clashes with Muslims who reside mainly in the southern group of islands comprising Mindanao. These ethno-religious differences are reflected in the demographic trends, with lower fertility and child mortality in the Luzon region than in the Mindanao region.

Back on the Asian mainland, we find that Vietnam has boomed demographically since the days when the United States was involved in this region's conflict. Population estimates for Vietnam in 2020 (98 million—fifteenth most populous in the world) show that the country has exactly doubled in size since the Vietnam War ended in 1975. That was largely a result of a swift drop in mortality unaccompanied immediately by a decline in fertility, thus leading to a huge youth bulge. Recognizing the threat to development, Vietnam introduced a national family planning policy in 1988 encouraging (although not forcing) couples to have only one or two children (Goodkind 1995). That policy, in concert with Chinese-style free-market economic reforms, led to an equally swift drop in the number of children per woman—from six each in 1975 to replacement level in 2000, where it has stayed. The result has been the same kind of demographic dividend that China has experienced, as we discuss below.

Iran   With 82 million people, Iran is the most populous Shia-majority Muslim country in the world (followed by Iraq, Azerbaijan, and Bahrain—the only other Shia-majority countries). Like Vietnam, it has experienced a very rapid fertility decline—from six children each as recently as 1985 to below replacement level today (Lutz, Crespo Cuaresma, and Abbasi-Shavazi 2010; Courbage and Todd 2011). This has gone hand-in-hand with a rise in female literacy and other forms of modernization taking place in the country, despite the generally conservative attitude of the government. Here again we see a population that now has low fertility and high life expectancy but which is still experiencing fairly rapid population growth because of the momentum built into the large youth bulge created by the high fertility of the recent past. We will return to the theme of population momentum in Chapter 8 in the discussion of the age transition.

East Asia

East Asia has 1.6 billion people, dominated demographically by China, the most populous country in the world with 1.4 billion people, and Japan, the eleventh most populous even though its 126 million is less than ten percent of China's size. Overall, East Asia includes just under 20 percent of the world's total population, though its share is diminishing as China continues to pump the brakes on its population growth and as Japan slowly depopulates (it is projected to decline to 106 million by the middle of this century).

China   The People's Republic of China dominates the map of the world drawn to scale according to population size, with one-fifth of all humans on the planet (see Figure 1.1). If we add in the Chinese in Taiwan (which the government of mainland China still claims as its own), Singapore, and the overseas Chinese elsewhere in the world, closer to one out of every four people is of Chinese origin. Nonetheless, China's share of the world's total population actually peaked in the middle of the nineteenth century. In 1850, more than one in three people were Chinese, and that fraction has steadily declined over time even as China's population continued to grow in absolute numbers, fueled by high birth rates that tended to compensate for the high death rates.

After the Communist overthrow of China in 1949, the government at first tried to ignore the country's demographic bulk, partly for Marxist ideological reasons that we will discuss in Chapter 3. However, after the death of Mao Zedong in 1976, China began to take stock of the magnitude of its problem. In 1982 it conducted its first national census since 1964 (which had been taken shortly after the terrible famine that we mentioned earlier). Though fertility had begun to decline in earnest by then, as we will discuss in more detail in Chapter 5, the census nonetheless counted more than one billion people. The general government attitude was summed up in the mid-1990s as follows:

> Despite the outstanding achievements made in population and development, China still confronts a series of basic problems including a large population base, insufficient cultivated land, under-development, inadequate resources on a per capita basis and an uneven social and economic development among regions. . . . Too many people has [sic] impeded seriously the speed of social and economic development of the country and the rise of the standard of living of the people. Many difficulties encountered in the course of social and economic development are directly attributable to population problems. (Peng 1996:7).

Fertility decline actually began in China's cities in the 1960s and spread rapidly throughout the rest of the country in the 1970s, when the government introduced the family planning program known as *wan xi shao*, meaning "later" (marriage), "longer" (birth interval), "fewer" (children) (Goldstein and Feng 1996). In 1979, this was transformed into the now famous (if not infamous) one-child policy, but fertility was already on its way down by that time (Riley 2004, 2017). Indeed, it dropped to replacement level in the 1990s and has stayed there since.

Although China's birthrate has now dropped to 1.8 children per woman, that does not yet mean that the population has stopped growing—population momentum again rears its head. Despite its low birth rate, the number of births each year in China is nearly twice the number of deaths just because China is paying for its previous high birth rate. There are so many young women of reproductive age (women born 25 to 45 years ago when birth rates were still above replacement level) that their babies still outnumber the people who are dying each year. As a result, the rate of natural increase in China is slightly higher than in the United States, despite nearly identical fertility rates.

China's rapid drop in fertility and mortality generated a demographic dividend which, as we noted above, is the period of time when a society is bulging with working-age adults unencumbered by a lot of children due to the rapid decline in fertility, while also unencumbered for the time being by a high proportion of older people to care for. China has famously used its demographic dividend over the past few decades to develop its economy and extend its global influence. But the dividend is transitory—a "golden era" between a very young population (China in the 1960s and before) and a very old population (China of the future). China may be unique in the world in "getting old" before it has gotten rich. Despite a loosening of the one-child policy by the government in 2013, and an end to it in 2016, there are as yet no signs (and no expectation) of a huge increase in China's birth rate, and the population is projected to decline in number between now and the middle of the century, yielding its long-held position of most populous to India, as you can see in Table 1.2.

Japan   Population size probably peaked in Japan in 2010 and is now slowly on the way down. The decline is actually slower than it might be due to the fact Japan has the lowest level of mortality in the world, with a female life expectancy at birth of 87 years. Japan's health (accompanied by its wealth) translates demographically into very high probabilities of survival to old age—indeed, more than half of all Japanese born this year will likely still be alive at age 80. This very low mortality rate is accompanied by very low fertility. Japanese women are bearing an average of 1.4 children each, leading some pundits to suggest that Japan has its own "one-child policy." To be sure, Japan experienced its own demographic dividend when fertility declined rapidly following the end of World War II. Like China, Japan used that dividend very wisely and successfully rebuilt its economy. But that too was transitory and Japan's current low mortality and low fertility have produced a population in which only 12 percent are under age 15, whereas 28 percent are 65 or older. The United Nations projects that by 2050 the percent under 15 will rise slightly to 13 percent, while the percent 65 and older will have jumped to 36. Despite aging and slowly depopulating, Japan will still be in the top 20 in 2050, as you can see in Table 1.2.

Oceania

None of the countries in Oceania is populous enough to be on the top 20 list. It is home to a wide range of indigenous populations, including Melanesian and Polynesian, but European influence has been very strong, and the region is generally thought of as being "overseas European." Its population of 41 million is just slightly more than Canada's and is less than one percent of the world's total. Australia accounts for two-thirds of the region's population, followed by Papua New Guinea and New Zealand.

In a pattern repeated elsewhere in the world, the lowest birth rates and lowest death rates (and the lowest rates of population growth) are found in countries whose populations are largely European-origin (Australia and New Zealand, in this case), whereas the countries with a higher fraction of the population of indigenous origin have higher birth rates, higher mortality, and substantially higher rates of population growth (exemplified in Oceania by Papua New Guinea). Much of Australia's current population growth is fueled by immigration, especially from Asia, and this is leading to a situation not unlike that in the United States, where an increasingly older European-origin population is supported by a younger generation of children of immigrants.

This whirlwind global tour highlights the tremendous demographic contrasts that exist in the modern world. In many of the less developed nations, especially in sub-Saharan Africa and South Asia, the population continues to grow quickly, both in absolute terms and rates of growth. Yet, in the more developed countries population growth has slowed, stopped, or in some places even started to decline. As we look around the world, we see that the more rapidly growing countries tend to have high proportions of people who are young, poor, prone to disease, and susceptible to political instability. The countries that are growing slowly or not at all tend to have populations that are older, richer, healthier, and more politically stable.

Summary and Conclusion

The goal of this book is to help you to understand and cope with the demographic change that is impacting you and your community and to better comprehend the changes occurring all over the world. Demographic analysis helps you do this by seeking out both the causes and the consequences of population change. The absolute size of population change is obviously very important as is the rate of change and, of course, the direction (growth or decline).

The past 200 years have witnessed almost nonstop growth in most places in the world. Even though the rate is slowing down, we are continuing to add more than 9,000 people to the world's total every hour of every day. You may not realize it, but everything happening around you is influenced by demographic events in faraway places as well as those close to where you live. This refers not just to the big things like regional conflict, globalization, climate change, exhaustion of resources, and massive migration movements, but even to little things that affect you directly, such as the kinds of stores that operate in your neighborhood, the goods that are stocked on your local supermarket shelves, the availability of a hospital emergency room, and the jobs aimed at college graduates in your community. Influential decision makers in government agencies, social and health organizations, and business firms now routinely base their actions at least partly on their assessment of the changing demographics of an area. So, both locally and globally, demographic forces are at work to change and challenge your future. The more you know about this, the better prepared you will be to deal with it (and perhaps even influence what the future will be).

High death rates kept the number of people in the world from growing rapidly until approximately the time of the Industrial Revolution. Then improved living conditions, public health measures, and, more recently, medical advances dramatically accelerated the pace of growth. As populations grow, the pressure or desire to migrate also increases. The vast European expansion into less developed areas of the world, which began in the fifteenth and sixteenth centuries but accelerated in the nineteenth century, is a notable illustration of massive migration and population redistribution. Today migration patterns have shifted, and people are mainly moving from less developed to more developed nations. Closely associated with migration and population density is the urban revolution—that is, the movement from rural to urban areas, and then from urban to urban places, changing the social and economic dynamics of places in the process.

The current world situation finds China and India to be the most populous countries, followed by the United States, Indonesia, and Brazil. Everywhere population is growing we find that death rates have declined more rapidly than have birth rates, but there is considerable global and regional variability in both the birth and death rates and thus in the rate of population growth. Dealing with the pressure of an expanding young population is the task of developing countries, whereas more developed countries, along with China and most of its East Asian neighbors, have aging populations and are coping with the fact that the demand for labor in their economies may have to be met by immigrants from more rapidly growing countries.

Demographic dynamics represent the leading edge of social change in the modern world. We live in a world of nearly 8 billion people, heading to more than 9 billion by the middle of this century and probably even more beyond that. In order to know what is happening demographically, we need to have accurate and reliable information and in the next chapter we turn our attention to the sources and uses of demographic data.

Main Points

1. Demography is concerned with everything that influences or can be influenced by population size, growth or decline, processes, spatial distribution, structure, and characteristics.

2. Demography is a force in the world that has influenced every improvement in human well-being that the world has witnessed over the past few hundred years.

3. The past was very different from the present in large part because of demographic changes taking place all over the globe; and the future will be different for the same reasons.

4. The cornerstones of population studies are the processes of mortality (a deadly subject), fertility (a well-conceived topic), and migration (a moving experience).

5. Examples of global issues that have deep and important demographic components include the relationship of population to food, water, and energy resources, as well as housing and infrastructure, environmental degradation, political instability, and the status of women.

6. Between 1750 and 1950, the world's population mushroomed from 800 million to 2.5 billion, and since 1950 it has expanded to nearly 8 billion.

7. Early population growth was slow not because birth rates were low but because death rates were high; on the other hand, continuing population increases are due to dramatic declines in mortality without a matching decline in fertility.

8. World population growth has been accompanied by migration from rapidly growing areas into less rapidly growing regions. Initially, that meant an outward expansion of the European population, but more recently it has meant migration from less developed to more developed nations.

9. The world's ten most populous countries are China, India, the United States, Indonesia, Brazil, Pakistan, Nigeria, Bangladesh, Russia, and Mexico. Together they account for 58 percent of the world's population.

10. Almost all of the population growth in the world today is occurring in the less developed nations, leading to an increase in the global demographic contrasts among countries.

Questions for Review

1. When did you first become aware of demography or population issues, and what were the things that initially seemed to be important to you?

2. Describe what you think might be the typical day in the life of a person living in a world where death rates and birth rates are both very high. How might those demographic imperatives influence everyday life? How would human existence be different from today as a result?

3. Migration of people into other countries is a major part of the demography of the modern world. How do you think the world of 2050 will look demographically as a consequence of the trends currently in place?

4. Five of the ten most populous nations in the world (India, United States, Nigeria, Pakistan, and Bangladesh) were part of the British Empire at one time. Do you think that having been a part of the British Empire influenced those countries' demographic futures? If so, how? If not, why not?

5. How would you explain the regional patterns that are very observable with respect to global demography? Are European countries more like each other than they are like Asian countries? Is Africa unique demographically? How meaningful are national boundaries when it comes to population trends?

CHAPTER 2
Demographic Data and Applied Demography

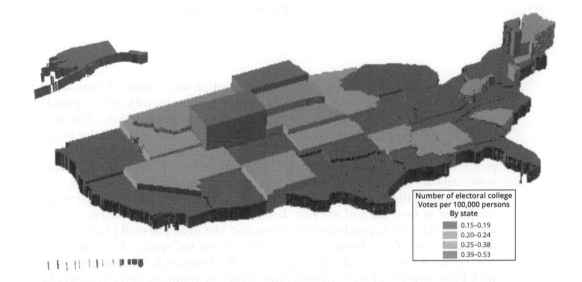

Figure 2.1   Electoral College Votes Per 100,000 Persons by State in the United States, for Presidential Elections in 2012, 2016, and 2020

Note: For each state the map shows the number of senators and members of Congress for each state (the combination of which comprises a state's votes in the Electoral College that actually votes for the president). A person in Wyoming, for example, at 0.53 votes per 100,000 people, has 3.5 the electoral power of a person in California, where there are only 0.15 votes per 100,000, based on the 2010 census. *Note that the sizes of Alaska and Hawaii are not to scale, but the colors and heights are correct.*

Source: Created by John R. Weeks using data from the U.S. Census Bureau.

Population Censuses
The Census of the United States
    Who Is Included in the Census?
    Coverage Error
    Content Error
    Sampling Error
    Continuous Measurement—American
       Community Survey
The Census of Canada
The Census of Mexico
IPUMS—Warehouse of Global Census Data

Registration of Vital Events

Combining the Census and Vital Statistics

Administrative Data

Sample Surveys
Demographic Surveys in the
    United States
Canadian Surveys
Mexican Surveys
European Surveys
Demographic and Health Surveys
Demographic Surveillance Systems

Historical Sources

Spatial Demography
Mapping Demographic Data
GIS and the Census

Applied Demography   Summary and Conclusion
Political Planning
Social Planning   Main Points
Business Planning/Marketing
                                                Questions for Review
Should You Pursue a Career in Demographics?   **ESSAY:** *Demographics of Politics*

Now that Chapter 1 has armed you with a riveting assortment of facts about the history of population growth and a solid overview of the world's current population situation, you are ready to delve into the sources and nature of the demographic data available to us to understand what is going on in the world. In order to analyze the demographic fundamentals of a particular society, we need to know how many people live there, how they are distributed geographically, how many are being born, how many are dying, how many are moving in, and how many are moving out.

Of course, this is only the beginning if we want to unravel the mysteries of *why* things are as they are and not just describe *what* they are. To do that we have to ferret out the social, psychological, economic and even physical characteristics of the people and places being studied. What's more, we need to know these things not just for the present but for the past as well. However, let's begin our discussion with those sources of basic information about the numbers and characteristics of people who are currently alive, babies being born (births), people dying (deaths), and people moving in and out (migrants).

The single most important source of data on population size and distribution, as well as demographic structure and characteristics, is the census of population. So, we will begin this chapter with an overview of the history of population censuses, followed by a closer look at how censuses are taken in the United States and its neighbors, Canada and Mexico. The major source of information on the population processes of births and deaths in most countries is the registration of vital statistics, although in a few countries this task is accomplished by population registers, and in most developing nations vital events are estimated from sample surveys. Administrative data and historical data provide much of the information about population changes at the local level including, of course, geographic mobility and migration. Indeed, the spatial component of demography is central to our understanding of population change, and these data are put to a wide range of social, economic, and political uses, as we will discuss later in this chapter.

Population Censuses

For centuries, governments have wanted to know how many people were under their rule because they wanted to know who the taxpayers were, and they wanted to identify potential laborers and soldiers. Obviously, the most direct way to find out how many people there are is to count them, and when you do that you are conducting a population census—ideally, a complete enumeration of the population. Over time this process has grown in size and complexity to the point that the United Nations Statistics Division (2008:1) notes that "the traditional census is among the most complex and massive peacetime exercises a nation undertakes. It requires mapping the entire country, mobilizing and training an army of enumerators, conducting a massive public information campaign, canvassing all households, collecting individual information, compiling vast amounts of completed questionnaires, and analysing and disseminating the data." Indeed, Massimo Livi-Bacci (2017:24) concludes that the 2010 Census of China "was the largest social investigation ever undertaken."

But, let's go back to the old days and where it all began. As far as we know, the earliest governments to undertake censuses of their populations were those in the ancient civilizations of Egypt, Babylonia, China, Palestine, and Rome (Bryan 2004). In fact, the term *census* is said to come from the Latin for "assessing" or "taxing" (Starr 1987). For several hundreds of years, citizens of Rome were counted periodically for those ever-popular tax and military purposes. Another early example occurred in the seventh century CE when the Prophet Mohammed led his followers from Mecca to Medina (in Saudi Arabia). After establishing a city-state there, one of his first activities was to conduct a written census of the entire Muslim population in the city (the returns showed a total of 1,500) (Nu'Man 1992).

William of Normandy used a similar strategy in 1086, twenty years after having conquered England. William ordered an enumeration of all the landed wealth in the newly acquired territory in order to determine how much revenue the landowners owed the government. Data were recorded in the Domesday Book, *domesday* being the word in Middle English for *doomsday*, which is the day of final judgment. The census document was so named because it was the final proof of legal title to land. The Domesday Book was not really what we think of today as a census in that it was an enumeration of "hearths," or household heads and their wealth, rather than of all the people. In order to calculate the total population of England in 1086 from the Domesday Book, you would have to multiply the number of "hearths" by some estimate of household size. More than 300,000 households were included, and researchers estimate they averaged five persons per household. Therefore, the population of the area enumerated by William at the time was approximately 1.5 million (Hinde 1995). The population of what is now modern England and Wales was actually substantially larger than that at the time because, in fact, the Domesday Book does not cover London, Winchester, Northumberland, Durham, or much of northwest England, and the only parts of Wales included are certain border areas (U.K. National Archives 2014).

When the European renaissance began in northern Italy in the fourteenth century, first the Venetians and then the Florentines were interested in counting the wealth of their region just as William had been after conquering England. They developed a *catasto* that combined a count of the hearth and individuals. Thus, unlike the Domesday Book, the Florentine catasto of 1427 recorded not only the wealth of households but also data about each member of the household. In fact, so much information was collected that most of it went unexamined until the modern advent of computers (Herlihy and Klapisch-Zuber 1985).

The value of a census was also well known to François de Salignac de la Mothe-Fénelon, a very influential French archbishop and political philosopher of the late seventeenth and early eighteenth centuries. He was tutor to the Duke of Burgundy and much of his writing was intended as a primer of government for the young duke:

> Do you know the number of men who compose your nation? How many men, and how many women, how many farmers, how many artisans, how many lawyers, how many tradespeople, how many priests and monks, how many nobles and soldiers? What would you say of a shepherd who did not know the size of his flock?. . . A king not knowing all these things is only half a king (quoted in Jones 2002:110).

Even armed with those valuable insights, however, France did not take the lead in conducting a regular census of population. Sweden was actually one of the first European nations to keep track of its population on a regular basis with the establishment in 1749 of a combined population register and census administered in each diocese by the local clergy (Statistika Centralbyran [Sweden] 1983). Denmark, as well as several Italian states (before the unification of Italy in the late nineteenth century), also conducted censuses during the eighteenth century (Carr-Saunders 1936), as did the United States (where the first census was conducted in 1790, as we will discuss below in more detail). England launched its first modern census in 1801.

By the latter part of the nineteenth century, the statistical approach to understanding business and government affairs was taking root in the Western world. In fact, the very term *statistic* is derived from the German word meaning "facts about a state." The population census began to be viewed as a potential tool for finding out more than just how many people there were and where they lived, and governments increasingly began to ask questions about age, marital status, whether and how people were employed, literacy, and so forth. Census data (in combination with other statistics) have, in fact, become the "lenses through which we form images of our society." Frederick Jackson Turner made this observation after the Census Bureau announced the end of the frontier based on data from the 1890 census, meaning there was no longer a frontier line in the west because land with less than two persons per square mile no longer existed. Our national self-image today is confirmed or challenged by numbers that tell of drastic changes in the family, the increase in ethnic diversity, and many other trends. Winston Churchill observed that "first we shape our buildings and then they shape us. The same may be said of our statistics" (Alonso and Starr 1982:39).

The potential power behind the numbers can be gauged by public reaction to a census. In Germany, the proposed enumeration of 1983 was postponed to 1987 because of public concern that the census was prying unduly into private lives. Germany did not conduct another census until 2002, well after reunification, and even then it was a sample census, not a complete enumeration. In the past few decades, protests have occurred in England, Switzerland, and the Netherlands, as well. In the Netherlands case, the census scheduled for the 1980s was actually canceled after a survey indicating that the majority of the urban population would not cooperate (Robey 1983). The Dutch have since used what they call a "virtual census" in which they generate population data from administrative sources, especially population registers.

In 2008, the European Union passed a set of regulations encouraging its member states to undertake census enumerations in 2011. The response by member countries was uneven, but Germany stepped up to do that. Even before the census, German officials had been concerned that they were overestimating the size of Germany's population, and the 2011 census data confirmed that fact. Although administrative data had been capturing people moving in, out-migrants were being missed, and that became clear once the complete enumeration was undertaken.

Since the end of World War II, the United Nations has encouraged all member states to enumerate their populations in censuses, often providing financial as well as technical aid to less developed countries. The world's two largest nations, China and India, each regularly conduct censuses, with the most recent (as of this date) being China in 2010 and India in 2011. India is, in fact, well into its second 100 years of census taking, the first census having been taken in 1881 under the supervision of the British.

In contrast to India's regular census-taking, another of England's former colonies, Nigeria (currently the world's seventh most populous nation, as you'll recall from Chapter 1), has had quite a bit more trouble with their census-taking efforts. Nigeria's population is divided among three broad ethnic groups: the Hausa-Fulani in the north, who are predominately Muslim; the Yoruba in the southwest, who are of various religious faiths; and the largely Christian Igbo in the southeast. The 1952 census of Nigeria indicated that the Hausa-Fulani had the largest share of the population, and they dominated the first postcolonial government set up after independence in 1960. The newly independent nation ordered a census to be taken in 1962, but the results this time showed that northerners accounted for only 30 percent of the population. A "recount" in 1963 led somewhat suspiciously to the north accounting for 67 percent of the population. This episode exacerbated underlying ethnic tensions, culminating in the Igbo declaring independence. The resulting Nigerian Civil War, commonly known as the Biafran War (1967–70) cost the lives of at least three million people before the Igbo rejoined the rest of Nigeria. A census in 1973 was never accepted by the government, and it was not until 1991 that the nation felt stable enough to try its hand at enumeration again. That was after agreeing that there would be no questions about ethnic group, language, or religion, and that population numbers would not be used as a basis for government expenditures. The official census count was 88.5 million people, well below the 110 million that many population experts had been guessing in the absence of any real data (Okolo 1999).

In March 2006, Nigeria completed its first census since 1991, but not without protests, boycotts, rows over payments to officials, and at least 15 deaths (Lalasz 2006). The final count from the 2006 census was about 140 million and, given the history of census-taking in the country, there was a lot of skepticism surrounding the numbers. Though the census had steered clear of questions about religion, the 2008 Nigeria Demographic and Health Survey (see later in this chapter for a discussion of those surveys) suggests that 54 percent of women and men aged 15–49 are Christian, while about 45 percent are Muslim, and one percent practice some other religion (National Population Commission [Nigeria] and ICF Macro 2009). As of this date the country has no plans for another census.

Lebanon has not been enumerated since 1932, when the country was under French colonial rule (Domschke and Goyer 1986). At that time the country's population was divided nearly equally between Christians and Muslims; that fact, combined with the political strife between those groups, made taking a census a very sensitive political issue. Before the nation was literally torn apart by civil war between 1975 and 1990, the Christians had held a slight majority with respect to political representation. But Muslims almost certainly now hold a demographic majority due both to the lower level of fertility and higher level of outmigration among Christians (Courbage and Todd 2011). Nonetheless, what we know about Lebanon comes from sources other than census data.

We should note that censuses have historically been unpopular in that part of the world. The Old Testament of the Bible tells us that in ancient times King David ordered a census of Israel in which his enumerators counted "one million, one hundred thousand men who drew the sword. . . . But God was displeased with this thing [the census], and he smote Israel. . . . So the Lord sent a pestilence upon Israel; and there fell seventy thousand men of Israel" (1 Chronicles 21). Fortunately, in modern times the advantages of census taking seem more clearly to outweigh the disadvantages in most cases. This has been especially true in the United States where records indicate that no census has been followed directly by a pestilence.

The Census of the United States

Censuses of population were actually part of colonial life prior to the creation of the United States. A census had been conducted in Virginia in the early 1600s, and most of the northern colonies had conducted a census prior to the Revolution (U.S. Census Bureau 1978). As we discuss in the essay accompanying this chapter, a population census has been taken every 10 years since 1790 in the United States as part of the constitutional mandate that seats in the House of Representatives be apportioned based on population size and distribution. Article 1 of the U.S. Constitution directs that "representatives . . . shall be apportioned among the several states which may be included within this union, according to their respective numbers. . . . The actual Enumeration shall be made within three years after the first meeting of the Congress of the United States, and within every subsequent term of ten years, in such manner as they shall by law direct." Even in 1790 the government used the census to find out more than just how many people were under their jurisdiction. The census asked for the names of the following: head of family, free white males aged 16 years and older, free white females, slaves, and other persons. The census questions reflected the social importance of those categories at that point in history. Since that time questions have been added and deleted by the Census Bureau through a process that involves consultation with Congress, other government officials, and census statistics users.

For the first 100 years of census taking in the United States, the population was enumerated by U.S. Marshals. In 1880, special census agents were hired for the first time and, finally, in 1902 the Census Bureau became a permanent government agency (Hobbs and Stoops 2002). Beyond a core of inquiries designed to elicit demographic and housing information, the questions asked on the census have fluctuated according to the concerns of the time. Interest in international migration, for example, rose in 1920 just before the passage of a restrictive immigration law, and the census in that year added a battery of questions about the foreign-born population. In 2000, a question was added about grandparent caregivers, replacing a question on fertility, to provide insight into the shift in focus from how many children women were having to the issue of who is taking care of those children.

One of the more controversial items for the Census 2000 questionnaire was the question about race and ethnicity. The growing racial and ethnic diversity of the United States has led to a larger number of interracial/interethnic marriages and relationships producing children of mixed origin (also called multiracial). Previous censuses had asked people to choose a single category of race to describe themselves, but there was considerable public sentiment that people should be able to identify themselves as being of mixed or multiple origins if, in fact, they perceived themselves in that way (Harris and Sim 2002). Late in 1997, the government accepted the recommendation from a federally appointed committee that people of mixed racial heritage be able to choose more than one race category when filling out the Census 2000 questionnaire. Simply put, this means a person whose mother is white and whose father is African American can check both "White" and "Black or African American," whereas in the past the choice would have had to be made between the two. This was carried over into the 2010 and 2020 Censuses, as well as incorporated into other government surveys.

Another bone of contention concerning how people can identify themselves on the census has not yet been resolved. Though there was still a separate question about "Hispanic/Latino/Spanish Origin" identity on the 2010 census as you can see in Figure 2.2, there remains a deep controversy about whether "race" is even an appropriate census category. The following excerpt from an article in *The Economist* (2013) tackled the issue of whether the Hispanic identity and race identity questions should be combined into a single question:

> Such a change, say officials, would not mean that "Hispanic" is now to be considered a new racial category. Still, the widespread reporting of Hispanic-specific data, acknowledges Roberto Ramirez at the Census Bureau, means that in some respects "Hispanic" has become a de facto race.

> Some are skeptical about the proposal. Rubén Rumbaut, a sociologist at the University of California, Irvine, accepts the need for good data but says the bureau is thinking about race in 18th-century terms. Hispanic identity in America, he adds is a "Frankenstein's monster" that has taken on a life of its own.

> The ethnic origins of some previous waves of immigrants have evaporated over time: Italians, Germans and Russians, dismissed by Benjamin Franklin in 1751 as of "swarthy Complexion," are now, for the most part, just white. Similar forces may be at play today: last year the Pew Hispanic Centre found that among Hispanics of the third generation or above, almost half preferred to call themselves "American."

United States Census 2010

This is the official form for all the people at this address. It is quick and easy, and your answers are protected by law.

U.S. DEPARTMENT OF COMMERCE
Economics and Statistics Administration
U.S. CENSUS BUREAU

Use a blue or black pen.

Start here

The Census must count every person living in the United States on April 1, 2010.

Before you answer Question 1, count the people living in this house, apartment, or mobile home using our guidelines.

- Count all people, including babies, who live and sleep here most of the time.

The Census Bureau also conducts counts in institutions and other places, so:

- Do not count anyone living away either at college or in the Armed Forces.
- Do not count anyone in a nursing home, jail, prison, detention facility, etc., on April 1, 2010.
- Leave these people off your form, even if they will return to live here after they leave college, the nursing home, the military, jail, etc. Otherwise, they may be counted twice.

The Census must also include people without a permanent place to stay, so:

- If someone who has no permanent place to stay is staying here on April 1, 2010, count that person. Otherwise, he or she may be missed in the census.

1. How many people were living or staying in this house, apartment, or mobile home on April 1, 2010?

Number of people =

2. Were there any additional people staying here April 1, 2010 that you did not include in Question 1? Mark [X] all that apply.

- Children, such as newborn babies or foster children
- Relatives, such as adult children, cousins, or in-laws
- Nonrelatives, such as roommates or live-in baby sitters
- People staying here temporarily
- No additional people

3. Is this house, apartment, or mobile home — Mark [X] ONE box.

- Owned by you or someone in this household with a mortgage or loan? Include home equity loans.
- Owned by you or someone in this household free and clear (without a mortgage or loan)?
- Rented?
- Occupied without payment of rent?

4. What is your telephone number? We may call if we don't understand an answer.

Area Code + Number

OMB No. 0607-0919-C: Approval Expires 12/31/2011.

Form **D-61** (9-25-2008)

5. Please provide information for each person living here. Start with a person living here who owns or rents this house, apartment, or mobile home. If the owner or renter lives somewhere else, start with any adult living here. This will be Person 1.
What is Person 1's name? Print name below.

Last Name

First Name   MI

6. What is Person 1's sex? Mark [X] ONE box.
- Male   Female

7. What is Person 1's age and what is Person 1's date of birth?
Please report babies as age 0 when the child is less than 1 year old. Print numbers in boxes.
Age on April 1, 2010   Month   Day   Year of birth

→ NOTE: Please answer BOTH Question 8 about Hispanic origin and Question 9 about race. For this census, Hispanic origins are not races.

8. Is Person 1 of Hispanic, Latino, or Spanish origin?
- No, not of Hispanic, Latino, or Spanish origin
- Yes, Mexican, Mexican Am., Chicano
- Yes, Puerto Rican
- Yes, Cuban
- Yes, another Hispanic, Latino, or Spanish origin — Print origin, for example, Argentinean, Colombian, Dominican, Nicaraguan, Salvadoran, Spaniard, and so on.

9. What is Person 1's race? Mark [X] one or more boxes.
- White
- Black, African Am., or Negro
- American Indian or Alaska Native — Print name of enrolled or principal tribe.

- Asian Indian   Japanese   Native Hawaiian
- Chinese   Korean   Guamanian or Chamorro
- Filipino   Vietnamese   Samoan
- Other Asian — Print race, for example, Hmong, Laotian, Thai, Pakistani, Cambodian, and so on.   Other Pacific Islander — Print race, for example, Fijian, Tongan, and so on.

- Some other race — Print race.

10. Does Person 1 sometimes live or stay somewhere else?
- No   Yes — Mark [X] all that apply.
  - In college housing
  - In the military
  - At a seasonal or second residence
  - For child custody
  - In jail or prison
  - In a nursing home
  - For another reason

→ If more people were counted in Question 1, continue with Person 2.

USCENSUSBUREAU

Figure 2.2   First Page of Questionnaire for United States Census 2010
Source: U.S. Census Bureau.

In response to these concerns raised by social scientists, the Census Bureau conducted a test of the 2010 census question using both the "standard" two questions (one on race and another on Hispanic origin) compared to a question that combined those into a single concept of "origin." The results were similar, suggesting that the single question might be a viable option (U.S. Census Bureau 2012b), but ultimately the Census Bureau decided to stick with the two separate questions in the 2020 Census. However, there will be one change in that people who indicate that their race is "White" will now be asked to fill in a box indicating their identity (e.g., German, Irish, English . . .), people who check that their race is "Black or African Am." will also be asked to fill in their identity (e.g., African American, Jamaican, Haitian . . .), and people who indicate that they are "American Indian or Alaska Native" will similarly be asked to write down their "principal tribe(s)" (U.S. Census Bureau 2018b). This is actually an extension of the existing set of questions that ask for details about Hispanic identity (e.g., Mexican, Puerto Rican, Cuban) and Asian identity (e.g., Chinese, Vietnamese, Filipino, etc.).

Though the census is designed as a complete *enumeration* of the population, in the United States only a few of the questions are actually asked of everyone. For reasons of economy, most items in the census questionnaire have been administered to a sample of household in the last several censuses. From 1790 through 1930, all questions were asked of all applicable persons, but as the American population grew and Congress kept adding new questions to the census, the savings in sampling grew. As a result, in 1940 the Census Bureau began its practice of asking only a small number of items of all households (the "short form"), and using a sample of one out of every six households to gather more detailed data (the "long form"). This was the procedure up through the 2000 census. A major change was made for the 2010 census in the United States so that it included only the short form. The detailed information has henceforth been collected through the ongoing American Community Survey (ACS), which we discuss later in the chapter, instead of being part of the decennial census.

The short form information represents everything necessary to meet the Constitutional requirements for congressional redistricting. Though everything else is really useful, it is not Constitutionally required. This is why there was a huge fuss in 2018 when the Trump administration proposed putting a question about citizenship on the 2020 census short form. The question had not been on the short form since 1950, but was always on the long form, and more recently has been incorporated into the ACS. Following congressional hearings and period for public comment on this proposed change, the National Academy of Sciences (2018) published a "letter" with its evaluation and conclusions:

1. The American Community Survey already meets the stated need for citizenship data;

2. Adding the citizenship question without proper testing will, in our judgment, impair the quality of the 2020 census as a whole; and

3. Adding the citizenship question and using the method described in the Secretary's memo and the Census Bureau's review would create a new population register, which has unclear statistical purposes and which could not, under current law, be used for nonstatistical purposes, such as law enforcement against individuals, and still comport with the mission of the Census Bureau.

Lawsuits sent the issue to the U.S. Supreme Court, which in 2019 ruled that the government had not provided sufficiently good reasons for including the question, and so it was dropped from the census.

Demographics of Politics: Why the Census Matters

Demographics are central to the political process in the United States. The constitutional basis of the Census of Population is to provide data for the **apportionment** of seats in the House of Representatives. After each enumeration, which historically takes place every 10 years in the month of April, the U.S. Census Bureau is required by law to deliver total population counts for all 50 states to the President on or before December 31 of that year. These data are then sent to the House of Representatives for use in determining the number of representatives to which each state is entitled.

As the population of the United States has grown and new states added, the number of Representatives has risen. However, since the 1910 census, the total number of House seats has been fixed at 435, and the Constitution requires that every state get at least one seat. The first 50 House seats are thus used up, taking into account the four states added subsequent to the 1910 census. The question remains of how to apportion the remaining 385 seats, remembering that congressional districts cannot cross state boundaries and there can be neither partial districts nor sharing of seats. Since 1940, the number of seats assigned to each state has been based on a formula called the method of equal proportions, which rank-orders a state's priority for each of those 385 seats based on its total population compared with all other states. The calculations themselves are cumbersome, but they produce an allocation of House seats that is now accepted without much criticism or controversy, except for the issue of whether and how to count overseas Americans, as we noted elsewhere in this chapter.

The results of the 2010 census determined the number of seats for each state in the United States House of Representatives starting with the 2012 elections and going through the elections of 2020, after which the results of the 2020 census will be used. This apportionment also affected the number of votes each state has in the Electoral College for the 2012 through 2020 presidential elections, since each state's total number of electoral votes is equal to its members of Congress (Representatives and Senators combined). You can see in Figure 2.1 that several less-populated states have disproportionate clout in the Electoral College since they have two senators even though their population size only gives them one member of the House of Representatives.

Because of population changes, 18 states had changes in their number of seats following the 2010 census. Eight states gained at least one seat, and 10 states lost at least one seat. The accompanying map shows where the gains and losses occurred. Texas gained the most—four seats—almost entirely on the basis on net in-migration, including many undocumented immigrants from Mexico. New York and Ohio both lost two seats, almost entirely on the basis of out-migration to southern or western states. Indeed, all but one of the states that lost at least one seat in the House of Representatives are in the northern half of the country. The lone exception is Louisiana, which lost a substantial number of people who went especially to Texas following Hurricane Katrina and have not returned. The only state for which migration was not the major contributor to population growth between 2000 and 2010 is Utah, which has the country's highest birth rate.

Once the number of seats per state has been reapportioned, the real fight begins. This involves **redistricting**, the spatial reconfiguration of congressional districts (geographic areas) that each seat will represent. The U.S. Constitution addressed the issue by requiring that ". . . The number of representatives shall not exceed one for every thirty thousand, but each state shall have at least one representative" (U.S. Constitution, Article 1, Section 2, Para 3). Thus, the framers of the Constitution were most worried about there being too few constituents per House member. This was in response to what in England at the time were known as "rotten" or "pocket" boroughs, which had plagued Parliament in England, and which were finally abolished by the Reform Act of 1832. These were boroughs in which a very small number of voters existed who could thus collude to (or be bribed to) elect a particular person to Parliament.

The framers of the Constitution decided, somewhat arbitrarily, that each congressional district had to have a minimum of 30,000 people in order to have enough voters so that this kind of

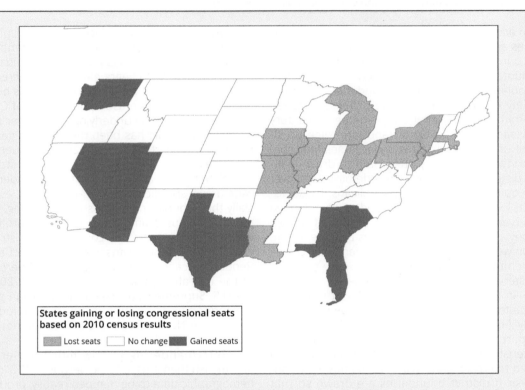

Note: The map shows only the continental states, but neither Alaska nor Hawaii lost or gained a seat as a result of the 2010 Census.

Source: Prepared by John R. Weeks from U.S. Census data.

corruption would be avoided. Note that originally those 30,000 people would have been ". . . determined by adding to the whole number of free persons, including those bound to service for a term of years, and excluding Indians not taxed, three-fifths of all other persons" (U.S. Constitution, Article 1, Section 2, Paragraph 3). The reference to "free persons" and "three-fifths of all other persons" was deleted by Section 2 of the 14th Amendment, passed in 1868 after the Civil War, and following the 13th Amendment in 1865 which abolished slavery and involuntary servitude.

In the 1960s, a series of Supreme Court decisions extended to the state and local levels the requirement that legislative districts be drawn in such a way as to ensure roughly the same number of constituents in each district ("one person, one vote"). In order to facilitate this, Public Law 94-171 mandates that the Census Bureau provide population counts by age (under 18 and 18 and over) and by race and ethnicity down to the block level for local communities (and, as noted in this chapter, these were the only data collected from everyone in the 2010 Census). These data are then used to redefine congressional district boundaries, as well as state and local legislative boundaries.

There are very few rules that govern the formation of a district beyond the requirement that, after the census is complete, each state must change its political boundaries to make sure each congressional district is equally populated. By law, newly drawn districts do not have to take

(continued)

Demographics of Politics: Why the Census Matters (*Continued*)

into account existing political boundaries, such as cities and counties, nor do they have to take into account natural geographic boundaries, such as mountains and rivers. They need only be equally populated. When political boundaries are drawn solely for partisan gain, the process is called "gerrymandering," after early-nineteenth-century Massachusetts governor (and later vice president of the United States under James Madison) Elbridge Gerry. Gerry attempted to draw political districts to favor his own Federalist Party over the opposing Democratic–Republicans. These districts looked like salamanders and so were dubbed "gerrymanders." Since that time, this mix of demography, geography, and politics has become a common weapon used by a majority party to increase its chance of winning an election by spatially clustering supportive voters together.

In 2004, the U.S. Supreme Court ruled that once the lines are drawn they can be challenged only if racial discrimination is involved. This means, in particular, that any other demographic characteristic such as political party affiliation can be used to create "safe" seats for members of Congress. If district boundaries are drawn so that one party has a clear majority within the district, it becomes very hard for the other party to challenge the incumbent. By contrast, a "swing" district is one in which there is roughly an equal number of voters in each political party, suggesting that an incumbent could more readily be challenged. An analysis by statistician Nate Silver of *fivethirtyeight*

.com following the 2012 elections in the United States indicated that the number of members elected from swing districts was only 35, compared to 103 members 20 years earlier. This increase in members coming from safe districts has been implicated in the increased polarization of Congress, and one of the underlying reasons for this surge in safe seats has been the uptick in gerrymandered districts (Silver 2012). Subsequently, there have been lawsuits filed in several states in which it is apparent that district boundaries were drawn specifically to favor candidates, especially the Republican Party. As of this writing, the most egregious example was in North Carolina, where 10 of that state's 13 congressional districts were held by Republicans, despite the fact that Republican candidates had won only 53 percent of the overall popular vote. However, in 2019, the U.S. Supreme Court ruled that partisan gerrymandering was beyond its authority to judge, and so the North Carolina districts will not be redrawn.

Gerrymandering is now much easier to accomplish than it used to be because GIS allows demographic data to be mapped readily, producing an almost infinite number of possible district boundaries to be drawn and compared with one another. In most states this work is overseen by the state legislature. So, the political party in power in that state as the census data come out will make those decisions, unless the legislature has designated some other agency to do the job.

The first page of the short form questionnaire for Census 2010 is reproduced as Figure 2.2 below—remember, the 2020 Census questionnaire will be slightly different. This first page asks for a count of everyone in the household, including people who may not be there at the moment, and those who may be homeless but are nonetheless in the housing unit. The first person listed is supposed to be someone in the household who owns, is buying, or rents this housing unit. This person used to be known as the "head of household" (and there is still a tax category in the United States for such a person), but the Census Bureau now refers to him or her on the census form simply as "Person 1." Subsequent pages then ask questions about each additional person in the household regarding his or her relation to Person 1, their sex, age and date of birth, whether the person is of Hispanic origin and, separately, what the person's race is. Finally, there is a specific question about whether or not

Currently non-partisan commissions undertake this task in nine states. In 2010, for example, voters in California approved Proposition 20, which added congressional redistricting to the tasks of the Redistricting Commission that already existed to redraw state legislative boundaries.

The Constitutional mandate to use the census for congressional redistricting did not explicitly anticipate partisan politics. Over time, however, people creating boundaries of these districts have been more concerned about the demographics of voters than about the total population being served by each member of the House of Representatives. The demographic characteristics of who votes is a huge political issue partly because the definition of who can vote has shifted substantially over time. The U.S. Constitution did not set a national standard for voter eligibility, leaving that decision to the states. Most states originally adopted the principle that only white male landowners were eligible to vote, and it was not until the middle of the nineteenth century that land ownership requirements were removed in all states, expanding the electorate to *all* white males.

The assumption is that you must be a citizen to vote and all states do require that, although it is not explicitly stated in the Constitution. This became an issue after the Civil War when southern states wanted to exclude former slaves from being able to vote by claiming that they were not U.S. citizens. So, just who *is* a citizen? That issue was settled by the 14th Amendment to the Constitution in 1868, which in Section 1 says that: "All persons born or naturalized in the United States and subject to the jurisdiction thereof, are citizens of the United States." This was followed in 1870 by the 15th Amendment, which provides that a person is eligible to vote regardless of race (and this was further reinforced by the Voting Rights Act of 1965). It was not until 1920 that women were given the vote by the passage of the 19th Amendment, and not until 1924 that all Native Americans were granted the right to vote. Most recently, in 1971, the 26th Amendment lowered the voting age throughout the U.S. from 21 to 18. You can see, then, that over time there has been a dramatic convergence between the number of people living in a congressional district (which determines how the boundaries of a district are defined) and the number of potential voters in that district (the people who will actually elect the Representative from that district).

Discussion Questions: (1) Discuss the way in which the purpose for which a census is taken may influence the kinds of questions asked, and the methodology used to collect those data; **(2)** What are some ways in which the redistricting procedures called "gerrymandering" could be limited? What might be the unintended consequences of your suggested changes?

this person sometimes lives or stays elsewhere. This is to help the Census Bureau eliminate duplicates, such as college students living away from home.

Table 2.1 lists the items on the U.S. Census 2010 questionnaire (the short form), the American Community Survey (from which "long form" data are collected), compared with a list of information obtained by the 2011 census of Canada and the 2010 census of Mexico, both of which countries will be discussed later in this chapter. The table indicates which items are asked of every household and which are asked of a sample of households.

So, in theory, a census obtains accurate information from everyone, but in practice that turns out to be more difficult than it may seem. For example, who is supposed to be included in the census? Are visitors to the country to be included? Are people who are absent from the country on census day to be excluded?

Table 2.1   Comparison of Items Included in the U.S. Census 2010 Questionnaire and the American Community Survey, the 2011 Census of Canada, and the 2010 Census of Mexico

Census Item	U.S. Census 2010 and ACS	Canada 2011	Mexico 2010
Population Characteristics:			
Age	XX	XX	XX
Sex	XX	XX	XX
Relationship to householder (family structure)	XX	XX	XX
Race	XX	X	
Ethnicity	XX	X	
Marital status	X	XX	XX
Fertility	X		XX
Child mortality			XX
Income	X	X	XX
Sources of income	X	X	X
Health insurance	X		XX
Job benefits			X
Unpaid household activities		X	
Labor force status	X	X	XX
Industry, occupation, and class of worker	X	X	XX
Work status last year	X		
Veteran status	X		
Grandparents as caregivers	X		
Place of work and journey to work	X	X	XX
Journey to work	X	X	
Vehicles available	X		
Ancestry	X	X	
Place of birth	X	X	XX
Birthplace of parents		X	
Citizenship	X	X	

Table 2.1 (*continued*)

Census Item	U.S. Census 2010 and ACS	Canada 2011	Mexico 2010
Year of entry if not born in this country	X	X	
Language spoken at home	X	XX	XX
Language spoken at work		X	
Religion		X	XX
Educational attainment	X	X	XX
School enrollment	X	X	XX
Residence one year ago (migration)	X	X	
Residence five years ago (migration)		X	XX
International migration of family members			X
Disability (activities of daily living)	X	X	XX
Housing Characteristics:			
Tenure (rent or own)	XX	XX	XX
Type of housing	XX	XX	XX
Agricultural use of property	X	XX	
Acreage of property	X		
Business use of property	X		
Material used for construction of walls			XX
Material used for construction of roof			XX
Material used for construction of floors			XX
Repairs needed on structure		X	
Year structure built	X	X	X
Units in structure	X		
Rooms in unit	X	X	XX
Bedrooms	X	X	XX
Kitchen facilities	X		XX
Electricity in house			XX

(continued)

Table 2.1   (continued)

Census Item	U.S. Census 2010 and ACS	Canada 2011	Mexico 2010
Water source			XX
Toilet facilities	X		XX
Sewerage			XX
Material possessions (TV, radio, etc.)	X		XX
House heating fuel	X		XX
Year moved into unit	X		
Value of property	X	X	
Selected housing costs	X	X	
Rent or mortgage payment	X	X	

Note: XX = Included and asked of every household; X = Included but asked of only a sample of households. Questions asked on each census may be different; similar categories of questions asked do not necessarily mean strict comparability of data.

Who Is Included in the Census?   There are several ways to answer that question, and each produces a potentially different total number of people. At one extreme is the concept of the de facto population, which counts all people in a given territory on the census day. At the other extreme is the de jure population, which represents people who legally "belong" to a given area in some way or another, regardless of whether or not they were there on the day of the census. For countries with few foreign workers and where working in another area is rare, the distinction makes little difference. But many countries, including nearly all the Gulf states in the Middle East, have large numbers of guest workers from other countries and thus have a larger *de facto* than *de jure* population. On the other hand, countries such as Nigeria or the Philippines that regularly have migrants working temporarily overseas in order to send remittances back home may have a larger *de jure* than *de facto* population.

Most countries (including the United States, Canada, and Mexico) have now adopted a concept that lies somewhere between the extremes of *de facto* and *de jure*. They include people in the census on the basis of usual residence, which is roughly defined as the place where a person usually sleeps. College students who live away from home, for example, are included at their college address rather than being counted in their parents' household. People with no usual residence (the homeless, including migratory workers, vagrants, and "street people") are counted where they are found. On the other hand, visitors and tourists from other countries who "belong" somewhere else are not included even though they may be in the country when the census is being conducted. At the same time, the concept of usual residence means that undocumented immigrants (who do not *legally* "belong" where they are found though it *is* their usual residence) will be included in the census along with everyone else.

Where you belong became a court issue following Census 2000 in the United States because the census includes members of the military and the federal government who are stationed abroad. They are counted as belonging to the state in the United States that was their normal domicile, and in 2000 this turned out especially to benefit North Carolina, which is home to several military bases. Utah then filed suit in federal court, objecting that Mormon missionaries from Utah who were serving abroad should also be counted as residents of Utah rather than being excluded because they were living outside the United States. In 2001, the U.S. District Court ruled against the Mormon case, so North Carolina gained a seat in Congress on the basis of its "overseas residents," whereas Utah did not. Utah pushed the idea again for the 2010 census, but the plan was again rejected by the Census Bureau, which pointed out that an estimated six million Americans who are not on the U.S. government payroll live abroad, and there is no reliable way to count them (Associated Press 2009).

Even knowing who should be included in the census does not, however, guarantee that they will all be found and accurately counted. There are several possible errors that can creep into the numeration process. We can divide these into the two broad categories of nonsampling error (which includes coverage error and content error) and sampling error.

Coverage Error   So we all agree that a census is designed to count everyone, but in the real world there are always people who are missed and some who are counted more than once. The difference between the undercount and overcount is called coverage error or net census undercount. There are several ways to measure and adjust for the undercount, but it becomes more complicated (and political) when there is a differential undercount, when some groups are more likely to be underenumerated than others.

In the United States, the differential undercount has meant that racial/ethnic minority groups (especially African Americans) have been less likely to be included in the census count than whites. Table 2.2 shows estimates of the net undercount in the last several censuses, along with the differential undercount of the black population. The overall undercount in the 1940 census was 5.6 percent, and you can see that it has been steadily declining since then as the Census Bureau institutes ever more sophisticated procedures. But you can also see that in 1940 more than 10 percent of African Americans in the country were missed by the census. This was the year that the differential undercount was discovered as a result of a "somewhat serendipitous natural experiment" (Anderson and Fienberg 1999:29). Because of World War II, men were registering for the draft when that census was taken, providing demographers with a chance to compare census returns with the count of men registering for the draft. It turned out that 229,000 more black men signed up for the draft than would have been expected based on census data (Price 1947), signaling some real problems with the completeness of the census coverage in 1940. Since then a great deal of time effort, and controversy have gone into attempts to reduce both the overall undercount and the differential undercount.

Table 2.2   Net Undercount and Differential Undercount in U.S. Censuses

Year	Net undercount for total population (%)	Undercount of black population (%)	Undercount of white population (%)	Differential undercount (percentage point difference between black and white undercount)
1940	5.6	10.3	5.1	5.2
1950	4.4	9.6	3.8	5.8
1960	3.3	8.3	2.7	5.6
1970	2.9	8.0	2.2	5.8
1980	1.4	5.9	0.7	5.2
1990	1.8	5.7	1.3	4.4
2000	(0.5)	1.8	(1.1)	2.9
2010	0.0	2.1	(0.8)	2.9

Sources: Data for 1940 through 1980 are from Anderson and Fienberg (1999:Table 4.1); data for 1990 are from Robinson, West, and Adlakha (2002:Table 6), and data for 2000 and 2010 are from the U.S. Census Bureau (2012a). The undercounts for 1940 through 1990 are based on demographic analysis, and the undercounts for 2000 and 2010 are based on Post-Enumeration Surveys.

Note: Numbers in parentheses indicate a net overcount; for 2000 and 2010 the white population refers to the non-Hispanic white only population.

Coverage is improved in the census by a variety of measures, such as having better address identification so every household receives a questionnaire and having a high-profile advertising campaign designed to encourage a high response to the mail-out questionnaire. Nearly three-fourths (72 percent) of households responded to the mailed questionnaire in 2010, and the rest were contacted by the Census Bureau in the Non-Response Follow-Up (NRFU) phase of data collection. The Census Bureau sends staff members into the field to interview people who do not complete the forms, and in some cases to find out about people whom they were unable to contact. When you combine this with the fact that one member of a household may have filled in the information for all household members, it is easy to see why so many people routinely think they have not been counted in the census—someone else answered for them. In 2020 the Census will offer online responses to the questionnaire for the first time in U.S. history, as well as the ability to phone in your responses if you don't want to fill out the paper questionnaire that you receive in the mail.

In China, coverage error in the recent past has focused not on racial/ethnic groups but on children. Daniel Goodkind (2011) estimated that there were nearly 37 million children under the age of 10 who were not counted in the 2000 census in China—a time when the one-child policy was in place. The reason census-takers could not find these children was that they were being hidden. Acknowledging them would have provided evidence that the government-mandated birth quotas had been exceeded. Since local officials, not just parents, were held responsible for failure to keep the birth rate down, everybody at the local level had an interest in suppressing information about these children. A related issue with coverage error is that it is dependent upon the definition of who should be counted. In 2000, the Chinese census enumerated only those people with Chinese citizenship; whereas in 2010 the Chinese shifted to people who usually reside in China—thus including immigrants (Feng 2012).

Right now you are probably asking yourself how a country's Census Bureau could ever begin to estimate the number of people missed in a census. It's certainly not an easy task, and statisticians in the United States and other countries have experimented with a number of methods over the years. The two principal methods used are (1) demographic analysis (DA), and (2) dual-system estimation (DSE) (which typically involves a post-enumeration survey).

The demographic analysis approach uses the demographic balancing equation to estimate what the population at the most recent census should have been, and then compares that number to the actual count. The demographic balancing equation says that the population at time 2 is equal to the population at time 1 plus the births between times 1 and 2, minus the deaths between times 1 and 2, plus the in-migrants between times 1 and 2, minus the out-migrants between times 1 and 2. Thus, if we know the number of people from the previous census, we can add the number of births since then, subtract the number of deaths since then, add the number of in-migrants since then, and subtract the number of out-migrants since then to estimate what the total population should have been. A comparison of this number with the actual census count, then, provides a big clue as to the accuracy of the census. Using these methods, the Census Bureau is able to piece together a composite rendering of what the population "should" look like. Differences from that picture and the one painted by the census can be used as estimates of under- or over-enumeration. By making these calculations for all age, sex, and racial/ethnic groups (using the cohort component method that will be discussed in more detail in Chapter 8), we can arrive at an estimate of the possible undercount among various groups in the population. This, for example, was the basis for deciding that China's 2000 census had missed 37 million children (Goodkind 2011), and that the 2010 Census in the United States had missed 400,000 Hispanic children aged 0–4 (though at the time of this writing we do not know why) (O'Hare et al. 2016).

Of course, if we do not have an accurate count of births, deaths, and migrants, then our demographic analysis estimate may itself be wrong, so this method requires careful attention to the quality of the non-census data. And, you say, why should we even take a census if we think we can estimate the number of people more accurately without it? The answer is that (1) we have to have a set of baseline numbers to start with, and they usually come from the previous census; and (2) the demographic analysis approach usually only produces an estimate of the total number of people in any age, sex, racial/ethnic group, without providing a way of knowing the details of the population—which is what we obtain from the census questionnaire.

The other technique for assessing accuracy, the dual-system estimation method, also involves comparing the census results with some other source of information about the people counted. For example, after Census 2010 in the United States, the Census Bureau implemented its Accuracy and Coverage Evaluation (A.C.E.) Survey, which was similar to, albeit somewhat more complex than, the post-enumeration A.C.E. survey conducted after the 2000 census, because it incorporated a variety of innovations suggested by a committee of the National Research Council (Bell and Cohen 2008). The process involves taking a carefully constructed sample survey right after the census is finished and then matching people in the sample survey with their responses in the census. This process can determine whether households and individuals within the households were counted in both the census and the survey (the ideal situation); in the census but not in the survey (possible but not likely); or in the survey but not in the census (the usual measure of underenumeration); or counted in the wrong place. Obviously, some people may be missed by both the census and the survey, but the logic underlying the method is analogous (with a few adjustments) to the capture-recapture method used by biologists tracking wildlife (Choldin 1994). That strategy is to capture a sample of animals, mark them, and release them. Later, another sample is captured, and some of the marked animals will wind up being recaptured. The ratio of recaptured animals to all animals caught in the second sample is assumed to represent the ratio of the first group captured to the whole population, and on this basis the wildlife population can be estimated.

Content Error   Now that we've dealt with coverage error and ways to mitigate its impact on the census, we have to turn our attention to possible problems with the accuracy of the data obtained (content error). Content error includes nonresponses to particular questions on the census or inaccurate responses if people do not understand the question. Errors can also occur if information is inaccurately recorded on the form or if there is some glitch in the processing (coding, data entry, or editing) of the census return. By and large, content error seems not to be a problem in the U.S. Census, although the data are certainly not 100 percent accurate. There is always the potential for misunderstanding the meaning of a question, and these problems appear to be greater for people with lower literacy skills (Iversen, Furstenberg, and Belzer 1999). In general, data from the United Nations suggest that the more highly developed a country is, the more accurate the content of its census data will be, and this is probably accounted for largely by higher levels of education.

In less developed countries, content error may be more problematic because interviewers may not be sufficiently trained or motivated to press respondents for accurate information. Over the years, a seemingly simple question such as age has been prone to error because of "age-heaping" in which people round their age to the nearest zero or five instead of giving a precise answer. This is why the U.S. Census asks about birth date (see Figure 2.2), not simply your age.

Sampling Error   If any of the data in a census are collected on a sample basis, then sampling error is most likely introduced into the results. Until the 2010 census in the United States, the long form was distributed to a random sample of the population, but that role has now been taken over by the American Community Survey, as we discuss below. The Canadian and Mexican censuses also collect some of the data from a sample rather than from everyone in the population. With any sample, scientifically selected or not, differences are likely to exist between the character-istics of the sampled population and the larger group from which the sample was chosen. However, in a *scientific* sample, such as that used in most census operations, sampling error is readily measured based on the mathematics of probability. To a certain extent, sampling error can be controlled—samples can be designed to ensure comparable levels of error across groups or across geographic areas. Furthermore, if the sample is very large, then sampling error will be relatively small.

Continuous Measurement—American Community Survey   Almost all the detailed data about population characteristics obtained from the decennial cen-suses in the United States come from the long form, which for several decades was administered to about one in six households. The success of survey sampling in obtaining reliable demographic data led the U.S. Census Bureau in 1996 to initi-ate a process of "continuous measurement" designed to replace the long form in subsequent decennial censuses, beginning with the 2010 census (Torrieri 2007). The vehicle for this is the monthly American Community Survey (ACS), which is a "rolling survey" of approximately three million American households each year, designed to collect enough data over a 10-year period to provide detailed informa-tion down to the census block level (a census block is the smallest geographic unit used by the U.S. Census, as we discuss later in the chapter), and in the process pro-vide updated information on an annual basis, rather than having to wait for data at 10-year intervals. Just as with the complete census, questionnaires are mailed out to the households selected for the sample, and people respond by mail, online, over the phone, or by way of a personal visit from a Census Bureau representative (U.S. Census Bureau 2018a).

The first data from the American Community Survey were made available on the Internet for the 2005 round of data, and data for the nation, states, and large populations within states are now updated annually online at the Census Bureau website and also on the IPUMS (Integrated Public Use Microdata Samples) website (as we discuss later in the chapter). By 2010 enough surveys had been collected to produce five-year estimates for areas with populations less than 20,000 and these are regularly updated. There are nearly 130 million households in the United States, and 3 million of those are surveyed each year, so over the course of the 10 years between the 2000 and 2010 censuses, the ACS covered about 30 million house-holds, meaning that almost one in four households wound up providing the detailed data no longer collected in the decennial census. The five-year estimates from the ACS produce data similar to that generated by Canada's five-year census cycle.

The Census of Canada

The first census in Canada was taken in 1666 when the French colony of New France was counted on the order of King Louis XIV. This turned out to be a door-to-door enumeration of all 3,215 settlers in Canada at that time. A series of wars between England and France ended with France ceding Canada to England in 1763, and the British undertook censuses on an irregular but fairly consistent basis. The several regions of Canada were united under the British North America Act of 1867, which specified that, not unlike the plan in the United States, censuses were to be taken regularly to establish the number of representatives that each province would send to the House of Commons. The first of these mandated censuses was taken in 1871, although similar censuses had been taken in 1851 and 1861. In 1905, the census bureau became a permanent government agency and is now known as Statistics Canada.

Canada began using sampling in 1941, the year after the United States experimented with it. In 1956, Canada conducted its first quinquennial census (every five years, as opposed to every 10 years—the decennial census), and in 1971 Canada mandated that the census be conducted every five years. The U.S. Congress passed similar legislation in the 1970s but never funded the efforts, so the United States stayed with the decennial census until the implementation of continuous measurement provided by the American Community Survey.

As in the United States, two census forms were used in Canada from 1941 through the 2006 census—a short form for all households with just a few key items (see Table 2.1) and a more detailed long form that went to a sample of 20 percent of Canadian households. However, for the 2011 Census, Statistics Canada dropped the mandatory long form and instead implemented the National Household Survey. This was sent out to 30 percent of households with the caveat that responding was voluntary, rather than compulsory. The Director of Statistics Canada resigned after the government made that decision, and there was a lot of concern that the high non-response rate (26 percent nationally but higher in some provinces) might make these data very difficult to interpret (Hulchanski et al. 2013). So, perhaps it was not too surprising that Statistics Canada abandoned the voluntary survey and returned to the traditional long form from a sample of the population for the 2016 census. The result was a record high 97.8 response rate.

Statistics Canada estimates coverage error by comparing census results with population estimates (the demographic analysis approach) and by conducting both a Reverse Record Check study to measure the undercoverage errors and an Overcoverage Study designed to investigate overcoverage errors. The Reverse Record Check is the more important part of the two, and involves taking a sample of records from other sources such as birth records and immigration records and then looking for those people in the census returns. An analysis of people known to exist from administrative data, but not found in the census, is a key component of estimating coverage error. The results of the Reverse Record Check and the Overcoverage Study are then combined to provide an estimate of net undercoverage (the difference between the overcount of some groups and the undercount of other groups) of 2.6 percent in the 2016 census (Statistics Canada 2018b), compared to 2.8 percent in 2006 (Statistics Canada 2013). Coverage in the 2016 census was enhanced by the ability of Canadians to fill out the census form online.

The Census of Mexico

Like Canada and the United States, Mexico has a long history of census taking. There are records of a census in the Valley of Mexico taken in the year 1116, and the subsequent Aztec empire also kept count of the population for tax purposes. Spain conducted several censuses in Mexico during the colonial years, including a general census of New Spain (Nueva España, as they knew it) in 1790. Mexico gained independence from Spain in 1821, but it was not until 1895 that the first of the modern series of national censuses was undertaken. A second enumeration was done in 1900, and since then censuses have been taken every 10 years (with the exception of the one in 1921, which was one year out of sequence because of the Mexican civil war—aka Mexican Revolution—between 1910 and 1920). From 1895 through the 1970s, the census activities were carried out by the General Directorate of Statistics (Dirección General de Estadística), and there were no permanent census employees. However, the bureaucracy was reorganized for the 1980 census, and in 1983 the Instituto Nacional de Estadística, Geografía e Informática (INEGI) became the permanent government agency in charge of the census and other government data collection.

A somewhat different set of questions are asked in Mexican censuses than in those of the United States and Canada, as you can see in Table 2.1. The 2000 census was the first in Mexico to use a combination of a basic questionnaire administered to most households, plus a lengthier questionnaire administered to a sample of households, and this was replicated in the 2010 census. Furthermore, the sampling strategy was a bit different than in the United States and Canada. Most of the questions are asked of all households, and the sample involves asking 10 percent of households to respond to a set of more detailed questions about topics included in the basic questionnaire. Especially noteworthy is a set of questions seeking information about family members who had been international migrants at any time during the previous five years.

In 1995 and 2005 Mexico also conducted a mid-decade census, which it called a "conteo" to distinguish it from the decennial censuses. The "conteo" used only the basic questionnaire, and did not include a sample to receive the extended questionnaire. However, in 2015 the strategy was altered and a sample of households was selected to receive a more detailed questionnaire, in what INEGI called the "Encuesta Intercensal 2015" (2015 Intercensal Study) (INEGI 2018).

Less income detail is obtained in Mexico than in Canada or the United States, and socioeconomic categories are more often derived from outward manifestations of income, such as housing quality, and material possessions owned by members of the household, about which there are several detailed questions. Because a majority of Mexicans are mestizos (Spanish for mixed race, in this case mainly European and indigenous), no questions are asked about race or ethnicity. The only allusion to diversity within Mexico on the basic questionnaire is found in the question about language, in which people are asked if they speak an indigenous language. If so, they are also asked if they speak Spanish. On the long form administered to a sample of households, a question is also asked specifically about whether or not they belong to an indigenous group.

In Mexico, the evaluation of coverage error in the census has generally been made using the method of demographic analysis. On this basis, Corona Vásquez (1991) estimated that underenumeration in the 1990 Mexican census was somewhere between 2.3 and 7.3 percent. No analysis has been published of the accuracy of subsequent censuses, which, in all events, would be difficult to establish because of the large number of Mexican nationals living outside of the country, especially in the United States. Perhaps more important is the fact that post-enumeration surveys and other types of coverage error analyses are expensive and budget cuts had already forced INEGI to trim several questions from the extended questionnaire administered in the 2010 census.

IPUMS—Warehouse of Global Census Data

It is taken for granted in North America that census data can be downloaded for free from the Internet. The United States, Canada, and Mexico all provide such free access to census data, as do an increasing number of countries around the world. In many of these cases, however, the data are already tabulated for you by the statistical agencies. For researchers interested in uncovering trends and patterns in the data, it is vastly preferable to have access to raw data from the individual census records so that detailed statistical analysis can be undertaken, as long you have the requisite statistical software such as SPSS, SAS, or STATA or you are fluent in R. Census agencies provide these kinds of data by creating what are known as Public Use Microdata Samples (PUMS). A small sample of all census records, typically 5 to 10 percent, is randomly selected. These records are stripped of all personally identifying information, but with a geographic code left in place so that a person's general location can be determined, and this data set is then made available to researchers for analysis.

Over the past few decades, the Minnesota Population Center at the University of Minnesota has been creating a genuinely amazing resource of public use microdata samples from the censuses of the United States (1850 to the present), the American Community Survey from 2001 to the present, the Current Population Survey of the United States (discussed later in the chapter) from 1962 to the present, and an ever-growing library of data from censuses all over the globe. The files are harmonized so that variable definitions are similar from one census to another, and they are provided in standard statistical software formats, along with links to digital maps for those countries. The Minnesota Population Center also hosts the National Historical Geographic Information System which includes georeferenced aggregated (not individual level) U.S. census data from 1790 to the present, all linked to digital maps that you can download and analyze yourself. They have several other related projects, and overall these are the kinds of data that truly move us forward in our understanding of what's going on in the world. We encourage you to investigate the resource at https://www.ipums.org.

Registration of Vital Events

If you were born in the United States, a birth certificate was filled out for you, probably by a clerk or volunteer staff person in the hospital where you were born. When you die, someone (again, typically a hospital clerk) will fill out a death certificate on your behalf. Standard birth and death certificates used in the United States are shown in Figure 2.3. Births and deaths, as well as marriages, divorces, adoptions and abortions, are known as vital events, and when they are recorded by the government and compiled for use they become vital statistics. These statistics are the major source of data on births and deaths in most countries, and they are most useful when combined with census data, since that allows us to create rates of births

U.S. STANDARD CERTIFICATE OF LIVE BIRTH

BIRTH NUMBER:

LOCAL FILE NO.

C H I L D
| 1. CHILD'S NAME (First, Middle, Last, Suffix) | | 2. TIME OF BIRTH (24 hr) | 3. SEX | 4. DATE OF BIRTH (Mo/Day/Yr) |

| 5. FACILITY NAME (If not institution, give street and number) | 6. CITY, TOWN, OR LOCATION OF BIRTH | 7. COUNTY OF BIRTH |

M O T H E R
| 8a. MOTHER'S CURRENT LEGAL NAME (First, Middle, Last, Suffix) | 8b. DATE OF BIRTH (Mo/Day/Yr) |

| 8c. MOTHER'S NAME PRIOR TO FIRST MARRIAGE (First, Middle, Last, Suffix) | 8d. BIRTHPLACE (State, Territory, or Foreign Country) |

| 9a. RESIDENCE OF MOTHER-STATE | 9b. COUNTY | 9c. CITY, TOWN, OR LOCATION |

| 9d. STREET AND NUMBER | 9e. APT. NO. | 9f. ZIP CODE | 9g. INSIDE CITY LIMITS? □ Yes □ No |

F A T H E R
| 10a. FATHER'S CURRENT LEGAL NAME (First, Middle, Last, Suffix) | 10b. DATE OF BIRTH (Mo/Day/Yr) | 10c. BIRTHPLACE (State, Territory, or Foreign Country) |

CERTIFIER
| 11. CERTIFIER'S NAME: _____ TITLE: □ MD □ DO □ HOSPITAL ADMIN. □ CNM/CM □ OTHER MIDWIFE □ OTHER (Specify)_____ | 12. DATE CERTIFIED ___/___/___ MM DD YYYY | 13. DATE FILED BY REGISTRAR ___/___/___ MM DD YYYY |

INFORMATION FOR ADMINISTRATIVE USE

M O T H E R
| 14. MOTHER'S MAILING ADDRESS: 9 Same as residence, or: State: Street & Number: | City, Town, or Location: Apartment No.:   Zip Code: |

| 15. MOTHER MARRIED? (At birth, conception, or any time between)   □ Yes   □ No IF NO, HAS PATERNITY ACKNOWLEDGEMENT BEEN SIGNED IN THE HOSPITAL? □ Yes   □ No | 16. SOCIAL SECURITY NUMBER REQUESTED FOR CHILD?   □ Yes □ No | 17. FACILITY ID. (NPI) |

| 18. MOTHER'S SOCIAL SECURITY NUMBER: | 19. FATHER'S SOCIAL SECURITY NUMBER: |

INFORMATION FOR MEDICAL AND HEALTH PURPOSES ONLY

M O T H E R
20. MOTHER'S EDUCATION (Check the box that best describes the highest degree or level of school completed at the time of delivery)	21. MOTHER OF HISPANIC ORIGIN? (Check the box that best describes whether the mother is Spanish/Hispanic/Latina. Check the "No" box if mother is not Spanish/Hispanic/Latina)	22. MOTHER'S RACE (Check one or more races to indicate what the mother considers herself to be)
□ 8th grade or less	□ No, not Spanish/Hispanic/Latina	□ White
□ 9th - 12th grade, no diploma	□ Yes, Mexican, Mexican American, Chicana	□ Black or African American
□ High school graduate or GED completed	□ Yes, Puerto Rican	□ American Indian or Alaska Native (Name of the enrolled or principal tribe)_____
□ Some college credit but no degree	□ Yes, Cuban	□ Asian Indian
□ Associate degree (e.g., AA, AS)	□ Yes, other Spanish/Hispanic/Latina	□ Chinese
□ Bachelor's degree (e.g., BA, AB, BS)	(Specify)_____	□ Filipino
□ Master's degree (e.g., MA, MS, MEng, MEd, MSW, MBA)		□ Japanese
□ Doctorate (e.g., PhD, EdD) or Professional degree (e.g., MD, DDS, DVM, LLB, JD)		□ Korean
		□ Vietnamese
		□ Other Asian (Specify)_____
		□ Native Hawaiian
		□ Guamanian or Chamorro
		□ Samoan
		□ Other Pacific Islander (Specify)_____
		□ Other (Specify)_____

F A T H E R
23. FATHER'S EDUCATION (Check the box that best describes the highest degree or level of school completed at the time of delivery)	24. FATHER OF HISPANIC ORIGIN? (Check the box that best describes whether the father is Spanish/Hispanic/Latino. Check the "No" box if father is not Spanish/Hispanic/Latino)	25. FATHER'S RACE (Check one or more races to indicate what the father considers himself to be)
□ 8th grade or less	□ No, not Spanish/Hispanic/Latino	□ White
□ 9th - 12th grade, no diploma	□ Yes, Mexican, Mexican American, Chicano	□ Black or African American
□ High school graduate or GED completed	□ Yes, Puerto Rican	□ American Indian or Alaska Native (Name of the enrolled or principal tribe)_____
□ Some college credit but no degree	□ Yes, Cuban	□ Asian Indian
□ Associate degree (e.g., AA, AS)	□ Yes, other Spanish/Hispanic/Latino	□ Chinese
□ Bachelor's degree (e.g., BA, AB, BS)	(Specify)_____	□ Filipino
□ Master's degree (e.g., MA, MS, MEng, MEd, MSW, MBA)		□ Japanese
□ Doctorate (e.g., PhD, EdD) or Professional degree (e.g., MD, DDS, DVM, LLB, JD)		□ Korean
		□ Vietnamese
		□ Other Asian (Specify)_____
		□ Native Hawaiian
		□ Guamanian or Chamorro
		□ Samoan
		□ Other Pacific Islander (Specify)_____
		□ Other (Specify)_____

Mother's Name   Mother's Medical Record No.

| 26. PLACE WHERE BIRTH OCCURRED (Check one) □ Hospital □ Freestanding birthing center □ Home Birth: Planned to deliver at home? 9 Yes 9 No □ Clinic/Doctor's office □ Other (Specify)_____ | 27. ATTENDANT'S NAME, TITLE, AND NPI NAME: _____ NPI:_____ TITLE: □ MD □ DO □ CNM/CM □ OTHER MIDWIFE □ OTHER (Specify)_____ | 28. MOTHER TRANSFERRED FOR MATERNAL MEDICAL OR FETAL INDICATIONS FOR DELIVERY? □ Yes □ No IF YES, ENTER NAME OF FACILITY MOTHER TRANSFERRED FROM: |

REV. 11/2003

Figure 2.3   Standard Birth and Death Certificates Used in the United States (latest versions as of 2019)

Source: U.S. Centers for Disease Control and Prevention, National Center for Health Statistics.

MOTHER	29a. DATE OF FIRST PRENATAL CARE VISIT _ _ /_ _ /_ _ _ _ MM DD YYYY ☐ No Prenatal Care	29b. DATE OF LAST PRENATAL CARE VISIT _ _ /_ _ /_ _ _ _ MM DD YYYY	30. TOTAL NUMBER OF PRENATAL VISITS FOR THIS PREGNANCY _____ (If none, enter ʌ0".)

31. MOTHER'S HEIGHT _____ (feet/inches)	32. MOTHER'S PREPREGNANCY WEIGHT _____ (pounds)	33. MOTHER'S WEIGHT AT DELIVERY _____ (pounds)	34. DID MOTHER GET WIC FOOD FOR HERSELF DURING THIS PREGNANCY? ☐ Yes ☐ No

35. NUMBER OF PREVIOUS LIVE BIRTHS (Do not include this child)	36. NUMBER OF OTHER PREGNANCY OUTCOMES (spontaneous or induced losses or ectopic pregnancies)	37. CIGARETTE SMOKING BEFORE AND DURING PREGNANCY For each time period, enter either the number of cigarettes or the number of packs of cigarettes smoked. IF NONE, ENTER ʌ0".	38. PRINCIPAL SOURCE OF PAYMENT FOR THIS DELIVERY
35a. Now Living Number _____ ☐ None	35b. Now Dead Number _____ ☐ None	36a. Other Outcomes Number _____ ☐ None	Average number of cigarettes or packs of cigarettes smoked per day. # of cigarettes # of packs Three Months Before Pregnancy _____ OR _____ First Three Months of Pregnancy _____ OR _____ Second Three Months of Pregnancy _____ OR _____ Third Trimester of Pregnancy _____ OR _____	☐ Private Insurance ☐ Medicaid ☐ Self-pay ☐ Other (Specify)_____

35c. DATE OF LAST LIVE BIRTH _ _ /_ _ _ _ MM YYYY	36b. DATE OF LAST OTHER PREGNANCY OUTCOME _ _ /_ _ _ _ MM YYYY	39. DATE LAST NORMAL MENSES BEGAN _ _ /_ _ /_ _ _ _ MM DD YYYY	40. MOTHER'S MEDICAL RECORD NUMBER

MEDICAL AND HEALTH INFORMATION	41. RISK FACTORS IN THIS PREGNANCY (Check that apply) Diabetes ☐ Prepregnancy (Diagnosis prior to this pregnancy) ☐ Gestational (Diagnosis in this pregnancy) Hypertension ☐ Prepregnancy (Chronic) ☐ Gestational (PIH, preeclampsia) ☐ Eclampsia ☐ Previous preterm birth ☐ Other previous poor pregnancy outcome (Includes perinatal death, small-for-gestational age/intrauterine growth restricted birth) ☐ Pregnancy resulted from infertility treatment-If yes, check all that apply: ☐ Fertility-enhancing drugs, Artificial insemination or Intrauterine insemination ☐ Assisted reproductive technology (e.g., in vitro fertilization (IVF), gamete intrafallopian transfer (GIFT)) ☐ Mother had a previous cesarean delivery If yes, how many _____ ☐ None of the above 42. INFECTIONS PRESENT AND/OR TREATED DURING THIS PREGNANCY (Check all that apply) ☐ Gonorrhea ☐ Syphilis ☐ Chlamydia ☐ Hepatitis B ☐ Hepatitis C ☐ None of the above	43. OBSTETRIC PROCEDURES (Check all that apply) ☐ Cervical cerclage ☐ Tocolysis External cephalic version: ☐ Successful ☐ Failed ☐ None of the above 44. ONSET OF LABOR (Check all that apply) ☐ Premature Rupture of the Membranes (prolonged, ≥12 hrs.) ☐ Precipitous Labor (<3 hrs.) ☐ Prolonged Labor (≥ 20 hrs.) ☐ None of the above 45. CHARACTERISTICS OF LABOR AND DELIVERY (Check all that apply) ☐ Induction of labor ☐ Augmentation of labor ☐ Non-vertex presentation ☐ Steroids (glucocorticoids) for fetal lung maturation received by the mother prior to delivery ☐ Antibiotics received by the mother during labor ☐ Clinical chorioamnionitis diagnosed during labor or maternal temperature >38°C (100.4°F) ☐ Moderate/heavy meconium staining of the amniotic fluid ☐ Fetal intolerance of labor such that one or more of the following actions was taken: in-utero resuscitative measures, further fetal assessment, or operative delivery ☐ Epidural or spinal anesthesia during labor ☐ None of the above	46. METHOD OF DELIVERY A. Was delivery with forceps attempted but unsuccessful? ☐ Yes ☐ No B. Was delivery with vacuum extraction attempted but unsuccessful? ☐ Yes ☐ No C. Fetal presentation at birth ☐ Cephalic ☐ Breech ☐ Other D. Final route and method of delivery (Check one) ☐ Vaginal/Spontaneous ☐ Vaginal/Forceps ☐ Vaginal/Vacuum ☐ Cesarean If cesarean, was a trial of labor attempted? ☐ Yes ☐ No 47. MATERNAL MORBIDITY (Check all that apply) (Complications associated with labor and delivery) ☐ Maternal transfusion ☐ Third or fourth degree perineal laceration ☐ Ruptured uterus ☐ Unplanned hysterectomy ☐ Admission to intensive care unit ☐ Unplanned operating room procedure following delivery ☐ None of the above

NEWBORN INFORMATION

NEWBORN	48. NEWBORN MEDICAL RECORD NUMBER 49. BIRTHWEIGHT (grams preferred, specify unit) _____ 9 grams 9 lb/oz 50. OBSTETRIC ESTIMATE OF GESTATION: _____ (completed weeks) 51. APGAR SCORE: Score at 5 minutes: _____ If 5 minute score is less than 6, Score at 10 minutes: _____ 52. PLURALITY - Single, Twin, Triplet, etc. (Specify)_____ 53. IF NOT SINGLE BIRTH - Born First, Second, Third, etc. (Specify)_____	54. ABNORMAL CONDITIONS OF THE NEWBORN (Check all that apply) ☐ Assisted ventilation required immediately following delivery ☐ Assisted ventilation required for more than six hours ☐ NICU admission ☐ Newborn given surfactant replacement therapy ☐ Antibiotics received by the newborn for suspected neonatal sepsis ☐ Seizure or serious neurologic dysfunction ☐ Significant birth injury (skeletal fracture(s), peripheral nerve injury, and/or soft tissue/solid organ hemorrhage which requires intervention) 9 None of the above	55. CONGENITAL ANOMALIES OF THE NEWBORN (Check all that apply) ☐ Anencephaly ☐ Meningomyelocele/Spina bifida ☐ Cyanotic congenital heart disease ☐ Congenital diaphragmatic hernia ☐ Omphalocele ☐ Gastroschisis ☐ Limb reduction defect (excluding congenital amputation and dwarfing syndromes) ☐ Cleft Lip with or without Cleft Palate ☐ Cleft Palate alone ☐ Down Syndrome ☐ Karyotype confirmed ☐ Karyotype pending ☐ Suspected chromosomal disorder ☐ Karyotype confirmed ☐ Karyotype pending ☐ Hypospadias ☐ None of the anomalies listed above

(Left margin: Mother's Name | Mother's Medical Record No. _____)

56. WAS INFANT TRANSFERRED WITHIN 24 HOURS OF DELIVERY? 9 Yes 9 No IF YES, NAME OF FACILITY INFANT TRANSFERRED TO:_____	57. IS INFANT LIVING AT TIME OF REPORT? ☐ Yes ☐ No ☐ Infant transferred, status unknown	58. IS THE INFANT BEING BREASTFED AT DISCHARGE? ☐ Yes ☐ No

Figure 2.3   (*continued*)

U.S. STANDARD CERTIFICATE OF DEATH

LOCAL FILE NO. _____   STATE FILE NO. _____

1. DECEDENT'S LEGAL NAME (Include AKA's if any) (First, Middle, Last)	2. SEX	3. SOCIAL SECURITY NUMBER

4a. AGE-Last Birthday (Years)	4b. UNDER 1 YEAR		4c. UNDER 1 DAY		5. DATE OF BIRTH (Mo/Day/Yr)	6. BIRTHPLACE (City and State or Foreign Country)
	Months	Days	Hours	Minutes		

7a. RESIDENCE-STATE	7b. COUNTY	7c. CITY OR TOWN

7d. STREET AND NUMBER	7e. APT. NO.	7f. ZIP CODE	7g. INSIDE CITY LIMITS? □ Yes □ No

8. EVER IN US ARMED FORCES? □ Yes □ No	9. MARITAL STATUS AT TIME OF DEATH □ Married □ Married, but separated □ Widowed □ Divorced □ Never Married □ Unknown	10. SURVIVING SPOUSE'S NAME: (If wife, give name prior to first marriage)

11. FATHER'S NAME (First, Middle, Last)	12. MOTHER'S NAME PRIOR TO FIRST MARRIAGE (First, Middle, Last)

13a. INFORMANT'S NAME	13b. RELATIONSHIP TO DECEDENT	13c. MAILING ADDRESS (Street and Number, City, State, Zip Code)

14. PLACE OF DEATH (Check only one: see instructions)

IF DEATH OCCURRED IN A HOSPITAL: □ Inpatient □ Emergency Room/Outpatient □ Dead on Arrival	IF DEATH OCCURRED SOMEWHERE OTHER THAN A HOSPITAL: □ Hospice facility □ Nursing home/Long term care facility □ Decedent's home □ Other (Specify):

15. FACILITY NAME (If not institution, give street & number)	16. CITY OR TOWN , STATE, AND ZIP CODE	17. COUNTY OF DEATH

18. METHOD OF DISPOSITION: □ Burial □ Cremation □ Donation □ Entombment □ Removal from State □ Other (Specify)	19. PLACE OF DISPOSITION (Name of cemetery, crematory, other place)

20. LOCATION-CITY, TOWN, AND STATE	21. NAME AND COMPLETE ADDRESS OF FUNERAL FACILITY

22. SIGNATURE OF FUNERAL SERVICE LICENSEE OR OTHER AGENT	23. LICENSE NUMBER (Of Licensee)

ITEMS 24-28 MUST BE COMPLETED BY PERSON WHO PRONOUNCES OR CERTIFIES DEATH	24. DATE PRONOUNCED DEAD (Mo/Day/Yr)	25. TIME PRONOUNCED DEAD

26. SIGNATURE OF PERSON PRONOUNCING DEATH (Only when applicable)	27. LICENSE NUMBER	28. DATE SIGNED (Mo/Day/Yr)

29. ACTUAL OR PRESUMED DATE OF DEATH (Mo/Day/Yr) (Spell Month)	30. ACTUAL OR PRESUMED TIME OF DEATH	31. WAS MEDICAL EXAMINER OR CORONER CONTACTED? □ Yes □ No

CAUSE OF DEATH (See instructions and examples)

32. PART I. Enter the chain of events--diseases, injuries, or complications--that directly caused the death. DO NOT enter terminal events such as cardiac arrest, respiratory arrest, or ventricular fibrillation without showing the etiology. DO NOT ABBREVIATE. Enter only one cause on a line. Add additional lines if necessary.

Approximate interval: Onset to death

IMMEDIATE CAUSE (Final disease or condition -------> resulting in death)   a._____
Due to (or as a consequence of):

Sequentially list conditions, if any, leading to the cause listed on line a. Enter the UNDERLYING CAUSE (disease or injury that initiated the events resulting in death) LAST   b._____
Due to (or as a consequence of):

c._____
Due to (or as a consequence of):

d._____

PART II. Enter other significant conditions contributing to death but not resulting in the underlying cause given in PART I	33. WAS AN AUTOPSY PERFORMED? □ Yes □ No
	34. WERE AUTOPSY FINDINGS AVAILABLE TO COMPLETE THE CAUSE OF DEATH? □ Yes □ No

35. DID TOBACCO USE CONTRIBUTE TO DEATH? □ Yes □ Probably □ No □ Unknown	36. IF FEMALE: □ Not pregnant within past year □ Pregnant at time of death □ Not pregnant, but pregnant within 42 days of death □ Not pregnant, but pregnant 43 days to 1 year before death □ Unknown if pregnant within the past year	37. MANNER OF DEATH □ Natural □ Homicide □ Accident □ Pending Investigation □ Suicide □ Could not be determined

38. DATE OF INJURY (Mo/Day/Yr) (Spell Month)	39. TIME OF INJURY	40. PLACE OF INJURY (e.g., Decedent's home; construction site; restaurant; wooded area)	41. INJURY AT WORK? □ Yes □ No

42. LOCATION OF INJURY: State:_____   City or Town:_____

Street & Number:_____   Apartment No.:_____   Zip Code:_____

43. DESCRIBE HOW INJURY OCCURRED:	44. IF TRANSPORTATION INJURY, SPECIFY: □ Driver/Operator □ Passenger □ Pedestrian □ Other (Specify)

45. CERTIFIER (Check only one):
□ Certifying physician-To the best of my knowledge, death occurred due to the cause(s) and manner stated.
□ Pronouncing & Certifying physician-To the best of my knowledge, death occurred at the time, date, and place, and due to the cause(s) and manner stated.
□ Medical Examiner/Coroner-On the basis of examination, and/or investigation, in my opinion, death occurred at the time, date, and place, and due to the cause(s) and manner stated.

Signature of certifier:_____

46. NAME, ADDRESS, AND ZIP CODE OF PERSON COMPLETING CAUSE OF DEATH (Item 32)

47. TITLE OF CERTIFIER	48. LICENSE NUMBER	49. DATE CERTIFIED (Mo/Day/Yr)	50. FOR REGISTRAR ONLY- DATE FILED (Mo/Day/Yr)

51. DECEDENT'S EDUCATION-Check the box that best describes the highest degree or level of school completed at the time of death.	52. DECEDENT OF HISPANIC ORIGIN? Check the box that best describes whether the decedent is Spanish/Hispanic/Latino. Check the "No" box if decedent is not Spanish/Hispanic/Latino.	53. DECEDENT'S RACE (Check one or more races to indicate what the decedent considered himself or herself to be)
□ 8th grade or less		□ White
□ 9th - 12th grade; no diploma	□ No, not Spanish/Hispanic/Latino	□ Black or African American □ American Indian or Alaska Native (Name of the enrolled or principal tribe)_____
□ High school graduate or GED completed	□ Yes, Mexican, Mexican American, Chicano	□ Asian Indian □ Chinese
□ Some college credit, but no degree	□ Yes, Puerto Rican	□ Filipino □ Japanese
□ Associate degree (e.g., AA, AS)	□ Yes, Cuban	□ Korean □ Vietnamese
□ Bachelor's degree (e.g., BA, AB, BS)	□ Yes, other Spanish/Hispanic/Latino (Specify)_____	□ Other Asian (Specify)_____ □ Native Hawaiian
□ Master's degree (e.g., MA, MS, MEng, MEd, MSW, MBA)		□ Guamanian or Chamorro □ Samoan
□ Doctorate (e.g., PhD, EdD) or Professional degree (e.g., MD, DDS, DVM, LLB, JD)		□ Other Pacific Islander (Specify)_____ □ Other (Specify)_____

54. DECEDENT'S USUAL OCCUPATION (Indicate type of work done during most of working life. DO NOT USE RETIRED).

55. KIND OF BUSINESS/INDUSTRY

Left margin (rotated): NAME OF DECEDENT — For use by physician or institution
To Be Completed/ Verified By: FUNERAL DIRECTOR
To Be Completed By: MEDICAL CERTIFIER
To Be Completed By: FUNERAL DIRECTOR

Figure 2.3   (continued)

and deaths, in which the vital events are the numerators and the census data provide the denominators.

Registration of vital events in Europe actually began as a chore of the church. Priests often recorded baptisms, marriages, and deaths, and historical demographers have used the surviving records to reconstruct the demographic history of parts of Europe (Wrigley 1974; Wrigley and Schofield 1981; Wall, Robin, and Laslett 1983; Landers 1993). Among the more demographically important tasks that befell the clergy was that of recording burials that occurred in England during the many years of the plague. In the early sixteenth century, the city of London ordered that the number of people dying be recorded in each parish, along with the number of christenings. Beginning in 1592, these records (or "bills") were printed and circulated on a weekly basis during particularly rough years, and thus they were called the London Bills of Mortality (Laxton 1987). Between 1603 and 1849, these records were published weekly (on Thursdays, with an annual summary on the Thursday before Christmas) in what amounts to one of the most important sets of vital statistics prior to the nineteenth-century establishment of official government bureaucracies to collect and analyze such data.

Initially, the information collected about deaths indicated only the cause (since one goal was to keep track of the deadly plague), but starting in the eighteenth century the age of those dying was also noted. Nonetheless, it was not until the middle of the nineteenth century that civil registration of births and deaths became compulsory and an office of vital statistics was officially established by the English government, mirroring events in much of Europe and North America. Birth and death certificates were standardized in the United States in 1900.

Unsurprisingly, today we find the most complete vital registration systems in the most highly developed countries and the least complete (often nonexistent) systems in the least developed countries. Such systems seem to be tied to literacy (there must be someone in each area to record events), adequate communication, and the cost of the bureaucracy required for such record keeping, all of which is associated with economic development. Among countries where systems of vital registration do exist, there is wide variation in the completeness with which events are recorded. Even in the United States, the registration of births is not 100 percent complete, yet the public so takes for granted the existence of vital statistics that the National Research Council was asked to convene a panel in 2009 to lay out the case for why continued funding is so vital (no pun intended) to our knowledge about the health of the nation (Siri and Cork 2009).

Although most nations have a system of birth and death registration that is separate from census activities, dozens of countries, mostly in Europe, maintain population registers, which are lists of all people in the country, and which can be used as a substitute for a census, as we mentioned earlier. Alongside each name are recorded the vital events for that individual, typically birth, death, marriage, divorce, and change of residence. Such registers are kept primarily for administrative (that is, social control) purposes, such as legal identification of people, election rolls, and calls for military service, but they are also extremely valuable for demographic purposes, since they provide a demographic life history for each individual. Even though registers are expensive to maintain, many countries that could afford them, such as the United States, tend to avoid them because of the perceived threat to personal freedom that can be inherent in a system that compiles and centralizes personally identifying information.

Combining the Census and Vital Statistics

Although recording vital events provides information about the number of births and deaths (along with other events) according to such characteristics as age and sex, we also need to know how many people are at risk of these events. Thus, vital statistics data are typically teamed up with census data, which do include that information. For example, you may know from the vital statistics that there were 3.8 million births in the United States in 2018 (the most recent year for which data are available at this writing), but that number tells you nothing about whether the birth rate was high or low. In order to draw any conclusion, you must relate those births to the 327 million people residing in the United States as of mid-2018, and only then do you discover a relatively low birth rate of 11.6 births per 1,000 population, down from 16.7 in 1990 (Hamilton et al. 2019).

The birth rate in 2018 required us to divide the number of births by the total population that year. No census had been taken in the United States since 2010, so an estimate of the population must be produced for the intercensal year. Once again census data are combined with vital statistics data (and migration estimates) using the demographic balancing equation that we discussed earlier in the chapter: the population in 2018 is equal to the population as of the 2010 census, plus the births, minus the deaths, plus the in-migrants, minus the out-migrants between 2010 and 2018. Naturally, deficiencies in any of these data sources will lead to inaccuracies in the estimate of the number of people alive at any time, but we typically won't know that until we conduct the next census.

Administrative Data

Knowing that censuses and the collection of vital statistics were not originally designed to provide data for demographic analysis has alerted demographers everywhere to keep their collective eyes open for any data source that might yield useful information. For example, an important source of information about immigration to the United States is the compilation of administrative records filled out for each person entering the country from abroad. These forms are collected and tabulated by the U.S. Citizenship and Immigration Service (USCIS) within the U.S. Department of Homeland Security. Of course, we need other means to estimate the number of people who enter without documents and avoid detection by the government, and we discuss that more in Chapter 6.

Data are not routinely gathered on people who permanently leave the United States, but the administrative records of the U.S. Social Security Administration provide some clues about the number and destination of such individuals because many people who leave the country have their Social Security checks follow them. An administrative source of information on migration within the United States used by the Census Bureau is a set of data provided to them by the Internal Revenue Service (IRS). Although no personal information is ever divulged, the IRS can match Social Security numbers of taxpayers each year and see if their address has changed, thus providing a clue about geographic mobility, at least among those people who file income tax returns. At the local level, a variety of administrative data can be tapped to determine demographic patterns. School enrollment data provide clues to patterns of population growth and migration. Utility data on connections and disconnections can also be used to discern local population trends, as can the number of people signing up for government-sponsored health programs (Medicaid and Medicare) and income assistance (various forms of welfare).

Sample Surveys

There are two major difficulties with using data collected in the census, by the vital statistics registration system, or derived from administrative records: (1) they are usually collected for purposes other than demographic analysis and thus do not necessarily reflect the theoretical concerns of demography; and (2) they are collected by many different people using many different methods and may be prone to numerous kinds of error. For these reasons, in addition to the cost of big data-collection schemes, sample surveys are frequently used to gather demographic data. (To be sure, as we noted above, sample surveys are incorporated into the census activities of the United States, Canada, Mexico, and many other countries.) Sample surveys may also provide the social, behavioral, economic, and even physical data we referred to earlier as being necessary to an understanding of why things are as they are. Their principal limitation is that they provide less extensive geographic coverage than a census or system of vital registration.

By using a carefully selected sample of even a few thousand people, demographers have been able to ask questions about births, deaths, migration, and other subjects that reveal aspects of the "why" of demographic events rather than just the "what." In some poor or remote areas of the world, sample surveys can also provide good estimates of the levels of fertility, mortality, and migration in the absence of census or vital registration data.

Demographic Surveys in the United States

We have already mentioned the American Community Survey (ACS), which is now a critically important part of the census itself. It is modeled after the Current Population Survey (CPS) conducted monthly by the U.S. Census Bureau in collaboration with the Bureau of Labor Statistics, and which has for many decades been one of the country's most important sample surveys. Since 1943, thousands of households (currently more than 50,000) have been queried each month about a variety of things, although a major thrust of the survey is to gather information on the labor force. Each March, detailed demographic questions are also asked about fertility and migration and such characteristics as education, income, marital status, and living arrangements.

Since 1983, the Census Bureau has also been conducting the Survey on Income and Program Participation (SIPP), which is a companion to the Current Population Survey. Using a rotating panel of more than 40,000 households that are queried several times over a two- to four-year period, the SIPP gathers detailed data on sources of income and wealth, disability, and the extent to which household members participate in government assistance programs. The Census Bureau also regularly conducts the American Housing Survey for the U.S. Department of Housing and Urban Development, and this survey generates important data on mobility and migration patterns in the United States. The National Center for Health Statistics (NCHS) within the U.S. Centers for Disease Control and Prevention (CDC) generates data about fertility and reproductive health through the National Survey of Family Growth (NSFG), which it conducts every five years or so. The government also obtains data on health and disability from the annual National Health Interview Survey (NHIS). These latter data are now available for each year from 1963 to the present on the Minnesota Population Center's IPUMS website.

There are also many privately funded surveys conducted in the United States that provide useful demographic information not available from the government surveys. Two of the more important of these are the General Social Survey (GSS), administered by the National Opinion Research Center (NORC) at the University of Chicago, and the sets of public opinion polls regularly conducted by the Pew Research Center in Washington, D.C.

Canadian Surveys

Canada conducts a monthly Labour Force Survey (LFS), initiated in 1945 to track employment trends after the end of World War II. Similar to the CPS in the United States, it is a rotating panel of 56,000 households, and although its major purpose is to gather data on the labor force (hence the name), it also obtains data on most of the core sociodemographic characteristics of people in each sampled household, so it provides a continuous measure of population trends in Canada. Since 1985, Statistics Canada has also conducted an annual General Social Survey, a sample of about 25,000 respondents. Each survey has a different set of in-depth topics designed to elicit detailed data about various aspects of life in Canada, such as health and social support, families, and time use.

Mexican Surveys

In Mexico, the government statistical agency INEGI conducts several regular national household surveys, one of which in particular is comparable to the CPS and the LFS. The National Survey of Occupation and Employment (Encuesta Nacional de Ocupación y Empleo [ENOE]) is a large (120,000-household) sample of households undertaken three times a year by INEGI and is designed to be representative of the entire country. As with the CPS and LFS, the goal is to provide a way of regularly measuring and monitoring the social and economic characteristics of the population beyond just data on current employment. Some of the population questions asked in the census (see Table 2.1) are also asked in the ENOE, along with a detailed set of questions about the labor force activity of everyone in the household who is 12 years of age or older.

European Surveys

Declining fertility and the concomitant aging of the population in Europe has generated a renewed interest in the continent's demography, and there are now several surveys in Europe that capture useful demographic information. The Population Unit of the United Nations Economic Commission for Europe funded the Family and Fertility Surveys (FFS) in 23 European nations during the 1990s. Since 2000, they have funded the "Generations and Gender Program," which is a longitudinal survey of 18–79-year-olds in 19 countries gathering data on a broad array of topics including fertility, partnership, the transition to adulthood, economic activity, care duties, and attitudes.

The European Social Survey (ESS) is a cross-national survey that has been conducted every two years across Europe since 2001 by researchers at City, University of London. The survey measures the attitudes, beliefs, and behavior patterns, along with the demographics of populations in more than 30 European nations. It is funded by the European Commission, the European Science Foundation, and the participating countries.

Demographic and Health Surveys

As we noted above, most developing countries do not have good systems of vital registration, without which it is difficult to track changes in mortality and fertility. Into this breach have stepped the Demographic and Health Surveys (DHS). The largest and globally most important set of demographic surveys are the product of the DHS Program of ICF International in Maryland. They are conducted with funding from the U.S. Agency for International Development (USAID), and are always done in collaboration with the national statistical agency of the country being surveyed.

The DHS is actually the successor to the World Fertility Survey, which was conducted between 1972 and 1982 under the auspices of the International Statistical Institute in the Netherlands. Concurrent with the World Fertility Survey was a series of Contraceptive Prevalence Surveys, conducted in Latin America, Asia, and Africa with funding from USAID. In 1984, the work of the World Fertility Survey and the Contraceptive Prevalence Surveys was combined into the Demographic and Health Surveys.

The focus of each DHS is on fertility, reproductive health, and child health and nutrition, but the data provide national estimates of basic demographic processes, structure, and characteristics, since a few questions are asked about all members of each household in the sample. With more than 300 surveys conducted in more than 90 developing countries in Africa, Asia, and Latin America, this is a rich source of information, as you will see in subsequent chapters. You can summarize data from the StatCompiler tool on the DHS website (https://www.dhsprogram.com), and you can also register to access their data directly from their website. Data from countries in Africa and Asia are also available through https://www.IPUMS.org.

A complementary set of surveys has been conducted in poorer countries that, for a number of reasons, have not had a Demographic and Health Survey. Known as the Multiple Indicators Cluster Surveys (MICS), they were developed by the United Nations Children's Fund (UNICEF) and are funded by multiple international agencies. These surveys collect data that are similar to those in the DHS and are available from the DHS Program.

Demographic Surveillance Systems

In Africa, many people are born, live, and die without a single written record of their existence because of the poor coverage of censuses and vital registration systems. To help correct this void, the INDEPTH Network was created in 1998 to provide a way of tracking the lives of people in specific "sentinel" areas of sub-Saharan Africa (and to a lesser extent south Asia), working with individual countries to select one or two defined geographic regions that are representative of a larger population. A census is conducted in that region and then subsequent demographic changes are continuously measured by keeping track of all births, deaths, migration, and related characteristics of the population. There are currently 42 surveillance sites in 20 different countries of Africa and Asia. INDEPTH was funded initially by governmental organizations, especially the Canadian government, and is now funded largely through private foundations.

Historical Sources

Our understanding of population processes is shaped not only by our perception of current trends but also by our understanding of historical events. Historical demography requires that we almost literally dig up information about the patterns of mortality, fertility, and migration in past generations to reconstruct "the world we have lost," as Peter Laslett (1971) once called it. You may prefer to whistle past the graveyard, but researchers at the Cambridge Group for the History of Population and Social Structure in the Department of Geography and the Faculty of History at Cambridge University (UK) have spent the past several decades developing ways to recreate history by reading dates on tombstones and organizing information contained in parish church registers and other local documents (Wrigley and Schofield 1981; Reher and Schofield 1993), extending methods developed especially by the great French historical demographer Louis Henry (1967; Rosental 2003).

Historical sources of demographic information do include censuses and vital statistics, but the general lack of good historical vital statistics is what typically necessitates special detective work to locate birth records in church registers and death records in graveyards. Even in the absence of a census, a complete set of good local records for a small village may allow a researcher to reconstruct the demographic profile of families by matching entries of births, marriages, and deaths in the community over a period of several years. Yet another source of such information is family genealogies, the compilation of which has become increasingly common in recent years throughout the world. Detailed genealogies in China, for example, allowed researchers at Cambridge University to develop simulation models of what the demographic structure of China must have been like in the past (Zhao 2001).

The results of these labors can be of considerable importance in testing our notions about how the world used to work. For example, through historical demographic research we now know that the conjugal family (parents and their children) is not solely a product of industrialization and urbanization, as was once thought (Wrigley 1974). In fact, such small family units, in contrast to the more traditional extended family units, were not uncommon in Europe prior to the Industrial Revolution and may actually have contributed to the process of industrialization by allowing at least some families more flexibility to meet the needs of the changing economy. In subsequent chapters, we will also have numerous occasions to draw on the results of the Princeton European Fertility Project, which gathered and analyzed data on marriage and reproduction throughout nineteenth- and early-twentieth-century Europe.

By quantifying (and thereby clarifying) our knowledge of past patterns of demographic events, we are also better able to interpret historical events in a meaningful fashion. In the United States extended families may have been more common prior to the nineteenth century than has generally been thought (Ruggles 1994). Indeed, R.V. Wells (1982) has reminded us that the history of the struggle of American colonists to survive, marry, and bear children may tell us more about the determination to forge a union of states than a detailed recounting of the actions of British officials.

Spatial Demography

Spatial demography represents the application of spatial concepts and statistics to demographic phenomena (Weeks 2004b; Voss 2007; Matthews and Parker 2013; Weeks 2016). It recognizes that demography is, by its very nature, concerned with people in places. Since people tend to do things differently in different places, demography is inherently spatial. Where you live is an important determinant of who you are, and social scientists are increasingly aware that spatial variation is a universal principle of human society. For example, the innovation of the early fertility declines in Europe, which we discussed in Chapter 1, provides a nearly classic example of Waldo Tobler's First Law of Geography that everything is related to everything else, but near things are more related than distant things

(Tobler 1970, 2004). This is a concept known as spatial autocorrelation. Thus, in Europe, had it not been for spatial autocorrelation, fertility might have declined in isolated settings, but the decline would not have spread as it did (we'll discuss this more in the next chapter). It turns out that all three demographic processes—mortality, fertility, and migration—exhibit spatial autocorrelation. Spatial autocorrelation is enhanced especially by migration patterns in which people in different geographic areas interact with each other over time, mixing and mingling in ways that can alter local cultures and influence demographic trends (Raymer, Willekens, and Rogers 2018). These are, in many ways, the essential ingredients that create neighborhoods, and the combination of census and GIS data helps us define and study neighborhoods (Logan 2018).

Culture underlies most aspects of demography, so if we can understand why some places have different cultures than others, we are in a good position to understand spatially varying levels of mortality, fertility, and migration. Recognizing and studying this spatial variability has been greatly enhanced by the technologies and tools that are wrapped into the overall field of Geographic Information Science (GIScience). As a result of these methods of analysis and of viewing the world, demography is evolving from being a primarily spatially *aware* science (which it has always been) to an increasingly more spatially *analytic* science (facilitated by the methods of GIScience). The advent of high-powered personal computers revolutionized our ability to analyze massive demographic data sets, and this has allowed the spatial component of demographic analysis to come into its own and further improve our knowledge of how the world works. The first uses of these concepts and methods actually occurred in business and government planning and then migrated, if you will, to academic research. Let us provide you with a good example of this from cluster marketing.

You often hear about the numbers and characteristics of people (their "demographic") in terms of the likelihood that they will buy certain kinds of products, watch certain kinds of movies, or vote for particular candidates. But where are those people? Where should you concentrate your resources in order to get their attention. The fact that "birds of a feather flock together" (i.e., that spatial autocorrelation is a regular feature of the world) means that neighborhoods can be identified on the basis of a whole set of shared sociodemographic characteristics. This greatly facilitates the process of marketing to particular groups in a process known as cluster marketing. This takes us back to the 1970s when:

> . . . a computer scientist turned entrepreneur named Jonathan Robbin devised a wildly popular target-marketing system by matching zip codes with census data and consumer surveys. Christening his creation PRIZM (Potential Rating Index for Zip Markets), he programmed computers to sort the nation's 36,000 zips into forty "lifestyle clusters." Zip 85254 in Northeast Phoenix, Arizona, for instance, belongs to what he called the Furs and Station Wagons cluster, where surveys indicate that residents tend to buy lots of vermouth, belong to a country club, read *Gourmet* and vote the GOP ticket. In 02151, a Revere Beach, Massachusetts, zip designated Old Yankee Rows, tastes lean toward beer, fraternal clubs, *Lakeland Boating* and whoever the Democrats are supporting (Weiss 1988:xii).

The PRIZM system made Robbin's company, Claritas Corporation (now part of Nielsen), one of the largest and most successful spatial demographics (aka geodemographics) firms in the world. A core principle is that *where* you live is a good predictor of *how* you live (Weiss 2000; Harris, Sleight, and Webber 2005; Sway 2018). It combines demographic characteristics with lifestyle variables and permits a business to home in on the specific neighborhoods where its products can be most profitably marketed. In keeping with the changing demographics of America, Nielsen Claritas adds new clusters as neighborhoods evolve. And, of course, neighborhoods evolve as their demographics change, and as technology alters the way people in different areas can be "approached" by retailers (e.g., by email, text messages, Facebook, Twitter, etc.).

Mapping Demographic Data

Demographers have been using maps as a tool for analysis for a long time. Some of the earliest analyses of disease and death relied heavily on maps that showed, for example, where people were dying from particular causes. In the middle of the nineteenth century, London physician John Snow used maps to trace a local cholera epidemic. In research that established the modern field of epidemiology, Snow was able to show that cholera occurred much more frequently among customers of a water company that drew its water from the lower Thames River (downstream from the city), where it had become contaminated with London sewage. However, neighborhoods drawing water from another company were associated with far fewer cases of cholera because that company obtained water from the upper Thames—prior to its passing through London, and thus before the city's sewage was dumped in the river (Snow 1936).

Today a far more sophisticated version of this same idea is available to demographers through geographic information systems (GIS), which form the major part of the field of GIScience. A GIS is a computer-based system that allows us to combine maps with data that refer to particular places on those maps and then to analyze those data using spatial statistics (part of GIScience) and display the results as thematic maps or some other graphic format. Computer software allows us to transform a map into a set of areas (such as a country, state, or census tract), lines (such as streets, highways, or rivers), and points (such as a house, school, or a health clinic). Our demographic data must then be geo-referenced (associated with some geographic identification such as precise latitude-longitude coordinates, a street address, ZIP code, census tract, county, state, or country) so the computer will link them to the correct area, line, or point.

Demographic data are always referenced to a specific geographic area, even if just at the level of the entire nation. In the United States, the Geography Division of the U.S. Census Bureau works closely with the Population Division to make sure that data are identified for appropriate levels of "census geography." The most specific location would be your home address (expressed in terms of latitude and longitude), but that is never made public. In order to maintain privacy, data are aggregated to the neighborhood in which you live, and then aggregated to larger geographic areas. The smallest area typically used by the U.S. Census is a census block, which is a contiguous area or neighborhood with locally identifiable boundaries. As you can see in Table 2.3, Census blocks are aggregated into block groups, which in turn are the building blocks (pun intended) of census tracts. Tracts generally have a population size between 1,200 and 8,000 people, with an optimum size of 4,000 people. Census tracts are always within counties or their equivalent.

Geo-referencing data to places on the map means we can combine different types of data (such as census and survey data) for the same place, and we can do it for more than one time (such as data for 2010 and 2020). Spatial demography thus improves and enhances our ability to visualize and analyze the kinds of

Table 2.3   The Census Provides Geographically-Referenced Data for a Wide Range of Geographic Areas

Basic Geographic Hierarchy of Census Data:

United States
  Region (4)
    Division (9)
      State (50 states plus the District of Columbia, plus the outlying areas of American Samoa, Guam, northern Mariana Islands, Puerto Rico, and the Virgin Islands)
        Public Use Microdata Areas (PUMAs) (contiguous areas nested within states and built on census tracts and counties, containing at least 100,000 people)
          Counties and Statistically Equivalent Entities (the basic administrative and legal subdivision of states)
            County Subdivisions and Places (including minor civil divisions, cities, towns and Census Designated Places)
              Census Tract (tracts are small, relatively permanent subdivisions of a county or equivalent entity, having a population size between 1,200 and 8,000, with an optimum size of 4,000 people)
                Block Group (a cluster of blocks within census tracts, usually containing between 600 and 3,000 people)
                  Block (the smallest geographic unit, usually bounded on all sides by readily identifiable features such as streets, railroad tracks, or bodies of water)

Other Commonly Used Geographic Entities:

Zip Code (the standard 5-digit or expanded 3-digit Zip Code, encompassing areas similar to, but not identical with, census tracts)

Congressional Districts (the 435 areas from which people are elected to the U.S. House of Representatives. After the apportionment of congressional seats among the states based on decennial census population counts, each state with multiple seats is responsible for establishing congressional districts for the purpose of electing representatives. Each congressional district is to be as equal in population to all other congressional districts in a state as practicable)

Source: U.S. Bureau of the Census, 2018, Geographic Areas Reference Manual; https://www.census.gov/geo/reference/garm.html (accessed 2018).

demographic changes taking place over time and space. Since 1997, for example, most of the Demographic and Health Surveys in less-developed countries have used global positioning system (GPS) devices (another geospatial technique) to record the location of (geo-reference) each household in the sample in order to allow for more sophisticated spatial demographic analysis of the survey data. An increasing number of other surveys are doing the same thing, thus exponentially increasing our ability to understand demographic change.

GIS and the Census

It is a gross understatement to say that the computer has vastly expanded our capacity to process and analyze data, and it is no coincidence that census data are so readily amenable to being "crunched" by the computer. The histories of the computer and the U.S. Census Bureau go back a long way together. Prior to the 1890 census, the U.S. government held a contest to see who could come up with the best machine for counting the data from that census. The winner was Herman Hollerith, who had worked on the 1880 census right after graduating from Columbia University. His method of feeding a punched card through a tabulating machine proved to be very successful, and in 1886 he organized the Tabulating Machine Company, which in 1911 was merged with two other companies and became the International Business Machines (IBM) Corporation (Kaplan and Van Valey 1980).

Then, after World War II, the Census Bureau sponsored the development of the first computer designed for mass data processing—the UNIVAC-I—which was used to help with the 1950 census and led the world into the computer age. Photo-optical scanning, which we now rely on heavily for entering data into the computer from printed documents (not to mention scanning the price of everything you buy at stores), was also a by-product of the Census Bureau's need for a device to tabulate data from census forms. FOSDIC (film optical sensing device for input to computers) was first used for the 1960 census.

Another useful innovation was the creation for the 1980 census of the DIME (Dual Independent Map Encoding) files. This was the first step toward computer mapping in which each piece of data was coded in a way that could be matched electronically to a place on a map. In the 1980s, several private firms latched onto this technology, improved it, and made it available to other companies for their own business uses.

By the early 1990s, the pieces of the puzzle had come together. The data from the 1990 U.S. census were made available for the first time on CD-ROM and at prices affordable to a wide range of users. Furthermore, the Census Bureau reconfigured its geographic coding of data, creating what it calls TIGER (Topologically Integrated Geographic Encoding and Referencing) files, which are digital boundary files that allow us to map the census data. At the same time, and certainly in response to increased demand, personal computers came along that were powerful enough and had enough memory to store and manipulate huge census files, including both the geographic database and the actual population and housing data. Not far behind was the software to run those computers, and several firms now make software for computers that allow interactive spatial analysis of census and other kinds of data resulting in the production of high-quality color maps of the analysis. Two of these firms—Environmental Systems Research Institute (ESRI) and Geographic Data Technology (GDT—now part of TomTom; your car's GPS may use its software)—worked with the Census Bureau prior to the Census 2000 to help update the Census Bureau's computerized Master Address File (the information used to continuously update the TIGER files) in order to improve census coverage and geographic accuracy. In a very real sense, the census and the TIGER files, more specifically, helped to spawn the now-booming GIS industry. By the time the 2010 census rolled around, it had become possible to map census data online through the Census Bureau's website and to download digital boundary files for use on your own computer.

Applied Demography

Spatial demography is an integral part of applied demography, or demographics, as it is more popularly known. The major difference between applied demography/demographics and the field of demography more generally is that the latter is concerned especially with producing new knowledge and improving our understanding of human behavior, whereas the former is concerned more with the use of existing knowledge and techniques to identify and solve problems and maybe make some money in the process.

Because we live in a social world, many if not most of the decisions that have to be made about life involve people, and when the issues relate to how many people there are, where they live and work, and what are they like, then demographics becomes part of the decision-making process (Pol and Thomas 2001; Thomas 2018), in which you systematically lay out a strategy for achieving your goal. These goals will obviously be different depending upon whether your problems relate to political, social, or business planning.

Political Planning

The original purpose of the Census of Population in the United States was for political planning—to determine how membership in the House of Representatives should be distributed, as we discuss in the essay in this chapter. Once elected, politicians regularly confront demographic reality in the course of legislating social change. They may ask questions, for example, about how population growth and distribution influence the allocation of tax dollars. Will the increase in the older population bankrupt the social security system? Would federal subsidies to inner-city areas help lower the unemployment rate? Are undocumented immigrants creating an undue burden on the criminal justice systems in border counties?

Politicians are not completely altruistic, of course, and now routinely use demographics for their own personal use when campaign time rolls around. What are the characteristics of a candidate's supporters (as well as the supporters of the "opposition" candidate) and where are these voters located? The strategies for "packaging and selling" a candidate are not unlike those used for any other product or service. Census and survey data are used to map the demographic characteristics of voters in a candidate's area and an appropriate plan of action is prepared. Remember, though, that to be elected, a candidate must appeal to voters, not necessarily to all people who reside in an area. Since not all residents may be eligible to vote (because they are too young, are not citizens, or are convicted felons whose rights have not been restored) and since not all who are eligible will actually vote, these differences may be crucial.

Social Planning

Social agencies have long recognized the value of demographics for planning. School districts ask: How many students will there be next year? Or: Do we need to redraw school attendance areas? Police departments need to ask what the changes in population growth might portend for criminal activity in their areas. Health officials plan services by identifying specific high-risk populations (people who have an unusually high need for particular services) and attempting to meet their needs: Where is the best location for a new skilled nursing facility? Or: Does the community hospital really need an additional 40 beds? When such planning breaks down, as it often does in cities of third-world nations where rapid population growth is occurring, the result can be a certain amount of chaos, social foment, and even political upheaval.

A demographic change that most communities in North America, Europe, and East Asia (especially Japan) currently face is the aging of the population. In the United States people aged 75 and older are four times more likely than those aged 18 to 44 to be admitted to a hospital, and they spend more time each year in the hospital than do younger people (National Center for Health Statistics 2017). The two ends of the age continuum are where the risks of death are highest (as we will discuss in greater detail in Chapter 4), and the pattern of death rates is a good (albeit not perfect) index of demand for health services. In 1960, 59 percent of all deaths in the United States occurred to people 65 or older, while those aged 85 or older accounted for 11 percent of all deaths. By 2015, 73 percent of all deaths in the U.S. were to people aged 65 and older, and 32 percent occurred to people 85 and older (Murphy et al. 2017). As these percentages increase, the kind of training required of physicians obviously shifts to those diseases and conditions that affect older people, and the demand increases for the types of facilities and workers required to care for the older population (Beckett and Morrison 2010; Hoque, McGehee, and Bradshaw 2013; Vogt 2018).

We also know that certain kinds of crimes—especially street crimes and drug-related crimes—are more likely to occur in neighborhoods with particular sociodemographic characteristics. Areas where the poverty and unemployment levels are high are especially prone to these visible kinds of crime in which the offenders and victims are local residents (as opposed to white-collar crime, for example). By geocoding where crime events are reported, and where people are arrested, police departments and crime analysts are able to use this kind of information in conjunction with a geographic information system to map reported crimes and to better manage policing resources.

Business Planning/Marketing

There are several major uses to which demographics are regularly put by people in business, including marketing strategies, site selection, investment decisions, and management of human resources. Marketing demographics answer questions such as: Who buys my product and where are those people located? Site selection answers the basic question of: Where should I locate my business? Investment demographics answer questions like: What are potentially the most profitable kinds of products in the future? What other countries might have a market for my products or services? Human-resource management demographics look at questions such as: Is my company hiring the proper demographic mix of employees? Will future labor force shortages prompt me to discourage older employees from retiring and/or recruit immigrants to fill the jobs? When it comes to understanding today's consumer marketplace, just about the only thing that's certain is that uncertainty reigns. The speed of technological change, the volatile global economy, and the emergence of globally connected, ever-more-demanding customers have coalesced into the blur that now characterizes business-as-usual.

The late business guru, Peter Drucker, warned us that grappling with uncertainty in the world requires more than guesswork. It demands looking at "what has already happened that will create the future. The first place to look," said Drucker, "is in demographics" (quoted in Russell 1999:54). It is as true today as when Drucker made that comment back in 1999. This point was further highlighted in a Forbes article in 2018 in which Pamela Danziger reviewed the "9 Demographic Trends Shaping Retail's Future" (Danziger 2018). Here are the nine "macro-trends" that as of this writing retailers need to be planning for: (1) fewer people means fewer people buying; (2) less fortunate middle class, more prosperous luxury class; (3) multigenerational households on the rise; (4) sheltering in place; (5) lots of young adults, but few kids; (6) going it alone; (7) who's working, who's not; (8) more phones, fewer cars; and (9) minority majority. Fertility trends and family demography are clearly spotlighted here, and we will discuss all of these trends in subsequent chapters.

A key demographic with which societies must cope is demographic metabolism, first popularized by sociologist Norman Ryder several decades ago (Ryder 1965), which refers to the ongoing replacement of people at each age in every society. Today's young people will be tomorrow's middle-aged people; they will eventually replace the older population; and so on. To the extent that each cohort has different characteristics from the one that preceded it, society will change over time. Of course, people have recognized this possibility of change forever, which helps to explain the strict rules guiding the rearing of children over history in most societies at least until recently—tamp down innovative behavior among the young before it upsets the social order.

The modern world is different in that we now tend to applaud, rather than discourage, innovation, and so each new cohort (popularly known as a "generation") is more likely than ever to create its own impact on society as it moves through life. The U.S. Census Bureau actually started the naming trend when it referred to the years 1946 through 1964 as the "Post War Baby Boom" (Francese and Piirto 1990). "As the kids born in this boom started to grow into adults (and thus, consumers), ad agencies found traction by marketing their products to so-called Baby Boomers. This would be the first (and so far last) time a generation's "official" name would come from a government organization" (Keyser 2018). The Baby Boom was followed by what we demographers have called the Baby Bust (spanning the birth years of 1965 through 1981—see Figure 2.4), but that name didn't really catch on. What did catch on was the name "Generation X" which became popular after Douglas Coupland published a novel with that name in 1991 (Coupland 1991). Generation X was followed by a cohort of babies born between 1982 and 1995 that has been famously labeled as "Millennials," especially from the writings of Neil Howe and William Strauss (1991, 2000). This generation represented the group coming of age in the twenty-first century—after the turn of the millennium. The most recent generation

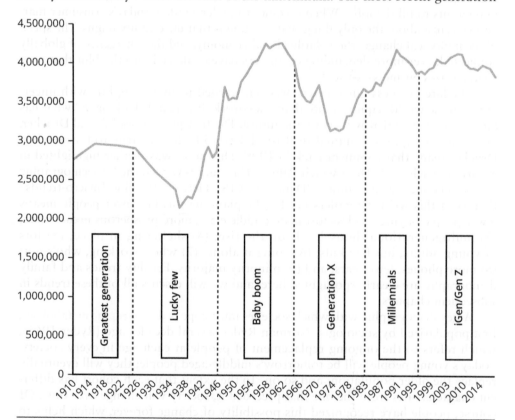

Figure 2.4   Births in the U.S. by year between 1910 and 2017 and their division into birth cohorts called "Generations"

Source: Prepared by John R. Weeks: birth data are from U.S. Centers for Disease Control and Prevention, National Center for Health Statistics; see text for definitions of each generation.

to come along has been variously labeled iGen or Generation Z, and encompasses people born from 1996 to the present. They are distinct for being the first generation to have had access to smartphones from adolescence on (Twenge 2017).

Though the first cohort to be popularly recognized was the Baby Boom generation, there are, of course, people still alive who were born prior to 1946, and their distinctiveness has been brought to the fore. Tom Brokaw's best-selling book on the "Greatest Generation" (Brokaw 1998) focused on people born between the beginning of the twentieth century and the Depression, who wound up being the core group fighting in World War II. Sandwiched between them and the Baby Boomers was a cohort born between 1929 and 1945 that Elwood Carlson (2008) has called the "Lucky Few." They were born during the hard times of the Depression but were too young to fight in World War II. However, after the war they were lucky to be needed as the Baby Boomers came along and created new economic demands for goods and services. The demographics of each of these groups is followed carefully by advertisers and business entrepreneurs, not to mention political and social planners.

Companies catering to the youngest age group have to keep track of the number of births (their potential market) as well as the characteristics of the parents and grandparents (who spend the money on behalf of the babies). Note that the baby market has witnessed considerable fluctuation in recent decades in the United States, as you can see in Figure 2.4. The number of babies being born each year dropped during the 1960s and 1970s, rebounded in the 1980s, peaked in 1990, and slacked off in the early 1990s before rebounding again until the Great Recession in the first part of this century, with a small decline from 2008 to the present. This is one of the things specifically mentioned by major retailer Toys R Us as it closed its stores in the United States in 2018 (Van Dam 2018):

> The decrease of birthrates in countries where we operate could negatively affect our business. Most of our end-customers are newborns and children and, as a result, our revenues are dependent on the birthrates in countries where we operate. In recent years, many countries' birthrates have dropped or stagnated as their population ages, and education and income levels increase. A continued and significant decline in the number of newborns and children in these countries could have a material adverse effect on our operating results.

As these different size cohorts flow through time, businesses have to adjust (as does all of society) since, for example, serving the Baby Boomers becomes a boom time for companies catering to their age group at any given time period. They are now moving into the young-old ages (more on this in Chapter 8), so we have seen a surge in things like laser eye surgery and sales of walking shoes (running shoe sales slowed to a walk for boomers). When not walking, the aging Baby Boomers have been driving their luxury or near-luxury sport utility vehicles (and are now snapping up electric cars).

Johnson & Johnson provides a good example of a company that has kept its eye on the changing demographics not only of the United States but of the world. The company got its start in the 1880s when Robert Wood Johnson began selling sterile bandages and surgical products—innovations built on Lister's germ theory that helped to lower death rates in hospitals. Later on, during the early years of the Baby Boom, Johnson & Johnson flourished by selling baby products. As Baby Boomers aged, the company continued to diversify its product line in a demographically relevant way, including acquiring ownership of both Ortho Pharmaceuticals (the largest U.S. manufacturer of contraceptives—helping to keep the birth rate low—and a large manufacturer of drugs to treat chronic diseases associated with aging) and Tylenol (one of the world's most popular pain relievers).

Basically, making sound investment decisions (as opposed to lucky ones) involves peering into the future, forecasting likely scenarios, and then acting on the basis of what seems likely to happen. After reading this book, you should have a good feel for the shape of things to come demographically. Most people do not, but those who do have an edge in life. A group of financial investors in the United Kingdom, for example, has established the Life and Longevity Markets Association in an attempt to spur the development of ways to make money from the pension funds into which an increasingly older population is pouring money. If people die sooner than expected, insurance companies lose money; whereas if they live longer than expected, the insurance companies reap a profit. The flip side of this is that if people live longer than expected, pension funds may be underfunded; whereas the pension funds profit if people die sooner, rather than later. You can see that people are betting one way or the other on your demographic future.

What else do the demographics suggest about future economic opportunities? The fact that 90 percent of the world's population growth in the foreseeable future will occur in the less developed nations is an important reason for the globalization of business and the internationalization of investment. In 2012 two financial analysts in California put together a demographic-economic model of 176 countries of the world. Their conclusion was that age structures with a disproportionate share of people of working age are good for economic growth (economies with a demographic tailwind), and age structures with lots of kids or lots of older people are not so good (economies with a headwind). They summarize the situation as follows (Arnott and Chaves 2012:42):

> Children are not immediately helpful to GDP. They do not contribute to it, nor do they help stock and bond market returns in any meaningful way; their parents are likely disinvesting to pay their support. Young adults are the driving force in GDP growth; they are the sources of innovation and entrepreneurial spirit. But they are not yet investing; they are overspending against their future human capital. Middle-aged adults are the engine for capital market returns; they are in their prime for income, savings, and investments. And senior citizens contribute to neither GDP growth nor stock and bond market returns; they disinvest to buy goods and services that they no longer produce.

All is not lost, however, in those countries with lots of kids because each one needs lots and lots of diapers. Procter & Gamble, maker of Pampers disposable diapers, has found a huge market out there. Babies, of course, grow up to be teenagers and young adults (trends that we will examine in detail throughout the book). From Malaysia to Argentina, young adults are buying iPads, cell phones, handheld electronic games, satellite dishes, and the perennial favorites, blue jeans and Coca-Cola. Companies selling in these markets are bound to make money.

International investors have been particularly intrigued by the world's two most populous countries, China and India. General Motors, Chrysler, and Ford all have invested in car manufacturing in China, as have Volkswagen and Peugeot Citroën from Europe. This is because China has become the world's largest market for new car sales. And where do they drive? Well, how about to the local Walmart, which opened its first store in China in the mid-1990s, and had 426 stores there as of 2018 (Walmart Stores 2018).

India, which is almost as populous but less well-off than China, does not yet allow full foreign ownership of retail businesses, except in very limited cases. However, the so-called "consuming class" in India (those with at least some discretionary income, although it may be as low as $2 per day) is estimated to comprise about 300 million people (Mustafi 2013). This is only about 25 percent of the population, yet it is a big market and thus represents an opportunity for some people to make money. Yum Brands, Inc., based in Louisville, Kentucky, which owns Pizza Hut, KFC, and Taco Bell (among other fast-food franchises), decided in 2010 that the growing young adult population (the youth bulge) in India represented a good market for Mexican food, so they opened a Taco Bell in Bangalore focusing on the vegetarian aspects of their menu (Sharma 2013).

As you can see, then, demography insinuates its way into an incredibly wide range of issues in our public and private worlds. This certainly underscores why it is so important for you to be aware of the underlying influences of demographics in nearly every aspect of your life—from the probability of finding a suitable mate to the probable size of your retirement check. If you take this interest in population change seriously, you may even wish to consider a career in demographics.

Should You Pursue a Career in Demographics?

A broad recognition on the part of businesses and planning organizations that demographics represents a useful and profitable resource means that many job opportunities exist in the field of applied demography, although in truth most such jobs are not labeled "demographer." They may be labeled corporate planner, economist, information analyst, market analyst, market researcher, research analyst, survey analyst, researcher, research scientist, or social scientist, but the substance of the job will be demographic analysis.

Many large companies and organizations in the United States have demographers on their payrolls. Jobs as applied demographers (especially those with GIS skills) will also be found in the myriad companies now offering geodemographic services. Google the term "geodemographics" and you'll see what we mean! Demographers are also employed by planning agencies at the federal, state, and local level, including regional agencies, counties, cities, chambers of commerce, economic development organizations, health departments, family planning agencies, and school districts. As long ago as 1982 the Population Association of America (PAA) created a Committee on Business Demography. Over time this has become the Applied Demography group in the PAA, organizing sessions at their annual meetings and putting out a very useful newsletter on a regular basis that provides insights into the people, organizations, and methods of applied demography/demographics.

What background should you have, besides reading this book, if you want to pursue a career in applied demography? Steven Murdock (former Director of the U.S. Census Bureau) and his colleagues (Murdock et al. 2006) suggest that it is useful to have a strong background in demographic techniques, especially in the areas of estimates, projections, and trend analysis. A good understanding of U.S. and international census data and census geography enables you to use demographic data correctly and effectively. And, of course, your employability will be especially enhanced if you have a good working knowledge of GIScience that you can combine with your demographic skills, as we have discussed throughout the chapter. Added to all of that, however, is a good appreciation of the overall pattern of demographic trends, so that you can offer meaningful and socio-culturally relevant interpretations of the demographic changes and relationships that you will be discovering in your work.

Summary and Conclusion

The focus in this chapter has been on the major sources of demographic information, the wells from which population data are drawn. Censuses are the most widely known and used sources of data on populations, and humans have been counting themselves in this way for a long time. However, the modern series of more scientific censuses dates only from the late eighteenth and early nineteenth centuries. The high cost of censuses, combined with the increasing knowledge we have about the value of surveys, has meant that even so-called complete enumerations often include some kind of sampling. That is certainly true in North America, as the United States, Canada, and Mexico all use sampling techniques in their censuses. Even vital statistics can be estimated using sample surveys, especially in developing countries, although the usual pattern is for births and deaths (and often marriages, divorces, and abortions) to be registered with the civil authorities. Some countries take this a step further and maintain a complete register of life events for everybody.

Knowledge can also be gleaned from administrative data gathered for non-demographic purposes. These are particularly important in helping us measure migration. It is not just the present that we attempt to measure; historical sources of information can add much to our understanding of current trends in population growth and change. Our ability to know how the world works is increasingly enhanced by incorporating our demographic data into a geographic information system, permitting us to ask questions that were not really answerable before the advent of the computer. Spatial demography expands our demographic perspective into a geographic realm about which demographers have long been aware, but only recently have been able to analyze.

Until the 1980s business did little business with demography, but the computerization of census and geographic data has changed all that. Applied demography/demographics, including geodemographics, has found a comfortable and important niche in the business world, especially in marketing, where demographic information permits more accurate segmentation of markets and the targeting of specific groups of consumers. Investors also pay attention to the way demographic trends point to future market growth and thus to potential profits. Human-resource managers are learning the value of knowing the demographics of their employees and of the labor force in general.

Before business got its hands on demographics, the major application of demographic theory and methods had been in planning—social planning, especially in education, but also in public and health services. Political planners have picked up on demographics, too. Besides the requirement in the United States that census data be used for congressional reapportionment and redistricting, demographics are now routinely used for analysis of potential legislation and for strategy in election campaigns.

The applied uses of demography may well help keep demography in front of you for the rest of your life. You will encounter demographics in the social media, magazines, newspapers, television, and in the course of your work, no matter what it might be. As that happens, we hope that you will not fail to use your demographic perspective (your demographic literacy, if you will) in its broadest scope to keep track of local, national, and international population trends, because demographic events will contribute to nearly all the major social changes you will witness over your lifetime, just as you will continue to contribute to those population trends with your own behavior.

This chapter has been about facts—how do we know what we know demographically? Next we turn to the more theoretical aspects of your demographic perspective and ask how we put these facts together to make sense of the world in which we live?

Main Points

1. In order to study population processes and change, you need to know how many people are alive, how many are being born, how many are dying, how many are moving in and out, and why these things are happening.

2. A basic source of demographic information is the population census, in which information is ideally obtained about all people in a given area at a specific time.

3. Not all countries regularly conduct censuses, but most of the population of the world has been enumerated since 2000.

4. Errors in the census typically come about as a result of nonsampling errors (the most important source of error, including coverage error and content error) or sampling errors.

5. Information about births and deaths usually comes from vital registration records—data recorded and compiled by government agencies. The most complete vital registration systems are found in the most highly developed nations, whereas they are often nonexistent in less-developed areas.

6. Sample surveys are sources of information for places in which census or vital registration data do not exist or where reliable information can be obtained less expensively by sampling than by conducting a census.

7. Spatial demography involves using geographic information systems to analyze demographic data from a spatial perspective, thus contributing substantially to our understanding of how the world works.

8. Applied demography/demographics is the application of population theory and methods to the solution of practical problems, including those that make businesses more profitable.

9. Demographics is the central ingredient in congressional reapportionment and redistricting in the U.S., while politicians also find demographics helpful in the analysis of legislation and in the strategy for their own election to office, and demographics are also useful for social and business planning.

10. You, too, could become a demographer. See your local professor for more details.

Questions for Review

1. In the United States, data are already collected from nearly everyone for Social Security cards and drivers' licenses. Why then does the country not have a population register that would eliminate the need for the census?

2. Survey data are never available at the same geographic detail as are census data. What are the disadvantages associated with demographic data that are not provided at a fine geographic scale?

3. Virtually all the demographic surveys and surveillance systems administered in developing countries are paid for by governments in richer countries. What is the advantage to richer countries of helping less-rich countries to collect demographic data?

4. What is the value to us in the twenty-first century of having an accurate demographic picture of earlier centuries?

5. Provide an example of spatial autocorrelation from your own personal experience. How might this concept influence your demographic perspective?

CHAPTER 3
Demographic Perspectives and Theories

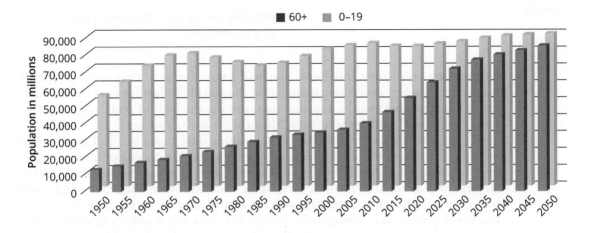

Figure 3.1   The Demographic Metabolism of the U.S. Population from 1950 Projected to 2050

Note: In 1950 there were almost 50 million more people in the United States. under the age of 20 than there were people aged 60 and older. That gap was widest as the last of the Baby Boomers were born. By 2050 the gap will have almost closed. Since the 1970s American society has had to adjust to an age structure in which the older population is increasing much more rapidly than the younger population.

Source: Adapted by John R. Weeks using data from the United Nations Population Division, World Population Prospects 2019.

Premodern Population Doctrines

The Prelude to Malthus

The Malthusian Perspective
Causes of Population Growth
Consequences of Population Growth
Avoiding the Consequences
Critique of Malthus
Neo-Malthusians

The Marxian Perspective
Causes of Population Growth
Consequences of Population Growth
Critique of Marx

The Prelude to the Demographic
    Transition Theory
Mill

Dumont
Durkheim

The Theory of the Demographic Transition
Critique of the Demographic Transition Theory
Reformulation of the Demographic Transition
    Theory
The Theory of Demographic Change and
    Response
Cohort Size Effects

The Theory of the Second Demographic
    Transition

The Demographic Transition Is Really
    a Set of Transitions
The Health and Mortality Transition
The Fertility Transition
The Age Transition

The Migration Transition
The Urban Transition
The Family and Household Transition
Impact on Local and Global
    Society

Summary and Conclusion

Main Points

Questions for Review

ESSAY: *Who Are the Neo-Malthusians and
        Why Do We Care?*

By the time you finish this book you will know for sure that demography is connected to nearly everything going on in the world. To further your understanding of how the world works, the next step is to put the facts of population together with the "whys" and "wherefores." In other words, you need a demographic perspective—a way of relating the demographic data described in Chapter 2 to theories about how the world operates demographically. A demographic perspective will guide you through the sometimes tangled relationships between population factors (such as size and growth, geographic distribution, age structure, and other sociodemographic characteristics) and the rest of what is going on in society. As you develop your own demographic perspective, you will acquire a new awareness about your own community, as well as about national and world political, economic, and social issues. You will be able to understand the influences that demographic changes have had, and you will consider the demographic consequences of events, which historically have been huge and transformative. The transformation of human society is intimately bound up with the evolution of demographic processes, and in this chapter we want to show you how demographers have arrived at that understanding over time.

As we discuss how population processes are intertwined with general social changes and trends, we need to recognize that there are actually two levels of population theory. At the core of demographic analysis is the technical side of the field—the mathematical and biomedical theories that predict the kinds of changes taking place in the biological components of demography: fertility, mortality, and the distribution of a population by age and sex. Demography has, in fact, played a central role in the development of the fields of probability, statistics, and sampling (Kreager 1993). This hard core is crucial to our understanding of human populations, but there is a "softer" (although no less important) outer wrapping of theory that relates demographic processes to the real events of the social world (Schofield and Coleman 1986). The linkage of the core with its outer wrapping is what produces a demographic perspective.

Two questions have to be answered before you will be able to develop your own perspective: (1) What are the *causes* of population change? and (2) What are the *consequences* of population change? In this chapter, we discuss several perspectives that provide broad answers to these questions and that also introduce the major lines of demographic theory. The purpose of this review is to give you a head start in developing your own demographic perspective by taking advantage of what others have learned and passed on to us.

We begin this chapter with a brief review of premodern thinking on the subject of population. Most of these ideas are what we call doctrine, as opposed to theory. Early thinkers were certain they had the answers and certain that their proclamations represented the truth about population growth and its implications for society. By contrast, the essence of modern scientific thought is to assume that you may *not* have the answer and to acknowledge that you are willing to consider evidence regardless of the conclusion to which it points. In the process of sorting out the evidence, we develop tentative explanations (hypotheses and then theories) that help guide our thinking and our search for understanding. In demography, as in all the sciences, theories replace doctrine when new, systematically collected information (censuses and other sources discussed in the previous chapter) becomes available, allowing people to question old ideas and formulate new ones. Table 3.1 summarizes the doctrines and theories discussed in the chapter.

Table 3.1   Demographic Perspectives over Time

	Date	Demographic Perspective
Examples of Premodern Doctrines	~1300 BCE	Book of Genesis—"Be fruitful and multiply."
	~500 BCE	Confucius—Population growth is good, but governments should maintain a balance between population and resources.
	360 BCE	Plato—Population quality more important than quantity; emphasis on population stability.
	340 BCE	Aristotle—Population size should be limited and the use of abortion might be appropriate.
	~50 BCE	Cicero—Population growth necessary to maintain Roman influence.
	400 CE	St. Augustine—Abstinence is the preferred way to deal with human sexuality; the second best is to marry and procreate.
	1280 CE	St. Thomas Aquinas—Celibacy is *not* better than marriage and procreation.
	1380 CE	Ibn Khaldun—Population growth is inherently good because it increases occupational specialization and raises incomes.
	1500–1800	Mercantilism—Increasing national wealth depends on a growing population that can stimulate export trade.
	1700–1800	Physiocrats—Wealth of a nation is in land, not people; therefore, population size depends on the wealth of the land, which is stimulated by free trade (laissez-faire).

(continued)

Table 3.1 (*continued*)

	Date	Demographic Perspective
Modern Theories	1798	Malthus—Population grows exponentially while food supply grows arithmetically, with misery (poverty) being the result in the absence of moral restraint.
	~1800	Neo-Malthusian—Accepting the basic Malthusian premise that population growth tends to outstrip resources, but unlike Malthus believing that birth control measures are appropriate checks to population growth.
	~1844	Marxian—Each society at each point in history has its own law of population that determines the consequences of population growth; poverty is not the natural result of population growth.
	~1873 to 1929	Prelude to the demographic transition, including Mill, Dumont, Durkheim, and Thompson.
	1945	Demographic transition in its original formulation—The process whereby a country moves from high birth and death rates to low birth and death rates with an interstitial spurt in population growth. Explanations based originally on modernization theory.
	1962	Earliest studies suggesting the need to reformulate the demographic transition theory.
	1963	Theory of demographic change and response—Demographic response made by individuals to population pressures is determined by the means available to them to respond; causes and consequences of population change are intertwined.
	1968	Easterlin relative cohort size hypothesis—Successively larger young cohorts put pressure on young men's relative wages, forcing them to make a tradeoff between family size and overall well-being.
	1987	Concept of the second demographic transition proposed to explain the evolution of below-replacement fertility levels in many societies.
	present	A broadening of the demographic transition theory to account for the complexity of the multiple types of demographic changes taking place in human society, including transitions in health and mortality, fertility, migration and urbanization, age/sex, families and households, and the local and global environments in which we live.

Premodern Population Doctrines

Until about 2,500 years ago, human societies probably shared a common concern about population: They valued reproduction as a means of replacing people lost through universally high mortality. Ancient Judaism, for example, provided the prescription to "be fruitful and multiply" (Genesis 1:28). Indeed, reproductive power was often deified, as in ancient Greece, where it was the job of a variety of goddesses to help mortals successfully bring children into the world and raise those children to adulthood. In two of the more developed areas of the world 2,500 years ago, however, awareness of the potential for populations to grow beyond their resources prompted comment by well-known philosophers. In the fifth century BCE, the writings of the school of Confucius in China discussed the relationship between population and resources (Sauvy 1969), and it was suggested that the government should move people from overpopulated to underpopulated areas. Nonetheless, the idea of promoting population growth was clear in the doctrine of Confucius (Keyfitz 1973).

Writing in *The Laws* in 360 BCE, Plato emphasized the importance of population stability rather than growth. Specifically, Plato proposed keeping the ideal community of free citizens (as differentiated from indentured laborers or slaves who had few civil rights) at a constant 5,040. Charbit (2002:216) suggests that "what inspired Plato in his choice of 5,040 is above all the fact that it is divisible by twelve, a number with a decisive sacred dimension." The number of people desired by Plato was still moderately small, because Plato felt that too many people led to anonymity, which would undermine democracy, whereas too few people would prevent an adequate division of labor and would not allow a community to be properly defended. Population size would be controlled by late marriage, infanticide, and migration (in or out as the situation demanded) (Plato 360BC [1960]). Plato was an early proponent of the doctrine that quality in humans is more important than quantity.

In the Roman empire, the reigns of Julius and Augustus Caesar were marked by clearly pronatalist doctrines—a necessity, given the very high mortality that characterized the Roman era (Frier 1999). In approximately 50 BCE, Cicero noted that population growth was seen by the leaders of Rome as a necessary means of replacing war casualties and of ensuring enough people to help colonize new lands. Several scholars have speculated, however, that by the second century CE, as the old, pagan Roman empire was waning in power, the birth rate in Rome may have been declining (Stangeland 1904; Veyne 1987). Indeed, Pliny ("the younger") complained that ". . . in our time most people hold that an only son is already a heavy burden and that it is advantageous not to be overburdened with posterity" (quoted in Veyne 1987:13).

The Middle Ages in Europe, which followed the decline of Rome and its transformation from a pagan to a Christian society, were characterized by a combination of both pronatalist and antinatalist Christian doctrines. Christianity condemned polygamy, divorce, abortion, and infanticide—practices that had kept earlier Roman growth rates lower than they otherwise might have been. The early and highly influential Christian leader, mystic, and writer Augustine (CE 354–430) interpreted the message of Paul in the New Testament to mean that virgins were the highest form of human existence. Human sexuality was, in Augustine's view, a supernaturally good thing but also an important cause of sin (because most people are unable or unwilling to control their desires) (O'Donnell 2006). He believed that abstinence was the best way to deal with sexuality (an antinatalist view), but the second-best state was marriage, which existed for the purpose of procreation (a pronatalist view). This duality shows up most clearly in the Roman Catholic Church where priests take a vow of abstinence, while urging their parishioners to have as many children as possible.

The time between the end of the Roman Empire (fifth century CE) and the Renaissance (fifteenth century CE) was an economically stagnant, fatalistic period of European history. While Europe muddled through the Middle Ages, Islam (which had emerged in the seventh century CE) was expanding throughout the Mediterranean. Muslims took control of southern Italy and the Iberian Peninsula and, under the Ottoman Empire, controlled the Balkans and the rest of southeastern Europe. Europe's reaction to this situation was the Crusades, a series of wars launched by Christians to wrestle control away from Muslims. These expeditions were largely unsuccessful from a military perspective, but they did put Europeans into contact with the Muslim world, which ultimately led to the Renaissance—the rebirth of Europe:

> The Islamic contribution to Europe is enormous, both of its own creations and of its borrowings—reworked and adapted—from the ancient civilizations of the eastern Mediterranean and from the remoter cultures of Asia. Greek science and philosophy, preserved and improved by the Muslims but forgotten in Europe; Indian numbers and Chinese paper; oranges and lemons, cotton and sugar, and a whole series of other plants along with the methods of cultivating them—all these are but a few of the many things that medieval Europe learned or acquired from the vastly more advanced and more sophisticated civilization of the Mediterranean Islamic world (Lewis 1995:274).

By the fourteenth century, one of the great Arab historians and philosophers, Ibn Khaldun, was in Tunis writing about the benefits of a growing population. In particular, he argued that population growth creates the need for specialization of occupations, which in turn leads to higher incomes, concentrated especially in cities: "Thus, the inhabitants of a more populous city are more prosperous than their counterparts in a less populous one. . . . The fundamental cause of this is the difference in the nature of the occupations carried on in the different places. For each town is a market for different kinds of labour, and each market absorbs a total expenditure proportionate to its size" (quoted in Issawi 1987:268). Ibn Khaldun was not a utopian. His philosophy was that societies evolved and were transformed as part of natural and normal processes. One of these processes was that "procreation is stimulated by high hopes and resulting heightening of animal energies" (quoted in Issawi 1987:268).

To be sure, the cultural reawakening of Europe took place in the context of a growing population, as we noted in Chapter 1. Not surprisingly, then, new murmurings were heard about the place of population growth in the human scheme of things. The Renaissance began with the Venetians, who had established trade with Muslims and others as the eastern Mediterranean ceased to be a Crusade war zone in the thirteenth century. In that century, an influential Dominican monk,

Thomas Aquinas, argued that marriage and family building were not inferior to celibacy, thus implicitly promoting the idea that population growth is an inherently good thing.

By the end of the fourteenth century, the plague had receded from Europe (as discussed in Chapter 1); by the sixteenth century, Muslims (and Jews) had been expelled from southern Spain, and Europeans had begun their discovery and exploitation of Africa, the Americas, and south Asia. Cities began to grow noticeably, and Giovanni Botero, a sixteenth-century Italian statesman, wrote that "the powers of generation are the same now as one thousand years ago, and, if they had no impediment, the propagation of man would grow without limit and the growth of cities would never stop" (quoted in Hutchinson 1967:111). The seventeenth and eighteenth centuries witnessed an historically unprecedented trade (the so-called Columbian Exchange) of food, manufactured goods, people, and disease between the Americas and most of the rest of the world (Crosby 1972), undertaken largely by European merchants, who had the best ships and the deadliest weapons in the world (Cipolla 1965; Diamond 1997).

This rise in trade, prompted at least in part by population growth, generated the doctrine of Mercantilism among the new nation-states of Europe. Mercantilism maintained that a nation's wealth was determined by the amount of precious metals it had in its possession, which were acquired by exporting more goods than were imported, with the difference (the profit) being stored in precious metals. The catch here was that a nation had to have things to produce to sell to others, and the idea was that the more workers you had, the more you could produce. Furthermore, if you could populate the new colonies, you would have a ready-made market for your products and possibly a new source of precious metals. Thus population growth was seen as essential to an increase in national revenue, and Mercantilist writers sought to encourage it by a number of means, including penalties for non-marriage, encouragements to get married, lessening penalties for illegitimate births, limiting out-migration (except to their own colonies), and promoting immigration of productive laborers. It is important to keep in mind that these doctrines were concerned with the wealth and welfare of a specific country, not all of human society. "The underlying doctrine was, either tacitly or explicitly, that the nation which became the strongest in material goods and in men would survive; the nations which lost in the economic struggle would have their populations reduced by want, or they would be forced to resort to war, in which their chances of success would be small" (Stangeland 1904:183).

Mercantilist doctrines were supported by the emerging demographic analyses of people like John Graunt, William Petty, and Edmund Halley (all English) in the seventeenth century and Johann Peter Süssmilch, an eighteenth-century chaplain in the army of Frederick the Great of Prussia (now Germany). In 1662, John Graunt, a Londoner who is sometimes called the father of demography, analyzed the series of Bills of Mortality in the first known statistical analysis of demographic data (Sutherland 1963). Although he was a haberdasher by trade, Graunt used his spare moments to conduct studies that were truly remarkable for his time. He discovered that for every 100 people born in London, only 16 were still alive at age 36 and only 3 at age 66 (Graunt 1662 [1939]; Dublin, Lotka, and

Spiegleman 1949)—suggesting very high levels of mortality. With these data he uncovered the high incidence of infant mortality in London and found, somewhat to the amazement of people at the time, that there were regular patterns of death in different parts of London. Graunt "opened the way both for the later discovery of uniformities in many social or volitional phenomena like marriage, suicide, and crime, and for a study of these uniformities, their nature and their limits; thus he, more than any other man, was the founder of statistics" (Willcox 1936:xiii). Indeed, Harrison and Carroll (2005) note that Graunt's studies are thought by many people to mark the beginning of *social science* as we know it today, not just statistics or demography.

One of Graunt's close friends (and probably the person who coaxed him into this work) was William Petty, a member of the Royal Society in London (Kreager 1988) and arguably the man who invented the field of economics (*The Economist* 2013a). Petty circulated Graunt's work to the Society (which would not have otherwise paid much attention to a "tradesman"), and this brought it to the attention of the emerging scientific world of seventeenth-century Europe. Several years later, in 1693, Edmund Halley (of Halley's comet fame) became the first scientist to elaborate on the probabilities of death. Although Halley, like Graunt, was a Londoner, he came across a list of births and deaths kept for the city of Breslau in Silesia (now Poland). From these data, Halley used the life-table technique (discussed in Chapter 4) to determine that the expectation of life in Breslau between 1687 and 1691 was 33.5 years (Dublin et al. 1949).

Then, in the eighteenth century, Süssmilch built on the work of Graunt and others and added his own analyses to the observation of the regular patterns of marriage, birth, and death in Prussia and believed that he saw in these the divine hand of God ruling human society (Hecht 1987), in much the same way that people are fascinated by patterns such as the Fibonacci sequence. His view, widely disseminated throughout Europe, was that a larger population was always better than a smaller one, and, in direct contradistinction to Plato, he valued quantity over quality. He believed that indefinite improvements in agriculture and industry would postpone overpopulation so far into the future that it wouldn't matter.

The issue of population growth was more than idle speculation, because we know with a fair amount of certainty that the population of England, for example, doubled during the eighteenth century (Petersen 1979), and as we discussed in Chapter 1, Europe as a whole was also increasing in population. The rising interest in population encouraged the publication of two important essays on population size, one by David Hume (1752 [1963]) and the other by Robert Wallace (1761 [1969]). These, in turn, influenced Malthus, whom we discuss later.

These essays sparked considerable debate and controversy, because there were big issues at stake: "Was a large and rapidly growing population a sure sign of a society's good health? On balance, were the growth of industry and cities, the movement of larger numbers from one social class to another—in short, all of what we now term 'modernization'—a boon to the people or the contrary? And in society's efforts to resolve such dilemmas, could it depend on the sum of individuals' self-interest or was considerable state control called for?" (Petersen 1979:139). These are questions we are still dealing with more than 250 years later.

The population had, in fact, increased during the Mercantilist era, although probably not as a result of any of the policies put forth by its adherents. However, it was less obvious that the population was better off. Rather, the Mercantilist period had become associated with a rising level of poverty (Keyfitz 1972). Mercantilism relied on a state-sponsored system of promoting foreign trade, while inhibiting imports and thus competition. This generated wealth for a small elite but not for most people, leading to considerable income inequality.

One of the more famous reactions against Mercantilism was that mounted in the middle of the eighteenth century by François Quesnay, a physician in the court of King Louis XV of France (and an economist when not "on duty"). Whereas Mercantilists argued that wealth depends on the number of people, Quesnay turned that around and argued that the number of people depends on the means of subsistence (a general term for level of living). The essence of this view, called physiocratic thought, was that land, not people, is the real source of wealth of a nation. In other words, population went from being an independent variable, causing change in society, to a dependent variable, being altered by societal change. As you will see throughout this book, both perspectives have their merits.

Physiocrats also believed that free trade (rather than the import restrictions demanded by Mercantilists) was essential to economic prosperity. This concept of "laissez-faire" (let people do as they choose) was picked up by Adam Smith, a Scotsman and one of the first modern economic theorists. Central to Smith's view of the world was the idea that, if left to their own devices, people acting in their own self-interest would produce what was best for the community as a whole (Smith 1776). Smith differed slightly from the physiocrats, however, on the idea of what led to wealth in a society. Smith believed that wealth sprang from the labor applied to the land (we might now say the "value added" to the land by labor), rather than it being just in the land itself. From this idea arose the belief that there is a natural harmony between economic growth and population growth, with the latter depending always on the former. Thus, Smith felt that population size is determined by the demand for labor, which is, in turn, determined by the productivity of the land. These ideas are important to us because Smith's work served as an inspiration for the Malthusian theory of population, as Malthus himself acknowledges (see the preface to the sixth edition of Malthus 1872), especially because Smith was not troubled by the consequences of population growth in the way that Malthus was:

> Contra Malthus, Smith is very positive about continued population growth as a necessary factor in economic and social improvement. The Wealth of Nations describes how developing economies, once they begin to expand into manufacturing and related commerce, experience increased labor specialization; such development naturally stimulates, and its continuation depends on, growth of the laboring population. Smith was unconcerned about potential demographic limits to this process since, in his view, the inherent capacity of the division of labor to expand production and meet human needs, if properly managed, is more than sufficient to resolve any such problem (Kreager 2017:513).

The Prelude to Malthus

The eighteenth century was the Age of Enlightenment in Europe, a time when the goodness of the common person was championed. This perspective, that the rights of individuals superseded the demands of a monarchy, inspired the American and French Revolutions and was generally very optimistic and utopian, characterized by a great deal of enthusiasm for life and a belief in the perfectibility of humans. It ushered in an era of critically questioning traditional ideas and authority that is still reverberating around the world.

In France, these ideas were well-expressed by Marie Jean Antoine Nicolas de Caritat, Marquis de Condorcet, a member of the French aristocracy who forsook a military career to pursue a life devoted to mathematics and philosophy. His ideas helped to shape the French Revolution, although despite his inspiration for and sympathy with that cause, he died in prison at the hands of revolutionaries. In hiding before his arrest, Condorcet wrote a *Sketch for an Historical Picture of the Progress of the Human Mind* (Condorcet 1795 [1955]). He was a visionary who "saw the outlines of liberal democracy more than a century in advance of his time: universal education; universal suffrage; equality before the law; freedom of thought and expression; the right to freedom and self-determination of colonial peoples; the redistribution of wealth; a system of national insurance and pensions; equal rights for women" (Hampshire 1955:x).

Condorcet's optimism was based on his belief that technological progress has no limits. "With all this progress in industry and welfare which establishes a happier proportion between men's talents and their needs, each successive generation will have larger possessions, either as a result of this progress or through the preservation of the products of industry, and so, *as a consequence of the physical constitution of the human race, the number of people will increase*" (Condorcet 1795 [1955]:188; emphasis added). He then asked whether it might not happen that eventually the happiness of the population would reach a limit. If that happens, Condorcet concluded, "we can assume that by then men will know that . . . their aim should be to promote the general welfare of the human race or of the society in which they live or of the family to which they belong, rather than foolishly to encumber the world with useless and wretched beings" (p. 189). Condorcet thus saw prosperity and population growth increasing hand in hand, and if the limits to growth were ever reached, the final solution would be birth control.

On the other side of the English Channel, similar ideas were being expressed by William Godwin (father of Mary Wollstonecraft Shelley, author of *Frankenstein*, and father-in-law of the poet Percy Bysshe Shelley). Godwin's *Enquiry Concerning Political Justice and Its Influences on Morals and Happiness* appeared in its first edition in 1793, revealing his ideas that scientific progress would enable the food supply to grow far beyond the levels of his day, and that such prosperity would not lead to overpopulation because people would deliberately limit their sexual expression and procreation. Furthermore, he believed that most of the problems of the poor were due not to overpopulation but to the inequities of the social institutions, especially greed and accumulation of property (Godwin 1793 [1946]).

Thomas Robert Malthus had recently graduated from Jesus College at Cambridge and was a country curate and a nonresident fellow of Cambridge as he read and contemplated the works of Godwin, Condorcet, and others who shared the utopian view of the perfectibility of human society. Although he wanted to be able to embrace such an openly optimistic philosophy of life, he felt that intellectually he had to reject it. In doing so, he unleashed a controversy about population growth and its consequences that rages to this very day.

The Malthusian Perspective

The Malthusian perspective derives from the writings of Thomas Robert Malthus ("Robert" to his family and friends), an English clergyman and subsequently a college professor. His first *Essay on the Principle of Population as it affects the future improvement of society; with remarks on the speculations of Mr. Godwin, M. Condorcet, and other writers* was published anonymously in 1798. Malthus's original intention was not to carve out a career in population studies, but only to show that the unbounded optimism of the physiocrats and utopian philosophers was misplaced. He introduced his essay by commenting that "I have read some of the speculations on the perfectibility of man and society, with great pleasure. I have been warmed and delighted with the enchanting picture which they hold forth. I ardently wish for such happy improvements. But I see great, and, to my understanding, unconquerable difficulties in the way to them" (Malthus 1798 [1965]:7).

These "difficulties," of course, are the problems posed by his now famous principle of population. He derived his theory as follows:

> I think I may fairly make two postulata. First, that food is necessary to the existence of man. Secondly, that the passion between the sexes is necessary, and will remain nearly in its present state. . . . Assuming then, my postulata as granted, I say, that the power of population is indefinitely greater than the power in the earth to produce subsistence for man. Population, when unchecked, increases in a geometrical ratio. Subsistence increases only in an arithmetical ratio. . . . By the law of our nature which makes food necessary to the life of man, the effects of these two unequal powers must be kept equal. This implies a strong and constantly operating check on population from the difficulty of subsistence.
>
> This difficulty must fall somewhere; and must necessarily be severely felt by a large portion of mankind. . . . Consequently, if the premises are just, the argument is conclusive against the perfectibility of the mass of mankind (Malthus 1798 [1965]:11).

Malthus believed that he had demolished the utopian optimism by suggesting that the laws of nature, operating through the principle of population, essentially prescribed poverty for a certain segment of humanity. Malthus was a shy person by nature (James 1979; Petersen 1979), and he seemed ill prepared for the notoriety created by his essay. Nonetheless, after owning up to its authorship, he proceeded to document his population principles and to respond to critics by publishing a substantially revised version in 1803, slightly but importantly retitled to read *An Essay on the Principle of Population; Or, A View Of Its Past And Present Effects*

On Human Happiness; With An Inquiry Into Our Prospects Respecting The Future Removal Or Mitigation Of The Evils Which It Occasions. In all, he published six editions of the book during his lifetime, followed by a seventh edition published posthumously (Malthus 1872 [1971]), and as a whole they have undoubtedly been the single most influential work relating population growth to its social consequences. Although Malthus initially relied on earlier writers such as David Hume (1752 [1963]) and Robert Wallace (1761 [1969]), he was the first to draw a picture that linked the consequences of growth to its causes in a systematic way.

Causes of Population Growth

Malthus believed that human beings, like plants and non-human animals, are "impelled" to increase the population of the species by what he called a powerful "instinct," the urge to reproduce. Further, if there were no checks on population growth, human beings would multiply to an "incalculable" number, filling "millions of worlds in a few thousand years" (Malthus 1872 [1971]:6). We humans, though, have not accomplished anything nearly so impressive. Why not? Because of the checks to growth that Malthus pointed out—factors that have kept population growth from reaching its biological potential for covering the earth with human bodies.

According to Malthus, the ultimate check to growth is lack of food (the "means of subsistence"). In turn, the means of subsistence are limited by the amount of land available, the "arts" or technology that could be applied to the land, and "social organization" or land ownership patterns. A cornerstone of his argument is that populations tend to grow more rapidly than the food supply, since population has the potential for growing geometrically—two parents could have four children, sixteen grandchildren, and so on—whereas he believed (incorrectly, as Darwin later pointed out) that food production could be increased only arithmetically, by adding one acre at a time. This led to his conclusion that in the natural order of things, population growth will outstrip the food supply, and the lack of food will ultimately put a stop to the increase of people (see Figure 3.2).

Of course, Malthus was aware that starvation rarely operates directly to kill people, since something else usually intervenes to kill them before they actually die of starvation. This "something else" represents what Malthus calls positive checks, primarily those measures "whether of a moral or physical nature, which tend prematurely to weaken and destroy the human frame" (Malthus 1872 [1971]:12). Today we would call these the causes of death. There are also preventive checks—limits to birth. In theory, the preventive checks would include all possible means of birth control, including abstinence, contraception, and abortion. However, to Malthus the only acceptable means of preventing a birth was to exercise moral restraint; that is, to postpone marriage, remaining chaste in the meantime, until a man feels "secure that, should he have a large family, his utmost exertions can save them from rags and squalid poverty, and their consequent degradation in the community" (1872 [1971]:13). Any other means of birth control, including contraception (either before or after marriage), abortion, infanticide, or any "improper means," was viewed as a vice that would "lower, in a marked manner, the dignity of human nature." Moral

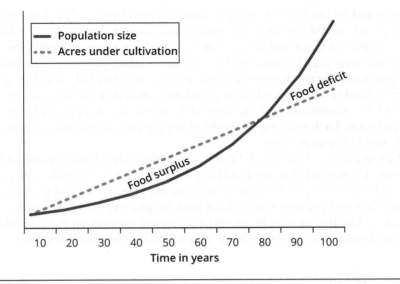

Figure 3.2   The Malthusian Principle—Over Time Geometric Growth of Population Overtakes Arithmetic Growth of Agricultural Land

Note: If we start with 100 acres supporting 100 people and then add 100 acres of cultivated land per decade (arithmetic growth) while the population is increasing by 3 percent per year (geometric growth), the result is a few decades of food surplus before population growth overtakes the increase in acres under cultivation, producing a food deficit, or "misery," as Malthus called it.

restraint was a very important point with Malthus, because he believed that if people were allowed to prevent births by "improper means" (that is, prostitution, contraception, abortion, or sterilization), then they would expend their energies in ways that are, so to speak, not economically productive. To put it another way, Malthus believed in self-control, not birth control.

As a scientific theory, the Malthusian perspective leaves much to be desired, since he was wrong about how quickly the food supply could increase, as we note below, and because he constantly conflates moralistic and scientific thinking (Davis 1955). Despite its shortcomings, however, which were evident even in his time, Malthus's reasoning led him to draw some important conclusions about the consequences of population growth that are still relevant to us.

Consequences of Population Growth

Malthus believed that a natural consequence of population growth was poverty. This is the logical end result of his arguments that (1) people have a natural urge to reproduce, and (2) the increase in the food supply cannot keep up with population growth. In his analysis, Malthus turned the argument of Adam Smith upside down. Instead of population growth depending on the demand for labor, as Smith (and the physiocrats) argued, Malthus believed that the urge to reproduce always forces population pressure to precede the demand for labor. Thus, "overpopulation" (as measured by the level of unemployment) would force wages down to the point where people could not afford to marry and raise a family. At such low wages, with a surplus of labor and the need for each person to work harder just to earn a subsistence wage, cultivators could employ more labor, put more acres into production, and thus increase the means of subsistence. Malthus believed that this cycle of increased food resources, leading to population growth, leading to too many people for available resources, leading then back to poverty, was part of a natural law of population. Each increase in the food supply only meant that eventually more people would live in poverty.

As you can see, Malthus did not have an altogether high opinion of his fellow creatures. He figured that most of them were too "inert, sluggish, and averse from labor" (1798 [1965]:363) to try to harness the urge to reproduce and avoid the increase in numbers that would lead back to poverty whenever more resources were available. In this way, he essentially blamed poverty on the poor themselves. There remained only one improbable way to avoid this dreary situation.

Avoiding the Consequences

Borrowing from John Locke, Malthus argued that "the endeavor to avoid pain rather than the pursuit of pleasure is the great stimulus to action in life" (1798 [1965]:359). Pleasure will not stimulate activity until its absence is defined as being painful. Malthus suggested that the well-educated, rational person would perceive in advance the pain of having hungry children or being in debt and would postpone marriage and sexual intercourse until he was sure that he could avoid that pain. If that motivation existed and the preventive check was operating, then the miserable consequences of population growth could be avoided. You will recall that Condorcet had suggested the possibility of birth control as a preventive check, but Malthus objected to this solution: "To remove the difficulty in this way, will, surely in the opinion of most men, be to destroy that virtue, and purity of manners, which the advocates of equality, and of the perfectibility of man, profess to be the end and object of their views" (1798:154). So the only way to break the cycle is to change human nature. Malthus felt that if everyone shared middle-class values, the problem would solve itself. He saw that as impossible, though, since not everyone has the talent to be a virtuous, industrious, middle-class success story, but if most people at least tried, poverty would be reduced considerably.

To Malthus, material success is a consequence of the human ability to plan rationally—to be educated about future consequences of current behavior—and he was a man who practiced what he preached. He planned his family rationally, waiting to marry and have children until he was 39, shortly after getting a secure job in 1805 as a professor of history and political economy at East India College in Haileybury, England (north of London). Interestingly enough, Marx thought that Malthus had taken the "monastic vows of celibacy" while other detractors attributed 11 children to him. In reality, Malthus and his wife, 11 years his junior, had only 3 children (Nickerson 1975; Petersen 1979).

To summarize, the major consequence of population growth, according to Malthus, is poverty. Within that poverty, though, is the stimulus for action that can lift people out of misery. So, if people remain poor, it is their own fault for not trying to do something about it. For that reason, Malthus was opposed to the English Poor Laws (welfare benefits for the poor), because he felt they would actually serve to perpetuate misery. They permitted poor people to be supported by others and thus not feel that great pain, the avoidance of which might lead to birth prevention. Malthus argued that if every man had to provide for his own children, he would be more prudent about getting married and raising a family. In his own time, this particular conclusion of Malthus brought him the greatest notoriety, because the number of people on welfare had been increasing and English parliamentarians were trying to decide what to do about the problem. Although the Poor Laws were not abolished, they were reformed largely because Malthus had given legitimacy to public criticism of the entire concept of welfare payments (Himmelfarb 1984). The Malthusian perspective that blames the poor for their own poverty endures, contrasted with the equally enduring view of Godwin and Condorcet that poverty is the creation of unjust human institutions. Two hundred additional years of debate have only sharpened the edges of the controversy.

Critique of Malthus

The single most obvious measure of Malthus's importance is the number of books and articles that have attacked him, beginning virtually the moment his first essay appeared in 1798 and continuing to the present (see, for example, Lee and Wang Feng 1999; Huzel 2006; Sabin 2013; Mayhew 2016). Dennis Hodgson (2009) quotes from a letter written by Thomas Jefferson in 1804 discussing the fact that he had just read Malthus's book and that he (Jefferson) was sure the principle of population did not apply to the United States, where the amount of available land meant that population growth could readily be absorbed. But Hodgson notes that later in the nineteenth century both sides in the debate over ending slavery in the United States called upon Malthusian arguments to bolster their case, even though Malthus himself was vociferously opposed to slavery.

The three most strongly criticized aspects of his theory have been (1) the assertion that food production could not keep up with population growth, (2) the conclusion that poverty was an inevitable result of population growth, and (3) the belief that moral restraint was the only acceptable preventive check. Malthus was not a firm believer in progress; rather, he accepted the notion that each society had a fixed set of institutions that established a stationary level of living. He was aware, of course, of the Industrial Revolution, but he was skeptical of its long-run value and agreed with the physiocrats that real wealth was in agricultural land. He was convinced that the increase in manufacturing wages that accompanied industrialization would promote population growth without increasing the agricultural production necessary to feed those additional mouths. Although it is clear that he was a voracious reader (Petersen 1999) and was a founder of the Statistical Society of London (Starr 1987), it is also clear that Malthus paid scant attention to the economic statistics that were available to him. "There is no sign that even at the end of his life he knew anything in detail about industrialization. His thesis was based on the life of an island agricultural nation, and so it remained long after the exports of manufacturers had begun to pay for the imports of large quantities of raw materials" (Eversley 1959:256). Thus, Malthus either failed to see or refused to acknowledge that technological progress was possible, and that its end result was a higher standard of living, not a lower one.

The crucial part of Malthus's ratio of population growth to food increase was that food (including both plants and non-human animals) would not grow exponentially, whereas humans could grow like that. Yet when Charles Darwin acknowledged that his concept of the survival of the fittest was inspired by Malthus's essay, he implicitly rejected this central tenet of Malthus's argument. In Chapter Three of *On the Origin of Species*, Darwin described his own theory as "the doctrine of Malthus applied with manifold force to the whole animal and vegetable kingdoms; for in this case there can be no artificial increase of food, and no prudential restraint from marriage. Although some species may be now increasing, more or less rapidly, in numbers, all cannot do so, for the world would not hold them" (Darwin 1872 [1991]:47). Put another way, every living thing has the potential for geometric increase, not just humans.

Malthus's argument that poverty is an inevitable result of population growth is also open to scrutiny. For one thing, his writing reveals a certain circularity in logic. In Malthus's view, a laborer could achieve a higher standard of living only by being prudent and refraining from marriage until he could afford it, but Malthus also believed that you could not expect prudence from a laborer until he had attained a higher standard of living. Thus, our hypothetical laborer seems squarely enmeshed in a catch-22. Even if we were to ignore this logical inconsistency, there are problems with Malthus's belief that the Poor Laws contributed to the misery of the poor by discouraging them from exercising prudence. Historical evidence has revealed that between 1801 and 1835 those English parishes that administered Poor Law allowances did not have higher birth, marriage, or total population growth rates than those in which Poor Law assistance was not available (Huzel 1969, 1980, 1984). Clearly, problems with the logic of Malthus's argument seem to be compounded by his apparent inability to see the social world accurately. "The results of the 1831 Census were out before he died, yet he never came to interpret them. Statistics apart, the main charge against him must be that he was a bad observer of his fellow human beings" (Eversley 1959:256).

We noted in Chapter 1 that the term "demography" was first used by a French scientist, Achille Guillard, in the middle of the nineteenth century. Schweber (2006) has argued that one of Guillard's motivations in trying to develop a new discipline of demography was to pressure French academics to see that statistical analyses of births and deaths would show that Malthus was wrong about his claim that population growth inevitably led to poverty. Once again, the power of Malthusian thought lies partly in the strength of opposition that he aroused in his lifetime, and even now two centuries later (see, for example, Mayhew 2016; Bashford and Chaplin 2016).

Neo-Malthusians

Those who criticize Malthus's insistence on the value of moral restraint, while accepting many of his other conclusions, are typically known as neo-Malthusians (see the essay in this chapter for more discussion). Specifically, neo-Malthusians favor contraception rather than simple reliance on moral restraint. During his lifetime, Malthus was constantly defending moral restraint against critics (many of whom were his friends) who encouraged him to deal more favorably with other means of birth control. In the fifth edition of his Essay, he did discuss the concept of *prudential restraint*, which meant the delay of marriage until a family could be afforded without necessarily refraining from premarital sexual intercourse in the meantime. He never fully embraced the idea, however, nor did he ever bow to pressure to accept anything but moral restraint as a viable preventive check.

Ironically, the open controversy actually helped to spread knowledge of birth control among people in nineteenth-century England and America. This was aided materially by the trial and conviction (later overturned on a technicality) in London in 1877–78 of two neo-Malthusians, Charles Bradlaugh and Annie Besant, for publishing a birth control handbook, *Fruits of Philosophy: The Private Companion of Young Married People*, written by Charles Knowlton, a physician in Massachusetts, and originally published in 1832. The publicity surrounding the trial enabled the English public to become more widely knowledgeable about those techniques (Chandrasekhar 1979). Eventually, the widespread adoption of birth control meant that fertility could be controlled *within* marriage, allowing couples to respond to economic changes in ways that were not anticipated by Malthus's Principle of Population.

Criticisms of Malthus do not, however, diminish the importance of his work:

> There are good reasons for using Malthus as a point of departure in the discussion of population theory. These are the reasons that made his work influential in his day and make it influential now. But they have little to do with whether his views are right or wrong. . . . Malthus' theories are not now and never were empirically valid, but they nevertheless were theoretically significant (Davis 1955b:541).

As we noted earlier, part of Malthus's significance lies in the storm of controversy his theories stimulated. Particularly vigorous in their attacks on Malthus were Karl Marx and Friedrich Engels.

The Marxian Perspective

Karl Marx and Friedrich Engels were both teenagers in Germany when Malthus died in England in 1834, and by the time they had met and independently moved to England, Malthus's ideas were already politically influential in their native land, not just in England. Several German states and Austria had responded to what they believed was overly rapid growth in the number of poor people by legislating against marriages in which the applicant could not guarantee that his family would

Who Are the Neo-Malthusians and Why Do We Care?

"Picture a tropical island with luscious breadfruits [a Polynesian plant similar to a fig tree] hanging from every branch, toasting in the sun. It is a small island, but there are only 400 of us on it so there are more breadfruits than we know what to do with. We're rich. Now picture 4,000 people on the same island, reaching for the same breadfruits: Number one, there are fewer to go around; number two, you've got to build ladders to reach most of them; number three, the island is becoming littered with breadfruit crumbs. Things get worse and worse as the population gradually expands to 40,000. Welcome to a poor, littered tropical paradise" (Tobias 1979:49). This scenario would probably have drawn a nod of understanding from Malthus himself, and even though written a few decades ago, it typifies the modern neo-Malthusian view of the world.

One of the most influential neo-Malthusians of the twentieth century was the University of California, Santa Barbara biologist Garrett Hardin. In 1968, Hardin published an article that raised the level of consciousness about population growth in the minds of professional scientists. His theme was simple and had been made by Kingsley Davis (1963) as he developed the theory of demographic change and response: Personal goals are not necessarily consistent with societal goals when it comes to population growth—Adam Smith was not completely correct to believe in laissez-faire. Hardin's metaphor is "the tragedy of the commons." He asks us to imagine an open field, available as a common ground for herdsmen to graze their cattle. "As a rational being, each herdsman seeks to maximize his gain. Explicitly or implicitly, more or less consciously, he asks, 'What is the utility to me of adding one more animal to my herd?'" (Hardin 1968:1244). The benefit, of course, is the net proceeds from the eventual sale of each additional animal, whereas the cost lies in the chance that an additional animal may result in overgrazing of the common ground. Since the ground is shared by many people, the cost is spread out over all, so for the individual herdsman, the benefit of another animal exceeds its cost. "But," notes Hardin, "this is

the conclusion reached by each and every rational herdsman sharing a commons. Therein is the tragedy. Each man is locked into a system that compels him to increase his herd without limit—in a world that is limited" (1968:1244). The moral, as Hardin puts it, is that "ruin is the destination toward which all men rush, each pursuing his own best interest in a society that believes in the freedom of the commons. Freedom in a commons brings ruin to all" (1968:1244).

Hardin reminds us that most societies are committed to a social welfare ideal. Families are not completely on their own. We share numerous things in common: education, public health, and police protection, and in all of the richer nations of the world people are guaranteed a minimum amount of food and income at the public expense. This leads to a moral dilemma that is at the heart of Hardin's message: "To couple the concept of freedom to breed with the belief that everyone born has an equal right to the commons is to lock the world into a tragic course of action" (Hardin 1968:1246). He was referring, of course, to the ultimate Malthusian clash of population and resources, and Hardin was no more optimistic than Malthus about the likelihood of people voluntarily limiting their fertility before it is too late.

Meanwhile, in the 1960s the world was becoming keenly aware of the population crisis through the writings of the person who is arguably the most famous of all neo-Malthusians, Paul Ehrlich. Like Hardin, Ehrlich is a biologist (at Stanford University), not a professional demographer. His *Population Bomb* (Ehrlich 1968) was an immediate sensation when it came out in 1968 and to this day often sets the tone for public debate about population issues. In the second edition of his book, Ehrlich (1971) phrased the situation in three parts: "too many people," "too little food," and, adding a wrinkle not foreseen directly by Malthus, "environmental degradation." Ehrlich called Earth "a dying planet."

In 1990, Ehrlich, in collaboration with his wife, Anne, followed with an update titled *The Population Explosion* (Ehrlich and Ehrlich 1990), reflecting their view that the bomb they worried about in 1968 had detonated in the meantime. The level of concern about the destruction of the environment has grown tremendously since 1968. Ehrlich's book had inspired the first Earth Day in the spring of 1970 (an annual event ever since in most communities across the United States and elsewhere in the world), yet in their 1990 book Ehrlich and Ehrlich rightly question why, in the face of the serious environmental degradation that had concerned them for so long, had people regularly failed to grasp its primary cause as being rapid population growth? "Arresting population growth should be second in importance only to avoiding nuclear war on humanity's agenda. Overpopulation and rapid population growth are intimately connected with most aspects of the current human predicament, including rapid depletion of nonrenewable resources, deterioration of the environment (including rapid climate change), and increasing international tensions" (Ehrlich and Ehrlich 1990:18).

Ehrlich thus argues that Malthus was right—dead right. But the death struggle is more complicated than that foreseen by Malthus. To Ehrlich, the poor are dying of hunger, while rich and poor alike are dying from the by-products of affluence—pollution and ecological disaster. Indeed, this is part of the "commons" problem. A few benefit; all suffer. What does the future hold? Ehrlich suggested that there are only two solutions to the population problem: the birth rate solution (lowering the birth rate) and the death rate solution (a rise in the death rate). He viewed the death rate solution as being the most likely to happen, because, like Malthus, he has had little faith in the ability of humankind to pull its act together. The only way to avoid that scenario, he argued, was to bring the birth rate under control, perhaps even by force. That idea generated death threats against him and his wife, but fortunately it turned out that fertility has been brought down to much lower levels by voluntary, rather than forceful means (with China the only real exception to this rule).

Neo-Malthusians differ from Malthus especially because they reject moral restraint as the only acceptable means of birth control and because they see population growth as leading not simply to poverty but also to widespread calamity. For neo-Malthusians, the "evil arising from the redundancy of population" that Malthus worried about has broadened in scope, and the remedies proposed are thus more dramatic.

Gloomy they certainly are, but the messages of Ehrlich and Hardin are important and have brought population issues to the attention of the entire globe. One of the ironies of neo-Malthusianism is that if the world's population does avoid future calamity, people will likely claim that the neo-Malthusians were wrong. Yet, much of the stimulus to bring down birth rates (including emphasis on the reproductive rights of women as the alternative to coercive means) and to find new ways to feed people and protect the environment has come as a reaction to the concerns they very publicly have raised.

It should be noted that the mention of Malthus or of the term neo-Malthusian has raised a lot of concern over the years (indeed, starting during Malthus's lifetime) that these ideas would lead to people being forced not to have children they might otherwise have wanted. Thus, the worry about the negative consequences of global population growth becomes a situation in which policy-makers may wind up making moral determinations about the relative value of actual and potential lives (McCann 2017; Murphy 2017; Merchant 2017).

Discussion Questions: (1) Discuss the tragedy of the commons in relation to global climate change and to the quality of water throughout the world, and relate that to population growth. **(2)** If Malthus was wrong in his idea that the food supply could not grow as quickly as population, as Darwin seemed to suggest, do you think that the neo-Malthusians are also wrong in their analysis of how the world works? Why or why not?

not wind up on welfare (Glass 1953). As it turned out, that scheme backfired on the German states, because people continued to have children, just out of wedlock. Thus, the welfare rolls grew as the illegitimate children had to be cared for by the state (Knodel 1970). The laws were eventually repealed, but they had an impact on Marx and Engels, who saw the Malthusian point of view as an outrage against humanity. Their demographic perspective thus arose in reaction to Malthus.

Causes of Population Growth

Neither Marx nor Engels ever directly addressed the issue of why and how populations grew. They seem to have had little quarrel with Malthus on this point, although they were in favor of equal rights for men and women and saw no harm in preventing birth. Nonetheless, they were skeptical of the eternal or natural laws of nature as stated by Malthus (that population tends to outstrip resources), preferring instead to view human activity as the product of a particular social and economic environment. The basic Marxian perspective is that each society at each point in history has its own law of population that determines the consequences of population growth. For capitalism, the consequences are overpopulation and poverty, whereas for socialism, population growth is readily absorbed by the economy with no side effects. This line of reasoning led to Marx's vehement rejection of Malthus, because if Malthus was right about his "pretended 'natural law of population'" (Marx 1890 [1906]:680), then Marx's theory would be wrong.

Consequences of Population Growth

Marx and Engels especially quarreled with the Malthusian idea that resources could not grow as rapidly as population, since they saw no reason to suspect that science and technology could not increase the availability of food and other goods at least as quickly as the population grew. Engels argued in 1865 that whatever population pressure existed in society was really pressure against the means of employment rather than against the means of subsistence (Meek 1971). Thus, they flatly rejected the notion that poverty can be blamed on the poor. Instead, they said, poverty is the result of a poorly organized society, especially a capitalist society. Implicit in the writings of Marx and Engels is the idea that the normal consequence of population growth should be a significant increase in production. After all, each worker obviously was producing more than he or she required—how else would all the dependents (including the wealthy manufacturers) survive? In a well-ordered society, if there were more people, there ought to be more wealth, not more poverty (Engels 1844 [1953]).

Not only did Marx and Engels feel that poverty, in general, was not the end result of population growth, they argued specifically that even in England at that time there was enough wealth to eliminate poverty. Engels had himself managed a textile plant owned by his father's firm in Manchester, and he believed that in England more people had meant more wealth for the capitalists rather than for the workers because the capitalists were skimming off some of the workers' wages as profits for themselves. Marx argued that they did that by stripping the workers of their tools and then, in essence, charging the workers for being able to come to the factory to work. For example, if you do not have the tools to make a car but want a job making cars, you could get hired at the factory and work eight hours a day. But, according to Marx, you might get paid for only four hours, the capitalist (owner of the factory) keeping part of your wages as payment for the tools you were using. The more the capitalist keeps, of course, the lower your wages and the poorer you will be.

Furthermore, Marx argued that capitalism worked by using the labor of the working classes to earn profits to buy machines that would replace the laborers, which, in turn, would lead to unemployment and poverty. Thus, the poor were not poor because they overran the food supply, but only because capitalists had first taken away part of their wages and then taken away their very jobs and replaced them with machines. Thus, the consequences of population growth that Malthus discussed were really the consequences of capitalist society, not of population growth per se. Overpopulation in a capitalist society was thought to be a result of the capitalists' desire for an industrial reserve army that would keep wages low through competition for jobs and, at the same time, would force workers to be more productive in order to keep their jobs. To Marx, the logical extension of this was that the growing population would bear the seeds of destruction for capitalism, because unemployment would lead to disaffection and revolution. If society could be reorganized in a more equitable (that is, socialist) way, then population problems would disappear.

It is noteworthy that Marx, like Malthus, practiced what he preached. Marx was adamantly opposed to the notion of moral restraint, and his life repudiated that concept. He married at the relatively young age (compared with Malthus) of 25, proceeded to father eight children, including one illegitimate son, and was on intimate terms with poverty for much of his life.

In its original formulation, the Marxian (as well as the Malthusian) perspective was somewhat provincial, in the sense that its primary concern was England in the nineteenth century. Marx was an intense scholar who focused especially on the historical analysis of economics as applied to England, which he considered to be the classic example of capitalism. However, as his writings have found favor in other places and times, revisions have been forced upon the Marxian view of population.

Critique of Marx

Not all who have adopted a Marxian worldview fully share the original Marx–Engels demographic perspective. Socialist countries have had trouble because of the lack of political direction offered by the Marxian notion that different stages of social development produce different relationships between population growth and economic development. For Marx, the Malthusian principle operated under capitalism only, whereas under pure socialism there would be no population problem. Unfortunately, he offered no guidelines for the transition period. At best, Marx implied that the socialist law of population should be the antithesis of the capitalist law. If the birth rate were low under capitalism, then the assumption was that it should be high under socialism; if abortion seemed bad for a capitalist society, it must be good for a socialistic society.

Thus, it was difficult over time for Russian demographers to reconcile the fact that demographic trends in the former Soviet Union were remarkably similar to trends in other developed nations. Furthermore, Soviet socialism was unable to alleviate one of the worst evils that Marx attributed to capitalism, higher death rates among people in the working class than among those in the higher classes (Brackett 1968). Moreover, birth rates dropped to such low levels throughout Marxist Eastern Europe in the years leading up to the breakup of the Soviet Union in 1991 that it was no longer possible to claim (as Marx had done) that low birth rates were bourgeois.

In China, the empirical reality of having to deal with the world's largest national population led to a radical departure from Marxian ideology. As early as 1953, the Chinese government organized efforts to control population by relaxing regulations concerning contraception and abortion. Ironically, after the terrible demographic disaster that followed the "Great Leap Forward" in 1958 (see Chapter 1), a Chinese official quoted Chairman Mao as having said, "A large population in China is a good thing. With a population increase of several fold we still have an adequate solution. The solution lies in production" (Ta-k'un 1960:704). Yet by the 1970s production no longer seemed to be a panacea, and with the introduction of the one-child policy in 1979, the interpretation of Marx took an about-face as another Chinese official wrote that under Marxism the law of production "demands not only a planned production of natural goods, but also the planned reproduction of human beings" (Muhua 1979:724).

Thus, despite Marx's denial of a population problem in a socialist society, the Marxist government in China dealt with one by rejecting those Marxist roots and embracing instead one of the most aggressive and coercive government programs ever launched to reduce fertility through restraints on marriage (the Malthusian solution), the promotion of contraception (the neo-Malthusian solution), albeit also with the use of legalized abortion (Teitelbaum and Winter 1988; Heer 1965). In a formulation such as this, Marxism was revised in the light of new scientific evidence about how people behave, in the same way that Malthusian thought has been revised. Bear in mind that although the Marxian and Malthusian perspectives are often seen as antithetical, they both originated in the midst of a particular milieu of economic, social, and demographic change in nineteenth-century Europe.

The Prelude to the Demographic Transition Theory

The population-growth controversy, initiated by Malthus and fueled by Marx, was the basis of a series of nineteenth-century and early-twentieth-century reformulations that have led directly to prevailing theories in demography. In this section, we briefly discuss three individuals who made important contributions to those reformulations: John Stuart Mill, Arsène Dumont, and Émile Durkheim.

Mill

The English philosopher and economist John Stuart Mill was an extremely influential writer of the nineteenth century. Mill was not as quarrelsome about Malthus as Marx and Engels had been; his scientific insights were greater than those of Malthus at the same time that his politics were less radical than those of Marx and Engels. Mill accepted the Malthusian calculations about the potential for population growth to outstrip food production as being axiomatic (a self-truth), but he was more optimistic about human nature than Malthus was. Mill believed that although your character is formed by circumstances, one's own desires can do much to shape circumstances and modify future habits (Mill 1873 [1924]).

Mill's basic thesis was that the standard of living is a major determinant of fertility levels. "In proportion as mankind rises above the condition of the beast, population is restrained by the fear of want, rather than by want itself. Even where there is no question of starvation, many are similarly acted upon by the apprehension of losing what have come to be regarded as the decencies of their situation in life" (Mill 1848 [1929]: Book I, Chap 10). The belief that people could be and should be free to pursue their own goals in life led him to reject the idea that poverty is inevitable (as Malthus implied) or that it is the creation of capitalist society (as Marx argued). One of Mill's most famous comments is that "the niggardliness of nature, not the injustice of society, is the cause of the penalty attached to overpopulation" (1848 [1929]: Book I, Chap. 13). This is a point of view conditioned by Mill's reading of Malthus, but Mill did not accept the Malthusian inevitability of a population growing beyond its available resources. Mill believed that people do not "propagate like swine, but are capable, though in very unequal degrees, of being withheld by prudence, or by the social affections, from giving existence to beings born only to misery and premature death" (1848 [1929]: Book I, Chap. 7). In the event that population ever did overrun the food supply, however, Mill felt that it would likely be a temporary situation with at least two possible solutions: import food or export people. He was, of course, referring to specific countries such as England, rather than thinking about this on a global scale, as we now must do.

The ideal state from Mill's point of view is that in which all members of a society are economically comfortable, an economic equality that is not inconsistent with Marx's perspective. At that point he felt (as Plato had centuries earlier) that the population would stabilize and people would try to progress culturally, morally, and socially instead of attempting continually to get ahead economically. It does sound good, but how do we get to that point? It was Mill's belief that before reaching the point at which both population and production are stable, there is essentially a race between the two. What is required to settle the issue is a dramatic improvement in the living conditions of the poor. If social and economic development are to occur, there must be a sudden increase in income, which could give rise to a new standard of living for a whole generation, thus allowing productivity to outdistance population growth. According to Mill, this was the situation in France after the Revolution:

> During the generation which the Revolution raised from the extremes of hopeless wretchedness to sudden abundance, a great increase of population took place. But a generation has grown up, which, having been born in improved circumstances, has not

learnt to be miserable; and upon them the spirit of thrift operates most conspicuously, in keeping the increase of population within the increase of national wealth (1848 [1929]: Book II, Chap. 7).

Mill was convinced that an important ingredient in the transformation to a non-growing population is that women do not want as many children as men do, and if they are allowed to voice their opinions, the birth rate will decline. Mill, like Marx, was a champion of equal rights for both sexes, and one of Mill's more notable essays, *On Liberty*, was co-authored with his wife. He reasoned further that a system of national education for poor children would provide them with the "common sense" (as Mill put it) to refrain from having too many children.

Overall, Mill's perspective on population growth was significant enough that we find his arguments surviving today in the writings of many of the twentieth- and twenty-first-century demographers whose names appear in the pages that follow. However, before getting to those people and their ideas, it is important to acknowledge at least two other nineteenth-century individuals whose thinking has an amazingly modern sound: Arsène Dumont and Émile Durkheim.

Dumont

Arsène Dumont was a late-nineteenth-century French demographer who felt he had discovered a new principle of population that he called "social capillarity" (Dumont 1890). Social capillarity refers to the desire of people to rise on the social scale, to increase their individuality as well as their personal wealth. The concept is drawn from an analogy to a liquid rising into the narrow neck of a laboratory flask. The flask is like the hierarchical structure of most societies, broad at the bottom and narrowing as you near the top. To ascend the social hierarchy often requires that sacrifices be made, and Dumont argued that having few or no children was the price many people paid to get ahead. Dumont recognized that such ambitions were not possible in every society. In a highly stratified aristocracy, few people outside of the aristocracy could aspire to a career beyond subsistence. However, in a democracy (such as late-nineteenth-century France), opportunities to succeed existed at all social levels. Joseph Spengler (1979) has succinctly summarized Dumont's thesis: "The bulk of the population, therefore, not only strove to ascend politically, economically, socially, and intellectually, but experienced an imperative urge to climb and a palsying fear of descent. Consequently, since children impeded individual and familial ascension, their number was limited" (p. 158).

Notice that Dumont added an important ingredient to Mill's recipe for fertility control. Mill argued that it was fear of social slippage that motivated people to limit fertility below the level that Malthus had expected. Dumont went beyond that to suggest that social aspiration was a root cause of a slowdown in population growth. Dumont was not happy with this situation, by the way. He was upset by the low level of French fertility and used the concept of social capillarity to propose policies to undermine it. He believed that socialism would undercut the desire for upward social mobility and would thus stimulate the birth rate. History, of course, has suggested otherwise, which would lead us back to the importance of Mill's view of the world.

Durkheim

While Dumont was concerned primarily with the causes of population growth, focusing mainly on the birth rate, another late-nineteenth-century French sociologist, Émile Durkheim, based an entire social theory on the consequences of population growth. In discussing the increasing complexity of modern societies, characterized particularly by increasing divisions of labor, Durkheim proposed that "the division of labor varies in direct ratio with the volume and density of societies, and, if it progresses in a continuous manner in the course of social development, it is because societies become regularly denser and more voluminous" (Durkheim 1893 [1933]:262). Durkheim proceeded to explain that population growth leads to greater societal specialization because the struggle for existence is more acute when there are more people. If you compare a primitive society with an industrialized society, the primitive society is not very specialized. By contrast, in industrialized societies there is a lot of differentiation; that is, there is an increasingly long list of occupations and social classes. Why is this? The answer is in the volume and density of the population. Growth creates competition for society's resources, and in order to improve their advantage in the struggle, people specialize.

Durkheim's thesis that population growth leads to specialization was derived (he himself acknowledged) from Darwin's theory of evolution. In turn, Darwin acknowledged his own debt to Malthus. You will notice that Durkheim also clearly echoes the words of Ibn Khaldun, although it is uncertain whether Durkheim knew of the latter's work.

The critical theorizing of the nineteenth and early twentieth centuries set the stage for a more systematic collection of data to test aspects of those theories and to examine more carefully those that might be valid and those that should be discarded. As population studies became more quantitative in the twentieth century, a phenomenon called the demographic transition took shape and took the attention of demographers.

The Theory of the Demographic Transition

Although it has dominated demographic thinking for the past several decades, and is now almost routinely included in introductory texts in the social and environmental sciences, the demographic transition theory actually began as only a description of the demographic changes that had taken place in the advanced nations over time. In particular, it described the transition from high birth and death rates to low birth and death rates, with an interstitial spurt in growth rates leading to a larger population at the end of the transition than there had been at the start. The idea emerged as early as 1929, when Warren Thompson gathered data from "certain countries" for the period 1908–27 and showed that the countries fell into three main groups, according to their patterns of population growth:

> *Group A (northern and western Europe and the United States):* From the latter part of the nineteenth century to 1927, these countries had moved from having very high rates of natural increase to having very low rates of increase "and will shortly become stationary and start to decline in numbers" (Thompson 1929:968).

> *Group B (Italy, Spain, and the "Slavic" peoples of central Europe):* Thompson saw evidence of a decline in both birth rates and death rates but suggested that "it appears probable that the death rate will decline as rapidly or even more rapidly than the birth rate for some time yet. The condition in these Group B countries is much the same as existed in the Group A countries thirty to fifty years ago" (p. 968).

> *Group C (the rest of the world):* In the rest of the world, Thompson saw little evidence of control over either births or deaths.

As a consequence of this relative lack of voluntary control over births and deaths (a concept we will question later), Thompson felt that the Group C countries (which included about 70–75 percent of the population of the world at the time) would continue to have their growth "determined largely by the opportunities they have to increase their means of subsistence. Malthus described their processes of growth quite accurately when he said 'that population does invariably increase, where there are means of subsistence. . . .'" (Thompson, 1929:971).

Thompson's work, however, came at a time when there was little concern about overpopulation. The "Group C" countries had relatively low rates of growth because of high mortality and, at the same time, by 1936, birth rates in the United States and Europe were so low that Enid Charles published a widely read book called *The Twilight of Parenthood*, which was introduced with the comment that "in place of the Malthusian menace of overpopulation there is now real danger of underpopulation" (Charles 1936:v). Furthermore, Thompson's labels for his categories had little charisma. It is difficult to build a compelling theory around categories called A, B, and C.

Sixteen years after Thompson's work, Frank Notestein (1945) picked up the threads of his thesis and provided labels for the three types of growth patterns that Thompson had simply called A, B, and C. Notestein called the Group A pattern incipient decline, the Group B pattern transitional growth, and the Group C pattern high growth potential. That same year, Kingsley Davis (1945) edited a volume of the *Annals of the American Academy of Political and Social Sciences* titled "World Population in Transition," and in the lead article (titled "The Demographic Transition") he noted that "viewed in the long-run, earth's population has been like a long, thin powder fuse that burns slowly and haltingly until it finally reaches the charge and explodes" (Davis 1945:1). The term population explosion, alluded to by Davis, refers to the phase that Notestein called transitional growth. Thus was born the term *demographic transition*. It is that process of moving from high birth and death rates to low birth and death rates, from high growth potential to incipient decline (see Figure 3.3).

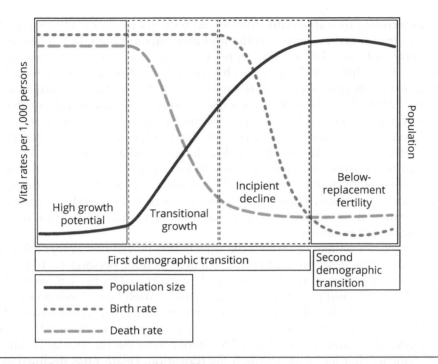

Figure 3.3   The First and Second Demographic Transitions

Note: The first demographic transition is the classic model of the transition from high birth and death rates to low birth and death rates, with in interstitial spurt in population growth; the second demographic transition tries to explain the drop to below-replacement fertility levels.

At this point in the 1940s, however, the demographic transition was merely a picture of demographic change, not a theory. But as each new country studied fit into the picture, it seemed as though some new universal law of population growth—an evolutionary scheme—was being developed. The apparent historical uniqueness of the demographic transition (all known cases have occurred within the last 200 years) spawned a host of alternative names, such as the "vital revolution" and the "demographic revolution." Between the mid-1940s and the late 1960s, rapid population growth became a worldwide concern, and demographers devoted a great deal of time to the demographic transition perspective. By 1964, George Stolnitz was able to report that "demographic transitions rank among the most sweeping and best-documented trends of modern times . . . based upon hundreds of investigations, covering a host of specific places, periods and events" (Stolnitz 1964:20). As the pattern of change took shape, explanations were developed for why and how countries pass through the transition. These explanations tended to be cobbled together in a somewhat piecemeal fashion from the nineteenth- and early-twentieth-century writers we discussed earlier in this chapter, but overall they were derived from the concept of modernization.

Modernization theory is based on the idea that in premodern times human society was generally governed by "tradition," and that the massive economic changes wrought by industrialization forced societies to alter traditional institutions: "In traditional societies fertility and mortality are high. In modern societies fertility and mortality are low. In between, there is demographic transition" (Demeny 1968:502). In the process, behavior has changed and the world has been permanently transformed. It is a macro-level theory that sees human actors as being buffeted by changing social institutions. Individuals did not deliberately lower their risk of death to precipitate the modern decline in mortality. Rather, society-wide increases in the standard of living and improved public health infrastructure brought about this change. Similarly, people did not just decide to move from the farm to town to take a job in a factory. Economic changes took place that created those higher-wage urban jobs while eliminating many agricultural jobs. These same economic forces improved transportation and communication and made it possible for individuals to migrate in previously unheard of numbers.

Modernization theory provided the vehicle that moved the demographic transition from a mere description of events to a demographic perspective. In its initial formulations, this perspective was perhaps best expressed by the sentiments "take care of the people and population will take care of itself" or "development is the best contraceptive" (Teitelbaum 1975). These were views that were derivable from Karl Marx, who was in fact one of the early proponents of the modernization theory (Inglehart and Baker 2000). The theory drew on the available data for most countries that had gone through the transition. Death rates declined as the standard of living improved, and birth rates almost always declined a few decades later, eventually dropping to low levels, although rarely as low as the death rate. It was argued that the decline in the birth rate typically lagged behind the decline in the death rate because it takes time for a population to adjust to the fact that mortality really is lower, and because the social and economic institutions that favored high fertility require time to adjust to new norms of lower fertility that are more consistent with the lower levels of mortality. Since most people value the prolongation of life, it is not hard to accept the idea of lower mortality, but the reduction of fertility is contrary to the established norms of societies that have required high birth rates to keep pace with high death rates. Such norms are not easily changed, even in the face of poverty.

Birth rates eventually declined, it was argued, as the importance of family life was diminished by industrial and urban life, thus weakening the pressure for large families. Large families are presumed to have been desired because they provided parents with a built-in labor pool, and because children provided old-age security for parents. The same economic development that lowered mortality is theorized to transform a society into an urban industrial state in which compulsory education lowers the value of children by removing them from the labor force, and people come to realize that lower infant mortality means that fewer children need to be born to achieve a certain number of surviving children. Finally, as a consequence of the many alterations in social institutions, "the pressures for high fertility weaken and the idea of conscious control of fertility gradually gains strength" (Teitelbaum 1975:421).

Critique of the Demographic Transition Theory

It has been argued that the concept underlying the demographic transition is that population stability, also known as homeostasis (Lee 1987), is the normal state of affairs in human societies and that change (the "transition") is what requires explanation (Kreager 1986). Not everyone agrees. Harbison and Robinson (2002) argue that transitions are the natural state of human affairs, and that each transition is followed by another one, a theme we will return to later in the chapter. In its original formulation, the demographic transition theory explained high fertility as a reaction to high mortality. As mortality declines, the need for high fertility lessens, and so birth rates go down. There is a spurt of growth in that transition period, but presumably the consequences will not be serious if the decline in mortality was produced by a rise in the standard of living, which, in its turn, produces a motivation for smaller families. But what will be the consequences if mortality declines and fertility does not? That situation presumably is precluded by the theory of demographic transition, but the demographic transition theory has not done a very good job of predicting levels of mortality or fertility or the timing of the fertility decline. This is because the initial explanation for the demographic behavior during the transition tended to be ethnocentric. It relied almost exclusively on the sentiment that "what is good for the goose is good for the gander." In other words, if this is what happened to the developed countries, why should it not also happen to other countries that are not so advanced? One reason might be that the preconditions for the demographic transition are considerably different now from what they were when the industrialized countries began their respective transitions.

For example, prior to undergoing the demographic transition, few of the currently industrialized countries had birth rates as high as those of most currently less-developed countries, nor indeed were their levels of mortality so high. Yet when mortality did decline, it did so as a consequence of internal economic development, not as a result of a foreign country bringing in sophisticated techniques of disease prevention, as is the case today. A second reason might be that the factors leading to the demographic transition were actually different from what for years had been accepted as true. Likely it is not just change that requires explanation but also differences in the starting and ending points of the transition. Perhaps, then, the modernization theory, in and of itself, did not provide an appropriate picture of historical development. These problems with the original explanations of the demographic transition led to new research and a reformulation of the perspective.

Reformulation of the Demographic Transition Theory

One of the most important social scientific endeavors to cast doubt on the classic explanation was the European Fertility Project, directed by Ansley Coale at Princeton University. In the early 1960s, J. William Leasure, then a graduate student in economics at Princeton, was writing a doctoral dissertation on the fertility decline in Spain, using data for each of that nation's 49 provinces. Surprisingly, his thesis revealed that the history of fertility change in Spain was not explained by a simple version of the demographic transition theory. Fertility in Spain declined in contiguous areas that were culturally similar, even though the levels of urbanization and economic development might be different (Leasure 1962). At about the same time, other students began to uncover similarly puzzling historical patterns in European data (Coale 1986). A systematic review of the demographic histories of Europe was thus begun in order to establish exactly how and why the transition occurred. The focus was on the decline in fertility, because it is the most problematic aspect of the classic explanation. These findings required demographers to consider some revisions to the theory of the demographic transition.

With the discovery that the decline of fertility in Europe occurred in the context of widely differing social, economic, and demographic conditions, it became apparent that economic development may be a sufficient cause of fertility decline, but not a necessary one (Coale 1973). For example, many provinces in Europe experienced a rapid drop in their birth rate even though they were not very urban, infant mortality rates were high, and a low percentage of the population was employed in industrial occupations. The data suggest that one of the more common similarities in those areas that have undergone fertility declines is the rapid spread of secularization. Secularization is an attitude of autonomy from otherworldly powers and a sense of responsibility for one's own well-being (Lesthaeghe 1977; Leasure 1982; Norris and Inglehart 2004). It is associated with an enlightened view of the world—a break from traditional ways of thinking and behaving.

It is difficult to know exactly why such attitudes arise when and where they do, but we do know that industrialization and economic development are, without any known exceptions, accompanied by secularization. At the same time, secularization can occur independently of industrialization. It might be thought of as a modernization of thought, distinct from a modernization of social institutions. When it pops up, secularization often spreads quickly, being diffused through social networks as people imitate the behavior of others to whom they look for clues to proper and appropriate conduct.

Education has been identified as one (indeed, probably the most important) potential stimulant to such altered attitudes, especially mass education, which tends to emphasize modernization and secular concepts. Education facilitates the rapid spread of new ideas and information, which would perhaps help explain another of the important findings from the Princeton European Fertility Project, that the onset of a long-term fertility decline tended to be concentrated in a relatively short period of time (van de Walle and Knodel 1980). The data from Europe suggest that once marital fertility had dropped by as little as 10 percent in a region, the decline spread rapidly. This "tipping point" occurred whether or not infant mortality had already declined (Watkins 1986).

Some areas of Europe that were similar with respect to socioeconomic development did not experience a fertility decline at the same time, whereas other provinces that were less similar socioeconomically experienced nearly identical drops in fertility. The data suggest that this riddle is solved by examining cultural factors, not just socioeconomic ones. Building on the concept of spatial demography, it was found that areas sharing a similar culture (same language, common ethnic background, similar lifestyle) were more likely to share a decline in fertility than areas that were culturally less similar (Watkins 1991). The principal reason for this is that the idea of family planning seemed to spread quickly until it ran into a barrier to its communication. Language is one such barrier (Leasure 1962; Lesthaeghe 1977), and social and economic inequality in a region is another (Lengyel-Cook and Repetto 1982). Social distance between people turns out to inhibit communication of new ideas and attitudes.

What kinds of ideas and attitudes might encourage people to rethink how many children they ought to have? To answer this kind of question we must shift our focus from the macro (societal) level to the micro (individual) level and ask how people actually respond to the social and economic changes taking place around them. In the 1990s Coleman and Fararo (1992) put forward what became a popular individual-level perspective: rational choice theory (sometimes referred to as RAT). The essence of rational choice theory is that human behavior is the result of individuals making calculated cost-benefit analyses about how to act and what to do. For example, Caldwell (1976:331) has suggested that "there is no ceiling in primitive and traditional societies to the number of children who would be economically beneficial." Children are a source of income and support for parents throughout life, and they produce far more than they cost in such societies. The wealth flow, as Caldwell called it, is from children to parents.

The process of modernization (the macro-level changes) eventually results in the tearing apart of large, extended family units into smaller, nuclear units that are economically and emotionally self-sufficient (micro-level changes). As that happens, children begin to cost parents more (including the cost of educating them as demanded by a modernizing society), and the amount of support that parents get from children begins to decline (starting with the income lost because children are in school rather than working). As the wealth flow reverses and parents begin to spend their income on children, rather than deriving income from them, the economic value of children vanishes. Economic rationality would now seem to dictate having zero children, but in reality, of course, people continue having children for a variety of social reasons that we detail in Chapter 5.

Rational choice theory is not just about economics, but even when it comes to economic issues, there has been a lot of research over the past few decades suggesting that we humans are not as rational as we might have thought. Daniel Kahneman, a psychologist at Princeton, won the Nobel Prize in Economics in 2002 for his work on how we think, and he summarized his research in a best-selling book, *Thinking, Fast and Slow* (Kahneman 2011). The key point is that most of our thinking is "fast" (intuitive and emotional), whereas only a small fraction is "slow" (deliberate and rational). This is what allows us to believe many things, regardless of their objective truth (Schermer 2012). It helps to explain why people do not always behave "rationally" and we have to take these ideas into account as we explain both the causes and consequences of demographic behavior. In 2002, Princeton demographer Douglas Massey suggested that people may generally be rational (with the capacity for "slow" thinking), but much of human behavior is still powered by emotional responses (the "fast" thinking) that supersede rationality (Massey 2002). We are animals, and though we may have vastly greater intellectual capacities than other species, we are still influenced by a variety of non-rational forces, including our hormones (Udry 1994, 2000).

Overall, then, the principal ingredient in the reformulation of the demographic transition perspective is to add "ideational" factors to "demand" factors as the likely causes of demographic change, especially changes in fertility. The original version of the theory suggested that modernization reduces the demand for children and so fertility falls—if people are rational economic creatures, then this is what should happen. But the real world is more complex, and the diffusion of ideas can shape fertility (and other demographic) behavior along with, or even in the absence of, the usual signs of modernization (Casterline 2001).

This does not necessarily mean that Wallerstein (1976) was correct when he declared that modernization theory was dead. On the contrary, there is evidence from around the world that "industrialization leads to occupational specialization, rising educational levels, rising income levels, and eventually brings unforeseen changes— changes in gender roles, attitudes toward authority and sexual norms; declining fertility rates; broader political participation; and less easily led publics" (Inglehart and Baker 2000:21). This is not a linear path, however. "Economic development tends to push societies in a common direction, but rather than converging, they seem to move on parallel trajectories shaped by their cultural heritages" (Inglehart and Baker 2000:49).

One strength of reformulating the demographic transition is that nearly all other perspectives can find a home here. Malthusians note with satisfaction that fertility first declined in Europe primarily as a result of a delay in marriage, much as Malthus would have preferred. Neo-Malthusians can take heart from the fact that rapid and sustained declines occurred simultaneously with the spread of knowledge about family planning practices. Marxists also find a place for themselves in the reformulated demographic transition perspective, because its basic tenet is that a change in the social structure (modernization of thought, if not also of the economy) is necessary to bring about a decline in fertility. This is only a short step away from agreeing with Marx that there is no universal law of population, but rather that each stage of development and social organization has its own law, and that cultural patterns will influence the timing and tempo of the demographic transition—when it starts and how it progresses. Furthermore, the macro-level changes are never sufficient to explain what happens—we must also pay attention to what is going on at the individual level.

The Theory of Demographic Change and Response

The work of the European Fertility Project focused on explaining regional differences in fertility declines. This was a very important theoretical development, but not a comprehensive one because it only partially dealt with a central issue of the demographic transition theory: How (and under what conditions) does a mortality decline lead to a fertility decline? To answer that question, Kingsley Davis (1963) asked what happens to individuals when mortality declines—what is happening at the micro-level? The answer is that more children survive to adulthood, putting greater pressure on family resources, and people have to reorganize their lives in an attempt to relieve that pressure; that is, people respond to the demographic change. But note that their response will be in terms of personal goals, not national goals. It rarely matters what a government wants. If individual members of a society do not stand to gain economically or socially by behaving in a particular way, they probably will not behave that way. Indeed, that was a major argument made by the neo-Malthusians against moral restraint. Why advocate postponement of marriage and sexual gratification rather than contraception when you know that few people who postpone marriage are actually going to postpone sexual intercourse, too? In fact, Ludwig Brentano (1910) quite forthrightly suggested that Malthus was insane to think that abstinence was the cure for the poor.

Davis argued that the response individuals make to the population pressure created by more members joining their ranks is determined by the means available to them. A first response, nondemographic in nature, is to try to increase resources by working harder—longer hours perhaps, a second job, and so on. If that is not sufficient or there are no such opportunities, then migration of some family members (typically unmarried sons or daughters) is the easiest demographic response. This is, of course, the option that people have been using forever, undoubtedly explaining in large part why human beings have spread out over the planet.

In the eighteenth century, Richard Cantillon, an Irish–French economist, was pointing out what happened in Europe when families grew too large:

> If all the labourers in a village breed up several sons to the same work, there will be too many labourers to cultivate the lands belonging to the village, and the surplus adults must go to seek a livelihood elsewhere, which they generally do in cities. . . . If a tailor makes all the clothes there and breeds up three sons to the same, yet there is work enough for but one successor to him, the two others must go to seek their livelihood elsewhere; if they do not find enough employment in the neighboring town they must go further afield or change their occupation to get a living (Cantillon 1755 [1964]:23).

But what will be the response of that second generation, the children who now have survived when previously they would not have, and who have thus put the pressure on resources? Davis argues that if there is in fact a chance for social or economic improvement, then people will try to take advantage of those opportunities by avoiding the large families that caused problems for their parents. Davis suggests that the most powerful motive for family limitation is not fear of poverty or avoidance of pain as Malthus argued; rather, it is the prospect of rising prosperity that will most often motivate people to find the means to limit the number of children they have (we discuss these means in Chapter 5). Davis here echoes the themes of Mill and Dumont, but adds that, at the very least, the desire to maintain one's relative status in society may lead to an active desire to prevent too many children from draining away one's resources. Of course, that assumes the individuals in question have already attained some status worth maintaining.

One of Davis's most important contributions to our demographic perspective is, as Aaron Cicourel put it, that he "seems to rely on an implicit model of the actor who makes everyday interpretations of perceived environmental changes" (Cicourel

1974:8). For example, people will respond to a decline in mortality only if they notice it, and then their response will be determined by the social situation in which they find themselves. Davis's analysis is important in reminding us of the crucial link between the everyday lives of individuals and the kinds of population changes that take place in society. Another demographer who extended the scope of the demographic transition with this kind of analysis is Richard Easterlin, who developed the relative cohort size hypothesis.

Cohort Size Effects

People who share something in common represent a cohort and in population studies this usually refers to people who share the same age (or at least age range) in common. As we alluded to in Chapter 2, cohorts represent a potential force for change through the process of demographic metabolism (check out Figure 3.1 at the beginning of this chapter). Societies have more trouble "tamping down" the effect of demographic metabolism when it involves a change in the size of successive cohorts, which happens as birth and or death rates (and to a lesser extent migration rates) change over time. The youth bulge discussed in Chapter 1 is one example of that. Indeed, the impact of changing cohort size on human society is a nearly constant theme in this book. It turns out, however, that this is not just a one-way street in which, for example, changes in the birth rate alter the size of cohorts, and that produces social change. Richard Easterlin has shown that relative cohort size can then feed back to influence the birth rate itself.

The Easterlin relative cohort size hypothesis (also sometimes known as the relative income hypothesis) is based on the idea that the birth rate does not necessarily respond to absolute levels of economic well-being but rather to levels that are relative to those to which one is accustomed (Easterlin 1968, 1978). Easterlin assumes that the standard of living you experience in late childhood is the base from which you evaluate your chances as an adult. If you can easily improve your income as an adult compared to your late childhood level, then you will be more likely to marry early and have several children. If young people are relatively scarce in society and business is good, they will be in relatively high demand. In nearly classic Malthusian fashion, they will be able to command high wages and thus be more likely to feel comfortable about getting married and starting a family—the "lucky few" as Carlson (2008) has called the small cohort born during the Depression and World War II (see Chapter 2 for more on this). On the other hand, if young people are in relatively abundant supply, then even if business is good, the competition for jobs will be stiff and it will be difficult for people to maintain their accustomed level of living, much less marry and start a family. This was the experience of the Baby Boomers, and helps to explain the changes in family demography that are discussed later in this chapter and especially in Chapter 9.

Easterlin's thesis presents a model of society in which demographic change and economic change are closely interrelated. Economic changes produce demographic changes, which in turn produce economic changes, and so on. The idea of a demographic feedback cycle, which is at the core of Easterlin's thinking, is compelling, and relative cohort size is certainly a factor that will influence various kinds of social change. But what about the situation that prevails in an increasing number of countries with relatively small cohorts of young adults who are not responding as the Easterlin hypothesis would suggest? Rather than marrying earlier and having more children, they are postponing marriage and having even fewer children. Demographers didn't see this coming, and one reaction to these unexpected trends is to suggest that parts of the world are experiencing something that goes beyond our earlier ideas about the demographic transition.

The Theory of the Second Demographic Transition

In its original formulation, the demographic transition was simply a movement from a demographic regime characterized by high birth and death rates to one characterized by low birth and death rates. When the latter was achieved, presumably the transition was over and things would stabilize demographically (homeostasis) and a country would enter a post-transitional era of equilibrium. However, the dramatic changes taking place in family and household structure since World War II, especially in Europe, led European demographers Dirk van de Kaa and Ron Lesthaeghe in 1986 to propose a "second demographic transition" as something that goes beyond a stable post-transitional period (see, for example, van de Kaa 1987; Lesthaeghe 1995, 2010). A demographic centerpiece of this change in the richer countries (they focused initially on Europe) has been a fall in fertility from slightly above replacement level (about 2.1 children per woman) to below-replacement levels (illustrated in Figure 3.3), but with the twist that this was less about not having babies than it was about the personal freedom to do what one wanted, especially among women. "The driving force behind this transition was ideational change—a dramatic shift from altruistic to individualistic norms and attitudes" (Zaidi and Morgan 2017:475). Put another way, "[i]deational change, as seen through the increase in individual autonomy, secularization, female emancipation, and postmaterialism, is the central explanation, without which other explanations are incomplete" (Zaidi and Morgan 2017: 479).

So, rather than the pattern of grow up, marry, but have fewer children than in the past because you know that they are almost certain to survive to adulthood (the essence of the First Demographic Transition), the Second Demographic Transition is associated with a host of changes in the demography of families because people, especially women, are viewing the world differently than they used to. These family demographic changes include a postponement of marriage, a rise in premarital cohabitation, a rise in nonmarital fertility, as well as a rise in voluntary childlessness. The flexibility in family forms and fertility was aided substantially by the contraceptive revolution which was associated with the increasing acceptance of the many personal and family advantages of controlling fertility (Lesthaeghe and Wilson 1986).

The Second Demographic Transition is not inconsistent with other theories that have pushed us beyond the initial explanations for the First Demographic Transition. The big issue revolves around the increasingly common pattern of below-replacement fertility in richer countries of the world. However, demographers have found that not all countries with low fertility necessarily wind up with below-replacement levels (Rindfuss and Choe 2015). The most likely explanation for the difference lies in the relative levels of gender equity. Structural changes typically come first, including greater equality in education, employment, and occupations. More difficult to change are the gender inequities at the home and personal levels. Men's roles in the family are key determinants of fertility because if women are employed outside of the home, but also are expected to be responsible for all the housework and childcare chores, then women may choose to have fewer children than they would if the husband was also helping with those family jobs (McDonald 2000; Esping-Anderson and Billari 2015; Goldscheider, Bernhardt, and Lappegård 2015). Following that line of thinking, it may be that as full gender equity is achieved, the below-replacement level fertility could rise to a level closer to replacement.

The Demographic Transition Is Really a Set of Transitions

The reformulation driven by the European Fertility Project, the theory of demographic change and response, the cohort size effects, the Second Demographic Transition, and other research all have generated the insight that the demographic transition (by which we mean the one that started a couple of hundred years ago) is actually a group of interrelated transitions that can be explained as part of a complex set of cultural demographic processes. Taken together, they help us understand not just the causes but the consequences of population change. The interrelationships among these transitions are shown in Figure 3.4.

The Health and Mortality Transition

Modern demographic changes have almost always started with a decline in mortality, which is brought about by changes in society that improve the health of people and thus their ability to resist disease, and by scientific advances in public health and medicine that prevent premature death and help extend life to increasingly older ages. However, we know that death rates do not decline evenly by age; rather it is the very youngest and the very oldest—but especially the youngest—whose lives are most likely to be saved by improved life expectancy. This is because deaths at the youngest ages are caused in particular by communicable diseases with which scientific advances have been the quickest to cope. Deaths at older ages are due especially to degenerative diseases, the prevention or management of which require more science and skill than is typically required for communicable disease. Thus, the initial impact of the health and mortality transition is to increase the number of young people who are alive, ballooning the bottom end of the age structure in a manner that looks just like an increase in the birth rate. This sets all the other transitions in motion.

The increase in our ability to stay alive longer is arguably the most dramatic thing that has ever happened to the human species—a true evolution. And it didn't

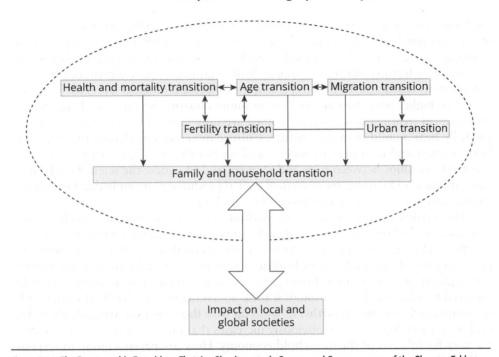

Figure 3.4   The Demographic Transitions That Are Simultaneously Causes and Consequences of the Changes Taking Place in the World at the Local and Global Scales

Note: Each box has its own set of theories that serve as explanations for the phenomena under consideration.

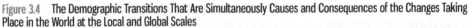

happen by chance. It has come about largely through scientific advances that are closely tied to the technological and economic transformations of the past 200 years. In theory there is no specific limit to how long humans might live (De Grey and Rossiter 2017), and to the extent that lives might be extended beyond what we have yet seen among humans, we will be in completely uncharted cultural demographic territory. In the next chapter (Chapter 4) we will discuss health and mortality in more detail.

The Fertility Transition

The extension of human existence as a result of falling mortality is typically followed by the fertility transition—the shift from natural (and high) to controlled (and low) fertility, usually in a delayed response to the improvements in health and mortality. If people did not respond to declining mortality by having fewer children, the population would quickly grow to locally unsustainable numbers in an almost classic Malthusian scenario. In the abstract, we can say that declining fertility is a necessary societal adjustment to declining mortality, but since it occurs at the individual level, we have to examine the various ways in which this sort of behavior evolves. Furthermore, our ability to control fertility is closely tied to the same kinds of scientific advances that led to the declines in mortality. You will remember that the First Demographic Transition Theory assumed that fertility would bottom out at replacement level, but many individuals and societies have, at least for the time being, dropped below that, as explained by the Second Demographic Transition Theory. Will fertility drop even more? Will it go back up? Culture, not biology, will show us that path. To be sure, if it were simply a biological issue, then fertility would be higher now than at any time in human history, because our better health and medical treatments mean that women are now more able to conceive and successfully bear a child than ever before. Culture intervenes to change the roles that both women and men play in society and within the family, altering sexual and other relationships between men and women, and of course the scientific advances that give men and women more control over reproduction are embedded in cultural change and in the diffusion of ideas and technology.

The fertility transition can begin without a decline in mortality (as happened in France in the late eighteenth and early nineteenth centuries), but in most places it is the decline in mortality, leading to greater survival of children, that eventually motivates people to think about limiting the number of children they are having. Throughout most of human history, the average woman had two children who survived to adulthood, even though it took an average of six live births (and additional miscarriages and stillbirths) to wind up with those two surviving children. The decline in mortality, however, obviously increases that number and thereby threatens the very foundation of the household economy. How are parents going to respond to this? Answering that question was at the core of Kingsley Davis's theory of demographic change and response. At the community or societal level, the increasing number of young people creates all sorts of pressures to change, often leading to peer pressure to conform to new standards of behavior, including the deliberate control of reproduction. How soon and how much people will respond with lower fertility will depend upon a lot of factors, including religious and other ideological beliefs, how deeply they are embedded in social networks, and the diffusion of new ideas from family, friends, and others in their community, as well as the availability and acceptability of effective methods of limiting fertility.

Another set of extremely important changes that occur in the context of the health and mortality transition is that the scope of life expands for women as they, too, live longer. They are increasingly empowered to delay childbearing and to have fewer children because they begin to realize that most of their children will survive to adulthood and they, themselves, will survive beyond the reproductive ages, beyond their children's arrival into adulthood. This new freedom gives them vastly more opportunities than ever before in human history to do something with their lives besides bearing and raising children. This realization may be a genuine tipping point in the evolution of fertility, leading to an almost irreversible decline at the societal level. Of course, we can anticipate that some women will still have several children, but they will be the exception, not the rule. The big question to which we do not currently have an answer is how many women will choose not to have any children at all.

As fertility declines, levels of health and mortality continue to evolve because the health of surviving children is enhanced when a woman has fewer children among whom to share resources. Also affected by the fertility decline is the age structure, which begins to cave in at the younger ages as fewer children are being born, and as most are now surviving through childhood. In its turn, that shift in the age transition to an increasingly older age structure has the potential to divert societal resources away from dealing primarily with the impact of children to dealing with broader social concerns, including raising the standard of living. A higher standard of living can then redound to the benefit of health levels throughout society, adding fuel to the fire of increasing life expectancy, which means that fewer children need to be born to maintain population size. The sets of theories underlying the fertility transition and its linkages to the other transitions are discussed in detail in Chapter 5.

The Age Transition

The demographically predictable changes in the age structure brought about by altered patterns of mortality and fertility, along with in- or out-migration, produce social and economic reactions as societies find themselves adjusting to constantly evolving age distributions. In many respects, this is the "master" transition and driver of broader cultural demographic evolutionary changes. The changing number of people at each age that occurs with the decline of mortality, and then the decline in fertility, and then fluctuations in fertility, presents the most obvious demographic pressure for social change—demographic metabolism on steroids.

When both mortality and fertility are high, the age structure is quite young, and that's what human societies looked like for most of history until about 200 years ago when mortality started falling in the economically developing parts of Europe and North America. The decline in mortality initially makes a population even younger by disproportionately increasing the number of young people. Then, as fertility declines, the youngest ages are again affected first, since births occur only at age zero, so a fertility decline shows up first as simply fewer young children than before. However, as the bulge of young people born prior to the fertility decline pushes into the older ages while fertility begins to decline, the age structure moves into a stage that can be very beneficial to economic development in a society. This has become commonly known as the demographic dividend: the period during which a large fraction of the population is composed of young adults of working age who are having fewer children as dependents at the same time that the older population has not yet increased in size enough to create problems of dependency in old age. As we will see, this phase in the age transition is often associated with a golden age of advancement in the standard of living because the demographic dividend offers an opportunity for the kind of economic leap forward that Mill was advocating.

That golden age can be transitory, however, if a society has not planned for the next phase of the age transition, when the older population begins to increase more rapidly than the younger population. The baby bulge created by the initial declines in mortality reaches old age at a time when fertility has likely declined, resulting in an age structure that has a much greater number and a higher fraction of older people than ever before (again, check out Figure 3.1 at the beginning of this chapter). We are only now learning how societies will respond to this challenge of an increasingly older population. These interrelationships between the age transition and society are discussed in detail in Chapter 8.

The Migration Transition

The theory of the First Demographic Transition emphasizes the three main ways by which a population changes—mortality, fertility, and migration. The first two have obvious biological components, whereas migration does not. Nonetheless, we know that humans have been migrating for tens of thousands of years, which is why we live on every part of the planet that is currently habitable. Meanwhile, back at the very young age structure put into motion by declining mortality in combination with a delayed decline in fertility, the theory of demographic change and response suggests that in rural areas, where most of the population lived for most of human history, the resulting growth in the number of young people will lead to an oversupply of young people looking for jobs, which will encourage them to go elsewhere in search of economic opportunity.

The Europeans who experienced the first wave of population growth, because they experienced the health and mortality transition first, still lived in a world where there was "empty" land. Of course, it wasn't really empty, as the Americas and the islands of the South Pacific (largely Australia and New Zealand) were populated mainly by hunter-gatherers who used the land extensively, rather than intensively, as we mentioned in Chapter 1. As Europeans arrived in the Americas, they perceived land as being not used and so claimed it for themselves. We all know the consequences of this for the indigenous populations, as all the land was eventually claimed for intensive human use. So, whereas the Europeans could initially spread out from rural Europe to rural areas in the Americas and the South Pacific, migrants from rural areas today no longer have that option.

Notice in Figure 3.4 that there is a double-arrow connecting the age and migration transitions. This is because migration takes people (mainly young adults) out of one area and puts them in another area, thus affecting the age structure in both places. As patterns of declining death and declining fertility have varied across the world, the difference in age structure between two places has contributed to one of the current migration patterns of people from younger societies filling in the "empty" places in the age structure of older societies. The details of the migration transition will be discussed in Chapter 6.

The Urban Transition

With empty lands filling up, migrants from the countryside in the world today have no place to go but to cities, and cities have historically tended to flourish by absorbing labor from rural areas. A majority of people in the world now live in cities and their environs, and by the end of the twenty-first century, almost all of us will be there. Migration between and within countries is increasingly the movement of people from one urban place to another, rather than from rural to urban places.

The urban transition thus begins with migration from rural to urban areas but then morphs into the urban evolution as most humans wind up being born in, living in, and dying in cities. The complexity of human existence is played out in cities, leading us to expect a constant dynamism of urban places for most of the rest of foreseeable human history. Because urban places are historically associated with lower levels of fertility than rural areas, as the world's population becomes increasingly urban we can anticipate that this will be a major factor in keeping fertility levels down all over the world.

Furthermore, the cultural differences between urban and rural populations are diminishing due to the rapid spread of communication between the two. Cell phones and the internet have connected urban and rural residents to one another in ways that would have been unimaginable only a few decades ago. The consequence of this is that people living in rural areas are less socially and culturally isolated than they used to be, even as they become a smaller fraction of the human population. Urban ideas and behavior, which are almost always more innovative than what's happening in rural places, are diffused into rural places, changing ways of thinking and doing that keeps rural populations in the evolutionary loop without necessarily having actually to live in a city. The urban transition is discussed more fully in Chapter 7.

The Family and Household Transition

As urban life evolves and diffuses, people's actions toward and reactions to others take on new and innovative forms, and this is nowhere more obvious than in families and households. Families include the people to whom we are related by birth, adoption, marriage, or a similar culturally denoted connection sometimes called "fictive kin" by anthropologists. The household includes just the people who actually share a living space. For most of human history, there was a huge overlap between family and household. Family members tended to all live together in the same household. In this kind of an environment, there is a high degree of surveillance and supervision, especially of younger family members by older members of the household. Everyone knows what everyone else is doing and everyone is involved in enforcing the "rules" by which the group is expected to live.

The *family* changes through hatching, matching, and dispatching—births, marriages, and deaths—and the occasional migration, whereas the *household* is organized around economic activities of feeding, clothing, and attending to people's daily needs. Historically, these household activities would most likely be influenced by outside events such as changes in weather, attacks from outsiders, or imposition of external government force—things over which household members have relatively little control. They will also be influenced by inside events—family politics—which will undoubtedly shift as the family demographics change.

As we discussed in relation to the Theory of Demographic Change and Response, all of the above transitions affect families and households, and demographically-inspired social change hits them the hardest. That is why all the boxes in Figure 3.4 point to the Family and Household Transition. From the very beginning, we can see that the health and mortality transition is pivotal because it gives women (and men, too, of course) a dramatically greater number of years to live in general, and more specifically a greater number of years that do not need to be devoted to children. Low mortality reduces the pressure for a woman to marry early and start bearing children while she is young enough for her body to handle the stress of repeated pregnancies and births. Furthermore, when mortality was high, marriages had a high probability of ending in widowhood when one of the partners was still reasonably young, and families routinely were reconstituted as widows and widowers remarried. However, low mortality leads to a much longer period of time that married couples will be alive together before one partner dies, which leads to an increase in divorce and remarriage rates, along with the rise in cohabitation, and alternative living arrangements.

The age transition also plays a role in the changes in families and households at the societal level, because over time the increasingly similar number of people at all ages—as opposed to a majority of people being very young—means that any society is bound to be composed of a greater array of family and household arrangements. Diversity in families and households is also encouraged by migration (which breaks up and reconstitutes families) and by the urban transition, especially since urban places tend to be more tolerant of diversity than are smaller rural communities, although of course this latter point may be evolving, as we mentioned above in the context of the increasing connections between urban and rural places. So important are these changes that they have given rise to an entire field of family demography, as is discussed in more detail in Chapter 9.

Impact on Local and Global Society

The modern world of science and technology has, over the past two centuries in particular, brought us increasingly high levels of control over our lives. We are less susceptible to death, more able to decide if we want sex to be associated with the chance of a pregnancy, more educated than ever before, with historically unheard of job skills, an incredible ability to move quickly across countries and continents, and we can be in nearly constant contact with people all over the globe. And there are more of us than ever before. Remember from the first chapter that at the beginning of the nineteenth century, shortly after the United States became an independent country, the world's population was just shy of one billion persons. As of the date this book was published, scarcely more than two centuries later, we are just shy of eight billion people—an astonishing change. Two hundred years ago, only about 3 percent of humans lived in cities—now more than half live in cities. The world is a dramatically different place now than it used to be, and those differences show up in our everyday lives—in our families and households. Those changes then turn around and influence demographic trends.

The modern field of population studies came about largely to encourage and inspire deeper insight into the causes and consequences of changes in fertility, mortality, migration, age and sex structure, and population characteristics and distribution. Demographers spent most of the twentieth century doing that, but always with an eye toward new things that could be learned about what demographic change means for human society. Unlike in Malthus's day, population growth is no longer viewed as being caused by one set of factors nor as having a simple prescribed set of consequences. At the same time, we are still dealing with one of the basic issues raised by Malthus: Can we sustain a large population at ever-higher standards of living? Chapter 10 focuses on that topic.

The rest of this book is devoted to more detailed examinations of each of the transitions highlighted in Figure 3.4, and you will discover that there are a variety of theoretical approaches that have developed over time to explain the causes and consequences of each set of transitions. Your own demographic perspective will be honed by looking for similarities and patterns in the transitions that link them together and, more importantly, link them to their potential impact on society.

Summary and Conclusion

A lot of thinking about population issues has taken place over a very long period of time, and in this chapter we have traced the progression of demographic thinking from ancient doctrines to contemporary systematic perspectives. Malthus was not the first, but he was certainly the most influential of the early modern writers. Malthus believed that a biological urge to reproduce was the cause of population growth and that the natural consequence of this growth was poverty. Marx, on the other hand, did not openly argue with the Malthusian causes of growth, but he vehemently disagreed with the idea that poverty is the natural consequence of population growth. Marx denied that population growth was a problem per se—it only appeared that way in capitalist societies. It may have seemed peculiar that we discussed a person who denied the importance of a demographic perspective in a chapter dedicated to that very importance. However, the Marxian point of view is sufficiently prevalent today among political leaders and intellectuals in enough countries that this attitude becomes in itself a demographic perspective of some significance. Furthermore, his perspective on the world finds its way into many aspects of current mainstream thinking, including modernization theory, that underlay aspects of the First Demographic Transition Theory.

The perspective of Mill, who seems very contemporary in many of his ideas, was somewhere between that of Malthus and Marx. He believed that increased productivity could lead to a motivation for having smaller families, especially if the influence of women was allowed to be felt and if people were educated about the possible consequences of having a large family. Dumont took these kinds of individual motivations a step further and suggested in greater detail the reasons why prosperity and ambition, operating through the principle of social capillarity, generally lead to a decline in the birth rate. Durkheim's perspective emphasized the consequences more than the causes of population growth. He was convinced that the complexity of modern societies is due almost entirely to the social responses to population growth—more people lead to higher levels of innovation and specialization.

More recently developed demographic perspectives have implicitly assumed that the consequences of population growth are serious and problematic, and they move directly to explanations of the causes of population growth. The original theory of the demographic transition suggested that growth is an intermediate stage between the more stable conditions of high birth and death rates to a new balance of low birth and death rates. Reformulations of the demographic transition perspective have emphasized its evolutionary character and have shown that the demographic transition is not one monolithic change, but rather that it encompasses several interrelated transitions: A decline in mortality will almost necessarily be followed by a decline in fertility, and by subsequent transitions in migration, urbanization, the age structure, and the family and household structures in society. The next six chapters explore each of these transitions in detail, beginning with the health and mortality transition.

Main Points

1. A demographic perspective is a way of relating basic population information to theories about how the world operates demographically.

2. Population doctrines and theories prior to Malthus vacillated between pronatalist and antinatalist and were often utopian.

3. According to Malthus, population growth is generated by the urge to reproduce, although growth is checked ultimately by the means of subsistence.

4. The natural consequences of population growth according to Malthus are misery and poverty because of the tendency for populations to grow faster than the food supply. Nonetheless, he believed that misery could be avoided if people practiced moral restraint—a simple formula of chastity before marriage and a delay in marriage until one can afford all the children that God might provide.

5. Marx and Engels strenuously objected to the Malthusian population perspective because it blamed poverty on the poor rather than on the evils of social organization.

6. Mill argued that the standard of living is a major determinant of fertility levels, but he also felt that people could influence their own demographic destinies.

7. Dumont argued that personal ambition generated a process of social capillarity that induced people to limit their number of children in order to get ahead socially and economically, while another French writer, Durkheim, built an entire theory of social structure on his conception of the consequences of population growth.

8. The First Demographic Transition theory is a perspective that emphasizes the importance of economic and social development, which leads first to a decline in mortality and then, after some time lag, to a commensurate decline in fertility, ultimately getting back to something close to zero population growth. It is based on the experience of the developed nations, and is derived especially from the modernization theory, but with important reformulations over time.

9. The Second Demographic Transition theory focuses on explanations for the unexpected emergence of below-replacement fertility levels in many, although not all, higher-income countries. It is driven by ideological changes, especially in the role of women and the family in society.

10. The demographic transition is really a set of transitions, including the health and mortality, fertility, age, migration, urban, and family/household transitions.

Questions for Review

1. What lessons exist within the ideas of pre-Malthusian thinkers on population that can be applied conceptually to the demographic situations we currently confront in the world?

2. It was obvious even in Malthus's lifetime that his theory had numerous defects. Describe those defects and discuss why, given them, we are still talking about Malthus.

3. Based on the information provided in this chapter, which writer—Malthus or Marx—would sound most modern and relevant to twenty-first-century demographers? Defend your answer.

4. What are the important aspects of culture that need to be brought into the picture if we are to fully understand the ideas behind the First and then the Second Demographic Transitions?

5. Review the basic premises of the theory of demographic change and response and discuss how it served to expand the concept of the demographic transition into the idea of a larger suite of transitions.

PART TWO

POPULATION PROCESSES

CHAPTER 4
The Health and Mortality Transition

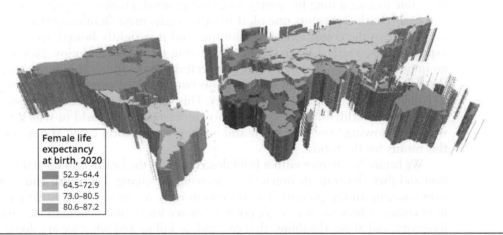

Female life
expectancy
at birth, 2020

■ 52.9–64.4
■ 64.5–72.9
■ 73.0–80.5
■ 80.6–87.2

Figure 4.1   Global Variability in Female Life Expectancy at Birth

Source: Adapted by John R. Weeks from data in United Nations Population Division, *World Population Prospects 2019*; data represent estimates for 2020.

Defining the Health and Mortality Transition

Health and Mortality Changes Over Time
The Roman Empire to the Industrial Revolution
Industrial Revolution to the Twentieth Century
World War II as a Modern Turning Point
Postponing Death by Preventing and Curing Disease
The Nutrition Transition

Life Span and Longevity
Life span
Longevity

Disease and Death Over the Life Cycle
Age Differentials in Mortality
Infant Mortality
Mortality at Older Ages
Sex and Gender Differentials in Mortality

Causes of Poor Health and Death
Communicable Diseases
Emerging Infectious Diseases
Maternal Mortality
Noncommunicable Diseases

Injuries
The "Real" Causes of Death

Measuring Mortality
Crude Death Rate
Age/Sex-Specific Death Rates
Age-Adjusted Death Rates
Life Tables
Life Table Calculations
Disability-Adjusted Life Years

Health and Mortality Inequalities
Educational and Socioeconomic Differentials
   in Mortality
Inequalities by Race and Ethnicity
Marital Status and Mortality
Urban and Rural Differentials
Neighborhood Differences in Mortality

Summary and Conclusion

Main Points

Questions for Review

ESSAY: *Mortality Control and the Environment*

It isn't that people now breed like rabbits; it's that we no longer die like flies—declining mortality, not rising fertility, is the root cause of the revolutionary increase in the world's population size and growth over the past two centuries. Only within that time has mortality been brought under control to the point that most of us are now able to take a long life pretty much for granted. Human triumph over disease and early death represents one of, if not the single, most significant improvements ever made in the condition of human life, and it is tightly bound up in all other aspects of the vastly higher standard of living that we now enjoy. Nevertheless, an important unintended by-product of declining mortality is the mushrooming of the human population from just 1 billion two hundred years ago to an expected 9–10 billion by the middle of this century. This increase has literally changed everything in the world, and you cannot fully understand the world in which you live without knowing how the health and mortality transition came about and what this means for the future.

We begin the chapter with a brief description of the health and mortality transition and then illustrate its impact by reviewing the changes in health and mortality over time, up to the present. The transition is by no means over, however, so we next consider how far it can go, given what we know about human life span and longevity, and about the things that can and do kill us and what we are doing about them. We will measure the progress of the transition using a variety of indices that we review in the chapter, and we employ some of those tools in the last part of the chapter to examine important inequalities that still exist in the world with respect to health and mortality, and which are almost always associated with a host of other disadvantages in life.

Defining the Health and Mortality Transition

Health and death are typically thought of as two sides of the same coin—morbidity and mortality, respectively—with morbidity referring to the prevalence of disease in a population and mortality the pattern of death. The link is a familiar one to most people—the healthier you are, the longer you are likely to live. At the societal level, this means that populations with high morbidity are those with high mortality; therefore, as health levels improve, so does life expectancy. Most of us in the richer countries take our long life expectancy for granted. Yet scarcely a century ago, and for virtually all of human history before that, death rates were very high and early death was commonplace. Within the past 200 years, and especially during the second half of the twentieth century, country after country has experienced a transition to better health and lower death rates—a long-term shift in health and disease patterns that has brought death rates down from very high levels in which people die young, primarily from communicable diseases, to low levels, with deaths concentrated among the elderly, who die from degenerative diseases. This phenomenon was originally defined by Abdel Omran (1971, 1977) as the "epidemiological transition," but because the term "epidemiology" technically refers only to disease and not to death, we have chosen to broaden the term to refer to the health and mortality transition.

As a result of this transition, the variability by age in mortality is reduced or *compressed,* leading to an increased *rectangularization* of mortality. This means that most people survive to advanced ages and then die pretty quickly (as we discuss in more detail later in the chapter). The vast changes in society brought about as more people survive to ever older ages represent important contributions to the overall demographic transition. We can begin to understand this most readily by examining how health and mortality have changed dramatically during the course of human history, especially European history, for which we tend to have better data than for the rest of the world.

Health and Mortality Changes Over Time

In much of the world and for most of human history, life expectancy probably fluctuated between 20 and 30 years (United Nations 1973; Weiss 1973; Riley 2005). At this level of mortality, only about two-thirds of babies survived to their first birthday, and only about one-half were still alive at age 5, as seen in Table 4.1. This means that one-half of all deaths occurred before age 5. At the other end of the age continuum, around 10 percent of people made it to age 65 in a premodern society. Thus, in the premodern world, about one-half the deaths were to children under age 5 and only about one in 10 were to a person aged 65 or older.

Table 4.1   The Meaning of Improvements in Life Expectancy

Period	Life Expectancy for Females	Percentage Surviving to Age				Percentage of Deaths		Number of Births Required for Zero Population Growth
		1	5	25	65	<5	65+	
Premodern	20	63	47	34	8	53	8	6.1
	30	74	61	50	17	39	17	4.2
U.S. and Europe in late 18th and early 19th centuries	40	82	73	63	29	27	29	3.3
Lowest in sub-Saharan Africa circa 2020	53	89	87	82	35	13	35	2.7
World average circa 2020	74	97	96	94	80	3	80	2.1
Mexico	80	99	98	98	86	1	86	2.1
United States	82	99	99	99	89	<1	89	2.1
Canada	84	99	99	99	92	<1	91	2.1
Japan (highest in world)	87	99	99	99	95	<1	95	2.1

Sources: Prepared by John R. Weeks; life expectancies less than 69 are based on stable population models in Ansley Coale and Paul Demeny, 1966, *Regional Model Life Tables and Stable Populations* (Princeton, NJ: Princeton University Press); other life table data are from United Nations Population Division, *World Population Prospects 2019 Revision.*

In hunter-gatherer societies, it is likely that the principal cause of death was poor nutrition—people literally starving to death—combined perhaps with selective infanticide and geronticide (the killing of older people) (McKeown 1988), although there is too little evidence to do more than speculate about this (Bocquet-Appel 2008). As humans gained more control over the environment by domesticating plants and animals (the Agricultural Revolution), both birth and death rates probably went up, as we mentioned in Chapter 1. It was perhaps in the sedentary, more densely settled villages common after the Agricultural Revolution that infectious diseases became a more prevalent cause of death. People were almost certainly better fed, but closer contact with one another, with animals, and with human and animal waste encouraged the spread of disease, with especially disastrous results for infants, a situation that prevailed for thousands of years.

The Roman Empire to the Industrial Revolution

Life expectancy in the Roman Empire is estimated to have been about 21 years (Frier 1983). Keep in mind that this does not mean that everybody dropped dead at age 21. Looking at Table 4.1, you can see that it means the majority of children born did not survive to adulthood. People who reached adulthood were not too likely to reach a very advanced age, but of course some did. The major characteristic of high mortality societies was that there was a lot more variability in the ages at which people died than is true today, but in general people died at a younger, rather than an older, age.

The Roman Empire began to break up by the third century, and the period from about the fifth to the fifteenth centuries represents the Middle Ages. Nutrition in Europe during this period probably improved enough to raise life expectancy to more than 30 years. The plague, or Black Death, hit Europe in the fourteenth century, having spread west from Asia (Cantor 2001; Christakos et al. 2005). It is estimated that one-third of the population of Europe may have perished from the disease between 1346 and 1350. The plague then made a home for itself in Europe and, as Carlo Cipolla says, "For more than three centuries epidemics of plague kept flaring up in one area after another. The recurrent outbreaks of the disease deeply affected European life at all levels—the demographic as well as the economic, the social as well as the political, the artistic as well as the religious" (Cipolla 1981:3). The constant uncertainty about life could crush you, but it could also encourage you to take risks, as some Europeans did by spreading out around the world.

We mentioned in Chapter 1 that Europe's increasing dominance in oceanic shipping and weapons gave it an unrivaled ability not only to trade goods with the rest of the world, but to trade diseases as well. The most famous of these disease transfers was the so-called Columbian Exchange, which we mentioned in Chapter 1 as involving (among many other things) the diseases that Columbus and other European explorers took to the Americas (and a few that they took back to Europe). Their relative immunity to the diseases they brought with them, at least in comparison with the devastation those diseases wrought on the indigenous populations, is one explanation for the relative ease with which Spain was able to dominate much of Latin America after arriving there around 1500. The populations in Middle America at the time of European conquest were already living under conditions of "severe nutritional stress and extremely high mortality" (McCaa 1994:7), but contact with the Spaniards turned a bad situation into what McCaa (1994) has called a "demographic hell," with high rates of orphanhood and with life expectancy probably dipping below 20 years. Spain itself was hit by at least three major plague outbreaks between 1596 and 1685, and McNeill (1976) suggests that this may have been a significant factor in Spain's decline as an economic and political power.

Industrial Revolution to the Twentieth Century

The plague had been more prevalent in the Mediterranean area (where it is too warm for the fleas to die during the winter) than farther north or east, and the last major sighting of the plague in Europe was in the south of France, in Marseilles, in 1720. It is no coincidence that this was the eve of the Industrial Revolution. The plague retreated (rather than disappeared) probably as a result of "changes in housing, shipping, sanitary practices, and similar factors affecting the way rats, fleas, and humans encountered one another" (McNeill 1976:174), and other causes of poor health were diminished by the receding of the Little Ice Age in Europe (Fagan 2000).

At the end of eighteenth century, after the plague had receded and as increasing income improved nutrition, housing, and sanitation, life expectancy in Europe and the United States was approximately 40 years (Vallin and Meslé 2009). As Table 4.1 shows, this was a transitional stage at which there were just about as many deaths to children under age 5 as there were deaths at age 65 and over. Infectious diseases (including influenza, acute respiratory infections, enteric fever, malaria, cholera, and smallpox) were still the dominant reasons for death, but their ability to kill was diminishing. Analyses of recently created sets of mortality data have shown, however, that the highest life expectancy recorded anywhere in the world began to go up almost without interruption beginning in about 1800 (Oeppen and Vaupel 2002; Vallin and Meslé 2009). This was led almost exclusively by Scandinavian countries until the 1980s, when Japan took over the lead.

Although death rates began to decline in the nineteenth century, improvements were at first fairly slow to develop for various reasons. Famines were frequent in Europe as late as the middle of the nineteenth century—the Irish potato famine of the late 1840s and Swedish harvest failures of the early 1860s are prominent examples. These crop failures were widespread, and it was common for local regions to suffer greatly from the effects of a bad harvest because poor transportation made relief very difficult. Epidemics and pandemics of infectious diseases, including the 1918 influenza pandemic, helped to keep death rates high even into the twentieth century. In August 1918, as World War I was ending, a particularly virulent form of the flu apparently mutated almost spontaneously in West Africa (Sierra Leone), although it was later called "Spanish influenza." For the next year, it spread quickly around the world, infecting as many as one-third of all humans and killing an estimated 50 million people in its path, including about 675,000 in the United States and Canada (U.S. Centers for Disease Control and Prevention 2018a). We now know that this pandemic was caused by the H1N1 virus, but viruses were unknown at that time, and there was little that could be done.

The 1918 influenza pandemic was a setback to health levels, but it does help to illustrate the fact that until recently, any increases in longevity were not due to better medical care, but rather were primarily due to environmental changes that improved health levels, especially better nutrition and increasing standards of living:

> Soap production seems to have increased considerably in England, and the availability of cheap cotton goods brought more frequent change of clothing within the economic feasibility of ordinary people. Better communication within and between European countries promoted dissemination of knowledge, including knowledge of disease and the ways to avoid it, and may help to explain the decline of mortality in areas which had neither an industrial nor an agricultural revolution at the time (Boserup 1981:124–125).

Thomas McKeown and R. G. Record (1962), who did the pioneering research in this area, along with Robert Fogel (2004), have argued that the factors most responsible for nineteenth-century mortality declines were improved diet and hygienic changes, with medical improvements largely restricted to smallpox vaccinations. Samuel Preston and Michael Haines (1991), though noting the importance of nutrition, also highlighted the role that knowledge (or lack thereof) about public health plays in controlling infectious disease. In 1900, the United States was already the richest country in the world, but its child mortality rate was very high. Why? Because at that time disease processes were still poorly understood.

Clean water, toilets, bathing facilities, systems of sewerage, and buildings secure from rodents and other disease-carrying animals are all public ingredients for better health because they help stop the spread of disease. We now accept the importance of washing our hands as common sense, but the important work of Ignaz Semmelweis in Vienna, Joseph Lister in Glasgow, and Louis Pasteur in Paris in validating the germ theory all took place in the mid-nineteenth century—just a heartbeat away from us in the overall timeline of human history. Public health is largely a matter of preventing the spread of disease, and these kinds of measures have been critical in the worldwide decline in mortality. The medical model of curing disease gets much more attention in the modern world, but its usefulness is predicated on the underlying foundation of good public health (Emch, Root, and Carrel 2017). David Cutler and Grant Miller (2005) point to the particularly important role played by the introduction of clean water technology (chlorination and filtration) in cities of the United States in the late nineteenth and early twentieth centuries, the time period when life expectancy made its single biggest jump in U.S. history. This was, of course, a direct application of the germ theory.

Public health improvements, as implied by their name, are viewed as public goods that are paid for societally, rather than individually. It was not until the early twentieth century in the United States that the health of children came to be seen as a joint responsibility of the community, rather than just a private family matter (Preston and Haines 1991). Working especially with the school system, this created a public health atmosphere in which, for example, vaccinations for childhood diseases became widespread. Later on, especially in Europe and Canada, albeit not in the United States, the idea emerged strongly that all aspects of health care, including medical care, should be treated as a public good rather than as an individual affair.

Life expectancy has increased enormously since the mid-nineteenth century. In 1851 in England, the life expectancy for males was only 40 years, and it was 44 for women. At the beginning of the twentieth century, it had increased to 45 for men and 49 for women. But, here in the first part of the twenty-first century, life expectancy in the United Kingdom is 79 for men and 83 for women. As you can see in Figure 4.2, this pattern has been closely followed in the United States. In 1850, the numbers in the United States were 38.3 years for males and 40.5 years for females. Referring to Table 4.1, this meant that about 73 babies out of 100 would survive to age 5, and about 29 percent of people born would still be alive at age 65. Figure 4.2 also shows that life expectancy began to increase more rapidly as we moved into the twentieth century, and public health measures, in particular, started to have a positive impact. Data for Canada are available only since 1920, but you can see that Canada has always had a slightly higher life expectancy than has the United States, while at the same time Mexico has been catching up with both countries.

Looking at Latin America, we can see that prior to the Spanish invasion in the sixteenth century, the area was dotted with primitive civilizations in which medicine was practiced as a magic, religious, and healing art. In an interesting reconstruction of history, Bernard Ortiz de Montellano (1975) conducted chemical tests on herbs used and claimed to have particular healing powers by the Aztecs in Mexico. He found that a majority of the remedies he was able to replicate were, in fact, effective. Most of the remedies were for problems very similar to those for which Americans spend billions of dollars a year on over-the-counter drugs: coughs, sores,

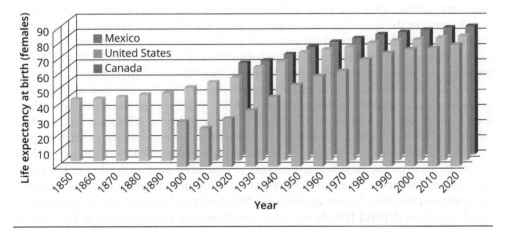

Figure 4.2   Life Expectancy Has Improved Substantially in the United States, Canada, and Mexico (Data for Females)

Sources: Data for the United States 1850 through 1970 are from the U.S. Census Bureau, 1975, *Historical Statistics of the United States, Colonial Times to the 1970 Bicentennial Edition, Part I* (Washington, DC: Government Printing Office); Tables B107–115 and B126–135 (data for 1850–1880 refer only to Massachusetts); data for Mexico 1900–1950 are from Martha Mier y Terán, 1991, "El Gran Cambio Demográfico," *Demos* 5:4–5; Data for Canada 1920–1970 are from Statistics Canada, Catalogue no. 82-221-XDE. All other data are from the World Health Organization (WHO), Global Health Observatory Data Repository, http://apps.who.int/gho/data/node.main.688?lang=en, accessed 2018, and United Nations Population Division, *World Population Prospects: The 2017 Revision,* File MORT/7-3: Female life expectancy at birth by region, subregion and country, 1950–2100.

nausea, and diarrhea. Unfortunately, these remedies were not sufficient to combat most diseases and mortality remained very high (life expectancy less than 30 years) in Mexico until the 1920s, when things started to improve at an accelerating rate. Since the 1920s, death rates have been declining so rapidly that Mexico has nearly caught up with the United States. Thus, in 1920, life expectancy for females in Mexico was 23 years less than in the United States, whereas by 2020 that difference is projected to be only 2 years.

World War II as a Modern Turning Point

As mortality has declined throughout the world, the control of communicable diseases has been the major reason, although improved control of degenerative disease has played an increasingly important part. This is true for the less developed nations of the world today, just as it was for Europe and North America before them. However, there is a big difference between the more developed and less developed countries in what precipitated the drop in death rates. Whereas socioeconomic development was a precursor to improving health in the developed societies, the less developed nations have been the lucky recipients of the transfer of public health knowledge and medical technology from the developed world. Most of this has taken place since the end of World War II.

World War II conjures up images of German bombing raids on London, desert battles in Egypt, D-Day, and the nuclear explosion in Hiroshima. It was a devastating war costing more lives than any previous combat in history. Yet it was also the staging ground for the most amazing resurgence in human numbers ever witnessed. To keep their own soldiers alive, each side in that war spent huge sums of money figuring out how to prevent the spread of disease among troops, including ways to clean up water supplies and deal with human waste, and at the same time to work on new ways to cure disease and heal sick and wounded soldiers. Very importantly, World War II brought us penicillin, the world's first "miracle drug" (Hager 2006:149).

All of this knowledge and technology was transferred to the rest of the world at the war's end, leading immediately to significant declines in the death rate. Thus, it took only half a century in Latin America for mortality to fall to a point that had taken at least five centuries in European countries, as we noted above with respect to Mexico. Countries no longer have to develop economically to improve their health levels if public health facilities can be emulated and medical care imported from richer countries. As Eduardo Arriaga (1970:5) noted during the time that this phenomenon was first becoming obvious: "Because public health programs in backward countries depend largely on other countries, we can expect that the later in historical time a massive public health program is applied in an underdeveloped country previously lacking public health programs, the higher the rate of mortality decline will be." As you can see in Figure 4.3, this applies especially to Latin America and Asia, where improvements in life expectancy have been nothing short of remarkable since the end of World War II.

Progress is not, however, automatic. Sub-Saharan Africa was generally experiencing a rise in life expectancy until being devastated by HIV/AIDS starting in the

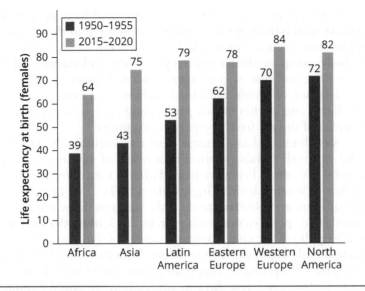

Figure 4.3 Regional Changes in Life Expectancy Since the End of World War II

Source: Adapted from data in United Nations Population Division, *World Population Prospects: The 2017 Revision*, File MORT/7-3: Female life expectancy at birth by region, subregion and country, 1950–2100.

1980s, as we will discuss later in the chapter. The continent has since recovered its upward path, but still lags behind the rest of the world with respect to health and mortality, as you can readily visualize looking back at Figure 4.1. Eastern Europe has consistently had lower life expectancy than Western Europe. And you can see in Figure 4.3 that though North America had higher life expectancy than Western Europe right after World War II, Western Europe has since overtaken North America because life expectancy gains have been slower in the United States than in other rich countries. In fact, life expectancy in the United States in 2016 was slightly lower than it had been in 2015 (Xu et al. 2018), almost certainly a consequence, at least in part, of the country's opioid crisis, which has led to an increase in unintended deaths from drug overdose and suicide, most notably among less-educated, middle-aged, non-Hispanic White men (Case and Deaton 2017).

Postponing Death by Preventing and Curing Disease

Improvements in health and medical care can only postpone death to increasingly older ages; we are obviously not yet able to prevent death altogether. There are two basic ways to accomplish the goal of postponing death to the oldest possible ages: (1) preventing diseases from occurring or from spreading when they do occur; and (2) curing people of disease when they are sick. Not getting sick in the first place is clearly the ideal route to travel, a route with both communal (public) and individual elements. Prevention of disease is aided by improved nutrition, both in terms of calories and in terms of vitamin and mineral content; clean water to prevent the spread of water-borne disease and to encourage good personal hygiene; piped sewers to eliminate contact with human waste; treatment of sewage so that it does not come back around to "bite" you; adequate clothing and shoes to prevent parasites from invading the body; adequate shelter to keep people dry and warm; eradication of or at least protection against disease-carrying rodents and insects; vaccinations against childhood diseases; use of disinfectants to clean living and eating areas; sterilization of dishes, bed linen, and clothes of sick people; and the use of gloves and masks to prevent the spread of disease from one person to another.

Smallpox was eliminated as a disease from the world in 1980 (although there are reportedly still vials in laboratories) as a result of massive vaccination campaigns, and polio is close to being eradicated after a long campaign of worldwide vaccination by the World Health Organization (WHO) of the United Nations. Pakistan, Afghanistan, and Nigeria are the only places in the world that still record significant numbers of polio victims each year. In 2013, more than a dozen children were crippled by polio in the civil war-torn country of Syria, and WHO concluded that the infection had originated with someone from Pakistan who had brought it with them to Syria. It is probable that if all of the nearly eight billion of us wore sterile face masks for just a few days in succession, we could eliminate several important diseases on a worldwide basis.

Cures for disease range from relatively simple but incredibly effective treatments, such as oral rehydration therapy for infants (widely available only since the 1970s), and antibiotics used in the treatment of bacterial infections (widely available only since the 1940s), to the more complex and technology-oriented treatments for cancer, heart disease, and other degenerative diseases, even including organ transplants, and stem cell therapies. These high-tech measures include combinations of drug therapy, radiation therapy, and surgery.

This wide range of options available for pushing back death reveals the complexity of mortality decline in any particular population. As Roger Schofield and David Reher (1991:17) noted in a review of the European mortality decline, "There is no simple or unilateral road to low mortality, but rather a combination of many different elements ranging from improved nutrition to improved education." Nonetheless, John Caldwell (1986) pointed out that although a high level of national income is nearly always associated with higher life expectancies, the bigger question is whether it is possible for poorer countries to lower their mortality levels. Global experience shows the answer to be yes, and there are several ways to do it (Taylor and Maurice 2018).

China offers an example of a country that was very poor and had a low life expectancy no higher than 40 years at the time of the communist revolution after the end of World War II. A combination of public health measures and the implementation of a very basic health care system (the "barefoot doctors") increased life expectancy to more than 60 years by the mid-1970s. Increasing incomes in China have helped life expectancy rise to 78 for females since then. Geography also makes some difference. Caldwell (1986) noted that islands and other countries with very limited territories have been able to lower their mortality more readily than territorially larger nations. Being "in the path" of European expansion has also been fortuitously beneficial to some countries (such as Costa Rica and Sri Lanka) because it increased the opportunities for the transfer of death control technology.

The Nutrition Transition

It used to be axiomatic that the poor were skinny and only the rich could afford to be fat. That's no longer true even in poorer countries where obesity is rapidly becoming a health problem. This is bound up in a phenomenon that Barry Popkin (Popkin 1993; Popkin 2002; Popkin, Adair, and Ng 2012) has named the nutrition transition—a marked worldwide shift toward a diet high in fat and processed foods and low in fiber, accompanied by lower levels of physical exercise, leading to corresponding increases in degenerative diseases.

Hunting and gathering populations were probably undernourished, and they experienced high disease rates. As humans became agriculturalists, their diets shifted more toward cereals and people were regularly at risk of famine from bad weather affecting the crops. Industrialization impacted agriculture by improving productivity and diminishing the chance of famine. More recently, especially in Western nations, the diet associated with industrialization has shifted to one high in fat, cholesterol, and sugar (and often accompanied by a sedentary lifestyle). There is ample evidence that people living in the wealthier societies of the world are larger in size than ever before in history (Pray 2014) and this promotes degenerative disease. Modern society, even in poorer nations, is increasingly associated with obesity and with less active lifestyles than ever before, and these factors threaten to limit our ability to push life expectancy to higher levels (Levine and Crimmins 2018).

Though our bodies are built to live on the edge of famine in a physically active world (the human condition until recently), the majority of humans now have a relatively secure food supply and the ability to avoid at least some of the manual labor of the past. The proliferation of motorized transportation also means that we are walking far less than ever before. All these things add up to the widely reported finding that more than 25 percent of children (ages 2 through 14) in the United States have at least one chronic health condition, especially obesity (Van Cleave, Gortmaker, and Perrin 2010). In fact, among children aged 2–19 in the United States, 18.5 percent were obese in 2015–2016 (Hales et al. 2017). The evidence seems clear that obesity is likely to shorten a person's life expectancy in rich and not-so-rich countries alike (Monteverde et al. 2010; Lieberman 2013), and it is an important reason why life expectancy improvements in the United States are occurring more slowly than in the past (Preston, Vierboom, and Stokes 2018).

Over the course of history, our body's ability to store fat is what saved us when the food ran out for a while. Especially in the richer nations, we no longer face such periodic shortages so that fat isn't used up unless we consciously limit its intake and/or engage in regular physical exercise. If we are going to reduce the burden of degenerative disease and prolong our health, we are almost certainly going to have to restructure our everyday life to reduce the consumption of fat and sugar (and processed foods more generally) while increasing our level of exercise. This goes hand-in-hand with the need for humans to revert to a more plant-based diet since the increasing consumption of meat is harmful not just to the person eating it, but also to the planet more generally, as we will discuss in greater detail in Chapter 10.

Life Span and Longevity

Could you live forever if you were able to avoid fatal accidents and fatal communicable diseases, and if you were scrupulous about lifestyle choices? The answer to that question is almost certainly "no," but there is a lot of scientific work currently being done to delay death to ever older ages. Biologists suggest that as we move past the reproductive years (past our biological "usefulness"), we undergo a set of concurrent processes know as senescence: a decline in physical viability accompanied by a rise in vulnerability to disease. Several theories are in vogue as to why people become susceptible to disease and death as age increases. These can be roughly divided into theories of "wear and tear" and "planned obsolescence." Wear and tear is one of the most popularly appealing theories of aging and likens humans to machines that eventually wear out due to the stresses and strains of constant use. But which biological mechanisms might actually account for the wearing out? One possibility is that errors occur in the synthesis of new proteins within the body. Protein synthesis involves a long and complex series of events, beginning with the DNA in the nucleus and ending with the production of new proteins. At several steps in this delicate process, it seems possible that molecular errors can occur that lead to irreversible damage (and thus aging) of a cell. Of special concern is the possibility that errors may occur in the body's immune system so that the body begins to attack its own normal cells rather than just foreign invaders. This process is called "autoimmunity." Alternatively, the immune system may lose its ability to attack the outside invaders, leading to a situation in which the body no longer can fight off disease. The planned obsolescence theories revolve around the idea that each of us has a built-in biological time clock that ticks for a predetermined length of time and then stops. This theory essentially proposes that you will die "when your number is up," because each cell in your body will regenerate only a certain number of times and no more.

Which of these theories makes the most sense? Will they be overtaken by newer and better ones? Good questions, and given the emerging advances in human genome analysis and regenerative therapies based on stem cells, we may well approach some answers in your lifetime (Olshansky 2018; Tchkonia and Kirkland 2018). Until that time comes, let us remind you that current evidence points to two basic conclusions: (1) aging is much more complex than we have previously assumed, so different theories tend to fill in only parts of the puzzle; and (2) we have not yet discovered the basic, underlying mechanism of aging that (if it exists) would explain everything. The planned obsolescence theory could explain why animal species each have a different life span; whereas the various aspects of wear and tear seem better able to explain why members of the same species show so much variability in the actual aging process.

Life Span

Demographers define **life span** as the oldest age to which human beings can survive; whereas longevity is the ability to remain alive from one year to the next—the ability to resist death. As noted above, we do not yet have a good enough theory about aging to help us to predict how long humans *could* live, so we must be content to assume that the oldest age to which a human actually *has* lived (a figure that may change from day to day) is the oldest age to which it is possible to live. Claims of long human life spans are widespread, but confirmation of those claims is more difficult to find. As of this writing, the oldest authenticated age to which a human has ever lived is 122 years and 164 days, an age achieved by a Frenchwoman, Jeanne Louise Calment, who died in August 1997. Her authenticated birth date was February 21, 1875, and on her 120th birthday in 1995, she was asked what kind of future she expected. "A very short one," she replied (Wallis 1995:85). You can stay up to date by visiting the following website: http://www.recordholders.org/en/list /oldest.html. You have almost certainly read the claim that the first person to live to be 150 years of age has already been born. Only time will tell, but keep in mind that more than 20 years after Jeanne Louise Calments's death, no one had met or exceeded her age at death.

Longevity

So, humans can live to at least age 122, yet very few people come even close to achieving that age. Most, in fact, can expect to live scarcely more than half that long (life expectancy at birth for the world as a whole is estimated to be about 72 years for both sexes combined). It is this latter concept, people's demonstrated ability to stay alive, as opposed to the theoretical maximum, that we refer to as longevity and it is usually measured by life expectancy, the statistically average length of life (or average expected age at death, which we will discuss in greater detail later in the chapter). This is greatly influenced by the society in which we live because of the variability in public health and medical care systems, as we discussed above. The very same person born into a poorer country such as Nigeria will have a lower life expectancy than if she had been born in the United States. Your own longevity is also influenced by the genetic characteristics with which you are born. The strength of vital organs, predisposition to particular diseases, metabolism rate, and so on are biological factors over which we presently have little control. Studies of identical twins separated at birth and raised in different environments show that their average age at death is more similar than non-identical twins, and that both groups of twins have life expectancies that are more similar than you would expect by chance. Nonetheless, the available evidence suggests that only about 25 percent of the variability in longevity is due to inherited characteristics (Carey and Judge 2001; Passarino, De Rango, and Montesanto 2016). The remaining differences in mortality are due to social, economic, environmental and even political factors that influence when and why death occurs.

The social world influences the risk of death in a variety of ways that can be reasonably reduced to two broad categories: (1) the social, economic, and political infrastructure (how much control we exercise over nature); and (2) lifestyle (how much control we exercise over ourselves). The infrastructure of society refers to the way in which wealth is generated and distributed, reflecting the extent to which water and milk are purified, diseases are vaccinated against, rodents and other pests are controlled, waste is eliminated, and food, shelter, clothing, and acute medical care and long-term assistance are made available to members of society. Within any particular social setting, however, death rates may also be influenced by lifestyle. Smoking, drug use, excessive alcohol use, exposure to environmental toxins, eating fatty and processed foods, and too little exercise are lifestyle factors that may shorten longevity.

Although one key to a long life may be your "choice" of long-lived parents, prescriptions for a long life are most often a brew of lifestyle choices. A typical list of ways to maximize longevity includes regular exercise, daily breakfast, normal weight, no smoking, only moderate drinking, seven to eight hours of sleep daily, regular meal-taking, taking your prescribed medications, and having an optimistic outlook on life. Note that the latter idea of "don't worry, be happy, you'll live longer" has the backing of medical research (Davidson, Mostofsky, and Whang 2010). These suggestions, by the way, are not unique to the Western world, nor are they particularly modern. A group of medical workers studying older people in southern China many years ago concluded that the important factors for long life are fresh air, moderate drinking and eating, regular exercise, and an optimistic attitude (Associated Press 1980). Similarly, note the words of a Dr. Weber, who was 83 in 1904 when he published an article in the *British Medical Journal* outlining his prescriptions for a long life:

> Be moderate in food and drink and in all physical pleasures; take exercise daily, regardless of the weather; go to bed early, rise early, sleep for no more than 6–7 hours; bathe daily; work and occupy yourself mentally on a regular basis—stimulate the enjoyment of life so that the mind may be tranquil and full of hope; control the passions; be resolute about preserving health; and avoid alcohol, narcotics, and soothing drugs (quoted in Metchnikoff 1908:102).

Disease and Death Over the Life Cycle

Age Differentials in Mortality

Disease and death are not randomly distributed across the life cycle. Humans are like most other animals with respect to the general pattern of death by age—the very young and the old are most vulnerable, whereas young adults are least likely to die. In Figure 4.4, you can see that the pattern of death by age is similar whether the actual death rates are high or low. After the initial five years of life, there is a period of time, usually lasting at least until middle age, when risks of death are relatively low. Beyond middle age, mortality increases, although at a decelerating rate (Horiuchi and Wilmoth 1998; Feehan 2018).

The genetic or biological aspects of longevity have led many theorists over time to believe that the age patterns of longevity shown in Figure 4.4 could be explained by a simple mathematical formula similar perhaps to the law of gravity and other laws of nature. The most famous of these was put forward in 1825 by Benjamin Gompertz and describes a simple geometric relationship between age and death

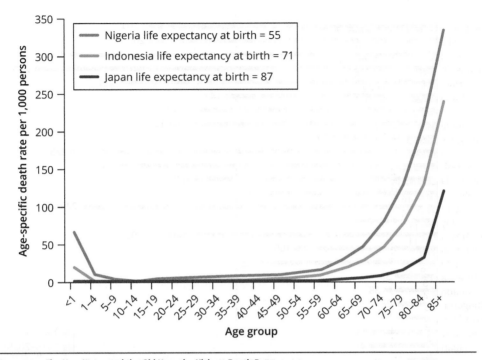

Figure 4.4   The Very Young and the Old Have the Highest Death Rates

Note: Nigeria has among the highest death rates in the world, Japan is among the lowest, and Indonesia is at the world average. Yet all three countries exhibit the universal age pattern of mortality—high at both ends and lowest in the middle. Data refer to 2016 and are for females, but the pattern is the same for males.

Source: Adapted from data in World Health Organization, Global Health Observatory Data Repository.

rates from the point of sexual maturity to the extreme old ages (Olshansky and Carnes 1997). These mathematical models are interesting, but they have so far not been able to capture the actual variability and complexity in the human experience with death (McAuley et al. 2015). Part of the problem is that we may know what *kills* us, but we are less certain about what it is that allows us to *survive*, although of course a lot of researchers are working on this problem. This is why, even if we were able to rid ourselves of all diseases, we do not know how long we might live. We do know, however, that since our susceptibility to disease and death varies over the life cycle, it is important to look at those differences in more detail.

Infant Mortality

There are few things in the world more frightening and awesome than the responsibility for a newborn child, fragile and completely dependent on others for survival. For most of human history until only the past century or so, and still in many developing nations, the fragility and dependency are translated into high infant mortality rates (IMR) (the number of deaths during the first year of life per 1,000 live births). Infant death rates are closely correlated with life expectancy, and Figure 4.5 shows the

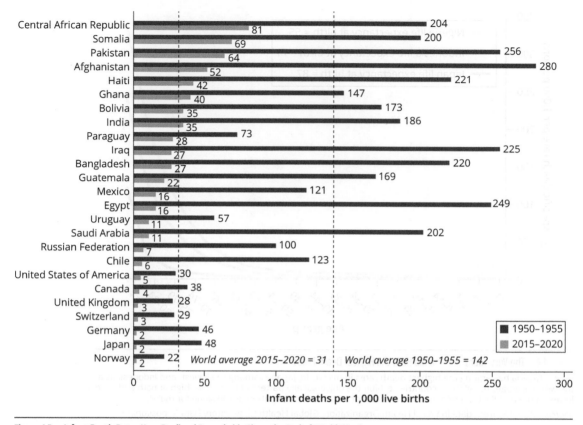

Figure 4.5   Infant Death Rates Have Declined Remarkably Since the End of World War II
Source: Data are from United Nations Population Division, *World Population Prospects: The 2017 Revision.*

infant mortality rates for a sample of countries around the world, with comparisons between rates prevailing in 1950–1955 compared to now. For the world as a whole, the average infant death rate has plummeted from 142 deaths per 1,000 live births in the period shortly after the end of World War II to 31 per 1,000 as of this writing. In the earlier period, Norway had the world's lowest IMR, at 22 per 1,000, and it is now tied with several other countries, including Japan, for the lowest IMR of 2 per 1,000.

The highest IMR in the world is currently found in the Central African Republic, where 81 out of 1,000 children born alive die before their first birthday. This is certainly dismal, but you can see that it is a huge improvement over the 204 deaths per 1,000 live births back in 1950–1955. Even more astounding is the change over time in Afghanistan. In 1950–1955, long before it was invaded first by Russia, and then the United States and its allies, the IMR was 280 per 1,000—the highest in the world at that time. It is now down to 52—still above the world average, but lower even than its next-door neighbor Pakistan. It is not a coincidence that the countries with huge declines in infant mortality in an historically short period of time (just a few decades) are among the nations with the highest rates of population growth. As we discuss in the next chapter, it is much easier to reduce death rates than birth rates.

Why are babies so vulnerable, and how can we intervene to bring death rates down in an almost miraculous manner? One of the most important causes of death among infants is dehydration, which can be caused by almost any disease or dietary imbalance, with polluted water being a common source of trouble for babies. How can dehydration and other causes of death among infants be avoided? In the broadest sense, the answer can be summed up by two characteristics common to people in places where infant death rates are low—high levels of education and income. These are key ingredients at both the societal and the individual levels. In general, those countries with the highest levels of income and education are those with enough money to provide the population with clean water, adequate sanitation, food and shelter, and, very importantly, access to health care services.

Higher incomes increase the chance that babies will have a nutritious, sanitary diet that prevents diarrhea. Nursing mothers can best provide this service if their diet is adequate in amount and quality. Income is also frequently associated with the ability of a nation to provide, or an individual to buy, adequate medical protection from disease. In places where infant death rates are high, communicable diseases are a major cause of death, and most of those deaths could be prevented with medical assistance (Liu et al. 2015). We know, for example, that between 1861 and 1960, the infant death rate in England and Wales dropped from 160 to 20, and more than two-thirds of that decline was due to the control of communicable diseases.

Throughout the world, infant health has been aided especially by the fact that the WHO has promoted the use of oral rehydration therapy (ORT), which involves administering an inexpensive glucose and electrolyte solution to replenish bodily fluids. Oral rehydration therapy was first shown to be effective in clinical trials in Bangladesh in 1968, and it has proven to be very effective in controlling diarrhea and dehydration among infants (and adults as well—think Gatorade) all over the world.

When infant mortality drops to low levels, as is true in advanced nations like the United States and Canada, prematurity becomes the single most important reason for deaths among infants, and in many cases prematurity results from lack of proper care of the mother during pregnancy. Pregnant women who do not maintain an adequate diet, who smoke, take drugs, or in general are not well cared for have an elevated chance of giving birth prematurely, thus putting their baby at a distinct disadvantage in terms of survival after birth.

Throughout the world, the infant mortality rate is a fairly sensitive indicator of societal development because as the standard of living goes up, so does the average level of health in a population, and the health of babies typically improves earlier and faster than that of people at other ages. This greater ability to resist death past infancy generally holds up throughout the reproductive years (with the exception of maternal mortality, which we discuss below), but beyond that time of life, death rates start to increase.

Mortality at Older Ages

It has been said that in the past, parents buried their children; now, children bury their parents. This describes the health and mortality transition in a nutshell.

The postponement of death until the older ages means that the number of deaths among friends and relatives in your own age group is small in the early years and then accelerates in the later decades of life. But even at the older ages, there are revolutionary changes taking place in death rates. In the more developed countries of the world, the risk of death has been steadily going down even at the very oldest ages. We have not yet unlocked the key to living beyond age 122, no matter the promises of biotech companies, but we are pushing toward the day when a large fraction of people will approach that age before they die.

As life expectancy has increased and people survive in greater proportions to older ages, societies experience less variability in the ages at which their members die. Instead of people being likely to die at almost any age (even if most at risk when young or old), death gets compressed into a narrow range of ages. Wilmoth and Horiuchi (1999) calculated, for example, that the variability in ages at death in Sweden in the 1950s was only about one-fourth of what it had been 100 years before that. The result of this **mortality compression** of death into a narrow range at the older ages is also known as rectangularization, as we noted earlier in the chapter. This means that the curve of the proportion of people surviving to any given age begins to square off, rather than dropping off smoothly. Figure 4.6 gives you an example of this using data for females in the United States.

Going back to 1901–10, when life expectancy at birth in the United States was 52 years, Figure 4.6 shows that the proportion surviving drops off fairly quickly at the younger ages because of high infant and child mortality, and then it drops off fairly smoothly after that until everybody has died off at around 100. By the middle

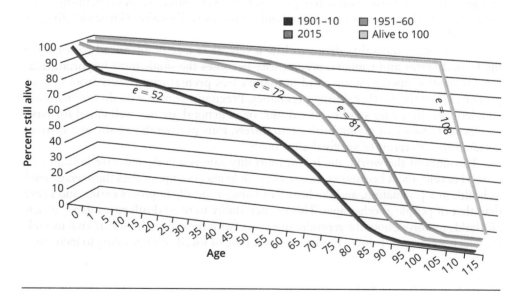

Figure 4.6   The Compression of Mortality in the United States

Sources: Data for 1901–10, 1951–60, and 2015 are from the United States Mortality Database, University of California, Berkeley, available at usa.mortality.org (data downloaded in 2018); the "Alive to 100" data were generated by John Weeks. Data are for females.

of the twentieth century, in 1951–60, when life expectancy had increased rather dramatically to 72 years, the proportions alive at each successive age are noticeably larger than they were at the beginning of that century, and the trend continued into the twenty-first century when, in the year 2015 (the most recent data available at this writing), life expectancy at birth for females had reached 81. An almost totally rectangular situation is shown as the extreme case in Figure 4.6. If everyone survived to age 100, and then died fairly quickly after that, mortality would be compressed into a very short time period, with an estimated life expectancy of 108 years, and the survival curve would be nearly squared off at the oldest ages, as you can see. In general, the limited data available seem to support the idea that compression and rectangularization are occurring (Wilmoth and Horiuchi 1999; Kannisto 2007; Brown et al. 2012), although not everybody agrees (Lynch and Brown 2001). The principal argument against it is that it assumes a fixed human life span of around 120 years. If we are somehow able to crack that barrier, then people could live to increasingly older ages (e.g., 150 years), which might "decompress" mortality and smooth out the mortality curve at the older ages (Caselli and Vallin 2001).

Even if we are never able to overcome the 120-year limit, one of the most dramatic changes in mortality in richer countries over the past few decades has been the drop in death rates at the older ages. It is not simply that deaths are being compressed into a relatively short period in old age, but that age has been getting progressively older. Consider that in 1900 a woman who reached age 65 in the United States could expect to live another 12 years. At the time of World War II that had increased a bit to 14 years, but by 2015 it was up to 21 years. These things may not matter much to you now, but as you approach old age, you'll start to give them more thought, especially since by then that number of additional years of life will almost certainly be higher than it is now.

Sex and Gender Differentials in Mortality

Although the age pattern of death is the most obvious way in which biology affects our lives, it is also true that at every age there are differences between males and females in the likelihood of death. Some of these differentials seem to be strictly biological in origin (the "sex" differences) whereas others are induced by society (the "gender" differences), although it is not always easy to tell the difference between the biological and social influences.

The most basic health difference between males and females is that males have higher death rates than females from conception to the very oldest ages. Seemingly to compensate for this, more males are conceived than females. Fetal mortality is higher for boys than girls, but there are still typically more males born than females. Infant and childhood mortality rates are higher for males, with a roughly equal number of males and females being reached, quite conveniently from an evolutionary perspective, in the prime reproductive ages of the late teens and early twenties. After that, the only bump in the road for females compared to males is high maternal mortality, and by the older ages we can almost always expect to find more women than men.

The difference in life expectancy between males and females has attracted curiosity for a long time, and it has been suggested facetiously that the early death of men is nature's way of repaying those women who have spent a lifetime with demanding, difficult husbands. However, the situation has been more thoroughly investigated by a variety of researchers. It appears that a real biological superiority exists for women in the form of an immune function, probably imparted by the hormone estrogen, although it is not yet easy to measure this biological advantage. It may be, for example, that the XY chromosome combination that males have is biologically less robust than the XX combination of females (Shabecoff 2014). In general, biological interpretations of the difference are supported by studies showing that throughout the animal kingdom females survive longer than males (Retherford 1975; Kohler, Preston, and Lackey 2006), suggesting some kind of basic biological superiority in the ability of females to survive relative to males (biologists refer to this as an aspect of *sexual dimorphism*).

In human populations, the survival advantage of women is widespread, but it is not quite universal. Until very recently there were still several countries—notably Afghanistan and a few nations in sub-Saharan Africa—where life expectancy for females was actually lower than for males. This implies that there are social factors at work when it comes to mortality, especially related to the status of women. It is in those countries where women are most dominated by men that women have been least likely to outlive men (Cardenas and Obermeyer 1997). In sub-Saharan Africa, for example, this has shown up in the victimization of women by men who have HIV but force women to have unprotected sex with them. In South Asia, it has been noticeable at the younger ages, when girls may be fed less well than boys, and parents may be less likely to seek health care for sick girls than for sick boys (Muhuri and Preston 1991; Yount 2003; Oster 2009).

The social aspect of mortality also shows up in what is certainly an important part of the explanation for the fact that over much of the twentieth century life expectancy was increasing faster for females than for males, whereas in the past two to three decades the gap has narrowed. For example, in 1900, women could expect to live an average of two years longer than men in the United States, and by 1975, the difference had peaked at 7.8 years. Since then, however, the difference has dropped to 4.8 years as of 2015. The solution to this mystery is smoking. During the first half of the 20th century, males were smoking cigarettes much more than females, and this helped to elevate male risks of death from cancer, degenerative lung diseases (such as chronic bronchitis and emphysema), and cardiovascular diseases (Preston 1970). However, cigarette smoking by women increased after World War II, and by now women are nearly as likely as men to be smokers (the smoking version of gender equality), although overall levels of smoking are much lower than they used to be. However, since deaths associated with smoking tend to occur many years after smoking begins, the decline in smoking takes a while to show up as a decrease in smoking-related deaths. Researchers have found that males and females who smoke heavily have similar (and lower-than-average) life expectancies, but nonsmoking males still have lower life expectancies than nonsmoking females (Rogers and Powell-Griner 1991; Rogers, Hummer, and Nam 2000; Lariscy, Hummer, and Rogers 2018).

Causes of Poor Health and Death

The World Health Organization puts deaths into one of three major categories: (1) communicable, maternal, perinatal, and nutritional conditions (which we will just abbreviate to "communicable"); (2) noncommunicable diseases; and (3) injuries. Each of these includes a long list of causes of death, and Table 4.2 summarizes the top 20 causes of death in the world, comparing data across the World Bank's four major income groupings of the world's countries.

Of the 57 million people who died anywhere in the world in 2016, WHO estimates that the top killer (9.4 million) was ischemic heart disease—a reduced flow of blood to the heart that causes a heart attack. You can see in Table 4.2 that 14 of the top 20 causes of death as of 2016 (the most recent data at this writing) are from noncommunicable diseases. As we have noted before, this is very new in human history because until recently communicable diseases have been the major cause of death, killing people before they had a chance to die of something else, and they are still the top two killers in low-income countries, as can be seen in Table 4.2.

Communicable Diseases

Communicable (or infectious) diseases include bacterial (such as tuberculosis, pneumonia, and the plague), viral (such as influenza and measles), and protozoan (such as malaria and diarrhea). They are spread in different ways (by different vectors), and have varying degrees of severity. Tuberculosis is an example of a bacterial infection that still kills more than one million people each year, despite the known treatments for it, and it is estimated that several times that number of people are infected with the disease worldwide but do not show symptoms. The disease remains untreated in many parts of the world, especially in Africa.

Measles is an example of an acute viral disease that is severe in infancy and adulthood but less so in childhood. It is usually spread by droplets passed through the air when an infected person coughs or sneezes. If left untreated in an infant or adult, the chance of death is 5–10 percent. Vaccinations now protect most people in the developed world from measles, and the United Nations has been working to increase immunization elsewhere, helping to lower the global number of deaths from measles dramatically to less than 100,000 per year (World Health Organization 2018a), dropping it off the top 20 list.

Malaria is an example of a complex protozoan disease typically spread by female mosquitoes first biting an infected person. Then the blood from the malarial person spends a week or more in the mosquito's stomach, where the malarial spores develop and enter the mosquito's salivary gland. The disease is passed along with the mosquito's next bite to a human. There are two major types of malaria: (1) *Plasmodium falciparum* is the most deadly, and it is prevalent in sub-Saharan Africa, but it is less commonly found elsewhere, probably because it requires consistently high temperatures; and (2) *Plasmodium vivax*, which is the most common form of malaria and is found especially in Latin America and South Asia. It is less deadly (albeit still serious) than *P. falciparum*, but it is less sensitive to low temperature and

Table 4.2   Top 20 Causes of Death in the World as of 2016

Cause of Death	Broad Category of Cause	No. of Deaths in World 2016 (millions)	Percent of Deaths Due to This Cause			
			High-Income Countries	Upper-Middle-Income Countries	Lower-Middle-Income Countries	Low-Income Countries
Ischemic heart disease	Noncommunicable	9.4	16.8	19.7	16.3	6.5
Stroke	Noncommunicable	5.8	7.2	15.2	8.4	5.2
Chronic obstructive pulmonary disease	Noncommunicable	3.0	5.4	6.3	5.4	2.0
Lower respiratory infections	Communicable	3.0	4.3	3.0	6.5	9.3
Alzheimer disease and other dementias	Noncommunicable	2.0	7.0	4.3	1.8	1.0
Trachea, bronchus, lung cancers	Noncommunicable	1.7	5.6	4.6	1.0	0.4
Diabetes mellitus	Noncommunicable	1.6	2.7	2.9	3.1	1.7
Road injury	Injury	1.4	0.9	2.7	2.7	3.6
Diarrhoeal diseases	Communicable	1.4	0.3	0.3	4.1	7.2
Tuberculosis	Communicable	1.3	0.1	0.6	4.2	4.2
Cirrhosis of the liver	Noncommunicable	1.3	1.6	1.8	3.0	1.6
Kidney diseases	Noncommunicable	1.2	2.2	2.1	2.3	1.0
Preterm birth complications	Noncommunicable	1.0	0.2	0.5	3.1	4.0
HIV/AIDS	Communicable	1.0	0.1	1.3	2.1	5.5
Hypertensive heart disease	Noncommunicable	0.9	1.4	2.2	1.3	0.9
Liver cancer	Noncommunicable	0.8	1.4	2.6	0.7	0.5
Colon and rectum cancers	Noncommunicable	0.8	3.2	1.6	0.6	0.4
Self-harm	Injury	0.8	1.6	1.4	1.4	0.8
Stomach cancer	Noncommunicable	0.8	1.5	2.4	0.6	0.3
Birth asphyxia and birth trauma	Noncommunicable	0.7	0.0	0.3	1.9	3.8
TOTAL		39.9	63.5	75.8	70.5	59.9
		=70.2% of all deaths				

Source: Adapted from data in World Health Organization (2018), Global Health Estimates 2016 Summary Tables: http://www.who.int/healthinfo/global_burden_disease/en/

was once endemic in southern Europe, as well as the southern United States (until the 1940s).

Children and pregnant women are most at risk of dying from malaria, and in areas where the disease is endemic (constantly present), such as sub-Saharan Africa, people who survive to adulthood may have built up an immunity as a result of repeated infections—a variation on the theme of "that which doesn't kill you makes you stronger." Malaria has been around for thousands of years, and it is likely that King Tut of Egypt died of malaria 33 centuries ago (Hawass et al. 2010). The disease may have emerged when humans cleared forests and settled into Neolithic agricultural villages thousands of years ago (Pennisi 2001). However, it was not until the late nineteenth century that it was proven that mosquito bites were the way in which the disease was transmitted, rather than it having something to do with bad air (*mal aria* in Italian). The first effective treatments, dating from the nineteenth century, were quinine, followed by chloroquine, and more recently artemisinin. Because of the complexity of the disease, no vaccines have been perfected as of this writing, although a great deal of work is under way. Preventing a bite is the best current strategy, and the Bill and Melinda Gates Foundation has helped pour resources into efforts to provide bed nets to keep people from being bitten while they sleep (mosquitos tend to be nocturnal), making sure that homes don't have standing water where mosquitos can breed, and various other ways to minimize human contact with the mosquito. These are the reasons why malaria is no longer on the top 20 list, but it still kills nearly 500,000 people each year.

An estimated 1.1 million people died of HIV/AIDS in 2016, making it the 14th most important cause of death in the world, as you can see in Table 4.2. That was a huge improvement from just a short time ago. As recently as the early 2000s, it was devastating to several southern African countries, such as Botswana, where life expectancy had dropped from 62 years in the 1980s to only 49 years in 2000–2005. It has since bounced back to the high 60s, as the world gets a handle on the disease after it exploded on the scene in the early 1980s. Millions of people have HIV/AIDS but treatment programs with antiretroviral drugs have been increasingly successful in keeping them alive. Treatment is expensive, however, underlining the importance of prevention. The spread of HIV can be prevented, as you undoubtedly know, especially by using condoms during intercourse and by not sharing needles to inject drugs. These relatively simple control measures have been very effective in North America and Europe, but they have been slower to catch on in sub-Saharan Africa, where prevalence rates and new infection rates are by far the highest in the world.

Emerging Infectious Diseases

Just as the world was getting HIV/AIDS under control, another emerging infectious disease came along in West Africa—Ebola. The virus was first identified in Zaire (now the Democratic Republic of Congo) in 1976, and has spread out from there. It is not clear how the disease wound up in Liberia and its West African neighbors, but the most likely carriers of the disease (besides infected humans) are bats, although monkeys may also be a reservoir (U.S. Centers for Disease Control and Prevention 2018b).

Global efforts to control the spread of Ebola have been at least partially successful, in that new cases are popping up almost exclusively in conflict zones in sub-Saharan Africa, especially the Democratic Republic of the Congo. However, in 2016, just as the Ebola scare was subsiding, a new disease hit the stage—the Zika virus. This mosquito-borne virus has the horrific effect of causing fetal brain damage if a pregnant woman is infected. When the disease was discovered in Brazil, and then in Central America, women were initially being advised to avoid getting pregnant. The disease was first identified in Uganda in 1947, so it too is originally out of Africa, just like Ebola and a lot of diseases. It is not known with certainty why the Zika virus showed up so suddenly in Brazil in 2016, but it was probably brought over by a visitor from one of the Pacific Islands where it had emerged a few years earlier after migrants had brought it there from Africa. It remains a global threat, so check with the U.S. Centers for Disease Control and Prevention (https://wwwnc.cdc.gov/travel/page/zika-travel-information) before making your travel plans. To be sure, the mobility of humans is the likely explanation for the regional dispersion of all infectious diseases, including Chagas disease, which is a parasitic disease that has long existed in rural areas of Latin America but has spread north with migrants from those areas (Conners et al. 2016).

The desire of humans to add more animal protein to their diet may be creating opportunities for coronaviruses (animal viruses) to be spread to humans. It is generally believed that HIV crossed to humans from monkeys and/or chimpanzees (Gao et al. 1999; de Groot et al. 2002), and the evidence suggests that severe acute respiratory syndrome (SARS) may have come from animals captured for food in China (Lingappa et al. 2004), and it is very possible that Ebola was transmitted by humans eating infected animals. Birds can also be sources of disease.

Although West Nile virus has existed in Africa and the Middle East for decades, it was brought to New York City in 1999, apparently by an imported infected bird that was bitten by a mosquito, which then bit a human who became sick and died. It has since spread to other communities all over the country. In 2003, a new H5N1 avian influenza (popularly called "bird flu") was reported in Asia. It originated in poultry farms, especially in Indonesia and Vietnam, and then crossed over to humans, spread especially by migratory birds. In 2009, yet another new strain of influenza, H1N1 (popularly known as "swine flu"), emerged as a worldwide pandemic. Because of the increasing ease of travel and greater global connectivity, the potential for new diseases to emerge is very high and WHO leads a coalition of groups that monitors these threats (Morens and Fauci 2013).

Maternal Mortality

A very special category of "communicable" diseases, as defined by WHO, is that associated with pregnancy and childbirth. Birth can be a traumatic and dangerous time not only for the infant, as discussed above, but for the mother as well. To be sure, until very recently, getting pregnant was probably one of the most dangerous things that a woman could do. This is because pregnancy and birth put both the fetus/infant and mother at risk of a wide range of infectious diseases that can be deadly if not identified and treated. Although global campaigns to reduce maternal death have been very effective, it is still true that more than 300,000 women die each year (the equivalent of two jumbo jets crashing every day and killing all passengers). The vast majority (perhaps as high as 99 percent) of those deaths occur in developing nations (World Health Organization 2018b).

These deaths leave a trail of tragedy throughout the world, and there are three factors, in particular, that increase a woman's risk of death when she becomes pregnant: (1) lack of prenatal care that might otherwise identify problems with the pregnancy before the problems become too risky; (2) delivering the baby somewhere besides a hospital, where problems can be dealt with immediately; and (3) seeking an unsafe abortion because the pregnancy is not wanted.

Women are obviously at risk of a maternal death only if they become pregnant. However, we do not have good data on the number of pregnancies worldwide, so we use the number of live births as an estimate of how many pregnancies have occurred within a particular group of women. The maternal mortality ratio (MMR) measures the number of maternal deaths per 100,000 live births. Estimates by WHO (2018) indicate that the MMR in developing countries in 2015 was 239 per 100,000 live births, compared to only 12 per 100,000 live births in developed countries. At the same time, the MMR in the United States is 14 per 100,000—twice the rate of Canada, and higher than any European country. More troubling is the fact that it has been going up in the United States since the mid-1980s, rather than down. It is not yet clear why this is happening, but the U.S. Centers for Disease Control and Prevention (2018c) suggests that an increasing number of pregnant women in the United States have chronic health conditions (noncommunicable diseases) such as hypertension, diabetes, and chronic heart disease, which may put a pregnant woman at higher risk of pregnancy complications.

Noncommunicable Diseases

As you already know, as we move through the health and mortality transition, noncommunicable diseases take precedence over communicable diseases as the important causes of death. As you can see looking back at Table 4.2, noncommunicable diseases account for the top five killers in the high-income countries, but only two of the top five in low-income countries.

Deaths from heart disease occur most commonly as a result of a reduced blood supply to the heart muscle, typically caused by a narrowing of the coronary arteries, which can be a consequence of atherosclerosis, "a slowly progressing condition in which the inner layer of the artery walls become thick and irregular because of plaque—deposits of fat, cholesterol, and other substances. As the plaque builds up, the arteries narrow, the blood flow is decreased, and the likelihood of a blood clot increases" (Smith and Pratt 1993:83). Stroke is also part of the family of cardiovascular diseases, but whereas heart disease produces death by the failure to get enough blood to the heart muscle, stroke is the result of the rupture or clogging of an artery in the brain. This causes a loss of blood supply to nerve cells in the affected part of the brain, and these cells die within minutes.

Mortality Control and the Environment

"Live long and prosper." Every newborn child should have such a toast offered on her or his behalf. For most of human history, children could look forward neither to a long life nor a prosperous one, and the achievement of both has required that we bring the environment under our control. We do this, for example, by growing a greater abundance of nutritious food than nature would otherwise provide, by killing the bacteria in our water supply, by protecting ourselves from disease-carrying insects and rodents, by using herbs and chemicals to create medications that kill the parasites that attack our bodies, and other devices and concoctions that help to repair or replace failing body parts. We control nature by draining swamps, clearing forests, plowing land, building roads and bridges, constructing water and sewerage systems, building dams and levees, and so forth. Then we protect ourselves from nature by building houses that keep predators at bay, keep the rain and snow outside, and adjusting the indoor atmosphere so we don't get too hot or too cold, using large amounts of generated energy in the process.

Controlling nature and protecting ourselves from its ravages are not accomplished without a cost, of course. In the process we rearrange our relationship to nature and risk degrading the environment to the point of unsustainability. This is all because of the natural linkage between living long and prospering—the two go together, as you can see in the accompanying diagram. The obvious impact of a declining death rate on the environment is that more people mean more resources used. This is the classical Malthusian view—population growth means more people trying to live at the same standard of living. That model simply says that we live long, but don't prosper. The prosperity comes from our greater per-person productivity as we become more clever and efficient in using environmental resources for our personal and collective improvement. Two important components of this are linked to the decline in mortality. The lower death rate is a result of our being healthier, and healthy people can work harder and longer and thus be more productive. But there is also a psychosocial aspect, which we have labeled an increase in the "scope" of life. The prospect of a long life, unburdened by the threat of imminent death, means that we can think about life in the long term, making plans and implementing changes and improvements that would have been unimaginable in the days when life was so uncertain.

This greater scope means that each of us has the potential to be more creative and productive in each year that we live. So, on the one hand, declining mortality increases the size of the population and increases the demand for resources. But, at the same time, the demand for resources is increasing more quickly than the growth of population because a healthier, longer-living population has the potential to prosper—to improve per person productivity, which also increases per person use of resources. One of the most elemental of these impacts is on the food supply. As we have become healthier, we have become bigger people, causing the demand for food to increase at a faster pace even than the population is growing (Fogel and Helmchen 2002; Floud et al. 2011). Consider this—in 1961, each of the 3.1 billion people then alive consumed an average of 2,255 calories of food per day; but 55 years later, in 2016 (the most recent estimates currently available from the United Nations Food and Agriculture Organization), the 7.4 billion people alive were consuming food at the rate of 2,904 calories per day. Population had increased by 139 percent—more than doubling in that time—but the total amount of food demanded (population times daily calories) had increased by 207 percent!

Can we go on this way? We will consider that question in more detail in Chapter 10, but let us give you an example from China, which in the period from 1961 to 2013 increased from 668 million to 1.383 billion people. This was a result of a death rate that was declining much more quickly than the birth rate—the Chinese added a whopping 31 years to their life expectancy during that

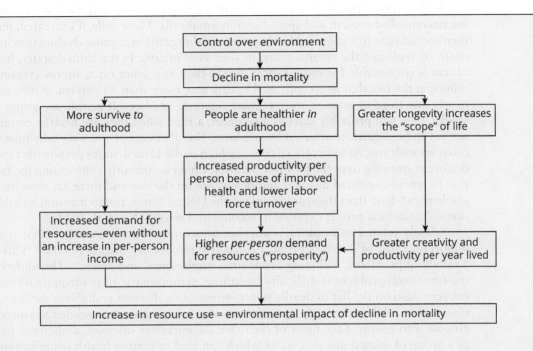

```
                    ┌──────────────────────────┐
                    │  Control over environment │
                    └────────────┬─────────────┘
                                 ▼
                    ┌──────────────────────────┐
                    │    Decline in mortality   │
                    └────────────┬─────────────┘
        ┌────────────────┬───────┴────────┬──────────────────┐
        ▼                ▼                ▼
┌───────────────┐ ┌───────────────┐ ┌──────────────────────┐
│ More survive  │ │ People are    │ │ Greater longevity    │
│ to adulthood  │ │ healthier in  │ │ increases the        │
│               │ │ adulthood     │ │ "scope" of life      │
└───────┬───────┘ └───────┬───────┘ └──────────┬───────────┘
        │                 ▼                     │
        │    ┌──────────────────────────┐       │
        │    │ Increased productivity per │      │
        │    │ person because of improved │      │
        │    │ health and lower labor     │      │
        │    │ force turnover             │      │
        │    └────────────┬─────────────┘       │
        ▼                 ▼                     ▼
┌───────────────┐ ┌───────────────┐ ┌──────────────────────┐
│ Increased     │ │ Higher per-   │ │ Greater creativity   │
│ demand for    │ │ person demand │ │ and productivity     │
│ resources—    │→│ for resources │←│ per year lived       │
│ even without  │ │ ("prosperity")│ │                      │
│ an increase in│ │               │ │                      │
│ per-person    │ │               │ │                      │
│ income        │ │               │ │                      │
└───────┬───────┘ └───────┬───────┘ └──────────┬───────────┘
        └─────────────────┼─────────────────────┘
                          ▼
┌────────────────────────────────────────────────────────────┐
│ Increase in resource use = environmental impact of decline  │
│ in mortality                                                 │
└────────────────────────────────────────────────────────────┘
```

52-year period. They, like many others in the world, were healthier at least partly because they were eating better, increasing their per-day calorie consumption from 1,439 in 1961 to 3,108 in 2013. Thus, China experienced a 107 percent increase in population—more than a doubling—and an astonishing 347 percent increase in the total amount of food consumed in the nation.

How did the country manage this? As you probably know already, and as we discussed in Chapter 1, this was a period of rapid economic development in China, which allowed people better nutrition and better health—these things all go together. China is the world's most populous country, so you can appreciate the impact on the Earth's environment of this combination of longer lives and higher food consumption per person.

Our greater productivity—that which makes us prosper—depends heavily on the use of energy, and the by-products of energy use include the emission of greenhouse gases, which have contributed to global climate change. Mosquitoes and other disease-carrying insects flourish in warmer weather, and there is a real concern that the re-emergence of infectious diseases will be among the many undesirable consequences of climate change. We are thus running the risk that by living longer and prospering, we have created a heap of other troubles with which we will have to cope. As Robert Louis Stevenson once famously said: "Everybody, sooner or later, sits down to a banquet of consequences."

Discussion Questions: (1) How do you think your life would be different if you were not pretty certain that you would survive to an old age? **(2)** The more rapid increase of the food supply than of population is contrary to what Malthus thought would happen—how might Malthus try to explain this? How would you explain it to him?

Malignant neoplasms (cancer) represent a group of diseases that kill by generating uncontrolled growth and spread of abnormal cells. These cells, if untreated, may then metastasize (invade neighboring tissue and organs) and cause dysfunction and death by replacing the normal tissue in your vital organs. In the United States, lung cancer is responsible for more cancer deaths than any other type, almost certainly reflecting the fact that as recently as 45 years ago, more than 50 percent of men and nearly one-third of women were regular cigarette smokers. If people are going to smoke, they will probably start as a teenager, a time when they are healthy enough not yet to be negatively affected by smoking. The ill effects of smoking take time to catch up with you, so lung cancer rates are high in the United States despite the rapid decline in smoking over the past few decades. China is currently confronting the fact that its smoking-related diseases and deaths are on the rise and there are now more smokers in China than there are people in the United States, not to mention an additional 700 million people exposed to secondhand smoke (Ng et al. 2014).

Closely related to smoking is another noncommunicable condition that is an important cause of death—chronic obstructive pulmonary disease (COPD). This is a family of problems, including bronchitis, emphysema, and asthma. The underlying functional problem is difficulty breathing, symptomatic of inadequate oxygen delivery. Also on the list of deadly noncommunicable diseases is diabetes mellitus, a disease that inhibits the body's production of insulin, a hormone needed to convert glucose into energy. Like most of the other degenerative diseases, diabetes is part of a group of related diseases, all of which can lead to further health complications such as heart disease, blindness, and renal failure. Finally, let us note that as populations age in the high-income countries, Alzheimer's disease has gotten closer to the top of the list. This dread condition produces memory loss and behavioral shifts in its victims and is a major cause of organic brain disorder among older people. Interestingly, it turns out to be a more important cause of death in the United States than in Japan, which has an older population than the United States. In Japan, on the other hand, respiratory diseases are more important than in the United States. This comparison cautions us to remember, as we pointed out earlier, that there are many routes to low mortality.

Injuries

Despite the widespread desire of humans to live as long as possible, we have devised all kinds of ways to put ourselves at risk of accidental or unintentional death as a result of the way in which we organize our lives and deal with products of our technology. Moreover, we are the only known species of animal that routinely kills other members of the same species (homicide) for reasons beyond pure survival, and we seem to be alone in killing ourselves intentionally (suicide). The latter is one of the top 10 causes of death in the United States for males, although not for females. In most countries, the suicide rate is higher for males than for females, and the general pattern is for suicide rates to rise through the teen years (a phenomenon that has always received considerable publicity), peak in the young adult ages, plateau in the middle years, and then rise in the older ages. However, the actual difference from one country to another in the suicide rate seems to be a cultural phenomenon (Cutright and Fernquist 2000). This was brought to light in 2018 when *The Economist* summarized data from the Institute of Health Metrics and Evaluation at the University of Washington to show that since the early 1990s, the death rate from suicide has been declining globally, but rising in the United States (*The Economist* 2018).

The global drop was driven especially by declines in suicide among women in China and India and among men in Russia. Urbanization and women's liberation seem to have been particularly important in China and India (the world's two most populous countries), where suicide was often a way out for women trapped in a relationship and family that was not of their choosing. As people have moved into cities and women have gained control over their own lives, they have been happier and thus less inclined to kill themselves. The rise in the United States seems to have been driven especially by the "sea of despair" that has taken root among white, working-class Americans and which, as we noted earlier in the chapter, is the likely reason for the recent drop in life expectancy in the United States (Case and Deaton 2015).

Men are not only more successful at killing themselves, they are also more likely to be killed by someone else. Homicide rates (as both victims and perpetrators) are highest for young adult males in virtually every country for which data are available (United Nations Office on Drugs and Crime 2014). Homicide death rates in the United States are higher than for any other industrialized nation except Russia, almost certainly reflecting the cultural acceptance of violence as a response to conflict combined with the ready availability of guns (which are used in two-thirds of homicides in the United States). Of special note is the remarkably higher rate of gun-related homicide among African American males within the United States (Murphy et al. 2017). This has existed for decades and appears to be most readily explained by high levels of poverty (Shaefer, Wu, and Edin 2017), which contribute to high rates of interpersonal violence (Gartner 1990:95) within a "subculture of exasperation" (Harvey 1986), especially in a society where guns are readily available (and those guns also increase the chance of a successful suicide attempt).

The "Real" Causes of Death

The causes of death discussed above reflect those items listed on a person's death certificate. The World Health Organization has worked diligently over the years to try to standardize those causes under a set of guidelines called the International Classification of Diseases (ICD), so that the pathological conditions leading to death will be identified consistently from one person to the next and from one country to the next. This enhances comparability, but it ignores the actual things going on that contribute to that death. Thus, when public concern first arose over the role of alcohol in traffic fatalities, there were no data available to suggest whether a person who died in an accident was a victim of his or her own alcohol use or the alcohol use of someone else. Similarly, a person who dies of lung cancer or heart disease may really be dying of smoking, no matter what the actual pathological condition that led immediately to death.

There is a vast amount of literature in the health sciences tracing the etiology (origins) of the diseases listed on death certificates, and in a path-breaking analysis, J. Michael McGinnis and William Foege (1993) culled those studies in order to estimate the "real" or "actual" causes of death in the United States in 1990, compared to the 10 leading causes of death as shown on death certificates and thus in vital statistics data. This study was so widely cited, and so important to our understanding of health risks, that it was later updated to reflect deaths as of 2000 (Mokdad et al. 2004). As of this writing, no one has updated the analysis, but it is unlikely to be very different.

The actual causes of death, as revealed by both studies, offer a different picture than that shown in a summary such as Table 4.2. The winner in the actual-cause-of-death sweepstakes was—tobacco. For example, of the 2,403,351 people who died in the United States in 2000, 435,000 (18 percent) died as a result of tobacco use. Tobacco has been traced to cancer deaths (especially cancers of the lung, esophagus, oral cavity, pancreas, kidney, and bladder), cardiovascular deaths (coronary heart disease, stroke, and high blood pressure), chronic lung disease, low birth weight, and other problems of infancy as a result of mothers who smoke, and to accidental deaths from burning cigarettes. Not surprisingly, smoking has emerged as an increasingly important real cause of death throughout the world. Many countries, especially in North America and Western Europe, have addressed this issue head on and have substantially lowered cigarette consumption. The health burden of smoking has now shifted to parts of Southern and Eastern Europe (especially Russia), China, and countries throughout South and Southeast Asia (Ng et al. 2014).

The second most important real cause of death in the United States relates to the diet and activity patterns of the U.S. population and accounted for 365,000 deaths or 15 percent of the total in 2000. This was a noticeable increase from the results for 1990. Most of these deaths were due to obesity, according to Ali Mokdad and associates (2004). Being overweight is associated with, among other things, major dietary abuses including high consumption of cholesterol, sodium, and animal fat. The principal activity pattern of concern is the lack thereof—a "couch potato" lifestyle. Poor diet and inactivity can lead to obesity, which then contributes to heart disease and stroke, cancers (especially colon, breast, and prostate), and diabetes mellitus.

Alcohol misuse was found to be the third (albeit a distant third) real cause of death in the United States. Alcohol contributes to death from cirrhosis, vehicle accidents, injuries in the home, drowning, fire fatalities, job injuries, murder, mayhem, and some cancers. This affects men much more than women, who are much less likely to drink alcohol in excess. Of course, the consequences of alcohol misuse are not just an early death, but also include the ruination of lives due to alcohol abuse.

Number four on the list of real causes is death by microbial agents—infectious diseases causing deaths that could have been largely prevented through appropriate vaccination and sanitation. Next on the list are toxic agents, which include occupational hazards, environmental pollutants, contaminants of food and water supplies, and components of commercial products. Toxins are known to contribute to cancer and to diseases of the heart, lungs, liver, kidneys, bladder, and the neurological system.

Motor vehicles were the direct cause of death of almost 39,000 people in the United States in 2016 (Xu et al. 2018), which is lot, but at least it was a decline from 2000. This drop is undoubtedly attributable to the improved safety of vehicles, greater attention to making sure that children and adults are properly belted in, and publicity campaigns to reduce drunk driving and texting while driving. However, road deaths (including pedestrians and bicyclists killed by motor vehicles) have become so increasingly common in developing countries that WHO has separated them out as a cause of death, and the World Bank issued a special report in 2013 focusing on the problem of road deaths in sub-Saharan Africa (Marquez and Farrington 2013).

Thus far, we have discussed life expectancy and death rates in some detail, but we have not actually defined those rates for you, because we didn't want to scare you away from a topic that is vitally important to our understanding of what's happening in the world. Nonetheless, in order to evaluate data on health and mortality, it is important to have a background on the rates and measures that are being used.

Measuring Mortality

In measuring mortality, we are attempting to estimate the force of mortality, the extent to which people are unable to live to their biological maximum age (whatever that might be). The ability to measure accurately varies according to the amount of information available. Consequently, the measures of mortality differ considerably in their level of sophistication. The least sophisticated measure of mortality is the crude death rate, which we discuss first.

Crude Death Rate

The crude death rate (CDR) is the total number of deaths in a year divided by the total population. In general form:

$$CDR = \frac{d}{p} \times 1,000$$

where d represents the total number of deaths occurring in a population during any given year, and p is the total midyear population in that year. This measure is called "crude" because it does not take into account the differences by age and sex in the likelihood of death. Nonetheless, it is frequently used because it requires only two pieces of information, total deaths and total population, which often can be estimated with reasonable accuracy even in developing countries where the cost of censuses and vital registration systems may limit the availability of more detailed data.

Differences in the CDR between two countries could be due entirely to differences in the distribution of the population by age, even though the force of mortality is actually the same. Thus, if one population has a high proportion of old people, its CDR will be higher than that of a population with a high proportion of young adults, even if at each age the probabilities of death are identical. For example, in 2018, Mexico had a CDR of 6 per 1,000, about half the 11 per 1,000 in Poland in that year. Yet, in that year a baby born in Poland could expect to live two years longer than one born in Mexico. The difference in CDRs was accounted for by the fact that only 7 percent of Mexico's population was aged 65 and older, whereas the elderly accounted for 17 percent of the Polish population (Population Reference Bureau 2018). In order to account for the differences in dying by age and sex, we can calculate age/sex-specific death rates if the necessary data are available.

Age/Sex-Specific Death Rates

To measure mortality at each age and for each sex, we must have a vital registration system (or a large survey) in which deaths by age and sex are reported, along with census or other data that provide estimates of the number of people in each age and sex category. The age/sex-specific death rate (ASDR or $_nM_x$) is measured as follows:

$$ASDR = \frac{_nd_x}{_nP_x} \times 100,000$$

where $_nd_x$ is the number of deaths in a year among people (measured separately for males and females) of a particular age group and in the age interval x to $x + n$ (typically a five-year age group, where x is the lower limit of the age interval and n represents the width of the interval in years of age) divided by the number of people of that age, $_nP_x$, in the population (again, usually defined as the midyear population). It is typically multiplied by 100,000 to get rid of the decimal point.

In the United States in 2015, the ASDR for males aged 65–69 was 1,812 per 100,000, while for females, it was 1,155 (Murphy et al. 2017). In 1900, the ASDR for males aged 65–69 was 5,000 per 100,000, and for females 5,500. Thus, we can see that over the course of the twentieth century and into the twenty-first century, the death rate for males aged 65–69 dropped by 64 percent, while for females, the decline was 79 percent. To be sure, in 1900, the death rate for females was actually higher than for males (likely for social reasons, not biological ones), whereas by 2015, it was well below that for males.

Age-Adjusted Death Rates

It is possible to compare crude death rates for different years or different regions, but it is analytically more informative if the data are adjusted for differences in the age structure of the populations prior to making those comparisons. The usual method is to calculate age-specific death rates (the ASDRs that we just discussed above) for two different populations and then apply those rates to a standard population. This means that we choose some population (e.g., the current U.S. population) as our "standard," and then we apply death rates from different populations to that standard population to see how the results differ based solely on the death rates. For this reason, this method is also known as standardization. The formula for the age-adjusted death rate (AADR) is as follows:

$$AADR = \left(\sum {}_nS_x *{}_nM_x\right)/\left(\sum {}_nS_x\right)$$

where ${}_nS_x$ is the number of people in this sex and age group of the standard population and ${}_nM_x$ is the ASDR, as calculated in the previous section. We can apply this methodology to compare the CDR in Egypt in 2015 (6 deaths per 1,000 population) with that in the United States in that same year (9 deaths per 1,000 population). Could it be that mortality was really higher in the United States than in Egypt?

Actually, no. To find out why, we use the U.S. population as the standard population and apply the age-specific death rates for Egypt (as estimated by the World Health Organization) to the United States age/sex structure in 2015 (as estimated by the U.S. Census Bureau) to see what the CDR would be in Egypt if its age-sex structure were identical to that of the United States. The result is that the AADR for Egypt in 2015 was 17 deaths per 1,000 population—almost twice the level of the United States.

Life Tables

Although the AADR takes the age differences in mortality into account, it does not provide an intuitively appealing measure of the overall mortality experience of a population. We would like to have a single index that sums that up, and so we turn to a frequently used index called expectation of life at birth, or more generally life expectancy. This measure is derived from a life table, which is part of a whole statistical family of "survival analysis," and even though it is complicated, it is used so widely that we have included a brief discussion of it here for you. You will recall from Chapter 1 that the life table has a long history, having been first used in 1662 by John Graunt to uncover the patterns of mortality in London.

Life expectancy can be summarized as the average age at death for a hypothetical group of people born in a particular year and being subjected to the risks of death experienced by people of all ages in that year. The expectation of life at birth for U.S. females born in 2015 of 81.4 years (see Table 4.3) does not mean that the average age at death in that year for females was 81.4. What it does mean is that if all the females born in the United States in the year 2015 had the same risks of dying throughout their lives as those indicated by the age-specific death rates in 2015, then their average age at death would be 81.4. Of course, some of them would have died in infancy while others might live to be 120, but the age-specific death rates for females in 2015 *implied* an average of 81.4.

One of the limitations of basing the life table on rates for a given year is that in most instances the death rates of older people in that year will almost certainly be higher than will be experienced by today's younger people when they reach that age. This will especially be true for a country that is in the midst of a rapid decline in mortality, but even in a low-mortality country such as the United States in the

Table 4.3   Life Table for Females in the United States, 2015

(1)	(2)	(3)	(4)	(5)	(6)	(7)	(8)	(9)	(10)
					Of 100,000 Hypothetical People Born Alive		Number of Years Lived		Expectation of Life
Age Interval	Number of Females in the Population	Number of Deaths in the Population	Age-Specific Death Rates in the Interval	Probabilities of Death (proportion of persons alive at beginning who die during interval)	Number Alive at Beginning of Interval	Number Dying During Age Interval	In the Age Interval	In This and All Subsequent Age Intervals	Average Number of Years of Life Remaining at Beginning of Age Interval
x to $x + n$	$_nP_x$	$_nD_x$	$_nM_x$	$_nq_x$	l_x	$_nd_x$	$_nL_x$	T_x	e_x
Under 1	1,942,904	10,395	0.005350	0.005326	100,000	533	99,547	8,132,321	81.3
1–4	7,786,776	1,713	0.000220	0.000880	99,467	87	397,660	8,032,774	80.8
5–9	10,028,044	1,103	0.000110	0.000550	99,380	55	496,763	7,635,114	76.8
10–14	10,101,942	1,212	0.000120	0.000600	99,325	60	496,478	7,138,351	71.9
15–19	10,311,036	3,093	0.000300	0.001499	99,266	149	495,957	6,641,873	66.9
20–24	11,071,459	5,314	0.000480	0.002397	99,117	238	494,991	6,145,917	62.0
25–29	11,052,155	7,073	0.000640	0.003195	98,879	316	493,607	5,650,926	57.1
30–34	10,785,909	9,384	0.000870	0.004341	98,563	428	491,748	5,157,319	52.3
35–39	10,201,161	11,731	0.001150	0.005734	98,136	563	489,271	4,665,572	47.5
40–44	10,185,045	16,296	0.001600	0.007968	97,573	777	485,921	4,176,300	42.8
45–49	10,518,915	25,666	0.002440	0.012126	96,795	1,174	481,043	3,690,379	38.1
50–54	11,370,470	43,435	0.003820	0.018919	95,622	1,809	473,586	3,209,336	33.6

55-60	11,210,375	62,890	0.005610	0.027662	93,813	2,595	462,576	2,735,750	29.2
60-64	9,952,697	78,726	0.007910	0.038783	91,218	3,538	447,244	2,273,175	24.9
65-69	8,471,278	98,267	0.011600	0.056365	87,680	4,942	426,044	1,825,931	20.8
70-74	6,186,891	114,829	0.018560	0.088685	82,738	7,338	395,345	1,399,887	16.9
75-79	4,512,927	135,974	0.030130	0.140097	75,400	10,563	350,592	1,004,542	13.3
80-84	3,386,676	174,786	0.051610	0.228560	64,837	14,819	287,136	653,950	10.1
85-89	2,422,101	218,619	0.090260	0.368213	50,018	18,417	204,046	366,814	7.3
90-94	1,261,957	198,203	0.157060	0.563889	31,601	17,819	113,455	162,768	5.2
95-99	366,919	94,529	0.257630	0.783510	13,781	10,798	41,912	49,313	3.6
100+	61,886	24,948	0.403124	1.000000	2,984	2,984	7,401	7,401	2.5

Sources: Calculated by John Weeks: death rates are from the Human Mortality Database. University of California, Berkeley, and Max Planck Institute for Demographic Research (Germany). Available at www.mortality.org or www.humanmortality.de (data downloaded 2018); population data are intercensal estimates from the U.S. Census Bureau, accessed 2018.

Table 4.4 Life Table for Males in the United States, 2015

(1)	(2)	(3)	(4)	(5)	(6)	(7)	(8)	(9)	(10)
	Number of Males in the Population	Number of Deaths in the Population	Age-Specific Death Rates in the Interval	Probabilities of Death (proportion of persons alive at beginning who die during interval)	Of 100,000 Hypothetical People Born Alive:		Number of Years Lived		Expectation of Life
					Number Alive at Beginning of Interval	Number Dying During Age Interval	In the Age Interval	In This and All Subsequent Age Intervals	Average Number of Years of Life Remaining at Beginning of Age Interval
Age Interval x to $x + n$	$_nP_x$	$_nD_x$	$_nM_x$	$_nq_x$	l_x	$_nd_x$	$_nL_x$	T_x	e_x
Under 1	2,035,134	12,964	0.006370	0.006336	100,000	634	99,461	7,640,057	76.4
1–4	8,142,467	2,280	0.000280	0.001119	99,366	111	397,199	7,540,596	75.9
5–9	10,459,132	1,360	0.000130	0.000650	99,255	64	496,115	7,143,397	72.0
10–14	10,520,388	1,788	0.000170	0.000850	99,191	84	495,743	6,647,282	67.0
15–19	10,797,867	7,451	0.000690	0.003444	99,106	341	494,679	6,151,539	62.1
20–24	11,667,854	15,868	0.001360	0.006777	98,765	669	492,152	5,656,860	57.3
25–29	11,409,399	18,141	0.001590	0.007919	98,096	777	488,537	5,164,708	52.6
30–34	10,889,739	19,602	0.001800	0.008960	97,319	872	484,415	4,676,171	48.0
35–39	10,173,424	21,262	0.002090	0.010396	96,447	1,003	479,729	4,191,756	43.5
40–44	10,030,153	26,179	0.002610	0.012965	95,444	1,237	474,128	3,712,027	38.9
45–49	10,334,929	39,273	0.003800	0.018821	94,207	1,773	466,602	3,237,899	34.4

50–54	10,963,847	66,660	0.006080	0.029945	92,434	2,768	455,250	2,771,297	30.0
55–60	10,597,567	97,816	0.009230	0.045109	89,666	4,045	438,218	2,316,047	25.8
60–64	9,117,180	121,441	0.013320	0.064454	85,621	5,519	414,310	1,877,829	21.9
65–69	7,596,190	138,706	0.018260	0.087314	80,103	6,994	383,028	1,463,520	18.3
70–74	5,296,158	145,009	0.027380	0.128130	73,109	9,367	342,124	1,080,492	14.8
75–79	3,610,906	153,572	0.042530	0.192213	63,741	12,252	288,076	738,368	11.6
80–84	2,412,665	167,897	0.069590	0.296386	51,489	15,261	219,295	450,292	8.7
85–89	1,442,244	166,796	0.115650	0.448560	36,229	16,251	140,516	230,997	6.4
90–94	588,978	112,118	0.190360	0.644895	19,978	12,884	67,680	90,481	4.5
95–99	127,988	37,904	0.296150	0.850822	7,094	6,036	20,381	22,801	3.2
100+	15,088	6,600	0.437464	1.000000	1,058	1,058	2,419	2,419	2.3

Sources: Calculated by John Weeks: death rates are from the Human Mortality Database. University of California, Berkeley, and Max Planck Institute for Demographic Research (Germany). Available at www.mortality.org or www.humanmortality.de (data downloaded 2018); population data are intercensal estimates from the U.S. Census Bureau, accessed 2018.

twenty-first century, life tables are assumed to underestimate the actual life expectancy of people at younger ages (Bongaarts and Feeney 2003; Schoen and Canudas-Romo 2005). Life tables are not really projections of future mortality as much as they are useful tools for comparing current levels of mortality.

Life Table Calculations

Life table calculations, as shown in Table 4.3 for U.S. females for 2015 and in Table 4.4 for U.S. males in 2015, begin with a set of ASDRs, and the first step is to find the probabilities of dying during any given age interval. Tables 4.3 and 4.4 are called "abridged life tables" because they group ages into five-year categories, rather than using single years of age. The probability of dying ($_nq_x$) between ages x and $x + n$ is obtained by converting ASDRs ($_nM_x$) to probabilities using the following formula:

$$_nq_x = \frac{(n)(_nM_x)}{1 + (a)(n)(_nM_x)}$$

The one tricky bit in this formula is the value for a which refers to the fraction of the time interval n that was lived by those who died during the interval. For most intervals, the fraction is 0.5, meaning that we assume that people who died lived on average through half of the interval, implying an even distribution of deaths through the interval. This is a reasonable estimate for every age from 5 through 100, regardless of race or sex (Arias, Rostron, and Tejada-Vera 2010). However, at age 1, we typically use a fraction of 0.85; for ages 1–4, we use a fraction of 0.6, and for the oldest age interval, we don't use the formula at all because the probability of death is simply 1.00—death is certain.

In Table 4.3, the age-specific death rates for females in 2015 in the United States are given in column (4). In column (5), they have been converted to probabilities of death from exact age x to exact age $x + n$. Once the probabilities of death have been calculated, the number of deaths that would occur to the hypothetical life table population is calculated. The life table assumes an initial population of 100,000 live births, which is then subjected to the specific mortality schedule. These 100,000 babies represent what is called the **radix** (l_0). During the first year, the number of babies dying is equal to the radix (100,000) times the probability of death. Subtracting the babies who died ($_1d_0$) gives the number of people still alive at the beginning of the next age interval (l_1). These calculations are shown in columns (6) and (7) of Table 4.3 (and are repeated for males in Table 4.4). In general:

$$l_{x+n} = l_x - _nd_x$$

where

$$_nd_x = (_nq_x)(l_x)$$

The next two columns that lead to the calculation of life expectancy are related to the concept of number of years lived. During the 5-year period, for example, between the 5th and the 10th birthdays, each person lives 5 years, assuming none of them dies. If there were 99,325 girls sharing their 10th birthdays [see column (6) of Table 4.3], and none of them died over the next 5 years, then they all would have lived a total of $5 \times 99,325 = 496,625$ years between their 10th and 15th birthdays. Of course, some girls died after their 10th but before their 15th birthday, so only those years that were lived prior to dying would be added in. This is why the number of years lived among girls between ages 10–14 is slightly less—496,478. You can appreciate that the lower the death rates, the more people there are who will survive through an entire age interval and thus the greater the number of years lived will be. The number of years lived $(_nL_x)$ can be estimated as follows:

$$_nL_x = n(l_x - a_nd_x)$$

The value of a is the same value described above. Note, however, that this formula will not work for the oldest, open-age interval (100+ in Tables 4.3 and 4.4) because there are no survivors at the end of that age interval, and the table provides no information about how many years each person will live before finally dying. The number of years lived in this group is estimated by dividing the number of survivors to that oldest age (l_{100}) by the death rate at the oldest age (M_{100}):

$$L_{100+} = \frac{l_{100}}{M_{100}}$$

The results of these calculations are shown in column (8) of Tables 4.3 and 4.4. The years lived are then added up, cumulating from the oldest to the youngest ages. These calculations are shown in column (9) and represent T_x, the total number of years lived in a given age interval and all older age intervals. At the oldest age (100+), T_x is just equal to $_nL_x$. But at each successively younger age (e.g., 95–99), T_x is equal to T_x at all older ages (e.g., 100+, which is T_{100}) plus the number of person-years lived between ages x and $x + n$ (e.g., between ages 95 and 99, which is $_5L_{95}$). Thus, at any given age:

$$T_x = T_{x+n} + {_nL_x}$$

The final calculation is the expectation of life (e_x), or average remaining lifetime. It is the total years remaining to be lived at exact age x and is found by dividing T_x by the number of people alive at that exact age (l_x):

$$e_x = \frac{T_x}{l_x}$$

Thus, for U.S. females in 2015, the expectation of life at birth (e_0) was $8,132,321/100,000 = 81.3$, whereas at age 25, a female could expect to live an additional 57.1 years (implying an age at death of 82.1). For males (Table 4.4), the comparable numbers are a life expectancy at birth of 76.4 and at age 25 an additional 52.6 years (implying an age at death of 77.6). Although it has required some work, we now have a sophisticated single index that summarizes the level of mortality prevailing in a given population at a particular time.

Disability-Adjusted Life Years

If increasing life expectancy meant simply that we spent more years at the end of our life being bedridden and/or mentally incompetent, few people would be interested in pursuing that goal. In the early 1990s, the World Bank initiated a joint project between the World Health Organization and the Harvard School of Public Health (with subsequent funding from the Bill and Melinda Gates Foundation and now led by a consortium headquartered at the Institute for Health Metrics and Evaluation at the University of Washington) designed to measure this aspect of health and mortality. The result has been the very influential Global Burden of Disease project, which looks at the economic downside of poor health (or, alternatively, the economic upside of good health) by asking how many years of productivity in a society are lost to its members because of poor health (Murray and Lopez 1996; Salomon et al. 2012; Dicker, Murray, and Gakidou 2018). This is a powerful argument that has been made strongly by labor unions and other groups that have argued for many years that if governments and/or employers will pay for health care, they will more than get their money back in increased productivity—healthy workers do more work than sick ones. It is the flip side of the idea that a high standard of living promotes good health; it suggests that good health promotes a high standard of living. It is likely that both sides of the argument are correct.

The important statistical index derived from the Global Burden of Disease project is the disability-adjusted life year (DALY). "The DALY is a health gap measure that extends the concept of potential years of life lost due to premature death to include equivalent years of healthy life lost by virtue of individuals being in states of poor health or disability. One DALY can be thought of as one lost year of healthy life and the burden of disease as a measure of the gap between current health status and an ideal situation where everyone lives into old age free from disease and disability" (Lopez et al. 2006:1).

How close we are to the latter situation can then be calculated for the more positive side of things to show what the healthy life expectancy (HALE) is in each country. Olshansky (2018) suggests that this can shift our focus from life span to healthspan. For example, we just calculated that in 2015 the life expectancy at birth for females in the United States was 81.3 (see Table 4.3). However, WHO calculates a HALE of 70.1, suggesting an 11.2-year gap between the two. For women in the United States who had reached 60 in 2015, the expected number of years remaining was 24.9 (see Table 4.3), whereas the HALE was 18.9—a difference of only 6.0 years. This is consistent with the idea that less healthy younger people are likely to die younger, but it also implies that at age 60, the average woman can expect to experience six years of disability before she dies.

A complementary way of looking at the issue is to compare your "biological" age with your "chronological" age. This is the idea underlying the question: Is 60 the new 50? Using data from the two most recent waves of the National

Health and Examination Survey, conducted by the U.S. National Center for Health Statistics, Eileen Crimmins and her colleagues found that the biological age of at least some Americans has, in fact, been declining (Levine and Crimmins 2018). That's a good thing because it means that a 60-year-old may now have the health functioning of a person 10 years younger. The reasons they found for the declines are highly reminiscent of the "prescriptions" for long life discussed earlier in this chapter: less smoking, not being obese, and taking your medications. These changes in healthspan and life span, or biological and chronological aging, have important implications for societies, and we will discuss those in greater detail in Chapter 8.

Health and Mortality Inequalities

Up to this point, we have emphasized the differences in health and mortality by age and sex. There are, however, a lot of other inequalities that exist in the world. The regional and country-level differences in mortality that have been revealed repeatedly in the chapter are clear reminders that cultural and economic features of societies have a major impact on human well-being. Our health is very dependent on massive infrastructure developments that we have discussed previously in this chapter. Regions in the world vary considerably in their access to these resources, and within the same regions and countries some people are more advantaged than others in these respects. Individual lifestyle choices that can affect both a person's healthspan and life span also make a significant difference.

Educational and Socioeconomic Differentials in Mortality

One of the strongest predictors of all demographic phenomena is education. It influences the number of children you will likely have, if and where you will migrate, and when and from what you might die. Indeed, your educational level may well influence the health levels of other family members, not just your own (Zimmer et al. 2007). Death data for the United States in 2015 show that the AADR for people with at least some college was one-third the level of people whose educational level was high school or less (Murphy et al. 2017). This is consistent with an earlier pioneering study by Kitagawa and Hauser (1973), in which they found that a White male in 1960 with an eighth grade education had a 6 percent chance of dying between the ages of 25 and 45, whereas for a college graduate the probability was only half as high. A number of subsequent studies in the United States and elsewhere confirm this finding that education is good for your health (Miech et al. 2011).

Closely associated with education in all societies is socioeconomic status, as we discuss in Chapter 9. In general, higher levels of education lead to higher levels of occupation and income, all of which define socioeconomic status (SES). Of course, growing up in a higher-SES family also increases the likelihood of reaching the higher levels of education. The linkages to health and mortality are pretty obvious: education to know the means whereby disease and occupational risks can be minimized, and income to buy protection against and cures for diseases.

Differences in mortality by social status are among the most pervasive inequalities in modern society, and the connection between income and health has been noticeable for a long time. In the nineteenth century, for example, Karl Marx attributed the higher death rate in the working classes to the evils of capitalism, and argued that mortality differentials would disappear in a socialist society. That may have been overly optimistic, but data do clearly suggest that by nearly every index of status, the higher your position in society, the longer you are likely to live. In England, researchers followed a group of 12,000 civil servants in London who were first interviewed in 1967–69, when they were aged 40 to 64. They were tracked for the next 10 years, and it was clear that even after adjusting for age and sex, the higher the pay grade, the lower the death rate. Furthermore, within each pay grade, those who owned a car (a more significant index of status in England than in the United States) had lower death rates than those without a car (Smith, Shipley, and Rose 1990). An update of this study revealed that even as life expectancy improved in the United Kingdom, the social class differences remained very stable (Hattersly 2005). The importance of these studies is that they relate to a country that has a highly egalitarian national health service. Even so, equal access to health services does not necessarily lead to equal health outcomes.

Inequalities by Race and Ethnicity

In most societies in which more than one racial or ethnic group exists, one group tends to dominate the others. This generally leads to social and economic disadvantages for the subordinate groups, and such disadvantages frequently result in lower life expectancies for the racial or ethnic minority group members. Some of the disadvantages are the obvious ones in which prejudice and discrimination lead to lower levels of education, occupation, and income, and thus to higher death rates. A large body of evidence suggests that there is a psychosocial component to health and mortality, as well, causing marginalized peoples in societies to have lower life expectancies than you might otherwise expect (Ross and Wu 1995; Barr 2008).

If we combine data for education and race, the result is a striking differential in life expectancy in the United States, as described by Olshansky and his collaborators (Olshansky et al. 2012:1803):

> We found that in 2008 US adult men and women with fewer than twelve years of education had life expectancies not much better than those of all adults in the 1950s and 1960s. When race and education are combined, the disparity is even more striking. In 2008 White US men and women with 16 years or more of schooling had life expectancies far greater than black Americans with fewer than 12 years of education—14.2 years more for White men than black men, and 10.3 years more for White women than black women.

This difference in life expectancy translates into a comparison between someone living in a high-income country (where life expectancy is 80 years) and someone living in a low-middle-income country (where life expectancy is 66 years). One person is living (in life-expectancy terms) in the United States, while the other is living, metaphorically, in Pakistan.

Even if we ignore the educational differences, U.S. data for 2015 from the National Center for Health Statistics show that at every age up to 85, African American mortality rates are significantly higher than for the non-Hispanic White population (Murphy et al. 2017). In 1900, African Americans in the United States had a life expectancy that was 15.6 years less than for Whites. Though that differential had been reduced to 3.5 years by 2015, that is still a larger gap than exists, for example, between the United States as a whole and the population of Mexico.

African Americans have higher risks of death from every major cause of death than do Whites. The only exception is deaths from Alzheimer's, for which non-Hispanic Whites have the higher rate. Since heart disease and cancer are the most common causes of death in the United States, the higher rates among African Americans are especially important (Murphy et al. 2017). There is also a spatial component because African Americans tend to have the highest levels of residential segregation of any group in the United States (which we discuss more in Chapter 7), and this has been shown to affect health levels negatively (Williams, Neighbors, and Jackson 2003; Pearlman et al. 2006). Wrapped into these disadvantages are behaviors that are specifically high risk. Age-adjusted death rates from homicides, especially from firearms, are an astonishing six times higher for Blacks than for Whites in the United States. Black males also are more likely to smoke than Whites and this may account for as much as 20 percent of the difference in Black-White mortality in the United States (Ho and Elo 2013).

If we look at what is now the largest ethnic minority in the United States—Hispanics—we find that the income and social status gap has narrowed between them and "Anglos" (non-Hispanic Whites). As this happened, differences in death rates between the groups disappeared and more recently have actually crossed over, so that AADRs among both males and females are lower for Hispanics in the United States than for non-Hispanic Whites (Murphy et al. 2017). That is impressive enough, but even if Hispanic mortality were simply the same as that for non-Hispanic Whites, it still highlights the tremendous disparity between Blacks and others in the United States.

Among all racial/ethnic groups in the United States, the highest death rates are almost certainly found among American Indians. There is, to be sure, a bit of uncertainty. The U.S. National Center for Vital Statistics does not prepare life tables for American Indians because of concern over misclassification of race/ethnicity on the vital statistics forms (Murphy et al. 2017; Arias, Heron, and Xu 2017). However, researchers in Portland and Seattle have recently used record-linkage techniques in order to create more accurate estimates of life expectancy and they conclude that life expectancy at birth and throughout the life span is several years less for American Indians and Alaska Natives (AI/ANs) than for non-Hispanic Whites: "As a group, AI/ANs have a profoundly different experience of morbidity and mortality throughout their lives than the general population: rates of diabetes, injuries, and cancer mortality are substantially higher" (Dankovchick et al. 2015:71). These populations tend to be rural, and levels of education and income are generally below average, all of which add to the probability of lower-than-average levels of health.

Marital Status and Mortality

It has long been observed that married people tend to live longer than unmarried people. This is true not only in the United States, but in other countries as well (Hu and Goldman 1990; Kaplan and Kronick 2006). A long-standing explanation for this phenomenon is that marriage is selective of healthy people; that is, people who are in ill health may have both a lower chance of marrying and a higher risk of death. At least some of the difference in mortality by marital status is certainly due to this.

Another explanation is that marriage is good for your health: protective, not just selective. Marriage may be associated with social and psychological support that keeps men, in particular, from committing suicide or from abusing themselves with alcohol and cigarettes, and which also provides a more nurturing environment when a person is ill. It is probably also protective in economic terms. Married women are healthier than unmarried women partly because they have higher incomes (as we discuss in Chapter 9). The flip side of marriage being good for you is that the ending of a marriage elevates the risk of death. In the United States, people who are currently divorced have the same age-adjusted death rate as people who never married, which is nearly twice the death rate of people who are currently married (Murphy et al. 2107). The increasing trends toward later marriage and higher levels of cohabitation before and after marriage complicate the relationship between marital status and mortality and is an area that will require new research if we are to fully understand what to expect in the future (Robards et al. 2012).

Urban and Rural Differentials

Until the twentieth century, cities were deadly places in which to live compared to the countryside. Mortality levels were invariably higher there than in surrounding areas since the crowding of people into small spaces, along with poor sanitation and contact with travelers who might be carrying disease, helped maintain fairly high levels of communicable diseases. For example, life expectancy in England in 1841 was 40 years for males and 42 years for females, but in London it was five years less than that (Landers 1993). In Liverpool, the port city for the burgeoning coal regions of Manchester, life expectancy was only 25 years for males and 27 years for females. In probability terms, a female child born in the city of Liverpool in 1841 had less than a 25 percent chance of living to her 55th birthday, while a rural female had nearly a 50 percent chance of surviving to age 55. Sanitation in Liverpool at that time was atrociously bad. G. H. Pumphrey (1940:141) notes that "pits and deep open channels, from which solid material (human wastes) had to be cleared periodically, often ran the whole length of streets. From June to October, cesspools were never emptied, for it was found that any disturbance was inevitably followed by an outbreak of disease." Longitudinal data for Paris likewise show that between 1880 and 1914, mortality in different neighborhoods was closely related to the availability of sewers (Kesztenbaum and Rosenthal 2017).

In general, we can conclude that the early differences in urban and rural mortality were due less to favorable conditions in the countryside than to decidedly unfavorable conditions in the cities (Alter and Oris 2005). Over time, however, medical advances and environmental improvements have benefited the urban population more than the rural, leading to the current situation of the worst mortality conditions existing in poor rural areas and the best mortality conditions existing in the richest urban areas (Murray, Kulkarni, and Ezzati 2006). As the world continues to urbanize (see Chapter 7), a greater fraction of the population in each country will be in closer contact with systems of prevention and cure. At the same time, the sprawling slums of many third world cities blur the health distinction between urban and rural and may produce their own unhealthy environments (Montgomery and Hewett 2005; Weeks, Hill, and Stoler 2013). For example, although child mortality rates in a city like Accra, the capital of Ghana, are lower than in rural areas, there are still important differences from one part of the city to another (Jankowska, Benza, and Weeks 2013).

Neighborhood Differences in Mortality

It is not just cities of developing countries where we might find neighborhood differences in mortality. This also turns out to be true in the United States, as we know from a recently developed set of neighborhood-level estimates of life expectancy at birth in the United States. In 2018, the U.S. National Center for Health Statistics collaborated with the Robert Wood Johnson Foundation and the National Association for Public Health Statistics and Information Systems (NAPHSIS) to create this unique dataset (Arias et al. 2018). They define a "neighborhood" as being the equivalent of a census tract which, as we noted in Chapter 2, is a small, relatively permanent subdivision of a county or equivalent entity, having a population size between 1,200 and 8,000, with an optimum size of 4,000 people. The Census Bureau works with local governments to define these boundaries, so they are likely to be similar to how you would define the neighborhood if you lived there. Given the discussion above about the differences in health and mortality levels by education and socioeconomic levels, by race/ethnicity, and by a key social variable such as marital status, and knowing that "birds of a feather tend to flock together" (i.e., the kind of residential clustering that we will discuss in Chapter 7), you can easily imagine that neighborhoods might differ in their estimated life expectancy at birth. You would be right.

Figure 4.7 shows a map of life expectancy at birth for each of San Diego County's 628 census tracts/neighborhoods using the data described above. Throughout this Southern California county, the life expectancy ranges from a low of 67.5 (comparable to Kenya) to a high of 93.4 (higher even than Japan!). As expected, there is a strong statistical association between life expectancy and income, education, and minority-group status. Two areas on the map help illustrate these relationships. Near the middle of the county is area "A," in which you see a large, residential upper-middle-class exurban area with life expectancy in the highest category. Just to the east of it is a large area with one of the lowest levels of life expectancy in the county. That area is an American Indian reservation where, despite income from a gambling casino, the average household income is still quite low and a relatively small percentage of adults are college graduates. Area "B" represents a string of older, more densely settled neighborhoods (which is why the census tracts are

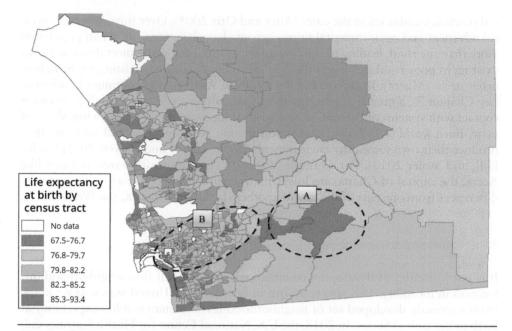

Figure 4.7   Life Expectancy at Birth, by Census Tract: San Diego County, 2010–2015

Source: Prepared by John Weeks from National Center for Health Statistics life expectancy data matched to Census Bureau census tract maps.

smaller in size). These neighborhoods range from low to fairly high life expectancy, explained again by the combination of income, education, and minority-group status. In particular, neighborhoods with high percentages of immigrants (San Diego County has many refugees from the Democratic Republic of the Congo and Iraq, as well as many immigrants from Mexico and elsewhere in Latin America) tend to have lower life expectancy. These demographic characteristics are highly correlated with health and mortality.

Summary and Conclusion

The control of disease has vastly improved the human condition and has, in the process, revolutionized life. Yet there are still wide variations between nations with respect to both the probabilities of dying and the causes of death. The differences between nations exist because countries are at different stages of the health and mortality transition, the shift from high mortality (largely from infectious diseases, with most deaths occurring at young ages) to low mortality (with most deaths occurring at older ages and largely caused by degenerative diseases). The different timing is due to a complex combination of political, economic, and cultural factors. There are many routes to low mortality, some of them involving genuine bumps in the road such as the HIV/AIDS pandemic in sub-Saharan Africa over the past few decades.

In general, females have a survival advantage over males at every age in most of the world, and a gender gap in mortality that favors women seems to be a feature of the health and mortality transition. We have been most successful at controlling communicable diseases, which are largely dealt with through public health measures, but medical technology has become increasingly good at limiting disability and postponing death from noncommunicable diseases, as well. This has helped to slow down the death rates at the older ages. It is ironic, however, that our very success at creating a life that is relatively free of communicable disease and that is built on a secure food supply has produced in its wake a transition in our pattern of nutrition that threatens to increase our risk of noncommunicable disease.

Differences in mortality within a society tend to be due to social status inequalities. As status and prestige (indexed especially by education, occupation, income, and wealth) go up, death rates go down. The social and economic disadvantages felt by minority groups, such as among Blacks in the United States, often lead to lower life expectancies. Marital status is also an important variable, with married people tending to live longer than unmarried people.

Although mortality rates are low in the more developed nations and are declining in most less developed nations, diseases that can kill us still exist if we relax our vigilance. The recent explosion of Ebola and the Zika virus onto the world stage was a reminder of that, as has been the emergence of new strains of influenza. Worldwide efforts have been put into malaria and tuberculosis control because those deadly diseases have been around forever and seem constantly to be on the verge of a resurgence in many regions of the world. Death control cannot be achieved and then taken for granted, for as Hans Zinsser (1935:13) so aptly put it:

> However secure and well-regulated civilized life may become, bacteria, protozoa, viruses, infected fleas, lice, ticks, mosquitoes, and bedbugs will always lurk in the shadows ready to pounce when neglect, poverty, famine, or war lets down the defenses. And even in normal times they prey on the weak, the very young, and the very old, living along with us, in mysterious obscurity waiting for opportunities.

If the thought of those lurking diseases scares you to death, then perhaps that too is part of the health and mortality transition (just a joke!). Also lurking around the corner is Chapter 5, in which we examine fertility concepts, measurements, and trends.

Main Points

1. The changes over time in death rates and life expectancy are captured by the perspective of the health and mortality transition.

2. Significant widespread improvements in the probability of survival date back only to the nineteenth century and have been especially impressive since the end of World War II. The drop in mortality, of course, precipitated the massive growth in the size of the human population.

3. The role played by public health preventive measures in bringing down death rates is exemplified by the saying a century ago that the amount of soap used could be taken as an index of the degree of civilization of a people.

4. World War II was a turning point in the transition because it led to new medicines and to a transfer of public health and medical technology all over the world, creating rapid declines in the death rate.

5. The things that can kill us are broadly categorized as communicable diseases, noncommunicable conditions, and injuries, whereas the most important "real" cause of death in the United States (and increasingly in the world as a whole) is the use of tobacco.

6. Life span refers to the oldest age to which members of a species can survive, whereas longevity is the ability to resist death from year to year, and healthspan refers to the number of healthy years you can expect to live, regardless of when you die.

7. Although biological factors affect each individual's chance of survival, social factors are also important overall determinants of longevity.

8. Among the important biological determinants of death are age and sex, with the very young and the very old being at greatest risk, and with males generally having higher death rates than females.

9. Mortality is measured with tools such as the crude death rate, the age/sex-specific death rate, the age-adjusted death rate, life expectancy, and disability-adjusted life years.

10. Living in a city used to verge on being a form of latent suicide, but now cities tend to have lower death rates than rural areas, and richer, better-educated people live longer than poorer, less-well-educated people on average, creating pockets of high- and low-mortality neighborhoods throughout the United States.

Questions for Review

1. Discuss how different the world of the twenty-first century would be if (1) death rates had not declined as they did in the first part of the twentieth century; and (2) if World War II had not happened.

2. What are the ways in which society is going to have to change in order to ward off the potentially fatal side effects of the nutrition transition?

3. What are the possible explanations for the apparent biological regularity that women live longer than men? How is the social world affected by this difference?

4. Although causes of death are neatly categorized, we know that there are complex reasons for many deaths. Discuss some of those complexities and what they reveal about the many different routes to low mortality for a population as a whole.

5. What changes do you think would have to be made in American society to eliminate the social and economic differences in disease and mortality that we currently observe? Would universal health coverage make a difference? Why or why not?

CHAPTER 5
The Fertility Transition

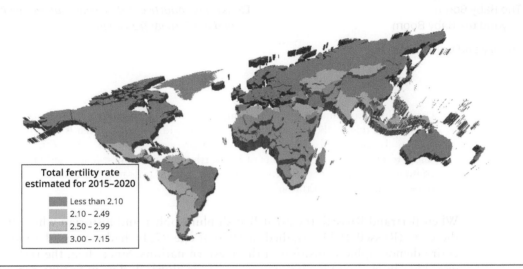

Figure 5.1   Total Fertility Rates Estimated for 2015–2020

Source: Prepared by John R. Weeks; adapted from data in United Nations, Department of Economic and Social Affairs, Population Division (2017). World Population Prospects: The 2017 Revision; data represent the medium variant projections for 2015–2020.

What Is the Fertility Transition?

How High Could Fertility Levels Be?
The Biological Component
The Social Component

Why Was Fertility High for Most of Human History?
Need to Replenish Society
Children as Security and Labor

The Preconditions for a Decline in Fertility

Ideational Changes That Must Take Place

Motivations for Lower Fertility Levels
The Supply-Demand Framework
The Innovation-Diffusion and "Cultural" Perspective

How Can Fertility Be Controlled?
Proximate Determinants of Fertility

Proportion Married—Limiting Exposure to Intercourse
Use of Contraceptives
Induced Abortion
Involuntary Infecundity from Breastfeeding
The Relative Importance of the Proximate Determinants

How Do We Measure Changes in Fertility?
Period Measures of Fertility
Cohort Measures of Fertility
Fertility Intentions

How Is the Fertility Transition Accomplished?

Geographic Variability in the Fertility Transition

Case Studies in the Fertility Transition
United Kingdom and Other European Nations
Historical Background
Current Fertility Patterns

China
The United States
   Historical Background
   The Baby Boom
   Beyond the Baby Boom

Summary and Conclusion

Main Points

Questions for Review

ESSAY: *Reproductive Rights, Reproductive Health, and the Fertility Transition*

> I am inclined to think that the most important of Western values is the habit of a low birth rate. If this can be spread throughout the world, the rest of what is good in Western life can also be spread. There can be not only prosperity, but peace. But if the West continues to monopolize the benefits of low birth rate(s), war, pestilence, and famine must continue, and our brief emergence from those ancient evils must be swallowed in a new flood of ignorance, destitution and war.

When Bertrand Russell, the great British philosopher and historian whose words these are (Russell 1951:49), died in 1970 at age 97, he had witnessed almost the entire demographic transition in the Western nations. Since then, the rest of the world has been absorbing his message, and the global decline in fertility represents a revolution in the control of human reproduction matched only by the unprecedented progress in postponing death discussed in the previous chapter.

What Is the Fertility Transition?

The fertility transition is the shift from high fertility, characterized by only minimal individual deliberate control, to low—perhaps very low—fertility, which is entirely under a woman's (or more generally a couple's) control. The phenomenon has been summarized by Cynthia Lloyd and Serguey Ivanov (1988) as the shift from "family building by fate" to "family building by design." The transition almost always involves a delay in childbearing to older ages (at least beyond the teen years) and typically an earlier end to childbearing. This process helps to free women and men alike from the bondage of unwanted parenthood and helps to time and space those children who are desired, which has the advantageous side effect of improving the health of mothers and their children.

To control fertility does not necessarily mean to limit it, yet almost everywhere you go in the world, the two concepts are nearly synonymous. This suggests, of course, that as mortality declines and the survival of children and their parents is assured, people generally want smaller families, and the wider the range of means available to accomplish that goal, the greater the chance of success.

The central questions of the fertility transition are why, when, and how does fertility decline from high to low levels? To answer them, we have to start with an understanding of why fertility has been high for all the previous millennia of human history and then proceed to explanations for its decline. In that process, we will also need to define some concepts related to human reproduction and review the ways in which we measure it so that we can talk more intelligently about trends in fertility over time and across the globe.

How High Could Fertility Levels Be?

When demographers speak of fertility, we are referring to the number of children born to women. This can be confusing, because physicians routinely use the term to refer to reproductive *potential*—how fertile a woman is. But in population studies fertility means the actual reproductive *performance* of women or men—how many children have they produced? Note that although our concern lies primarily with the total impact of childbearing on a society, we must recognize that the birth rate is actually the accumulation of millions of individual decisions to have or not have children. Thus, when we refer to a "high-fertility society," we are referring to a population in which most couples make the decision to have several children, whereas a "low-fertility society" is one in which most couples have few children. Naturally, some women in high-fertility societies have few children, and vice versa.

Fertility, like mortality, is composed of two parts, one biological and one social. The biological component refers to the capacity to reproduce, and though obviously a necessary condition for parenthood, it is not sufficient. Whether children will actually be born and, if so, how many, is largely a result of the social environment in which people live.

The Biological Component

The physical ability to reproduce is usually called fecundity by demographers. A fecund person can produce children; an infecund (sterile) person cannot. However, since people are rarely tested in the laboratory to determine their level of fecundity, most estimates of fecundity are actually based on levels of fertility (by which we mean the number of children a person has actually produced). Couples who have tried unsuccessfully for at least 12 months to conceive a child are usually called "infertile" by physicians (demographers would say "infecund"). The 2011–2015 round of the National Survey of Family Growth (NSFG) in the United States showed that 6.7 percent of American couples (where the wife was aged 15 to 44) are infecund/infertile by that criterion (Martinez, Daniels, and Febo-Vazquez 2018)—a decline from 8.5 in 1982 (Chandra, Copen, and Stephen 2013).

For most people, fecundity is not an all-or-none proposition and varies according to age. Among women it usually increases from menarche (the onset of menstruation, which usually occurs in the early teens), peaks in the twenties, and then declines to menopause (the end of menstruation). Male fecundity increases from puberty to young adulthood, and then gradually declines, though men are generally fecund to a much older age than are women.

At the individual level, very young girls occasionally become mothers. In 2017, there were 1,917 babies born to mothers under 15 years of age in the United States (Martin et al. 2018). Fortunately, that was a big drop from more than 8,000 in 2000 (Mathews and Hamilton 2018). The biggest decline was among non-Hispanic Black girls. At the other end of the age continuum, there were 840 mothers in 2017 whose age was listed as 50–54, which was higher than the 255 in 2000. It is possible but very rare for a woman to conceive naturally into her 50s. However, since the 1990s, hormone treatment of postmenopausal women suggests that a woman of almost any age might be able to bear a child by implantation of an embryo created from a donated egg impregnated with sperm, and this has been done successfully for several women over the age of 50, including a 66-year-old unmarried Spanish woman, who was successfully impregnated in 2006 at a clinic in Los Angeles, and gave birth to twins in Spain before dying of cancer shortly thereafter (Tremlett and Walker 2009).

Guinness World Records claims that the world's verified most prolific mother was a Russian woman in the eighteenth century who gave birth to 69 children. She actually had "only" 27 pregnancies, but experienced several multiple births (Guinness World Records 2018). Putting the extremes of individual variation aside, however, and assuming that most couples are normally fecund, how many babies could be born to women in a population that uses no method of fertility control? If we assume that an average woman can bear a child during a 35-year span between the ages of 15 and 49, that each pregnancy lasts a little less than nine months (accounting for some pregnancy losses such as miscarriages), and that in the absence of fertility limitation there would be an average of about 18 months between the end of one pregnancy and the beginning of the next, then the average woman could bear a child every 2.2 years, for a potential total of 16 children per woman (Bongaarts 1978). This can be thought of as the maximum level of reproduction for an entire group of people.

No known society has ever averaged as many as 16 births per woman, however, and there are biological reasons why such high fertility is unlikely. For one thing, pregnancy is dangerous (in the previous chapter, we noted the high rates of maternal mortality in many parts of the world), and many women in the real world would die before (if not while) delivering their sixteenth child, assuming they had not died from any other disease in a high-mortality society. Another problem with the calculation is the assumption that all couples are "normally" fecund. The principal control a woman has over her fecundity is to provide herself with a good diet and physical care. Without such good care, of course, the result will probably be lower fertility.

The role of nutrition in the ability of a woman to conceive a child was first researched by Rose Frisch (1978, 2002). Her analysis suggested that a certain amount of fat must be stored as energy before menstruation and ovulation can occur on a regular basis. Thus, if a woman's level of nutrition is too low to permit fat accumulation, she may experience amenorrhea (a temporary absence or suppression of menstruation) and/or anovulatory cycles, in which no egg is released. For younger women, the onset of puberty may be delayed until an undernourished girl reaches a certain critical weight (Komlos 1989). Conversely, improved nutrition has been linked to girls beginning menstruation at earlier ages than their less well-fed counterparts. Increased levels of fat among girls in the United States appear to have stimulated hormonal change and induced puberty in an increasing proportion of preteens.

Frisch (2002) calculated that in 1800 the average age at menarche in the United States was 16.0, dropping to 14.7 by 1880, and to 12.7 in the post–World War II era. The nutrition transition, discussed in the previous chapter, thus has had the effect of making it easier for younger women to conceive, even though it is paradoxically associated with the lower mortality that would reduce the need for women to bear children at a young age.

Since the maximum level of fertility described above would require modern levels of health and nutrition, it is not the level that we would expect to find in premodern societies. Therefore, a slightly different concept, natural fertility, has historically been defined as the level of reproduction that exists in the absence of deliberate fertility control (Henry 1961; Coale and Trussell 1974). This seems to be closer to an average of six or seven live births per woman. This is clearly lower than the maximum possible level of fertility, and it may be that the secret of human success lies in the very fact that as a species we have not actually been content to let nature take its course (Potts and Short 1999); that rather than there being some "natural" level of fertility, humans have always tried to exercise some control over reproduction. The clear implication is that the social component of human reproductive behavior is at least as important as the biological capacity to reproduce.

The Social Component

Opportunities and motivations for childbearing vary considerably from one social environment to another, and the result is great variability in the average number of children born to women over time and space. As we mentioned in Chapter 1, hunter-gatherer societies may have been motivated to space children several years apart, thus keeping fertility lower than it might otherwise have been. It would be difficult to be pregnant, have other small children, and be on the move. It may also have been, of course, that women in hunter-gatherer societies had sufficiently little body fat that their risk of conception was low enough to provide adequate spacing between children. Agricultural societies provide an environment in which more children may be advantageous, and where improved nutrition might well have improved a woman's chances of becoming pregnant more often. Moving forward in time, the low mortality and high standard of living of rich modern urban societies reduce the demand for children well below anything previously imagined in human existence (and creating the basis for the Second Demographic Transition, which we discussed in Chapter 3). Yet paradoxically the biological capacity to reproduce is probably the highest it has ever been in human history because people are healthier than they have ever been before.

It was the combination of modern medical science and a prosperous agricultural community that produced the world's most famous high-fertility group. The Hutterites are an Anabaptist (Christians who believe in adult baptism) religious group who live in agrarian communes in the northern Plains states of the United States and the western provinces of Canada. In the late nineteenth century, about 400 Hutterites migrated to the United States from Russia, having originally fled there from Eastern Europe (Kephart 1982), and recent estimates suggest that there are now more than 100 times that many—46,000 (Evans and Peller 2015). In the 1930s, the average Hutterite woman who survived her reproductive years could expect to have given birth to at least 11 children (Eaton and Mayer 1954). The secret to high Hutterite fertility has been a fairly early age at marriage, a good diet, good medical care, and a passion to follow the biblical prescription to "be fruitful and multiply." That prescription is best filled by engaging regularly in sexual intercourse without using contraception or abortion, believing as they do that any form of birth control is a sin.

Each Hutterite farming colony typically grows to a size of about 130 people. Then, in a manner reminiscent of Plato's *Republic,* the division of labor becomes unwieldy and part of the colony branches off to form a new group. Branching requires that additional land be purchased to establish the new colony, and over time the gobbling up of vacant land by Hutterites has caused considerable alarm, especially in Canada, where the majority of Hutterites now live. Laws were passed in Canada—although subsequently repealed—restricting the Hutterites' ability to buy land and, at the same time, new technological changes in farming methods (which the Hutterites tend to keep up with) have changed the pattern of work in the colonies. These social dynamics have apparently had the effect of raising Hutterite women's average age at marriage by as many as four or five years. Furthermore, access to modern health care has led many women at the other end of their reproductive years to agree to sterilization for "health reasons" (Peter 1987; White 2002). Overall fertility levels among Hutterites in 1980 were only half what they had been in 1930 (Nonaka, Miura, and Peter 1994), and this downward trend continued into the twenty-first century as Hutterites confronted the ongoing scarcity of new land for the expansion of their colonies, even as they dealt with external and internal cultural changes (White 2002). As a result, Hutterite women are now estimated to be having fewer than four children each (Evans and Peller 2015).

In Figure 5.2, you can see the fertility rates by age that produced the Hutterites' 11 children per woman several decades ago (from Robinson 1986). For comparison, the figure also offers you the age pattern of fertility for women as estimated for 2015–2020 by the United Nations Population Division for Niger (the world's highest fertility level as of 2015–2020 at 7.2 children per woman—check out Figure 5.1 again, where it clearly stands out), Mexico (2.1 children per woman), the United States (1.9 children per woman), and Canada (1.6 children per woman). The overall pattern is that in the higher fertility societies women in their 20s have the highest birth rates, and it drops off after that. However, in both Canada and the United States, where fertility is below replacement level, women delay their childbearing to the late 20s and early 30s, as we will discuss later in the chapter.

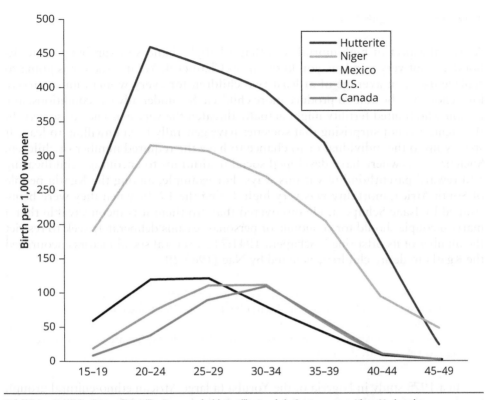

Figure 5.2 Hutterite "Natural" Fertility Compared with Fertility Levels in Contemporary Niger, Mexico, the United States, and Canada

Sources: Prepared by John R. Weeks; Hutterite data are from Robinson (1986), Table 6, and the data for Niger, Canada, Mexico, and the United States are from United Nations Population Division (2017).

Why Was Fertility High for Most of Human History?

You will recall that for the first 99 percent of human history, mortality was very high. Therefore, only those societies with sufficiently high fertility managed to survive over the years. There may have been lower-fertility societies in the past that we know nothing about because they did not produce enough offspring to make the grade. Societies that did survive probably did not take for granted that people would have enough children to keep the population going. They instituted multiple inducements—pronatalist pressures—to encourage the appropriate level of reproduction: high enough to maintain society, but not so high as to threaten its existence. It is the undoing of those social pressures to have children, and the replacing of them with different kinds of pressures to keep fertility low, that we have to understand if we are to explain the fertility transition. So, let us now discuss the general idea of the need to replenish society and then review the major inducements used by high-mortality societies, including the value of children as security and labor and the desire for sons, especially as it relates to the lower status of women in traditional societies.

Need to Replenish Society

A crucial aspect of high mortality is that a baby's chances of surviving to adulthood are not very good, as you know from Chapter 4. Yet if a society is going to replace itself, an average of at least two children for every woman must survive long enough to be able to produce more children. So, under adverse conditions, any person who limited fertility might actually threaten the very existence of society. In this light, it is not surprising that societies have generally been unwilling to leave it strictly up to the individual or to chance to have the required number of children. Societies everywhere have developed social institutions to encourage childbearing and reward parenthood in various ways. For example, among the Kgatla people of South Africa, mortality was very high during the 1930s when they were being studied by Isaac Schapera. He discovered that "to them it is inconceivable that a married couple should for economic or personal reasons deliberately seek to restrict the number of its offspring" (Schapera 1941:213). Several social factors encouraged the Kgatla to desire children, as noted by Nag (1962:29):

> A woman with many children is honored. Married couples acquire new dignity after the birth of their first child. Since the Kgatla have a patrilineal descent system (inheritance passes through the sons), the birth of a son makes the father the founder of a line that will perpetuate his name and memory . . . [and the mother's] kin are pleased because the birth saves them from shame.

In a 1973 study in Nigeria of the Yoruba (a large African ethno-cultural group), families with fewer than four children were looked upon with horror (Ware 1975). Apparently, they still are! The 2013 Demographic and Health Survey in Nigeria revealed that in northwestern Nigeria women had an ideal family size of 8.4 children (no, we're not making this up) but were having "only" 6.7 on average.

By and large, the social institutions and norms that encourage high fertility would have been so taken for granted by the members of a premodern, high-mortality society that anyone who consciously said, "I am having a baby in order to continue the existence of my society" would have been viewed as a bit weird. In modern times, if people really acted solely on the basis that they had to replace society, then modern higher-fertility societies such as Nigeria would now actually have much lower levels of fertility since in all such countries the birth rates exceed the death rates by a substantial margin; whereas the very low fertility societies would have higher fertility since in many of those countries the birth rate is now lower than the death rate.

This is not to say, however, that there is not a long-term relationship between mortality and fertility. There obviously is. It is just that the generation of parents who experience the improvement in their children's chances of survival is unlikely to be the generation that responds to that change with a decline in fertility. It will be their children (or even grandchildren) who become aware that lower mortality is changing the way society works, and thus they respond by lowering the number of children they have relative to their parents or grandparents. Indeed, as noted above, fertility is a lot lower now among this generation of Hutterites than it used to be.

Children as Security and Labor

In a premodern society, human beings were the principal economic resource. Even youngsters were helpful in many tasks, and as people matured into young adulthood they provided the bulk of the labor force that supported those, such as the aged, who were no longer able to support themselves. More broadly, children can be viewed as a form of insurance that rural parents, in particular, have against a variety of risks, such as a drought or a poor harvest. Though at first blush it may seem as though children would be a burden under such adverse conditions, many parents view a large family as providing a safety net—at least one or two of the adult children may be able to bail them out of a bad situation. One important way in which this may happen in the modern world is that one or more children may migrate elsewhere and send money home. Although children may clearly provide a source of income for parents until they themselves become adults (and parents), it is less certain that children will actually provide for parents in their old age.

It is most noteworthy that in a premodern setting, the *quantity* of children may matter more than the *quality*, and the nature of parenting is more to *bear* children than to *rear* them (Gillis, Tilly, and Levine 1992). Still, the noneconomic, nonrational part of society (the sexist part) intrudes by often suggesting that male children are more desirable than female children. This can have the unintended side effect of raising the birth rate. In most (albeit not all) societies until quite recently, males were typically valued more highly than females. Thus, many families would continue to have children until they had at least one son. Furthermore, if babies are likely to die, a family may have had at least two sons in order to increase the likelihood that one of them would survive to adulthood (an "heir and a spare").

India is a country where the desire for a surviving son is strong because the Hindu religion requires that a male family member—usually the son—perform the last rites when people die. Malthus was very aware of this stimulus to fertility in India and, in his *Essay on Population*, quoted an Indian legislator who wrote that under Hindu law a male heir is "an object of the first importance. 'By a son a man obtains victory over all people; by a son's son he enjoys immortality; and afterwards by the son of that grandson he reaches the solar abode'" (Malthus 1872 [1971]:116). Such beliefs, of course, also serve to ensure that society will be replaced in the face of high mortality. Yet, as Fred Arnold and associates (Arnold, Choe, and Roy 1998) remind us, the desire for sons cannot alone account for continuing high birth rates. Note that in Japan, South Korea, China, and Vietnam—Asian societies that still have strong male preferences—the drop in fertility has nonetheless been rapid.

Remember that for most women in most of human history, it was easier to have several children than to limit the number to one or two, regardless of the level of motivation. For the average person, a high level of desire and access to the means of fertility control are required to keep families small. Thus, the fertility transition was by no means automatically assured just because mortality declined. Certain preconditions need to be in place before birth rates will drop.

The Preconditions for a Decline in Fertility

In 1973, in response to the findings emerging from the Princeton European Fertility Project (which we discussed in Chapter 3), Ansley Coale tried to deduce how an individual would have to perceive the world on a daily basis if fertility were to be consciously limited. In this revised approach to the demographic transition, he argued that there are three preconditions for a substantial fertility decline: (1) the acceptance of calculated choice as a valid element in marital fertility, (2) the perception of advantages from reduced fertility, and (3) knowledge and mastery of effective techniques of control (Coale 1973). Although the societal changes that produced mortality declines may also induce fertility change, they will do so, Coale argued, only if the three preconditions exist. As a type of shorthand, these three preconditions are sometimes summarized as the ready, willing, and able (RWA) model. These things may seem obvious to you now, but they are remarkably recent in the overall timeline of history.

Coale's first precondition goes to the very philosophical foundation of individual and group life: Who is in control? If a supernatural power is believed to control reproduction, then it is unlikely that people will run the risk of offending that deity by impudently trying to limit fertility. On the other hand, the more secular people are (even if still religious), the more likely it is that they will believe that they and other humans have the right and ability to control important aspects of life, including reproduction. Control need not be in the hands of a god for a person not to be empowered. If a woman's life is controlled by her husband or other family members, then she is not going to run the risk of insult or injury by doing things that she knows are disapproved of by those who dominate her (Bledsoe and Hill 1998). The status of women, not just secularization, is an important part of this first, basic precondition for a decline in fertility.

The second precondition recognizes that more is required than just the belief that you can control your reproduction. You must have some reason to want to limit fertility. Otherwise, the natural attraction between males and females will lead to unprotected intercourse and, eventually, to numerous children. What kinds of changes in society might motivate people to want fewer children? Kingsley Davis (1963, 1967) suggested that people will be motivated to delay marriage and limit births within marriage if economic and social opportunities make it advantageous for them to do so. Having children is generally a means to some other end, so if the important goals change, then the desire to have children may also change.

Coale's third precondition involves the knowledge and mastery of effective means of fertility control. Specific methods of fertility control may be thought of as technological innovations, the spread of which is an example of diffusion. As we will detail later in the chapter, women in North America, for example, now typically use the pill to space children and then often choose female sterilization to end reproduction after the desired number of children are born (Daniels and Abma 2018). This is a different set of techniques than prevailed 30 years ago, and 30 years from now the mix will doubtless be different still. At the same time that new methods are evolving and knowledge of all methods is being diffused, part of the decision about what method of fertility regulation to use is based on the individual's cost-benefit calculations. As we just noted, the economic and psychosocial costs of various methods of birth control may well change over time and cause people to alter their fertility behavior accordingly, keeping in mind that not all possible avenues of fertility control are open to all people. Abortion is a good example. Although it is a legal method of birth control in the United States, it is not "available" to people who object to it for religious or personal reasons, or live in a state where access has been limited.

The remainder of the chapter uses these three preconditions for a fertility decline as an organizing framework to understand the fertility transition. First, we briefly review the changes in social structure that may be associated with the way in which humans view their role in reproduction (the first precondition) and that also influence the motivations to limit childbearing (the second precondition), which lead people to seek the means whereby they can do so (the third precondition). During this discussion, you should keep in mind that the three preconditions do not necessarily operate in a strictly linear fashion. In particular, it is possible that the availability of a particular type of contraceptive method (e.g., sterilization becoming available to Hutterite women) can encourage people to think in different ways about their control over reproduction and to reassess the number of children they want or intend to have.

Ideational Changes That Must Take Place

Tradition is, by definition, the enemy of change, so it is not surprising that so-called traditional societies are those that are most resistant to the idea that women, or couples working as a team, should be in charge when it comes to reproduction. Among the earliest nations to undergo a change in this regard were those that first experienced the Enlightenment, as we discussed in Chapter 3. The Enlightenment allowed people to break free from traditional ideas about the role of humans in the universe and, as we pointed out in the previous chapter, this was the opening door to science, which has provided us with the long lives that we now pretty much take for granted. The acceptance of secular ideas, associated especially with nonreligious education, occurred first in Europe and the overseas European countries such as the United States, Canada and Australia. Thus, it is not surprising that it was these countries that first experienced the fertility transition and now have among the lowest levels of fertility in the world.

An essential element in this process is a rise in the status of women (as we detail in the essay that accompanies this chapter), but historically this has been a slow and sometimes painful set of changes. A decline in mortality leads to an increase in child survival that forces people to think differently about the world than they did before. Having more children survive than ever imagined demands attention from everyone in a group. It is a wonderful prospect in the abstract, but it forces a new balance to be struck between people and resources. This is, of course, the basic point that Malthus—an early product of the Enlightenment—was making more than 200 years ago. But Malthus was pessimistic that people would or could change their ways and work out ways to limit the number of children born in order to prevent resources from being overrun and pushing everyone into perpetual poverty. History has, fortunately, generally proven him wrong on that point. Most people, though not all, do recognize that one way to cope with declining mortality is to limit fertility as well.

Motivations for Lower Fertility Levels

The motivational and ideational aspects of the fertility transition are most often explained as some combination of rational factors embodied in the supply-demand framework and sociocultural influences captured by the innovation-diffusion perspective. Let's discuss each of these complementary perspectives in turn.

The Supply-Demand Framework

The original formulation of the demographic transition envisioned a world in which the normal state of affairs is a balance between births and deaths (homeostasis). Mortality is assumed to decline for reasons that are often beyond the control of the average person (exogenous factors), but a person's reproductive behavior is dominated by a rational calculation of the costs and benefits to himself or herself (endogenous factors) of maintaining high fertility in the face of declining mortality. The idea is that people will eventually perceive that lower mortality has produced a situation in which more children are going to survive than can be afforded, and at that point, fertility will decline.

The economist Richard Easterlin (mentioned earlier in Chapter 3) is especially notable for his work in this regard, and the resulting perspective is somewhat clumsily called "the theory of supply, demand, and the costs of regulation," or, in shorthand, "the supply-demand framework." It is also known as "the new household economics" because the household (the group of people living together under the same roof), rather than the individual or the couple, is often taken as the unit of analysis, since reproductive decisions can affect all household members. High fertility, for example, may help households avoid risk in the context of low economic development, especially when children generate a positive net flow of income to the parents. Under those conditions, it is rational to want to produce a large number of children.

The supply-demand framework draws its concepts largely from the field of neoclassical economics, which assumes that people make rational choices about what they want and how to go about getting it. The essence of the theory is that the level of fertility in a society is determined by the choices made by individual couples within their cultural (and household) context (Easterlin 1978; Bulatao and Lee 1983; Easterlin and Crimmins 1985; Bongaarts 1993; McDonald 1993; Robinson 1997; McDonald 2000; Bongaarts 2014).

Couples strive to maintain a balance between the potential supply of children (which is essentially a biological phenomenon determined especially by fecundity) and the demand for children (which refers to a couple's ideal number of surviving children). If mortality is high, the number of surviving children may be small, and the supply may approximate the demand. In such a situation, there is no need for fertility regulation. However, if the supply begins to exceed the demand, either because infant and child survival has increased, or because the opportunity costs of children are rising, then couples may adjust the situation by using some method of fertility regulation. The decision to regulate fertility will be based on the couple's perception of the costs of doing so, which include the financial costs of the method and the social costs (such as stigmas attached to the use of methods of fertility control).

What are the opportunity costs of children? Let us assume that people are rational and make choices based on what they perceive to be in their best self-interest. The idea that children might be thought of as "commodities" was introduced in 1960 by University of Chicago economist Gary Becker, whose work on the economic analysis of households and fertility earned him a Nobel Prize in 1992. Becker's theory treated children as though they were consumer goods that require both time and money for parents to acquire. Then he drew on classic microeconomic theory to argue that for each individual a utility function could be found that would express the relationship between a couple's desire for children and all other goods or activities that compete with children for time and money (Becker 1960). It is important to note that time as well as money is being considered, for if money were the only criterion, then one would expect (in a society where there are social pressures to have children) that the more money a person had, the more children he or she would want to have. Yet we know that in almost every rich nation, those who are less well off financially tend to have more children than do those who are more well off. This relationship shifts only when fertility gets to very low levels, at which point there is evidence that couples with higher socioeconomic status tend to have slightly higher fertility levels than less well-off couples.

With the introduction of time into the calculations, along with an implicit recognition that social class determines a person's tastes and lifestyle, Becker's economic theory turns into a trade-off between *quantity* and *quality* of children. For the less well off, the expectations that exist for children are presumed to be low, and thus the cost is at its minimum. In the higher economic strata, the expectations for children are presumed to be greater, both in terms of money and especially in terms of time spent on each child. The theory asserts that parents in the higher strata are also exposed to a greater number of opportunities to buy goods and engage in time-consuming activities. Thus, to produce the kind of children desired, their number must be limited.

When an advanced education, a prestigious career, and a good income were not generally available to women, the lack of such things was not perceived as a cost of having children. But when those advantages are available, reducing or foregoing them for the sake of raising a family may be perceived as a sacrifice. Again, the reflexive nature of the connection between fertility and women's status is apparent. As fertility has gone down, more time has become available for women to pursue alternate lifestyles; and as the alternatives grow in number and attractiveness, the costs of having children have gone up. The benefits of having children are less tangible, though no less important, than the costs. They include psychological satisfaction and proof of adulthood, not to mention being more integrated into the family and community.

Reproductive Rights, Reproductive Health, and the Fertility Transition

The ability of women to control their own reproduction and their overall level of reproductive health is closely related to the changes that occur in the context of the fertility transition. By now you are familiar with the fact that pronatalist pressures have always been strong in societies characterized by high mortality, where several children must be born just to ensure that enough will survive to replace the adults who will be dying. Thus, one component of the social status of women is that with a regime of high mortality (and thus high fertility), women are busy with pregnancy, nursing, and child care, whereas men, who are biologically removed from the first two of these activities, are able to manipulate and exploit women by tying the status of women to their performance in reproduction and the rearing of children. Furthermore, high mortality means that childbearing must begin at an early age because the risk of a woman's death even as an adult may be high enough that those younger, prime reproductive years cannot afford to be "wasted" on activities other than family building. In a premodern society with a life expectancy of about 30 years, fully one-third of women age 20 died before reaching age 45, making it imperative that childbearing begin as soon as possible. Of course, the catch in all this is that pregnancy and childbirth are major causes of death for women between the ages of 20 and 45. This means that reducing fertility is a major cause of the improvement in women's reproductive health, an idea captured by the phrase "family planning saves lives" (Smith et al. 2009).

Women who marry young and begin having children may be "twice cursed"—having more years to be burdened with children and also being in a more vulnerable position to be dominated by a husband. Men need not marry as young as women, since they are not the child-bearers, and they also remain fecund longer. The older and more socially experienced a husband is compared to his wife, the easier it may be for him to dominate her. It is no coincidence that in Africa, Western Asia, and Southern Asia, where women are probably less free than anywhere in the world (and where fertility is higher than anywhere else), men are consistently several years older than their

wives. For example, in Niger, where fertility is very high (more than 7 children per woman), data from the Demographic and Health Surveys show the average woman marries at age 16 to a man 8 years her senior. By contrast, in Norway, where fertility is very low (fewer than 2 children per woman), the average woman marries at age 32 to a man who is 2 years older (United Nations Population Division 2017a).

Among the uglier aspects of traditional approaches to reproductive "health" is the practice of **female genital mutilation (FGM)**, sometimes known as female circumcision, which involves practices that are technically clitoridectomy and infibulation. Clitoridectomy is the more common practice and involves the total removal of the clitoris, whereas infibulation involves cutting the clitoris, the labia minora, and adjacent parts of the labia majora, and then stitching up the two sides of the vulva. These are useless and dangerous practices to which an estimated 3 million girls and women in at least 28 countries in northern and sub-Saharan Africa and parts of Asia are subjected annually (World Health Organization 2018). The effect is to dramatically lower a woman's enjoyment of sexual intercourse, but as was true for foot binding in an earlier era in China, the real purpose is to "control access to females and ensure female chastity and fidelity" (Mackie 1996:999). The migration of refugees from African countries such as Somalia, where the practice is common, to North America and Europe helped to ignite worldwide knowledge of and outrage about FGM, and there are now international movements in place bringing pressure on governments to make it illegal.

Three demographic processes—a decline in mortality, a drop in fertility, and increasing urbanization—have importantly influenced the ability of women to expand their social roles and improve their life chances. *A major factor influencing the rise in the status of women has been the more general liberation of people from early death.* The decline in mortality does not mean that pressures to have children have evaporated. That is far from the case, but there is a greater chance that the pressures will be less; indeed, remaining single and/or childless is more acceptable for a woman now than at any time in history, as we discuss in more detail in Chapter 9.

In North America, Europe, and much of Latin America and Asia, most of a woman's adult life is now spent doing something besides bearing and rearing children because she is having fewer children than in previous generations and she is also living longer. An average American woman, for example, bearing two children in her late 20s and early 30s would at most spend about 20 years bearing and rearing them. Of course, she will actually have far more than 20 years of relative (indeed increasing) independence from child-rearing obligations, because if her two children are spaced two years apart and the first child is born when she is 30, by age 38 her youngest child will be in school all day, and she will still have 44 more years of expected life, as you can see by looking back at Table 4.3. Is it any wonder, then, that women have searched for alternatives to family building

and have been recruited for their labor by the formal economic sector? In a sociocultural setting in which the reproduction of children consumes a great deal of societal energy, the domestic labor of women is integral to the functioning of the economy. With a slackening in demand for that type of activity, it is only natural that a woman's time and energy would be employed elsewhere, and elsewhere is increasingly likely to be in a city.

Cities are more likely than rural areas to provide occupational pursuits for both women and men that encourage a delay in marriage (thus potentially lowering fertility) and lead to a smaller desired number of children within marriage. Furthermore, since urbanization involves migration from rural to urban areas, this has meant that as they migrate, women are distanced a bit from the pressures to marry and have children that may have existed for them while living in their parents' homes. Thus, migration may lead to a

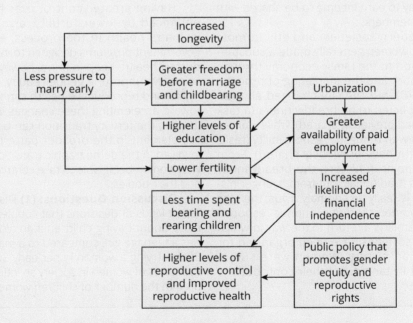

The Demographic Linkages Between the Fertility Transition and Reproductive Health

(continued)

Reproductive Rights, Reproductive Health, and the Fertility Transition (*Continued*)

greater ability to respond independently to the social environment of urban areas, which tend to value children less than rural areas. Young adults are especially prone to migration and every adult who moves may well be leaving a mother and her immediate influence behind. This means the migrant will have more freedom to look for alternatives and question the social norms that prescribe greater submissiveness, lower status, and fewer out-of-the-home opportunities for women than for men.

Of course, it isn't quite that simple. For one thing, the process of urbanization in the Western world initially led to an increase in the dependency of women before promoting increased gender equity (Nielsen 1978). Urbanization is typically associated with a transfer of the workplace from the home to an outside location—a severing of the household economy and the establishment of what Kingsley Davis (1984) called the breadwinner system, in which a member of the family (traditionally the male) leaves home each day to earn income to be shared with other family members.

In premodern societies, and still in most rural settings, women generally made a substantial contribution to the family economy through agricultural work and the marketing of produce (Boserup 1970), but the city changed all that. Men were expected to be breadwinners (a task that women had previously shared), while women were charged with domestic responsibility (tasks that men might have previously shared). From our vantage point in history, the breadwinner system seems "traditional," but from a longer historical view, it is really an anomaly. Thus, the idea of men and women sharing economic responsibility for the family is a return to the way in which most human societies have been organized for most of human history. Women were subjugated in most instances, but their contributions were crucial.

As the life expectancy of the urban woman increased and as her childbearing activity declined, the lack of alternative activities was bound to create pressures for change, and over time the urban opportunities for women have multiplied. In the figure accompanying this essay, we have diagrammed the major paths by which mortality, fertility, and urbanization influence the status of women and lead to more egalitarian gender roles and improved reproductive health. Increased longevity eventually lessens the pressure for high fertility and the pressure to marry early. These changes permit a woman greater freedom for alternative activities before marrying and having children, as well as providing more years of life beyond childbearing. Women are left to search for the alternatives, which are importantly wrapped up in higher levels of education. Society is then offered a "new" resource—nondomestic female labor. This creates new opportunities for a woman's economic independence, which is key to controlling her life, including her reproduction.

Having greater control over her own life, enhanced by lower fertility, also improves a woman's health in the process, even without government programs designed to increase reproductive health. Keep in mind, however, that public policy supporting gender equity, reproductive rights, and reproductive health can go a long way toward accelerating these changes in society. For its part, the fertility transition can be viewed as a key element in the broader pattern of changes involved in the demographic transition associated with women being able to take control of their lives and their bodies.

Discussion Questions: (1) Discuss the different kinds of decisions that couples are likely to make about having children if an older man marries a teenage girl, compared to a man in his early 30s marrying a woman in her early 30s. **(2)** Why is the status of women in society so intimately bound up with the number of children women have?

The latter reasons reflect a broad category of reward that society offers for parenthood—social approval. In addition, most people are most comfortable in families with children, since by definition everyone was raised in a situation involving at least one child. Thus, having children may allow you to relive vicariously (and perhaps revamp) your own childhood, helping to recreate the past and take the sting out of any failures you may experience as an adult. In a more instrumental way, children tend to provide a means for establishing a network of social relationships in a community through school, organized sports, and activity groups. The rewards of childbearing thus are greatest in terms of the personal and social satisfaction derived from them since in richer nations there is certainly little, if any, economic advantage derived from having children.

The fertility transition is not something that has occurred in a vacuum—it has occurred because other changes have been taking place in society to which individual couples or people within households respond. The health and mortality transition actually increases the potential supply of children because healthier women are better able to conceive successfully and bear a child. But the changes in society that are generating that improved health are assumed by the supply-demand framework to be largely economic in nature, and it is the changing economic circumstances, not the decline in mortality per se, that couples are believed to respond to as they choose to lower their demand for children.

An improved economy generates other things in life that compete with children. Other sources of income are higher than what child labor can produce, and there are more ways to spend one's time and money besides just on children. Thus, if the means for fertility regulation are sufficiently effective, the lowered demand for children will lower fertility. In 1938, an Englishman put it rather succinctly: "In our existing economic system, apart from luck, there are two ways of rising in the economic system; one is by ability, and the other by infertility. It is clear that of two equally able men—the one with a single child, and the other with eight children—the one with a single child will be more likely to rise in the social scale" (Daly 1971:33).

As we have already mentioned, education is the best clue to a person's attitude toward reproduction. An increase in education is strongly associated with the kind of rational decision making implied in the supply-demand framework. Furthermore, the better-educated members of society are most likely to be the secular agents of change who will encourage the diffusion of an innovation such as fertility limitation.

It is nearly axiomatic that better-educated women have lower fertility than less-educated women in any given society—at least until overall levels of fertility drop to well below replacement level, as they have especially in many European countries, and as we will discuss later in the chapter. It is the identification of this kind of fertility differential that helps to build our understanding of reproductive dynamics in human societies, because it causes us to ask what it is about education that makes reproduction so sensitive to it. In general terms, the answer is that education offers to people (men and women) a view of the world that expands their horizon beyond the boundaries of traditional society and causes them to reassess the value of children and reevaluate the role of women in society. Education also increases the opportunity for social mobility, which, in turn, sharpens the likelihood that people

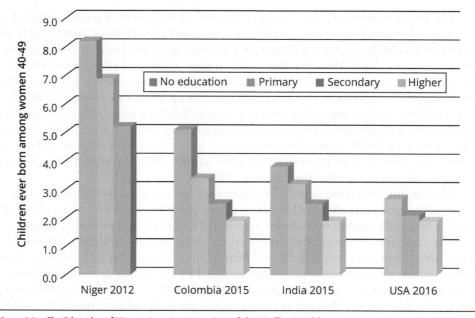

Children ever born among women 40-49

■ No education   ■ Primary   ■ Secondary   ■ Higher

Niger 2012   Colombia 2015   India 2015   USA 2016

Figure 5.3   The Education of Women Is an Important Part of the Fertility Transition

Note: For the United States, the lowest education category refers to women who did not complete high school, followed by high school graduates, and then women with a graduate or professional degree.

Sources: Prepared by John R. Weeks; data for Niger, Colombia, and India are from the respective Demographic and Health Surveys (www.dhsprogram.com). U.S. data are derived from the U.S. Census Bureau, Current Population Survey 2016 (released in 2017—www.census.gov).

will be in the path of innovative behavior, such as fertility limitation, that they may try themselves. Indeed, the role of education is so important that demographers at the Vienna Institute of Demography created a whole set of population projections incorporating trends in educational attainment as a predictor of fertility levels (Samir et al. 2010).

Figure 5.3 summarizes data from four countries that range from high to low overall levels of fertility, showing the relationship between fertility and education. The data are for women aged 40–49, so the number of children ever born approximates the completed fertility rate—the total number of children these women will ever have. The countries are arranged by the fertility level of women with no education (except in the United States, where it refers to women with less than a high school education), representing the situation in virtually all human societies prior to the fertility transition. At each successively higher level of education, the number of children is lower, representing the kind of structural change that increases the costs and lowers the benefits of having lots of children.

Some of the variability in the differential fertility by education is, of course, economic: Education will buy you more in some societies than in others, and the more it will buy you, the higher the opportunity costs of children may be. Another reason may be cultural: Education is not necessarily comparable from one country to another, and the means available to limit fertility may be different from one place to the next, no matter your level of education. All the same, education is such a critical factor that fertility is unlikely to decline without an improvement in educational levels, especially among women, even if we cannot exactly predict how much of a decline in the birth rate will accompany each higher level of educational attainment.

Once fertility has dropped to very low levels, however, its relationship to education appears to get more complicated, as we are now learning from case studies in Europe. Data for Denmark show that better educated women are having more children each (albeit still at less than replacement level) than women with the lowest levels of education. Data from Europe show that this pattern also exists in Finland and Portugal (Lanzieri 2013). The explanation probably lies at least in part in the greater economic advantages among better-educated women and men in low-fertility societies, putting them in a better position to have a slightly larger family than those with lower levels of income and wealth. It would seem that this situation should be true throughout Europe, not just in a few countries, yet for reasons that are not entirely clear, in the majority of European nations it is still true that more education leads to fewer children born.

One possibility is that higher fertility in low-fertility nations is encouraged by family-friendly public policies, especially daycare provision for pre-school children (Testa 2013). These are also likely to be countries in which the gender equality is greater than in other places, thus providing an environment in which it is easier for women to combine a family (even if a small one) with a career, rather than having to make a choice between the two.

One must also recognize that motivations for specific family size (lower or higher) do not appear magically just because one aspires to wealth or has received a college education. Motivations for low fertility arise out of our communication with other people and other ideas. Fertility behavior, like all behavior, is in large part determined by the information we receive, process, and then act on. The people with whom, and the ideas with which, we interact in our everyday lives shape our existence as social creatures.

The Innovation-Diffusion and "Cultural" Perspective

Most social scientists would agree that human behavior is not fully described by rational neoclassical economic theory. Rather, they are also drawn to the idea that many changes in society are the result of the diffusion of innovations (Brown 1981; Rogers 1995), which spread through our various social networks (Bernardi and Klärner 2014). We know, for example, that much of human behavior is driven by fads and fashions. Last year's style of clothing will go unworn by some people this year, even though the clothes may be in very good repair, just because that is not what "people" are wearing—it is so five minutes ago. These "people" are important agents of change in society—those who, for reasons that may have nothing to do with money or economic factors, are able to set trends.

You may call it charisma, or karma, or just plain influence, but there are those who set trends and those who do not—some people are just cool. We see it happen many times in our lives. Often these change agents are members of the upper strata of society. They may not be the inventors of the innovation, but when they adopt it, others follow suit. Notice, too, that the innovation may be technological, such as the cell phone, or it may be attitudinal and behavioral, such as deciding that two children is the ideal family size and then using the most popular means to achieve that number of children.

In Chapter 3, we mentioned that the fertility history of Europe suggests a pattern of geographic diffusion of the innovation of fertility limitation within marriage. The practice seemed to spread quickly across regions that shared a common language and ethnic origin, despite varying levels of mortality and economic development (Watkins 1991). This finding led to speculation that fertility decline could be induced in a society, even in the absence of major structural changes such as economic development, if the innovation could be properly packaged and adopted by the appropriately influential change agents. Importantly, this is where the concept of "culture" comes into play, because some societies are more prone to accept innovations than are others (Pollack and Watkins 1993).

To accept an innovation and change your behavior accordingly, you must be "empowered" (to use an overworked term) to believe that it is within your control to alter your behavior. Not all members of all societies necessarily feel this way. In many, if not most, "traditional" societies (or groups within a society), people accept the idea that their behavior is governed by God, or multiple gods, or more generally by "fate," or more concretely by their older family members (dead or alive). In such a situation, an innovation is likely to be seen as an evil intrusion and is not apt to be tolerated, which gets us back to the first precondition for a fertility decline—the ideational shift.

You can perhaps appreciate, then, that the diffusion of an innovation requires that people believe that they have some control over their life, which is the essence of the rational-choice model that underlies the economic approach to the fertility transition. In other words, the supply-demand model and the innovation-diffusion model tend to be complementary to one another, not opposed to one another. Both approaches can be helpful in explaining why fertility declines. In any social situation in which influential couples are able to improve their own or their children's economic and social success by concentrating resources on a relatively smaller number of children, other parents may feel called upon to follow suit if they and their offspring are to be socially competitive.

The importance of "influential couples" is sometimes ignored by North Americans who prefer the ideal of a classless society. European demographers offer the reminder that two enduring theories of social stratification have strong implications for fertility behavior: (1) cultural innovation typically takes place in higher social strata as a result of privilege, education, and concentration of resources, whereas lower social strata adopt new preferences through imitation, and (2) rigid social stratification or closure of class or caste inhibits such downward cultural innovation (Lesthaeghe and Surkyn 1988). Thus, the innovative behavior of influential people will be diffused downward through the social structure, as long as there are effective means of communication among and between social strata. From our perspective, the innovation of importance is the preference for smaller families, implemented through delayed marriage/sexual partnership and/or fertility limitation.

Because it is in the modern world of nation-states that the fertility transition has taken place, we cannot ignore the role that public policy may play as a force for implementing or attempting to thwart cultural innovations that affect levels of reproduction. In particular, governments can make it more or less difficult for women to become educated, avoid early marriage, seek a divorce, enter the labor force, and have access to a wide range of fertility limitation methods. We will discuss some of these policy issues later in the chapter.

How Can Fertility Be Controlled?

Assuming that people feel that they can control their fertility, and they have a desire to do so, how can they accomplish this? What means are available to them? The answers have varied across both time and space. Earlier in the chapter, we mentioned that "natural" fertility is rarely as high as the maximum level that would be possible. In most societies, families are trying (or at least hoping) to have the number of surviving children that will be most beneficial to them. But people for most of human history have lived close to the subsistence level and in the shadow of high death rates. Thus, it is not surprising that in such circumstances, couples are unlikely to have a preference for a specific number of children (van de Walle 1992). The vagaries of both child mortality and the food supply were apt to cause people to "play things by ear" rather than plan in advance the number of children desired. With high mortality, how many children are born is less important than how many survive. Once mortality started to come under human control, questions about limiting fertility also arose in ways that were very different from the past.

Proximate Determinants of Fertility

The means for regulating fertility have been popularly labeled (popular, at least, in population studies) the intermediate variables (Davis and Blake 1955). These represent 11 variables through which any social factor influencing the level of fertility will operate. Davis and Blake point out that there are actually three phases to fertility: *intercourse*, *conception*, and *gestation*. Intercourse is required if conception is to occur; if conception occurs, successful gestation is required if a baby is to be born alive. Table 5.1 lists the 11 intermediate variables according to whether they influence the likelihood of intercourse, conception, or gestation. Although each of the 11 intermediate variables plays a role in determining the overall level of fertility in a society, the relative importance of each varies considerably.

John Bongaarts (1978, 1982) has been instrumental in refining our understanding of fertility control, first by calling these variables the proximate determinants of fertility instead of intermediate variables, and second by suggesting that differences in fertility from one population to the next are largely accounted for by only four of those variables: proportion married, use of contraceptives, incidence of abortion, and involuntary infecundity (especially postpartum infecundity, as affected by breastfeeding practices). These variables are noted with a check mark

Table 5.1 The Proximate Determinants of Fertility—Intermediate Variables Through Which Social Factors Influence Fertility

Most Important of the Proximate Determinants	Proximate Determinants or Intermediate Variables
	I. Factors affecting exposure to intercourse ("intercourse variables")
	A. Those governing the formation and dissolution of unions in the reproductive period
✔	1. Age of entry into sexual unions
	2. Permanent celibacy: proportion of women never entering sexual unions
	3. Amount of reproductive period spent after or between unions
	a. When unions are broken by divorce, separation, or desertion
	b. When unions are broken by death of husband
	B. Those governing the exposure to intercourse within unions
	4. Voluntary abstinence
	5. Involuntary abstinence (from impotence, illness, unavoidable but temporary separations)
	6. Coital frequency (excluding periods of abstinence)
	II. Factors affecting exposure to conception ("conception variables")
✔	7. Fecundity or infecundity, as affected by involuntary causes, but including breastfeeding
✔	8. Use or nonuse of contraception
	a. By mechanical and chemical means
	b. By other means
	9. Fecundity or infecundity, as affected by voluntary causes (sterilization, medical treatment, and so on)
	III. Factors affecting gestation and successful parturition ("gestation variables")
	10. Fetal mortality from involuntary causes (miscarriage)
✔	11. Fetal mortality from voluntary causes (induced abortion)

Sources: Adapted by John R. Weeks from Kingsley Davis and Judith Blake (1955); and John Bongaarts (1982).

in Table 5.1. Bongaarts does not mean to imply, however, that the other intermediate or proximate determinants are irrelevant to our understanding of fertility among humans, only that they are relatively less important. We will focus attention on the most important determinants—those checked in Table 5.1. As we review these determinants, you will discover, by the way, that there is heavier emphasis on the behavior of women than of men. That is simply because if a woman never has intercourse, she will never have a child (aside from the still relatively rare cases of *in vitro* fertilization in a woman who is not otherwise having intercourse with a man), whereas a man will never have a child no matter what he does. Of course, preventing conception by sterilization or contraceptives can be done by either sex, but if conception occurs, it is obviously only the woman who bears the burden and the risk of either pregnancy or abortion.

Proportion Married—Limiting Exposure to Intercourse

Permanent virginity is obviously very rare, but the longer past puberty a woman waits to begin engaging in sexual unions, the fewer children she will probably have because of the shorter time she will be at risk of bearing children (Variable 1 in Table 5.1). According to data from the 2011–2013 National Survey of Family Growth, 13 percent of females in the United States had experienced sexual intercourse by age 15, and by age 19 the percentage had risen to 68 percent, with similar numbers for males (Martinez and Abma 2015). Not surprisingly, the likelihood that a teenage girl will have had sex is lower if she is in a family with both a mother and father (probably related to closer surveillance of her activities), and if her mother is well educated (probably related to her awareness of the potential costs to her of an unintended pregnancy). Consistent with the overall trend in lower fertility levels in the United States, the percentage of teenagers having sex has gone down since the 1980s, while at the same time the percentage of both males and females using contraception during their first sexual intercourse is very high.

Use of Contraceptives

It is probable that at least some people in most societies throughout human history have pondered ways to prevent conception (Himes 1976). Abstinence, withdrawal, and the douche are the most ancient of such premodern means, but there is some historical evidence that various plants were used in earlier centuries to produce "oral contraceptives" and early-stage abortifacients (Riddle 1992). We do not know much about the actual effectiveness of such methods, but they were almost certainly far less effective in preventing conception or birth and far riskier for a woman's health than are modern methods. The lack of effectiveness of the premodern methods meant that a badly unwanted pregnancy was more likely to end in an attempted abortion (and perhaps the woman's death) or the woman trying to conceal her pregnancy and then abandoning the baby (probably leading to the infant's death) after a secret delivery (van de Walle 2000).

There have been references to douching throughout recorded history, stretching back to ancient Egypt (Baird et al. 1996), and it is one of the principal means of contraception mentioned by Charles Knowlton in his famous *Fruits of Philosophy* in the nineteenth century (which we mentioned in Chapter 3). Over time, it has been recommended as a means of treating specific gynecological conditions and also as a contraceptive, on the theory that washing sperm out of the vagina right after intercourse (the "dash for the douche") might prevent conception. Unfortunately, for the one doing the douching, the sperm take only about 15 seconds to travel through the vagina into the cervical canal, so the effectiveness of douching is very limited.

Withdrawal is an essentially (although not exclusively) male method of birth control. It has a long history (it is, in fact, referenced in the Bible). It is actually a form of incomplete intercourse (thus its formal name, *coitus interruptus*) because it requires removal of the erect penis from the vagina just before male ejaculation. The method leaves little room for error, especially since there may be an emission of semen just before ejaculation, but it is one of the more popular methods historically for trying to control fertility.

Another historically important method is the male condom, a rubber or latex sheath inserted over the erect penis just prior to intercourse. During ejaculation, the sperm are trapped inside the condom, which is then removed immediately after intercourse while the penis is still erect, to avoid spillage. The condom is reasonably effective, especially if used in conjunction with a spermicidal foam. The condom is of course also useful in preventing the spread of sexually transmitted diseases, including venereal disease and HIV/AIDS. The condom is a method that is associated with the decline in the birth rate in the United States and Europe, having been around in Europe since at least the seventeenth century, when it was made of animal intestines. The modern type, made of rubber, dates to the mid-nineteenth century— the time that fertility was clearly beginning to drop in Europe and North America.

Given the discussion in this chapter's essay about the important role of gender equity as a factor in the fertility transition, it should not surprise you that historically the most important methods of contraception were male methods— withdrawal and the condom. The more recent addition of the oral contraceptive pill put women much more squarely in the driver's seat on the issue of pregnancy avoidance. The oral contraceptive, or "the pill" as it is popularly known, has revolutionized birth prevention for millions of women all over the world. The pill is a compound of synthetic hormones that suppress ovulation by keeping the *estrogen* level high in a female. This prevents the pituitary gland from sending a signal to the ovaries to release an egg. In addition, the *progestin* content of the pill makes the cervical mucus hostile to implantation of the egg if it is indeed released and may block the passage of sperm as well.

A closely related and increasingly popular set of contraceptives are called long-acting, reversible contraceptives (LARC). Instead of a having to remember to take a pill every day and worry about getting refills, these ovulation-suppressing hormones can also be administered by means of a small stick implanted under the skin, or through an intrauterine device (IUD) which is inserted into the uterus. Because you don't have to be reminded regularly to use them, they wind up being the most effective of all of the contraceptive methods, as you can see in Table 5.2.

The principal method of contraception that requires couple cooperation is the calendar rhythm method, more formally known as periodic abstinence or fertility awareness. Though users of this technique are jokingly referred to as parents, you can see that the use-effectiveness is still an improvement over using no method at all.

Periodic abstinence may seem old-fashioned, but it is actually a reasonably new technique because the timing of ovulation in the menstrual cycle (which is central to the method) was unknown until the 1930s when Kyusako Ogino and Herman Knaus independently discovered the fact that peak fecundity in women occurs at the approximate midpoint between menses and that, despite the variability in the amount of time between the onset of menses and ovulation, the interval between ovulation and the next menses is fairly constant at about 14 days.

Other methods of couple-oriented contraception represent non-vaginal sexual activity, such as mutual masturbation and oral-genital sex. In Davis and Blake's 1955 article, these forms of incomplete intercourse were listed as "perversions," but in more recent decades, with a significant change in openness about sex, they have become more widely acceptable techniques for engaging in sexual activity with limited risk of pregnancy.

If unprotected intercourse has taken place, it may still be possible for a woman to prevent conception, if she acts immediately—and we don't mean by douching. Emergency contraception (or *postcoital contraception*) is meant to avert pregnancy within a few days after intercourse. There are two principal means to do this: (1) emergency contraceptive pills—"the morning after pill" or "Plan B"—and (2) the Copper-T Intrauterine device (IUD) (Princeton University Office of Population Research 2013). The IUD method tends to be more effective than the pill method, but it needs to be fitted by a physician, whereas the pill is available at drug stores without a prescription.

The importance of any kind of contraception can be gauged by comparing it to the likelihood of getting pregnant if no method is used. The right-hand column of Table 5.2 illustrates the number of pregnancies per 100 women during the first year of use of any given method. This is a rate of use-effectiveness that approximates the chances of getting pregnant when using any method. Thus, a sexually active woman who is using no method at all has an 85 percent chance of getting pregnant over the course of a year. Even though withdrawal is one of the least reliable methods on the list, you can see that its use reduces the chance of pregnancy to 22 percent. This is not great by modern standards, but it is a large improvement on doing nothing. Data from a variety of surveys also have shown clearly that the more highly motivated couples (that is, those who do not want any more pregnancies, as opposed to those merely spacing their children) have higher use-effectiveness rates than less motivated couples, regardless of the method chosen.

It can be seen in Table 5.2 that 35 percent of American women of reproductive age are not using a method of contraception. Data from the 2015–2017 National Survey of Family Growth suggest that about 20 percent are fecund and sexually active but are choosing not to protect themselves from pregnancy, whereas 10 percent have never had intercourse, and 5 percent are non-surgically sterile, are pregnant, or are trying to get pregnant (Daniels and Abma 2018). The methods used by the 65 percent of women who are protecting themselves from pregnancy are listed in an order that approximates their use-effectiveness. Thus female and male sterilization and long-acting reversible contraception (LARC) tend to be the most effective methods. The latter includes the intrauterine device and the contraceptive implant. The most common method of female sterilization is tubal ligation, although there are other, more extreme surgical techniques such as a hysterectomy (the removal of the

Table 5.2   Contraceptive Use Among U.S. Women, 2015–2017, and Use-Effectiveness

Characteristic	Percent	Number of Pregnancies per 100 Women During First Year of Use
All women aged 15–49	100.0	
Not using contraception	35.1	85.0
Using contraception (contraceptors)	64.9	
Female sterilization	18.6	0.5
Male sterilization	5.9	
Long-acting reversible contraception (LARC)	10.3	0.1
Intrauterine device	7.9	
Implant	2.3	
3-month injectable (Depo-Provera)	2.1	6.0
Oral contraceptive pill	12.6	9.0
Contraceptive ring or patch	1.2	9.0
Condom	8.7	18.0
Withdrawal	3.9	22.0
Periodic abstinence	1.5	24.0
Other methods (including emergency contraception, female condom, foam, cervical cap, sponge, suppository, jelly))	0.2	

Sources: Prepared by John R. Weeks; contraceptive use data are from Daniels and Abma (2018: data for Figure 2); use-effectiveness data are from U.S. Centers for Disease Control and Prevention (2014).

uterus) that are normally done for health reasons, rather than contraceptive reasons (although the result is the same). For males, there are also drastic as well as simple means of sterilization. The drastic means is castration, which is removal or destruction of the testes. This generally eliminates sexual responsiveness in the male, causing him to be impotent (incapable of having an erection). Eunuchs (males who have been castrated) have an interesting place in history, but castration is practiced now mainly in the case of life-threatening disease. Vasectomy is the more popular male surgical contraceptive, and like a tubal ligation, it does not alter a person's sexual response. A vasectomy involves cutting and tying off the vas deferens, which are the tubes leading from each testicle to the penis. The male continues to generate sperm, but they are unable to leave the testicle and are absorbed into the body.

A close inspection of Table 5.2 will show you that there are only four methods that account for the majority of contraceptive use: female sterilization, the pill, LARC, and the male condom. Among women under the age of 30, the pill and LARC are most important, but at ages 30 and older—as women have had all the children they are likely to want—surgical methods take over as most popular (Daniels and Abma 2018).

Induced Abortion

Assuming that conception has occurred, a live birth may still be prevented. This could happen as a result of involuntary fetal mortality (Variable 10 among the intermediate variables shown in Table 5.1), which is either a spontaneous abortion (miscarriage) or a stillbirth. More important for our discussion, though, is voluntary fetal mortality, or induced abortion (Variable 11). Induced abortions became legal in Canada in 1969 and in the United States in 1973, and they are legal in all three of the world's most populous nations (China, India, and the United States), as well as in Japan and virtually all of Europe, including Ireland, where a new law went into effect in 2019 allowing abortion during the first 12 weeks of a pregnancy.

Back in the 1970s, abortion in many countries "changed from a largely disreputable practice into an accepted medical one, from a subject of gossip into an openly debated public issue" (Tietze and Lewit 1977:21). Worldwide, the demand for abortion has been dropping, but it is still high, even in places where it is not legal, and it is estimated that 56 million abortions occur each year worldwide. The rates per women of childbearing age are highest in Latin America and the Caribbean, and lowest in North America (Singh et al. 2018). The World Health Organization (2012) estimates that half of all abortions in the world are illegal (and thus have a high probability of being unsafe). The vast majority of abortions occur to women in their early 20s who experience an unintended pregnancy. Indeed, the number of abortions per woman is inversely related to the use of other contraceptive methods, clearly suggesting that the best way to reduce the abortion rate is to increase the availability of other forms of fertility limitation.

Abortion is probably the single most often used form of birth control in the world, and abortions have played a major role in fertility declines around the world. The number of legally induced abortions reported in the United States increased steadily from 1974 to 1981, peaking in that year, and has been declining since then (Guttmacher Institute 2014). It is estimated that nearly half of pregnancies in the United States are unintended, and 4 in 10 of these pregnancies end in abortion. Abortion rates are higher for unmarried women than for married, higher for African Americans than for other racial/ethnic groups, and higher for teenagers than for older women. This profile has not changed much over time.

Canadian women are less likely than women in the United States to use abortion, and since the fertility rate in Canada is slightly lower than in the United States, the implication is that Canadian women are also more efficient users of other methods of contraception. Abortions have played a role in Mexico's fertility decline as well, despite the fact that elective abortion is not legally available to most women in that country. Each state makes its own law in this regard, and although Mexico City legalized abortion in 2007, no other state has followed suit as of this writing. Nonetheless, women from anywhere in Mexico can legally go to Mexico City to obtain an abortion if they have the means to do so.

Involuntary Infecundity from Breastfeeding

Breastfeeding prolongs the period of postpartum amenorrhea and suppresses ovulation, thus producing in most women the effect of temporarily impaired fecundity. In fact, nature provides the average new mother with a brief respite from the risk of conception after the birth of a baby whether she breastfeeds or not; however, the period of infecundity is typically only about two months among women who do not nurse their babies, compared with 10–18 months among lactating mothers, albeit only if the mother is not supplementing breast milk with other food. Research suggests that stimulation of the nipple during nursing sets up a neuroendocrine reflex that reduces the secretion of the luteinizing hormone (LH) and thus suppresses ovulation. The cessation of lactation signals a prompt return of menstruation and the concomitant risk of conception in most women.

Over the past few decades, there has been concern that women in less developed nations were abandoning breastfeeding in favor of bottle feeding. In the absence of some method of contraception, a decline in breastfeeding would, of course, increase fertility by spacing children closer to one another. Closer spacing poses a threat to the health of both mother and child, and bottle feeding is also likely to raise the infant death rate since in less developed nations, bottle feeding may be accompanied by watered-down formulas that are less nutritious than a mother's milk, and/or the water used may be unsafe. Bacteria growing in unsterilized bottles and reused plastic liners can also lead to disease, especially diarrhea, which is often fatal to infants. In response to these concerns, UNICEF and the World Health Organization approved a voluntary code in 1981 to regulate the advertising and marketing of infant formula. However, it was not until 10 years later that that the giant Swiss firm Nestlé finally decided to limit its supply of free baby formula to Third World hospitals, and other baby formula suppliers quickly followed suit.

The Relative Importance of the Proximate Determinants

As we noted above, Bongaarts (1978, 1982) helped us to narrow down the original list of intermediate variables to the most important group of four proximate determinants. But even these four are not equally important, and their importance varies across time and space. In the now-developed countries, delayed marriage (without much premarital intercourse) and then the use within marriage of whatever contraceptive methods were available at the time, along with abortion, were almost certainly the paths to low fertility. Induced abortion has been a major factor in bringing fertility to low levels in Eastern Europe and East Asia, with modern contraception being more important in almost all other areas of the world, at least since the 1960s.

Contraceptive methods tend to be lumped into two broad categories: modern and traditional. The modern methods include the methods listed in Table 5.2, whereas traditional methods include things such as douching or taking herbal teas. Figure 5.4 shows the average percentage of married women aged 15–49 using any method of modern contraception in countries with differing levels of fertility. Here we have used the total fertility rate (TFR, an index similar to the total number of children born to women, as we discuss below), as estimated by the United Nations Population Division for the year 2020. Of the 134 countries for which these data are available, 47 have levels of fertility that are at or below replacement level (2.10 children per woman), and an average of 55 percent of women are using a modern contraceptive. Note that this measure does not include abortion.

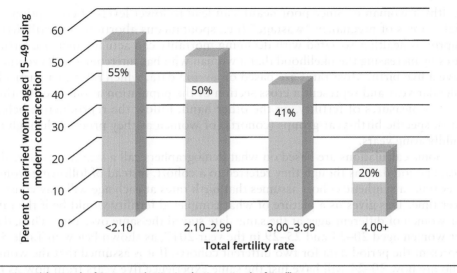

Figure 5.4   Higher Levels of Contraceptive Use Lead to Lower Levels of Fertility
Source: Prepared by John R. Weeks; data are from United Nations Population Division (2017b, 2018b).

Among the 32 countries where the TFR is in the range of 2.11 to 2.99 children, the percent using modern contraceptives drops a bit, to 50 percent. There are 18 countries with a TFR in the range of 3.00 to 3.99 children and the average percent of women using modern contraception in those countries is 41 percent. Finally, among the 37 countries with the highest level of fertility (4 or more children per woman), only 20 percent of women are using modern contraception.

You might wonder why the lowest-fertility countries don't have a much higher percentage of women using modern contraception. Abortion explains most of this, as we suggested above. In parts of Eastern Europe, especially the former Balkan states, abortion is still the principal means of fertility control. Several Asian nations, including China, are also in this category. Furthermore, in many Middle Eastern countries, where both contraceptive use and abortion rates are fairly low, the recent declines in fertility have been especially associated with a rise in the age at marriage. Because these are societies in which women are very unlikely to have sex outside of marriage, a delay in marriage also signals a delay in childbearing (Weeks et al. 2004). If contraceptive effectiveness were increased generally, and in particular if effective contraceptive use replaced abortion, the fit between fertility and contraceptive prevalence would be even higher than shown in Figure 5.4 (Bongaarts and Westoff 2000; Guengant and May 2013).

How Do We Measure Changes in Fertility?

How do we know that fertility has changed over time? To find out, we need measures that allow us to make the comparisons. The measures of fertility used by demographers generally attempt to gauge the rate at which women of reproductive age are bearing live children. Remember that this is partly a function of how healthy a woman is. Since poor health can lead to lower levels of conception and higher rates of pregnancy "wastage" (i.e., spontaneous abortions and stillbirths), improved health associated with declining mortality can actually increase fertility rates by increasing the likelihood that a woman who has intercourse will eventually have a live birth. Most rates are based on period data, which refer to a particular calendar year and represent a cross section of the population at one specific time. Cohort measures of fertility, on the other hand, follow the reproductive behavior of specific birth-year groups (cohorts) of women as they proceed through the childbearing years.

Some calculations are based on what demographers call a synthetic cohort that treats period data as though they referred to a cohort. Instead of following women over time, a synthetic cohort assumes that birth rates at each age will stay constant over time. This gives us a picture of what completed fertility would be if the rates for women of different ages at the same date stayed the same over time. Thus, data for women aged 20–24 and 25–29 in the year 2017, as shown below in Table 5.3, represent the period data for two different cohorts. If it is assumed that the women who are now 20–24 will have just the same experience five years from now as the women who are currently 25–29, then a synthetic cohort has been constructed from the period data.

Period Measures of Fertility

A number of period measures of fertility are commonly used in population studies, including the crude birth rate, the general fertility rate, the child-woman ratio, the age-specific fertility rate, the total fertility rate, the gross reproduction rate, and the net reproduction rate. Each one tells a little different story because each is based on a slightly different set of data. We will discuss the one that requires the least data first. Then each successive measure requires a bit more information (or at least harder-to-get information) for its calculation.

The crude birth rate (CBR) is the number of live births (b) in a year divided by the total midyear population (p). It is usually multiplied by 1,000 to reduce the number of decimals:

$$CBR = \frac{b}{p} \times 1,000$$

The CBR is "crude" because (1) it does not take into account which people in the population were actually at risk of having births, and (2) it ignores the age structure of the population, which can greatly affect how many live births can be expected in a given year. Thus, the CBR (which is sometimes called simply "the birth rate") can mask significant differences in actual reproductive behavior between two populations and, on the other hand, can imply differences that do not really exist.

For example, if a population of 1,000 people contained 300 women who were of childbearing age and 10 percent of them (30) had a baby in a particular year, the CBR would be 30 (i.e., 30 births/1,000 total people = 30 births per 1,000 population). However, in another population, 10 percent of all women may also have

Table 5.3   Calculation of Fertility Rates, United States 2017

(1)	(2)	(3)	(4)	(5)	(6)	(7)	(8)	(9)	(10)	(11)
		F	b	ASFR	b_f	ASFR_f				
Age group	Midpoint of interval	Number of women in age group	Number of births to women in age group	Age-specific birth rates	Number of female births to women in age group	Female births per woman	Female birth rate during 5-year interval	Proportion of female babies surviving to midpoint of age interval	Surviving daughters per woman during 5-year interval	Column (2) × Column (9)
15–19	17.5	10,331,169	194,377	18.8	94,953	0.00919	0.04595	0.9919	0.04558	0.79770
20–24	22.5	10,769,493	764,780	71.0	373,595	0.03469	0.17345	0.9900	0.17171	3.86354
25–29	27.5	11,468,230	1,123,577	98.0	548,867	0.04786	0.23930	0.9872	0.23624	6.49658
30–34	32.5	10,883,081	1,091,917	100.3	533,401	0.04901	0.24506	0.9835	0.24102	7.83300
35–39	37.5	10,616,012	554,796	52.3	271,018	0.02553	0.12765	0.9785	0.12491	4.68401
40–44	42.5	9,890,258	114,813	11.6	56,086	0.00567	0.02835	0.9718	0.02756	1.17112
45–49	47.5	10,587,683	8,483	0.8	4,144	0.00039	0.00196	0.9621	0.00188	0.08943
Total		74,545,926	3,852,743	1,764.0	1,882,065		0.86172		0.84890	24.93538
			GFR= sum of column (4)/sum of column (3) × 1,000 = 51.7	=TFR [sum of column (5) × 5]; expressed as 1.764 births per woman		= GRR [sum of column (7) × 5]	= NRR			divided by NRR = 29.37 = mean length of generation

Source: Prepared by John R. Weeks; birth data are from Martin et al. (2018), Table 3; death data are from Table 4.3.

had a child that year. Yet, if out of 1,000 people there were only 150 women of childbearing age, then only 15 babies would be born, and the CBR would be 15 per 1,000. Crude birth rates in the world in 2018, for example, ranged from a low of 7 per 1,000 in South Korea (the lowest rates tend to be in East Asia and Europe) to a high of 48 per 1,000 in Niger (all of the highest rates are in sub-Saharan Africa). The CBR in Canada was 11, compared with 12 in the United States, and 19 in Mexico (Population Reference Bureau 2018).

Despite its shortcomings, the CBR is often used because it requires only two pieces of information: the number of births in a year and the total population size. If, in addition, a distribution of the population by age and sex is available, usually obtained from a census (but also obtainable from a large survey, especially in less developed nations), then more sophisticated rates can be calculated.

The general fertility rate (GFR) uses information about the age and sex structure of a population to be more specific about who actually has been at risk of having the births recorded in a given year. As you can see in Table 5.3, the GFR (which is sometimes simply called "the fertility rate") is the total number of births in a year (b) divided by the number of women in the childbearing ages (F), which we usually consider to be ages 15–49, although sometimes the narrower age range of 15–44 is used because only a very small fraction of babies are born to mothers aged 45 or older, as you can see in Table 5.3. The formula is as follows, where $_{35}F_{15}$ denotes females starting at age 15 with an interval width of 35 years (i.e., women aged 15–49):

$$GFR = \frac{b}{_{35}F_{15}} \times 1,000$$

David Smith (1992) has noted that the GFR tends to be equal to about 4.5 times the CBR. Thus, in 2017 (the latest detailed information available as of this writing, reflecting the data in Table 5.3), the GFR in the United States of 51.7 was just slightly less than 4.5 times the CBR of 11.8 that year.

If vital statistics data are not available, it is still possible to estimate fertility levels from the age and sex data in a census or large survey. The child–woman ratio (CWR) provides an index of fertility that is conceptually similar to the GFR but relies solely on census data. The CWR is measured by the ratio of young children (aged 0–4) enumerated in the census to the number of women of childbearing age (15–49):

$$CWR = \frac{_4P_0}{_{35}F_{15}} \times 1,000$$

In the United States in 2017, there were an estimated 19,938,860 children aged 0–4 according to the U.S. Census Bureau (2018), and as you can see from Table 5.3, there were 74,545,926 women aged 15–49; thus, the CWR was 267 children aged 0–4 per 1,000 women of childbearing age. The CWR can be affected by the underenumeration of infants, by infant and childhood mortality (some of the children born will have died before being counted), and by the age distribution of women within the childbearing years, and researchers have devised various ways to adjust for each of these potential deficiencies (Smith 1992; Weeks et al. 2004). Furthermore, just as the GFR is roughly 4.5 times the CBR, the CWR is approximately 4.5 times the GFR. The CWR for the United States in 2017, as noted above, was 267, which was pretty close to 4.5 times the GFR in 2017 of 51.7.

One of the more precise ways of measuring fertility using period data is the age-specific fertility rate (ASFR). This requires a rather complete set of information: births according to the age of the mother and a distribution of the total population by age and sex. The ASFR is the number of births (b) occurring in a year to mothers aged x to $x + n$ ($_nb_x$) per 1,000 women (F) of that age (usually given in five-year age groups):

$$ASFR = \frac{_nb_x}{_nF_x} \times 1,000$$

As you can see in Table 5.3, in 2017 in the United States, there were 71 births per 1,000 women aged 20–24. However, in 1955 in the United States, in the middle of the baby boom, childbearing activity for women aged 20–24 had been more than three times higher, reflected in an ASFR of 242. In 2017, the ASFR for women aged 25–29 was 98, nearly half the ASFR of 191 in 1955. Thus, we can conclude that between 1955 and 2017 fertility dropped more for women aged 20–24 (a 71 percent decline) than for women aged 25–29 (a 49 percent drop). This is consistent with the rise in the age at marriage and the subsequent delay in childbearing during that time span.

ASFRs require that comparisons of fertility be done on an age-by-age basis. Demographers have also devised a method for combining ASFRs into a single fertility index covering all ages. This is called the total fertility rate (TFR), which we have mentioned several times up to this point without giving you a precise definition. The TFR uses the synthetic cohort approach and approximates knowing how many children women will have had when they are all through with childbearing by using the age-specific fertility rates at a particular date to project what could happen in the future if all women went through their lives bearing children at the same rate as women at that given date. For example, as noted above (and in Table 5.3), in 2017 American women aged 25–29 were bearing children at a rate of 98 births per 1,000 women per year. Thus, over a five-year span (from ages 25– through 29), for every 1,000 women, we could expect 490 (= 5 × 98) births for every thousand women if everything else remained the same. By applying that logic to all ages, we can calculate the TFR as the sum of the ASFRs over all ages:

$$TFR = \sum ASFR \times 5$$

As shown in Table 5.3, the ASFR for each age group is multiplied by five only if the ages are grouped into five-year intervals. If data by single year of age are available, that adjustment is not required. The TFR can be readily compared from one population to another because it takes into account the differences in age structure, and its interpretation is simple and straightforward. The TFR is an estimate of the average number of children born to each woman, assuming that current birth rates remain constant and that none of the women die before reaching the end of the childbearing years. In 2017, the TFR in the United States was 1,764 children per 1,000 woman, or 1.76 children per woman, which was almost exactly half the 1955 figure of 3.60 children per woman. A rough estimate of the TFR (measured per 1,000 women) can be obtained by multiplying the GFR by 30 or by multiplying the CBR by 4.5 and then again by 30. Thus, in the United States in 2017 the TFR of 1,764 children per 1,000 women was fairly close to (albeit less than) 30 times the GFR of 51.7.

A further refinement of the TFR is to look at female births only (because it is only the female babies who eventually bear children), producing a measure called the gross reproduction rate (GRR). The most precise way to do this is to calculate age-specific birth rates using only female babies ($ASFR_f$), and then the calculation of the TFR for females represents the GRR, as shown in Table 5.3:

$$GRR = \left(\sum ASFR_f \times 5 \right)$$

Note that in this case we did not multiply the $ASFR_f$ by 1,000, since we wanted the result to be in terms of individual women, not on a per 1,000 woman basis. The GRR is interpreted as the number of female children that a female just born may expect to have during her lifetime, assuming that birth rates stay the same and ignoring her chances of survival through her reproductive years. A value of one indicates that women will just replace themselves, whereas a number less than one indicates that women will not quite replace themselves, and a value greater than one indicates that the next generation of women will be more numerous than the present one. In the United States in 2017, the value of 0.86 suggests that if fertility levels in that year persisted into the future, the next generation of women would be only about 86 percent as large as in 2017.

The GRR is called "gross" because it assumes that a woman will survive through all her reproductive years. Actually, some women will die before reaching the oldest age at which they might bear children. The risk of dying is taken into account by the net reproduction rate (NRR). The NRR represents the number of female children that a female child just born can expect to bear, taking into account her risk of dying before the end of her reproductive years. It is calculated as follows:

$$NRR = \sum \left(ASFR_f \times \frac{_nL_x}{500,000} \right)$$

where $ASFR_f$ is the female-only age-specific fertility rate that we just calculated as part of the formula for the GRR. Each $ASFR_f$ is then multiplied by the probability that a woman will survive to the midpoint of the age interval, which is found from the life table by dividing $_nL_x$ (the number of women surviving to the age interval x to $x + n$) by 500,000 (which is the radix multiplied by 500,000—check back in Chapter 4 for those details). Note that if single-year-of-age data were used, the denominator would be 100,000 rather than 500,000. For the calculations in Table 5.3, we have used the life table data for females that are found in Table 4.3.

The NRR is always less than the GRR, since some women always die before the end of the reproductive period. How much before, of course, depends on death rates. In a low-mortality society such as the United States, the NRR is only slightly less than the GRR—the GRR of 0.86 is associated with a NRR of 0.85, whereas in a high-mortality society, the GRR may be considerably higher than the NRR. As an index of generational replacement, an NRR of one indicates that each generation of females is just replacing itself. A value less than one indicates a potential decline in numbers, and a value greater than one indicates the potential for growth, unless fertility and mortality change. It must be emphasized that the NRR is not equivalent to the rate of population growth in most societies. For example, in the United States, the NRR in 2017 was below replacement level, yet the population was still increasing by more than 2.3 million people each year. The NRR represents the future potential for growth inherent in a population's fertility and mortality regimes. However, peculiarities in the age structure (such as large numbers of women of childbearing age), and especially migration (see the next chapter), affect the actual rate of growth at any point in time.

By adding one more column to Table 5.3 (column 11), we are able to provide another useful index called the mean length of generation, or the average age at childbearing. Column 11 illustrates the calculation. You multiply the midpoint of each age interval (column 2) by the surviving daughters per woman for that age interval (column 10), and then you divide the sum of those calculations by the net reproduction rate (the sum of column 10), yielding a figure for 2017 in the United States of 29.4 years.

Cohort Measures of Fertility

Cohort data follow people through time as they age, rather than taking snapshots of different people at regular intervals, which is what period data do. Thus, the basic measure of cohort fertility is births to date, measured as the cumulative cohort fertility rate (CCFR), or the total number of children ever born (CEB) to women.

For example, women born in 1915 in the United States began their childbearing during the Depression. By the time those women had reached age 25 in 1940, they had given birth to 890 babies per 1,000 women (Heuser 1976). By age 44 (in 1959), those women had finished their childbearing in the baby boom years with a completed fertility rate of 2,429 births per 1,000 women. We can compare those women with another cohort of women who were born during the Depression and began their childbearing right after World War II. The cohort born in 1930 had borne a total of 1,415 children per 1,000 women by the time they were age 25 in 1955. This level is 60 percent greater than the 1915 cohort. By age 44 (in 1974), the 1930 cohort had borne 3,153 children per 1,000 women, 30 percent higher than the 1915 cohort. Indeed, examining cohort data for the United States, it turns out that the women born in 1933 were the most fertile of any group of American women since the cohort born in 1881. By contrast, the women who had just completed their childbearing in 2016 represented members of Generation X, born in the mid-1970s, and they reached age 40–44 with an average of only 2,068 births per 1,000 women (U.S. Census Bureau 2017).

Cohort information is obviously very illuminating, but because we cannot always wait for women to go through their childbearing years to estimate their level of fertility, we typically use the synthetic cohort approach to calculate the TFR. If fertility has not changed much over time, however, as has recently been true in the United States, then completed fertility of women in 2016 (2,068) is, as you can see, not that different from the TFR based on synthetic cohort data in 2017 (1,764).

Fertility Intentions

Our understanding of the fertility transition in the world has been quietly, but importantly, influenced by research on fertility intentions. These are data on what the women who are presently of childbearing age say they intend to do in the future in terms of having children. The idea for collecting this kind of information was inspired by demographers who had failed to forecast the baby boom that occurred after World War II. They realized after the fact that many couples had been postponing having babies before the war (because of the Depression) and during the war (because of the uncertainty and disruptions caused by the war), but they still intended to have more babies. The eventual fulfillment of these intentions helped to fuel the baby boom.

Period rates are prone to this problem of being influenced by the *timing* or *tempo* of births (when births occur), which may distort the underlying *quantum* of births (how many babies are actually born at a given time) (Bongaarts and Feeney 1998; Rodriguez 2006). Data on lifetime births expected by women can provide a clue to the number of births that will eventually be produced, even if the timing cannot be well predicted. For example, between 1976 and 1998, the TFR increased from 1.7 to 2.1 births per woman in the United States, seeming to show that fertility was on the rise during that 22-year period of time. However, data on lifetime births expected by women who were ages 30 to 34 actually went down from 2.4 in 1976 to 2.1 in 1998, while the number of lifetime births expected by women ages 18–24 and 25–29 remained virtually the same, at 2.1 and 2.0, respectively. This tells us that the TFR in 1976 was lower than it should have been because, as mentioned above, women were just postponing births to a later date. Although the timing had changed, young women in 1998 had exactly the same family size in mind (an average of 2.1 children), as did young women back in 1976.

Charles Westoff (1990) used data from 134 different fertility surveys conducted in 84 different countries to conclude that "the proportion of women reporting that they want no more children has high predictive validity and is therefore a useful tool for short-term fertility forecasting" (p. 84). An exhaustive review of the literature a decade later led S. Philip Morgan (2001:160) to conclude that "the evidence is clear: intentions strongly predict subsequent behavior." However, Morgan and a colleague found that this strong relationship holds for groups or societies, but not so much for individuals (Quesnel-Vallée and Morgan 2003). In other words, you can get a good idea about the direction of fertility trends in a country or a group within a country by knowing fertility intentions, but you are much less likely to predict an individual woman's completed family size from her specific intentions, because some women have more than intended and some have fewer (Morgan and Rackin 2010).

You can see that measures of fertility and their interpretations are no less complex than the fertility transition itself. With this set of measuring tools in hand, we can now return to the questions raised earlier in the chapter: What is it that eventually convinces people that they should want to have a small family, given that people seemed to want large families until very recently in human history? And what is the global variation in these patterns?

How Is the Fertility Transition Accomplished?

There is no single straight path that a population is likely to take to get from high fertility to low fertility, but there are some patterns that show up more regularly than others. Keep in mind that Coale's three preconditions for a fertility decline suggest that nothing will happen as long as women do not feel that they are in control of their own reproduction, so the first part of the transition is ideational in nature. Even assuming such an ideational change in society, fertility will only decline if people are motivated to break the old rules of life's game that funneled women into a world of having children early and often. Finally, women or couples must decide how they are going try to limit the children born.

One of the first signs of a fertility decline in a population is an increase in the age at which a woman has her first birth. You might call this the transition from children having children to women having children, and it is part and parcel of the rising status of women in society. This may be accomplished more through abstinence than anything else, but in societies where girls are sexually active prior to marriage this will obviously require either an effective contraceptive or the availability of abortion. At older ages, women who already have children may decide not to have an additional one, and completed family size becomes five children born instead of six, or four instead of five. Thus, during the fertility transition birth rates are apt to drop noticeably at the two age extremes of a woman's reproductive career.

Research suggests that even when couples have an ideal family size in mind, they make decisions about children one at a time. This information is captured by what demographers call parity progression ratios, which represent the proportion of women with a given number of children (parity refers to how many children have already been born) who "progress" to having another child. Thus, as fertility declines, parity progression ratios will decline at the higher parities. The consequence is a "compression" of reproduction (to borrow the term used in Chapter 4 in discussing mortality) into a shorter number of years. Instead of women routinely having babies between the ages of 15 and 49, most women will have all of their children in their 20s and early 30s. If you look at the data in Table 5.3 you can see that more than three-fourths (77 percent) of all babies born in the United States in 2017 had mothers between the ages of 20 and 34. The decline in parity progression ratios at the older ages is now accomplished especially with female or male sterilization, as we discussed earlier. In between the younger and older ages, the use of effective temporary contraception or the availability of abortion or emergency contraception provides couples with the opportunity to space children as they see most appropriate. In that process, they may decide, for example, not to have a third child now that they have two—making their own personal contribution to the fertility transition. Or, they may decide not to have a second child—making their contribution to the second demographic transition of below-replacement fertility.

All of the perspectives on the fertility transition discussed above assume that fertility will not decline until people see limiting fertility as being in their interest. The supply-demand framework assumes that people are making rational economic choices between the quantity and quality of children; whereas the innovation-diffusion perspective argues that social pressure is the motivation, regardless of the underlying economic circumstances. Coale's three preconditions do not specify what the motivating factors might be, leaving open the possibility of some mix of economic and social motivations, sometimes stimulated or retarded by public policy decisions that make it easier or harder for people interested in controlling their reproduction actually to do so. You can appreciate, then, that a combination of forces produces the observed fertility transitions, and these forces operate in different ways and speeds depending upon where you are in the world.

Geographic Variability in the Fertility Transition

It is fair to say that here in the twenty-first century, there is no region of the world that has not experienced at least the early stages of the fertility transition. In 1950, Europe had the lowest fertility levels in the world, followed by the predominantly "overseas European" regions of North America and Oceania (dominated by Australia and New Zealand). Now in the twenty-first century, Europe and East Asia, especially, have seen fertility drop to below replacement level, and the major question being asked is whether or not it will ever rise, or indeed if it might even drop to a lower level. You can see in Figure 5.5 that the United Nation's medium projections (typically the ones their demographers think are most likely) suggest that fertility might go up again in Europe and, in fact, the evidence suggests that this may already be happening (Bongaarts and Sobotka 2012), as it becomes easier for women to juggle working and motherhood.

Figure 5.5 is arranged so that the regions of the world that experienced the biggest declines in fertility between 1950 and 2020 are on the left, and the regions with the least decline are on the right. Thus, the Polynesian areas of Oceania experienced the most dramatic decline, although the decline in East Asia was most consequential globally because it involves such a large population—China, Japan, and the Koreas. As a region, East Asia went from women having 5.6 children on average (essentially at "natural fertility" levels) in 1950 to having only 1.6 children (well below replacement level) on average by 2020. Latin America and the Caribbean went through similar marked declines during that 70-year period.

Africa had the highest regional fertility in 1950, as it still does, and as it is projected to have in the middle of the century. However, Figure 5.5 separates out North Africa from sub-Saharan Africa because the former has experienced a substantial decline in fertility, even if it remains well above replacement level, whereas the latter has been much slower in its transition. The United Nations expects that at the middle of this century, sub-Saharan Africa will still have by far the highest fertility levels

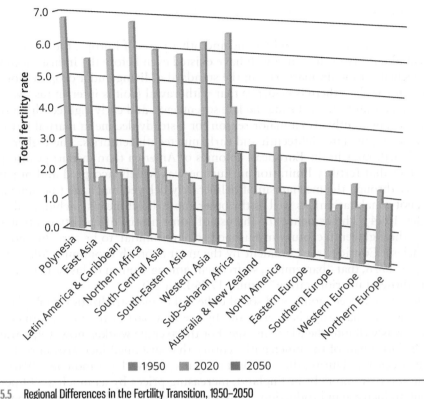

Figure 5.5   Regional Differences in the Fertility Transition, 1950–2050

Source: Prepared by John R. Weeks; data are from United Nations Population Division (2017b); Total fertility rates for 2020 and 2050 are based on the medium projections.

in the world, even if they are significantly lower than current levels. Desired family size remains very high in western and middle sub-Saharan Africa, where women prefer to have six children and men have an even higher preference (DHS Program 2019). However, North Africa, where fertility still remains well above replacement level, is expected to continue its decline over this century.

These regional trends give us a feel for what is happening, but not necessarily for why it's happening. It helps to take a look at a few countries in more detail to understand the fertility transition better.

Case Studies in the Fertility Transition

There are as many interesting stories of the fertility transition as there are countries and even subregions within countries, but for illustrative purposes, let's look first at the places that have had low fertility for the longest time and where it is now below replacement level—the United Kingdom and other European nations. Then we review the situation in two of the world's most populous nations—China and the United States—each of which has taken a different path through the fertility transition. Just as there are many roads to low mortality, there are many roads to low fertility.

United Kingdom and Other European Nations

Historical Background In England and other parts of Europe, the beginnings of a potential fertility decline may well have existed even before the Industrial Revolution touched off the dramatic rise in the standard of living and a drop in mortality. In English parishes, there is evidence that withdrawal (coitus interruptus) was used to reduce marital fertility during the late seventeenth and early eighteenth centuries, and it was apparently also a major reason for a steady decline in marital fertility in France during the late eighteenth and early nineteenth centuries. The higher preindustrial birth rates in the European colonies of America than in Europe also point to the fact that fertility limitation in Europe was widely accepted and practiced, especially through the mechanism of deliberately delayed marriage (meaning abstinence, not cohabitation), as well as the other, more direct means, including abortion (Wrigley 1974). The evidence for the use of some means of fertility control as far back as the eighteenth century in Europe is circumstantial, to be sure, but powerful nonetheless. Consider the comment by the great Scottish economist Adam Smith, writing in 1776, that "barrenness, so frequent among women of fashion, is very rare among those of inferior station" (Smith 1776:I.viii.37).

The enormous economic and social upheaval of industrialization took place earlier in England than anywhere else, and by the first part of the nineteenth century, England was well into the Machine Age. For the average worker, however, it was not until the latter half of the nineteenth century that sustained increases in real wages actually occurred. During the first part of that century, the Napoleonic Wars were tripling the national debt in England, increasing prices by as much as 90 percent without an increase in production. Thus, during most of Malthus's professional life, his country was experiencing substantial inflation and job insecurity. These relatively adverse conditions undoubtedly contributed to a general decline in the birth rate during the first half of the nineteenth century, brought about largely by delayed marriage (Wrigley 1987). After about 1850, economic conditions improved considerably, and the first response was a rise in the birth rate (as the marriage rate increased), followed by a long-run decline. This was a period in which all of Ansley Coale's preconditions for a fertility decline existed: (1) People had apparently accepted calculated choice as a valid element; (2) people perceived advantages from lowered fertility; and (3) people were aware of at least reasonably effective means of birth control. As we already mentioned, the British were accustomed to thinking in terms of family limitation. Delayed marriage, abstinence, and coitus interruptus within marriage were known to be effective means to reduce fertility. In the second half of the nineteenth century, then, motivation to limit family size came in the form of larger numbers of surviving children combined with aspiration for higher standards of living.

It is important to remember that the restriction of fertility was in many ways a return to preindustrial family patterns, in which an average of about two children survived to adulthood in each generation, as we discussed earlier in the chapter. Thus, mortality declines produced changes in the lives of people to which they had to respond. The English reacted in ways consistent with the theory of demographic change and response. They responded to population growth by migrating (to America, especially) and by delaying marriage, and then, only when those options were played out, did marital fertility clearly decline (Friedlander 1983). In a world now characterized by very open sexuality, it is sometimes hard to believe that large numbers of people were willing to suppress their sexuality in order to achieve some measure of economic success, but Simon Szreter and Eilidh Garrett (2000:70) remind us that "the available historical evidence suggests that the late marriage regime of early modern Britain entailed systematic sexual restraint among young adults up to their mid-20s, the point at which marriage could be realistically anticipated. A sexual culture of this sort might lend itself to restraint *after* marriage, as well, if and when the need arose."

The best-known explanation of the fertility decline in England in the latter half of the nineteenth century is that offered by J. A. Banks (1954) in *Prosperity and Parenthood* and its sequel, *Feminism and Family Planning in Victorian England* (Banks and Banks 1964). Banks's thesis is by now a familiar one: The rising standard of living in England, especially among the middle classes, gave rise to a decline in fertility by (1) raising expectations of upward social mobility, (2) creating fears of social slippage (you had to "keep up with the Joneses"), and (3) redefining the roles of women (in this case, from that of housewife to a fragile luxury of a middle-class man).

Though it is true that birth rates dropped more quickly in the upper social strata of English society than in the lower social strata, by 1880 all segments of English society were experiencing fertility declines. From about 1880 to 1910, England shared with much of continental Europe in what John Knodel and Etienne van de Walle (1979) called "the momentous revolution of family limitation." Fertility has continued on a slow downward trend since then, albeit interrupted by a postwar baby boom, which peaked in the mid-1960s. After that, however, birth rates resumed their downward trend and England has settled into a Second Demographic Transition pattern of just below-replacement-level fertility, with a TFR of only 1.9 children per woman, accomplished by widespread use of contraceptives (especially the pill), LARC, delayed marriage, delayed childbearing, abortion, and the use of female or male sterilization when the desired family size has been achieved (Neyer et al. 2013; Poston, Lee, and Kim 2018).

Figure 5.6 shows the change in fertility that has taken place in England over the course of the past 200 years. As dramatic as the change has been, it follows the nearly universal pattern of the biggest declines in motherhood being at the youngest and oldest ages. In 1800, the TFR in England is estimated to have been 5.6 children per woman (Livi-Bacci 2017), which was still lower than the TFR in India or China as recently as 1960. The transition in England down to its current TFR of 1.9 was helped along by the fact that contraception is used by 84 percent of married women of reproductive age (Population Reference Bureau 2018) and that, along with abortion, means that women do not have to delay sexual activity even though they delay marriage and/or having children. And, female and male sterilization means that when they decide to stop having children, it is a permanent decision.

Current Fertility Patterns   England mirrors other European nations, all of which currently have below-replacement-level fertility. There has been a good deal of hand-wringing over this in Europe because the low fertility, especially when combined with increasing life expectancy, is producing an increasingly older population with a shrinking base in the younger ages. Governments are worried about how

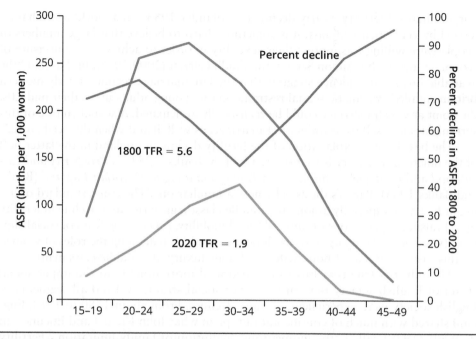

Figure 5.6   The Fertility Transition in England

Sources: Prepared by John R. Weeks; data for 1800 are from Livi-Bacci (2000); data for 2020 are from United Nations Population Division (2017).

old-age pensions will be funded and how economic growth will be maintained if there are too few young people to carry the load. However, this low fertility should not be too surprising because it can be explained in terms of both the supply-demand framework and the diffusion of innovations.

Europeans grow up knowing that they and any children they have will almost certainly survive to a rather old age. They also know that highly effective contraceptives make it possible to engage in sexual activity without fear of pregnancy (and, of course, the use of condoms will protect them from sexually transmitted diseases, including HIV). Should the contraceptive fail, either emergency contraception or abortion is available. Thus, European women are in almost total control over the supply of children. The important question is how large is the demand for children? Surveys throughout Europe suggest that most Europeans would prefer two children (Testa 2013), but at the same time, women are investing heavily in their own education and are seeking jobs and careers comparable to those of men. Though gender equity may be approachable on those two fronts, it is harder to attain within marriage. Women are still expected to be the principal providers of care to children and to their husbands, not to mention their aging parents, and this extra burden placed on women has created a climate of caution about settling into a relationship and having those two children. Women know that they most likely will bear a disproportionate share of the burden of child-rearing and household labor, while suffering substantial opportunity costs from delayed careers and lost wages.

The movement toward gender equity in education and in the labor force has thus not been matched by gender equity in domestic relationships, and so the demand for children has dropped to what we might think of as female replacement—a woman having a child (whether male or female) that allows her to experience reproduction and replacement, but not much more than that. This mismatch seems to be greatest in southern and eastern Europe, where attitudes about the woman's role in the family are more traditional than in the rest of Europe (Kertzer et al. 2009). Over time, demographers have been drawn to the idea that in highly developed countries, a *rise* in the status of women within family-oriented institutions may be necessary to bring fertility back up to, or at least closer to, replacement level (Chesnais 1996; McDonald 2000). Consistent with this view, a study in Spain has shown that fertility is higher in that country in those regions where childcare is more readily available (Baizan 2009). At the same time, the persistence of low fertility in Europe (and East Asia, as well) suggests to some researchers that fertility may never go back up to replacement level (Basten, Lutz, and Scherbov 2013), and that assumption is also built into the United Nations Population Division medium projections for European countries (United Nations Population Division 2017). As Nancy Riley (1997:115) put it so well: "To understand demographic processes, you must understand the place of women in society."

China

At the time of the Communist revolution in 1949, the average woman in China was bearing 6.2 children and the population, which was already more than half a billion, was growing rapidly. The government of the People's Republic of China realized decades ago that the population problem was enormous, and it implemented the largest, most ambitious, most significant, and certainly the most controversial policy to slow population growth ever undertaken in the world. In 1971, the government instituted the *wan xi shao* (later, longer, fewer) campaign that helped to accelerate fertility decline in China. However, it was viewed by the government as being insufficiently effective. The 1978 constitution of the People's Republic of China declared that "the state advocates and encourages birth planning" and the reasons for this were that (1) too rapid an increase in population is detrimental to the acceleration of capital accumulation, (2) rapid population increase hinders the efforts to raise the scientific and cultural level of the whole nation quickly, and (3) rapid population growth is detrimental to the improvement of the standard of living (Muhua 1979).

The goal of the Chinese government at that time was, incredibly enough, to achieve zero population growth (ZPG) by the year 2000, with the population stabilizing at 1.2 billion people. To accomplish this meant that at least one generation of Chinese parents had to limit their fertility to only one child, because the youthful age structure in China in the 1970s meant a high proportion of people were in their childbearing years. If all of those women had two children, the population would still be growing too fast. How did they go about trying to achieve this goal? The first step was to suggest that people should delay marriage and childbearing, while also trying to convince women not to have a third child (third or higher-order births accounted for 30 percent of all births in 1979). The second step was to promote the one-child family. These goals were accomplished partly by increased social pressure (propaganda, party worker activism, and almost certainly coercion as well), partly by the increased manufacture and distribution of contraceptives, especially the IUD, the wide availability of sterilization, and, of course, abortion.

The heart of the policy as originally formulated, though, was a carefully drawn system of economic incentives (rewards) for one-child families and disincentives (punishments) for larger families. Although the one-child policy was put into place by the central government, it was implemented at the local level in ways that varied from place in place (Gu et al. 2007), with the Han majority (the largest ethnic group in China) finding themselves under greater pressure to conform (and thus having lower fertility) than minority group members, who comprise about 10 percent of the Chinese population (Poston, Chang, and Dan 2006). In particular, since local leaders were held accountable by the central government for achieving low fertility, the door was opened for a variety of abuses, including the widely publicized cases of forced abortion (Jing 2013; Riley 2017).

In the countryside, the incentives were designed to be a bit different. Depending upon the local area, one-child rural families might receive additional monthly work points (which determined the rural payments in cash and in kind) until the child reached age 14. These one-child families also got the same grain ration as a two-child family. In addition, all rural families received the same-sized plot for private cultivation, regardless of family size, thus indirectly rewarding the small family. Although each province and prefecture in China had been encouraged by the central government to tailor specific policies to meet the particular needs of its residents, some of the more widely implemented policies included an increasingly heavy tax on each child after the first and the expectation that for each child after the second, parents would pay full maternity costs as well as full medical and educational costs. The decentralization of the policy, however, had negative local side-effects, as Jing (2013:396) noted: "Fines collected on unplanned births since 1980 are estimated to be RMB 1.5 to 2 trillion [250 to 330 million USD] and have become a major revenue source for some poor local governments. The collection and spending of fines is not fiscally disciplined, lacking standards, transparency, and monitoring. Local officials have developed a keen economic interest in collecting unplanned birth fines." Furthermore, the fact that local officials were held accountable if the birth rate was too high contributed to the widely publicized abuses, especially forced abortions.

One of the unintended side effects of the one-child policy was a markedly skewed sex ratio at birth, with an unusually high fraction of babies being boys, leading to the phenomenon of the "missing females" in China (Coale and Banister 1994)— fewer girls enumerated in censuses at younger ages than you would expect, given the number of boys enumerated. In the 1980s, there was a great deal of speculation and concern that the missing females were victims of female infanticide. Because female infanticide was fairly common during the pre-Communist era, the probability seemed great that the one-child policy in China would lead a couple to kill or abandon a newborn female infant, reserving their one-child quota for the birth of a boy (Mosher 1983). But further analyses of data in both China and South Korea (where a similar pattern of fertility decline has occurred without a coercive one-child policy) suggest that sex-selective abortion (which came into practice during the first years of the one-child policy), combined with the nonregistration of some female births, accounts for almost all of the "missing" females, and that the role of infanticide probably was exaggerated (Banister 2004; Goodkind 2011; Riley 2017). Furthermore, despite the intense publicity over time about forced abortions, the United Nations estimates that 84 percent of married women of reproductive age are using a modern contraceptive in China, with the IUD being the most popular "temporary" method, backed up by abortion (United Nations Population Division 2018a). Female and male sterilization are the methods of choice once a couple has completed childbearing.

Although China's leaders seemed convinced that the one-child policy was necessary to produce and maintain low fertility, it is intriguing to note the cultural similarities between mainland China and Taiwan (which, as you know, is actually claimed by China as part of its territory) and the coincidence of rapid fertility declines in the two countries—one with a clearly defined set of incentives and disincentives (China), and the other with a more normal voluntary family planning program (Taiwan), but both with rapidly expanding economies during the latter part of the twentieth century. The overall comparisons are shown in Figure 5.7, where you can see that Taiwan now has a self-imposed one-child level of fertility—one of

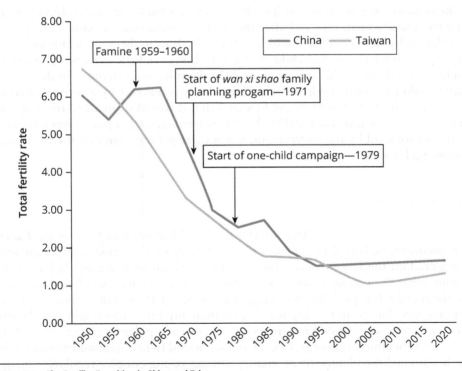

Figure 5.7   The Fertility Transition in China and Taiwan

Source: Prepared by John R. Weeks; data are from United Nations Population Division (2017); data for Taiwan from 1955 to 1990 are from Freedman, Chang, and Sun (1994), and for more recent dates from U.S. Census Bureau International Data Base (accessed 2014).

the lowest fertility levels in the world. It is thus possible, if not likely, that the drop in fertility in China would also have occurred even in the absence of the one-child policy. To be sure, you can see in Figure 5.7 that the total fertility rate was already declining in China at the time the government implemented the one-child policy, and it may well be argued that the government policy merely reinforced changes in reproduction that were already well under way. Furthermore, fertility fell not only in urban areas where the motivation for small families might be greatest, but in rural areas as well (Attané 2001).

The one-child policy in China was initially intended to be only an interim measure that would finally put the brake on population growth in that country (Greenhalgh 1986). The plan had been to ease back to a two-child family after hitting the 1.2 billion level of population size. Estimates by demographers at the United Nations suggest that China had already reached that point by 1995, but it was not until well into the current century that the government started loosening the rule. This was almost certainly in response to the rapidly shifting age structure brought about by the rapid drop in the birth rate. China very inventively used its demographic dividend (which we explained in Chapter 1 and will discuss in more detail in Chapter 8), but a rapidly increasing older population, accompanied by declines in the number of young people entering the labor force, led many people to project that China would grow old before it grew rich.

Reluctantly, the government has slowly walked back the one-child policy in order to raise the birth rate and alter the country's demographic course. In 2013, rules changed so that couples in which either or both were themselves only children could apply to have a second child. There was, however, little evidence that many couples were taking up this option, so in 2016 the rules were changed so that every couple could have two children each. That, too, was not met by a surge in births, and in 2018 the government began to signal that it would drop all restrictions on family size (Myers and Ryan 2018). As of this writing, such a policy has not been clearly put forward by the government, nor is there yet any sign that the birth rate is bouncing back.

The United States

Historical Background   Around 1800, when Malthus was writing his *Essay on Population*, he found the growth rate in America to be remarkably high and commented on the large frontier families about which he had read. Indeed, it is estimated that the average number of children born per woman in colonial America was about eight. It is probably no exaggeration to say that early in the history of the United States, American fertility was higher than any European-origin population had ever experienced. Children were a clear asset to a population trying to establish a thriving agricultural economy. Good harvests helped to maintain nutritional levels that heightened the chance of pregnancy among young couples regularly engaging in unprotected intercourse. Early data are not very reliable, but Ansley Coale and Melvin Zelnick (1963) made estimates of crude birth rates in the United States going back as far as 1800; these indicate that the crude birth rate of nearly 55 per

1,000 population would have been higher than in any country today. Even in 1855, the crude birth rate in America was 43 per 1,000, comparable to the highest levels that exist currently in a few sub-Saharan African countries. The American Civil War seems to have been a turning point in marital fertility, and fertility declined unabated from about 1870 until the Great Depression of the 1930s (Hacker 2003), during which time it bottomed out at a low level only recently reapproached. Why the precipitous drop?

Almost all voluntary migrants to the North American continent up to the late nineteenth century were western Europeans. The people who made up much of the population of the early United States came from a social environment in which fertility limitation was known and practiced. Despite the frontier movement westward, America in the century after the Revolution was urbanizing and commercializing rapidly. Furthermore, the United States was experiencing the process of secularization, and people's lives were increasingly loosened from the control of both the church and state. Malthus had commented that, with respect to all aspects of life, including reproduction, "despotism, ignorance, and oppression produced irresponsibility; civil and political liberty and an informed public gave grounds for expecting prudence and restraint" (Wrigley 1988:39). Craig Bolton and J. William Leasure (1979) have shown that throughout Europe, the early decline in fertility occurred near the time of revolution, democratic reform, or the growth of a nationalist movement. Analogously, Leasure (1989) found that the decline in fertility in the United States in the nineteenth century was closely associated with a rise in what he calls the "spirit of autonomy," measured early in the century by the proportion of the population in an area belonging to the more tolerant Protestant denominations (Congregational, Presbyterian, Quaker, Unitarian, and Universalist) and measured later in the century by educational level.

Lower fertility was accomplished by a rise in the average age at marriage and by various means of birth control within marriage, including coitus interruptus, abortion (even though it was illegal), and extended breastfeeding (Sanderson 1995). Nineteenth-century America also witnessed the secret spread of knowledge about douching and periodic abstinence (Brodie 1994), neither of which is necessarily very effective on the face of it, but the fact that women were searching for ways to prevent pregnancy is clear evidence of the motivation that women had to limit fertility.

New immigrants arriving in the United States in the late nineteenth and early twentieth centuries came especially from southern and eastern Europe, where ideas of contraception were less well known than in western Europe. As a nurse in New York City working among immigrants in the first decade of the twentieth century, Margaret Sanger witnessed firsthand the tragic health consequences for mothers and their babies of having too many children. Sanger herself decided to have only three children after watching her own Irish Catholic mother die prematurely as a result of having 11 children. Her patients kept asking her about the secrets that middle-class women must know that allowed them to keep their families small. But the secrets she did have at that time, including coitus interruptus and abstinence, were dismissed by women as being impossible without a husband's cooperation, which they knew they would never get. In 1912, after helplessly watching a young mother with several children die from a botched self-inflicted abortion, she "resolved to seek out the root of evil, to do something to change the destiny of mothers whose miseries were vast as the sky" (Sanger 1938:92).

Sanger immersed herself in finding out all she could about contraception and began to write on the subject, landing herself in continuing legal difficulty for publishing "pornographic" material. In 1915, she was introduced to a newly designed diaphragm developed in the Netherlands. It required a health professional to fit a woman for the right size, but it was far more effective than anything else that existed at that time, and it was probably the most effective contraceptive in the world until the pill came along in the 1960s (Douglas 1970). The next year, in 1916, Sanger opened her notorious birth control clinic in Brooklyn. She spent the remainder of her life trying to legalize the publication of information about family planning, and to legalize the distribution and use of contraceptives themselves.

Sanger, then, played a very critical role in the contraceptive revolution; she was the founder in 1939 of the Planned Parenthood Federation of America and in 1952 helped to create the International Planned Parenthood Federation. Astoundingly, until 1965, it was technically illegal in the United States for even a married couple to use any method of birth control. In that year the U.S. Supreme Court ruled in *Griswold v. Connecticut* that married couples had a right to privacy that extended to the use of contraceptives. The Court granted that same right to unmarried couples in 1972, and the following year, in the *Roe v. Wade* decision, extended the same argument to the legalization of abortion.

After World War I, the use of condoms became widespread in the United States (and in Europe as well) and, along with withdrawal and abstinence (and the clandestine use of the diaphragm), contributed to very low levels of fertility during the Depression (Himes 1976). The condom was available for sale not because it was a contraceptive (that use was illegal) but rather because it was a "prophylactic" that prevented the spread of sexually transmitted disease. During the Depression, fertility fell to levels below generational replacement. Though the United States was not unique in this respect, that bottoming out in the United States did cap the most sustained drop in fertility the world had seen up to that time. It was undoubtedly a response to the economic insecurity of the period, especially because that insecurity had come about as a quick reversal of increasing prosperity. Fear of social slippage, not to mention sheer desperation, was thus a very likely motive for keeping families small. The American demographic response for many couples was to defer marriage and to postpone having children, hoping to marry later on and have a larger family. Gallup polls starting in 1936 indicate that the average ideal family size was three children, and that most people felt that somewhere between two and four was what they would like. Thus, people were apparently having fewer children than they would have liked to have under ideal circumstances.

In 1933, the birth rate hit rock bottom because women of all ages, regardless of how many children they already had, lowered their level of reproduction. This was, however, mainly a matter of timing (the "tempo" of fertility, as discussed earlier). From 1934 on, the birth rates for first and second children rose steadily (reflecting people getting married and having small families), while birth rates for third and later children continued to decline (reflecting the postponement of larger families) until about 1940 (Grabill, Kiser, and Whelpton 1958). Just as the United States was entering World War II in late 1941 and 1942, there was a momentary rise in the birth rate as husbands went off to war, followed by a lull during the war. However, the end of World War II signaled one of the most dramatic demographic phenomena in North American history—the baby boom.

The Baby Boom   Most of you can probably appreciate that immediately after the end of a war, families and lovers are reunited and the birth rate goes up temporarily as people make up for lost time. This occurred in the United States as well as in England and Canada and several of the European countries actively involved in World War II. Surprisingly, though, these baby booms lasted not for one or two years, but for several years after the war. Birth rates in the United States continued to rise through the 1950s, as the total fertility rate went from 2.30 in 1940 to 3.67 in 1957 (U.S. National Center for Health Statistics 2019). In the United States the term "baby boomers" is usually applied to people born between 1946 and 1964, as we discussed in Chapter 2, but the "boom" peaked in 1957—12 years after the war ended, as you can see in Figure 5.8.

An important contribution to the baby boom was the fact that after the war women started marrying earlier and having their children sooner after marriage. For

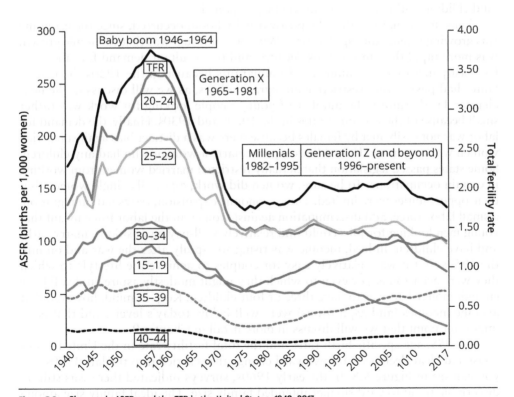

Figure 5.8   Changes in ASFRs and the TFR in the United States: 1940–2017

Sources: Prepared by John R. Weeks; data are from U.S. National Center for Health Statistics (2019) and Martin et al. (2018).

example, in 1940, the average first child was born when the mother was 23.2 years old, whereas by 1960, the average age had dropped to 21.8. This had the effect of bunching up the births of babies, which in earlier times would have been more spread out. Further, not only were young women having children at younger ages, but older women were having babies at older-than-usual ages, due at least in part to their having postponed births during the Depression and the war. After the war, many women stopped postponing and added to the crop of babies each year. These somewhat mechanical aspects of a "catching up" process (the "tempo" of fertility, as discussed early) explain only the early part of the baby boom. What accounts for its prolongation?

We do not have a definitive answer to this question (and remember that it occurred in other countries besides just the United States), but a widely discussed explanation is offered by Richard Easterlin (1968, 1978), which we mentioned in Chapter 3 as the relative cohort size hypothesis—a spin-off of the supply-demand perspective. Easterlin begins his analysis by noting that the long-term decline in the birth rate in the United States was uneven, sometimes happening more rapidly than at other times. In particular, the birth rate declined less rapidly during times of greater economic growth. If a young man could easily find a well-paying job, he could get married and have children; if job hunting was more difficult, marriage (and children within marriage) would be postponed.

Thus, it was natural that the postwar baby boom occurred, since the economy was growing rapidly during that time. What was unusual was that economic growth was more rapid than in previous decades, and the resultant demand for labor was less easily met by large numbers of immigrants because in the 1920s the United States had passed very restrictive immigration laws, as we will discuss in the next chapter. Furthermore, the number of young people looking for work was rather small because of the low birth rates in the 1920s and 1930s. Finally, the demand for labor was not easily met by females because there was a distinct bias against married women working in the United States, particularly a woman who had any children. Some states passed legislation that actually restricted married women from working in certain occupations. To be sure, women did work, especially single women, but their opportunities were limited. Thus, economic expansion, restricted immigration, a small labor force, and discrimination against women in the labor force meant that young men looking for jobs could find relatively well-paying positions, marry early, and have children. Indeed, income was rising so rapidly after the war and on into the 1950s that it was relatively easy for couples to achieve the lifestyle to which they were accustomed, or even to which they might modestly aspire, and still have enough money left over to have three or four children. Keep in mind, however, that average incomes (and aspirations) were well below today's levels, and that is an important point that we will discuss in more detail in Chapter 9.

In 1958, age-specific birth rates and the total fertility rate in the United States registered clear declines—a downward change that carried into the late 1970s—as you can see in Figure 5.8. In the early 1960s, surveys indicated there was still no discernible trend toward smaller intended family size. The ideal family size among Americans had remained quite stable between 1952 and 1966, ranging only between 3.3 and 3.6 children. But in 1967, Judith Blake discovered in a national sample taken the year before that "young women (those under age 30) gave 'two' children as their ideal more frequently than they had in any surveys since the early nineteen-fifties" (Blake 1967:20). This was the first solid evidence that fertility intentions might be on the way down—that the baby bust period had arrived, ushering in what later became known as Generation X.

Beyond the Baby Boom   Social and economic factors in the late 1960s suggested that fertility might continue to decline for a while. The rate of economic growth had slackened off, and there was no longer a labor shortage. As Norman Ryder (1965:845) very presciently noted:

> In the United States today the cohorts entering adulthood are much larger than their predecessors. In consequence they were raised in crowded housing, crammed together in schools, and are now threatening to be a glut on the labor market. Perhaps they will have to delay marriage, because of too few jobs or houses, and have fewer children. It is not entirely coincidental that the American cohorts whose fertility levels appear to be the highest in this century were those with the smallest number.

This was, of course, the kernel of Easterlin's relative cohort hypothesis, and younger couples did indeed alter their fertility behavior. Almost all of the fertility decline was due to a drop in marital fertility, rather than delayed marriage, mainly as a result of the arrival of "the pill," and to a rise in the use of abortion. As fertility dropped, family size ideals dropped as well. Gallup surveys showed that the proportion of white women under age 30 saying that two children was an ideal number rose dramatically from a low of 16 percent in 1957 to 57 percent in 1971 (Blake 1974). The decline in fertility following the baby boom peak thus seemed to signal a major shift in the norms surrounding parenthood in American society. "Motherhood is becoming a legitimate question of *preferences*. Women are now entitled to seek rewards from the pursuit of activities other than childrearing" (Ryder 1990:477, emphasis added).

At its peak in 1957, the TFR was 3.76 children per woman, but by 1976, it was less than half of that—having dropped to an historic low of 1.73. Never since then has the TFR in the United States been that low, as you can see in Figure 5.8. After that, the total fertility rate pushed upward, almost reaching replacement level in 2007, just before the Great Recession of 2008, after which it dropped off again. The latest data as of this writing show the TFR to have dropped down to a level (1.76) which is nearly as low as back in 1976. These general trends hide a great deal of complexity in American fertility patterns over the past three decades that have given us new and unexpected insights into family demography. Some of these include: (1) a steep drop in teenage births, as you can see in Figure 5.8; (2) a steep drop in fertility among women in their 20s, as you can see in Figure 5.8; (3) a rise in fertility among women in their 30s, as you can see in Figure 5.8; (4) a rise in out-of-wedlock births as people delay getting married; (5) an increasing variability in family size, including a rise in the proportion of women who are voluntarily childless; and (6) an increase in the proportion births to racial/ethnic minority groups, especially Hispanics. The implications of these trends are discussed in more detail in Chapter 9.

Summary and Conclusion

Fertility has both a biological and a social component. The capacity to reproduce is biological (although it can certainly be influenced by the environment), but we have to look to the social environment to find out why women are having a particular number of children. For most of human history, fertility was high and "natural" because every group had to overcome high mortality if it was to survive and not disappear. However, the confluence of increasing standards of living and lower mortality has changed those dynamics and led to the fertility transition.

Ansley Coale's three preconditions for a fertility decline (the ready, willing, and able model) offer a useful framework for conceptualizing the kinds of changes that must occur in a society if reproduction is going to drop to significantly lower levels. These include the acceptance of calculated choice about reproductive behavior, a motivation to limit fertility, and the availability of means by which fertility can be limited. The fertility transition is viewed by many as having an essentially economic interpretation, emphasizing the relationship between the supply of children (which is driven by biological factors) and the demand for children (based on a couple's calculations about the costs and benefits of children), given the costs (monetary and psychosocial) of fertility regulation. This is the supply-demand framework. It is complemented by those who argue that fertility limitation is a cultural innovation diffused through societies across social strata and over distances in ways that may be independent of economic factors. Once motivated to limit fertility, people must have some means available to do so. These are generally referred to as the proximate determinants of fertility, and they especially include the age at which regular intercourse begins, the use of contraception, breastfeeding, abortion, and surgical sterilization.

In order to know how fertility levels are changing, we must have ways to measure fertility. Demographers employ a range of statistical techniques, drawing upon vital statistics, censuses, and survey data. These methods use period data (from one point in time), cohort data (following women born at the same time through their reproductive life span), and synthetic cohort data (treating period data for women of different ages as though they represented a cohort). From the latter approach are derived two of the most widely used measurement tools—the total fertility rate and the net reproduction rate.

Theories of the fertility transition emphasize the role of wealth and economic development in lowering levels of fertility, although it is clear that these are sufficient but not necessary reasons for fertility to decline. You must also assess the overall social environment in which change is occurring. Desired and often scarce resources such as wealth, prestige, status, education, and other related factors often help to lower fertility because they change the way people perceive and think about the social world and their place in it. Human beings are amazingly adaptable when they want to be. When people believe that having no children or only a few children is in their best interest, they behave accordingly. Sophisticated contraceptive techniques make it easier, but they are not necessary, as the histories of fertility decline in places like the United Kingdom and the United States illustrate.

One of the most important ways in which societies change in the modern world is through migration. Migrants bring not only their bodies, but also their ideas with them when they move, and as communication and transportation get increasingly easier, they are more apt to diffuse ideas and innovations back to their place of origin, initiating change in those places just as they contribute to the evolution of the society into which they have migrated. In the following chapter, we turn our attention, then, to this next aspect of the demographic transition: the migration transition.

Main Points

1. The fertility transition represents the shift from "natural fertility" to more deliberate fertility limitation, and is associated with a drop in fertility at all ages, but especially at the older ages (beyond the 30s) and younger ages (under 20).

2. Fertility refers to the number of children born to women (or fathered by men), whereas fecundity refers to the biological capacity to produce children.

3. For most of human history, high mortality meant that societies were more concerned with maintaining reasonably high fertility levels, rather than contemplating a decline in fertility—surviving children, not children ever born, was the goal.

4. Ansley Coale's three preconditions for a fertility decline include: (1) acceptance of calculated choice in reproductive decision making ("ready"); (2) motivations to limit fertility ("willing"); and (3) the availability of means by which fertility can be regulated ("able").

5. The supply-demand perspective on the fertility transition suggests that couples strive to maintain a balance between the potential supply of children and the demand (desired number of surviving children), given the cost of fertility regulation.

6. The innovation-diffusion model of fertility draws on sociological and anthropological evidence that much of human behavior is driven by the diffusion of new innovations—both technological and attitudinal—that may have little to do with a rational calculus of costs and benefits.

7. Fertility is measured in a variety of ways using period data (crude birth rate, general fertility rate, child-woman ratio, age-specific birth rates), synthetic cohorts (total fertility rate, gross reproduction rate, net reproduction rate), and cohort data (children ever born and birth intentions).

8. The fertility transition is typically accomplished through a later age at marriage, through older women deciding not to have that additional child, and through women in their prime reproductive years using effective means of fertility control, including especially contraception and abortion.

9. Virtually all wealthy societies now have below-replacement fertility levels, and in almost all less-developed nations in the world today there are genuine fertility declines, as high-fertility norms and behavior give way to low-fertility preferences.

10. The level of fertility in the world is such that a woman gives birth to more than four children every second (we've got to find this woman and stop her!).

Questions for Review

1. How have the three preconditions for a fertility decline played out thus far in your own life?

2. Do you agree that the supply-demand framework and the innovation-diffusion theories seem like complementary perspectives on the fertility transition, rather than competing with each other? Defend your answer.

3. How do you think your perspective on the number of children you want to have in your lifetime would differ if you lived in western Europe, as compared to living in sub-Saharan Africa?

4. What are the arguments for and against the idea that fertility control is a moral dilemma rather than preventive medicine?

5. Why is the status of women in society so important to determining the level of fertility?

CHAPTER 6
The Migration Transition

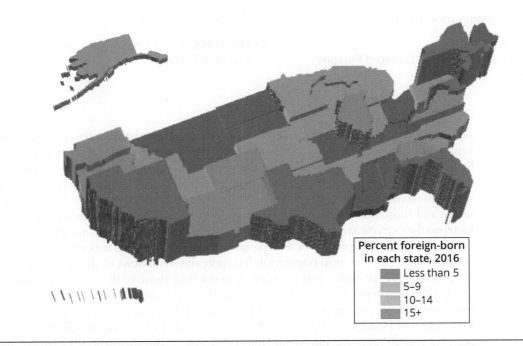

Figure 6.1 **Percent of the Population That Is Foreign-Born by State, United States, 2016**

Source: Prepared by John R. Weeks using American Community Survey data from IPUMS-USA, University of Minnesota, www.ipums.org (Ruggles et al. 2018).

What Is the Migration Transition?

Defining Migration
Internal Migrants
International Migrants
Stocks versus Flows

Measuring Migration

Why Do People Migrate?
Migration Selectivity
    Selectivity by Age
    Selectivity by Gender
The Push-Pull Theory
A Conceptual Model of Migration
    Decision Making

Explaining International Migration
    Neoclassical Economics Approach
    New Household Economics of Migration
    Dual Labor Market Theory
    World Systems Theory
    Network Theory
    Institutional Theory
    Cumulative Causation
    Which Theories Are Best?

Migration Within the United States

Global Patterns of Migration
The Current Situation
How Did We Get to This Point?

America's Immigration Trends
Historical Background of Migration and
   Immigration Laws
Current Immigration Trends

Canada's Immigration Trends

Forced Migration
Refugees and Internally Displaced Persons
Slavery

Impact of Migration on Society

Summary and Conclusion

Main Points

Questions for Review

ESSAY: *Is Migration a Crime? Illegal Immigration
   in Global Context*

Blaise Pascal, the famous seventeenth-century French mathematician, physicist, inventor, and philosopher once quipped: "The sole cause of man's unhappiness is that he does not know to stay quietly in his room." If this is so, unhappiness is enjoying unprecedented popularity today as people are choosing to leave their rooms, so to speak, in record numbers. People move most often in search of a better life for themselves and those dear to them, even though popular news about migration tends to focus on the extreme stories of those who are fleeing violence, oppression, or the effects of climate change. Regardless of why people move, however, migrants often wind up in destinations where the local population has quite different views of the world, ways of approaching life, attitudes, and behavior patterns than those of the migrants. Unfortunately, this contributes to many of the tensions that confront the world. Anti-immigrant sentiment has popped up over the past few years in the United States, contributing to the election of Donald Trump as president; in the United Kingdom, contributing to the popular vote to leave the European Union ("Brexit"); and throughout Germany and other European countries that have opened their doors to immigrants, especially to refugees from the conflict in Syria.

The fact is that more than 80 million people are being added to the world's population each year, and there is still a youth bulge in many less developed countries that already strains local economic resources because there just aren't enough jobs to go around. What are these people to do? Many of them are going to migrate.

What Is the Migration Transition?

Humans have been migrating throughout history (or else we would not be found in every nook and cranny of the globe), but until very recently this was almost entirely rural to rural migration, since cities were few and far between. Aboriginal populations in the Americas, for example, migrated out of Asia into lands never previously peopled by humans. Thousands of years later, Europeans migrated to the Americas, effectively displacing the aboriginal populations from their land, but most of these European migrants were farmers, not city-dwellers. Then, in an historically very short period of time, death rates dropped among European and overseas European populations and the demographic transition came into being. The drop in the death rate was, of course, associated with same economic changes that came with industrialization and the rise of science. These were activities that emerged in conjunction with the rise of cities as centers of control.

As death control diffused to rural populations more quickly than did fertility control, the rates of population growth in rural areas took off, creating a surplus of people in relation to available jobs. The migration transition was initially a rise in the percentage of people who were moving, with many of those people headed to new key destinations—cities. So, humans transitioned from migration being practiced by a relatively small fraction of people who moved largely from one rural area to another rural area (rural-rural migration) to a pattern of a higher percentage of people moving and with major destinations being urban places (rural-urban)—an important enough process that we devote the entire next chapter to the urban transition. More recently, as the majority of humans are now in urban places, the pattern of migration is largely urban to urban. So, the migration transition involves two elements: (1) an increase in the fraction of humans who migrate; and (2) a shift in the places to which and from which they are migrating.

The relationship of migration to the demographic transition arises from the fact that control of mortality and fertility has historically occurred within the context of urban places and then been diffused to rural areas. The population growth resulting from the decline in mortality in rural areas has created the paradoxical situation in which many of the people working in agriculture need to be replaced by machines so that enough food can be grown for a burgeoning population. Thus, people become less useful in agriculture as the population grows. Fortunately, the same forces creating this situation typically are creating employment opportunities in cities, and together these changes in both rural and urban economies help to spur the movement of the population from rural to urban places.

The migration transition within countries is thus the story of population growth in rural areas leading to a redundancy of that population, causing people to look elsewhere for a livelihood. With few new agricultural areas left in the world to be taken over by migrants, the city is now almost always where the jobs are, making the migration transition largely an urban transition (which we discuss in more detail in the next chapter). Eventually, of course, the size of the rural population stabilizes at the relatively low fraction of the total population that is required to grow and process the food and harvest any other natural resources (coal, oil, gold, diamonds, etc.) required by the nation's economy. At that point, it may no longer be appropriate to speak of a migration transition, but rather to a migration evolution, which implies that the population is largely urban-based, and people are moving between and within urban places (Pumain 2004).

Defining Migration

Migration has no known biological components in the way that mortality and fertility do. At the same time, the fact that we study migration rather than immobility means we assume that most people prefer not to move and that it is the moving that requires explanation. We accept the idea that humans have an innate sense of and attachment to place that may transcend rational decision making about the desirability of staying in one place or moving to another. At the same time, migration is an important societal force because it has the potential to alter a community or an entire country profoundly within a short time. In-migration and out-migration can increase or decrease population size, respectively, far more quickly than either mortality or fertility can. And even if the number of in-migrants just equals the number of out-migrants, the flow of people in and out will affect the social and economic structure of a community.

Migration is defined as any permanent change in residence. It involves the "detachment from the organization of activities at one place and the movement of the total round of activities to another" (Goldscheider 1971:64). Thus migration is spatial by definition. You cannot be a migrant unless you "leave your room." However, just because you leave your room, you are not necessarily a migrant. You may be a traveler, or perhaps a daily commuter from your home to work. These activities represent mobility, but not *migration*. You might be a temporary resident elsewhere (such as a construction worker on a job away from home for a few weeks or even months), or a seasonal worker (returning regularly to a permanent home), or a sojourner (typically an international migrant seeking temporary paid employment in another country). Again, though such people are most certainly mobile, they are not migrants because they have not changed their residence permanently. Of course, even when you change your permanent residence, if your new home is only a short distance away and you do not have to alter your round of activities (you still go to the same school, have the same job, shop at the same stores), then you are a mover (and maybe even a shaker), but not a migrant. All migrants are movers, but not all movers are migrants.

Defining migration as a permanent change of residence still leaves several important questions open that have to be answered before we can measure the phenomenon and know who is a migrant and who is not. For example, how far does a person have to move to be considered a migrant instead of just a mover? That is fairly straightforward in the case of international migrants (you are crossing a defined international border), but not so easily determined for internal migrants. As a rule of thumb, people moving only within a country are classified as migrants if they move across administrative boundaries. For example, the U.S. Census Bureau usually defines a migrant as a person who has moved to a different county within the United States. Note, however, that from the standpoint of a city within a county, a migrant would be anyone moving into or out of the city limits. From the standpoint of a local school district, a migrant would be anyone moving into or out of the school district's boundaries, even if the person was still in the same city. This issue of geographic scale is one that must be dealt with in all migration research. A birth is a birth, and a death is a death, but whether or not you are considered a migrant when you move varies according to who is asking the question.

Another question that has to be asked is: What do we mean by permanent? Most people who move at all tend to move more than once in a lifetime, so we have to decide how long you must stay at the new place before your move is considered permanent. The United Nations has somewhat arbitrarily decided that anyone who spends at least one year in the new locale is a migrant. It is sometimes the case that the data you are dealing with will determine what your definition of permanent will be. The decennial census in the United States up through Census 2000 routinely asked people a question about where they lived five years prior to the census. So, a migrant is defined from these census data as someone who lived in a different county (or a different state or a different country) five years prior to the census, regardless of how many times they may have moved in between. Of course, such a definition fails to capture the migration of someone who moved out and then back to the point of origin within that five-year time period. The Current Population Survey, by contrast, has asked a question in each year's March demographic supplement about where a respondent lived a year prior to the survey. This one-year time frame has also been incorporated into the American Community Survey which, as you know from Chapter 2, replaced the census long form as of the 2010 Census.

Internal Migrants

Internal migration, that which occurs within a country, has traditionally been thought of as "free" or voluntary in the sense that people are choosing to migrate or not, often basing that decision on economic factors. This is not to say that, within a country, people are never forced to move. Later in the chapter, we will see that internally displaced persons (IDPs) in fact account for a very large proportion of the world's refugee population. Especially in developing nations whose boundaries may have been created without due regard to ethnic and religious differences among inhabitants, civil strife can force people out of their homes to seek safety and refuge somewhere else in their own country.

People have also been forcibly moved within a country by government-led efforts in response to political and ideological factors. The history of the Western Hemisphere is one in which European migrants displaced the indigenous populations, many of whom still live on reservations created for them against their will. More recently the world has witnessed the migration of more than a million Chinese who were forced to relocate so that the Three Gorges Dam could be built in the 1990s and early 2000s.

International Migrants

Migration across international boundaries is usually voluntary, but it typically means that a person has met fairly stringent entrance requirements, or is entering without documents (which carries a load of stress with it), or is being granted refugee status, fleeing from a political, social, or military conflict. You can easily imagine that most kinds of international migration are apt to be more stressful than internal migration. On top of the move itself is heaped the burden of accommodating to a new culture and often a new language, being dominated perhaps by a different religion, being provided different types and levels of government services, and adjusting to different sets of social expectations and obligations.

To go any further in our discussion, we have to define terms. With reference to your area of origin (the place you left behind), you are an out-migrant, whereas you become an in-migrant with respect to your destination. We add a twist to these terms if you are an international migrant. You are an emigrant in terms of the area of origin and an immigrant in terms of the area of destination. Because commuters and sojourners also may cross international boundaries, the United Nations has tried to tighten the definition of an international migrant by developing the concept of a long-term immigrant, which includes all persons who arrive in a country during a year and whose length of stay in the country of arrival is more than one year (Kraly and Warren 1992).

As noted above, international migration can be differentiated further between legal immigrants, illegal (or undocumented) immigrants, refugees, and asylees. Legal immigrants are those who have governmental permission to live in the place to which they are migrating, whereas illegal or undocumented migrants do not. A refugee is defined by the United Nations (and by most countries of the world) as a person who "owing to a well-founded fear of being persecuted for reasons of race, religion, nationality, membership of a particular social group, or political opinion, is outside the country of his nationality, and is unable to or, owing to such fear, is unwilling to avail himself of the protection of that country" (UNHCR 2010). Asylees are refugees—with a geographic twist: they are already in the country to which they are applying for admission, whereas refugees are outside the country at the time of application.

To tangle the situation further, migration may involve more than a single individual—a family or even an entire village may migrate together. A ghost town, it has been suggested, does not necessarily signal the end of a community, only its relocation. More immediately, you may recall that in 2018 a migrant caravan of several thousand people formed in Honduras with help from a North American immigrant rights organization called *Pueblo sin Fronteras* (people without borders). This caravan, and the ones that have come in its wake, differ from previous migration streams to the U.S.-Mexico border because they were comprised especially of entire young families—not just individual migrants. These were people fleeing gang activity and government corruption in Central American countries, where U.S. Embassy personnel are very unlikely to grant refugee status for those kinds of reasons. The caravan traveled north through Guatemala, and then through Mexico to the U.S.-Mexico border where people hoped to cross the border and claim asylum in the United States. In the process, the Trump administration created a media show, declaring a "crisis" at the border, leading to policies such as the separation of immigrant children from their parents, and a lengthy partial government shutdown as a way of trying to force Congress to authorize funding a wall along the entire 2,000 mile U.S.-Mexico border.

Stocks Versus Flows

One of the more important things to keep in mind as we discuss the migration transition is that it involves both a process and a transformation. The *process* is that people move from one place to another—the migration flow. The *transformation* is that the migrant stock—those people living in a different place than where they were born—changes as people move into and out of a given place. The fact that an average of one million legal immigrants per year were admitted to the United States between 2000 and 2017 (U.S. Department of Homeland Security 2018) represents a measure of the flow of people from other places into the country. Those people were added to the stock of immigrants (the foreign-born population) already residing in the United States at the time.

Based on data from the American Community Survey, we can estimate that the total stock of foreign-born persons in the United States in 2016 was 45 million, accounting for almost 14 percent of the population. These data include undocumented persons since they are included in the census enumerations and American Community Survey. Figure 6.1 at the beginning of this chapter illustrates how the stock of immigrants varies state-by-state. California leads the nation with 28 percent of its population having been born outside the United States. This is followed by New York with 24 percent, New Jersey with 23, Florida and Nevada with 21, Hawaii with 20, Texas with 18, Massachusetts with 17, Maryland and the District of Columbia with 16. You can see that 8 of these top 10 states in terms of migrant stock are at the edge of the country, places where migrants are most likely to enter. Thus, the states with a large stock of immigrants are also places with the higher migration flows.

The conceptual contrast between stocks and the flows can be illustrated by the idea that if a million previous migrants had left the country just as a million new migrants were entering, the in- and out-flows would have been pretty large, but the stock itself would not have changed numerically. On the other hand, the demographic composition of the stock of migrants (e.g., their places of origin) could have been changed by the flows, even if the stock did not change numerically.

Information about the migrant stock comes largely from censuses and surveys where everybody is asked a question about whether or not they used to live in a different place. If they did (and they meet the criteria for being a migrant rather than just a mover), then they are part of the stock of migrants. If one additional question is asked about where they came from, then we can infer something about migration flows, as well, because we can then measure the number of people in the stock who flowed from point A to point B. Migration flow data can come from a variety of other sources, such as the U.S. Department of Homeland Security, which keeps track of people entering the United States.

Table 6.1 illustrates two different ways of evaluating the flow of immigrants to the United States in 2016. The official U.S. data on legal immigrants come from the Yearbook of Immigration Statistics compiled every year by the Department of Homeland Security (2019), and in Table 6.1 the numbers refer to people obtaining lawful permanent resident status (i.e., "green card" holders) in the United States during 2016, according to the country of their last residence. For most people this will be the same as the country of birth, but some people may have previously migrated and were living in a different place when they decided to migrate to the United States.

The other data in Table 6.1 come from responses to the American Community Survey, aggregated for the five-year period up to and including 2016. If a person responded that they had lived outside the United States a year ago, and they were also not already a U.S. citizen, then we can assume they are immigrants. They

Table 6.1   Top Countries of Origin for Immigrants to the United States, 2016

Country of Last Residence	Homeland Security Legal Immigrants—Persons Obtaining Lawful Permanent Resident Status, 2016, by Country of Last Residence	ACS 2016 5-Year Data—Foreign-Born, Not U.S. Citizen, Lived Abroad 1 Year Ago, by Country of Last Residence (Weighted Sample Data)
Mexico	172,726	125,591
China	77,658	127,156
Cuba	66,120	30,576
India	61,691	137,981
Dominican Republic	60,613	23,538
Philippines	50,609	34,880
Vietnam	40,412	17,731
Haiti	23,185	12,206
Jamaica	22,833	12,732
South Korea	21,329	35,328
El Salvador	21,268	21,880
Canada	19,349	52,916
Colombia	16,830	18,258
United Kingdom	14,887	29,035
Ethiopia	13,699	n/a
Brazil	13,528	25,798
Egypt	13,367	7,585
Honduras	12,996	19,079
Guatemala	12,548	18,847
Ecuador	10,779	n/a
TOTAL	1,183,505	1,217,937
Top 20 as % of total	63	62

Source: Prepared by John R. Weeks; Homeland Security data are from (U.S. Department of Homeland Security 2019); American Community Survey data are from IPUMS-USA (Ruggles et al. 2018).

are asked to name the country in which they lived a year ago, so that is information similar to the data from Homeland Security. The top 20 countries of last residence from the Department of Homeland Security account for 63 percent of the 1,183,505 people who entered the country legally that year, with the list being led by Mexico, China, Cuba, and India.

The estimates from the ACS show a very similar number of immigrants, and the top 20 countries from the Homeland Security list account for a nearly identical 62 percent of all immigrants that year. However, the country of last residence from the ACS data produces a different order of countries than the Homeland Security data. Instead of Mexico, China, Cuba, and India, the list is led by India, followed by China, Mexico, and Canada. A key difference between the two sources of data is that the ACS is administered to a sample of all households and thus includes undocumented immigrants, as well as people who may be in the country on temporary work or student visas, whereas the Homeland Security numbers refer only to legal immigrants—people with permission to live permanently in the country. We will talk about these issues below as we discuss the measurement of migration. At this point, it is mainly useful to remind ourselves once again how complicated migration can be.

People tend to be more concerned about who is coming in than who is leaving, and this is one reason why most countries do not have a good source of data on the number and destinations of out-migrants. In the United States, we tend to rely on estimates such as the number of Social Security checks sent to people living outside the country. We know, for example, that in December 2018, the Social Security Administration sent 413,426 checks to foreign addresses (U.S. Social Security Administration 2019), and it is likely that most of these are being sent to people who migrated to the United States to work, and then when they reached retirement age went back from whence they came—where their retirement check in dollars is likely to go further than in the United States.

The same can be said for Canada, where Citizenship and Immigration Canada (CIC) records the arrival of immigrants but has no data on people who leave the country. This problem arises even in the European nations that, as we mentioned in Chapter 2, maintain population registers. After Germany conducted a census in 2011, it discovered that the population was slightly smaller than that estimated from population register data because people were leaving the country without telling the authorities. Most countries have little available information on emigration, and we either do not know what is happening or have to rely on sample surveys or other indirect evidence (such as the stock of foreign-born people from a given country counted in censuses of destination nations) to infer patterns of emigration flow.

With respect to internal migration, data for the United States are obtained from the Current Population Survey and the American Community Survey, as noted above. The U.S. Census Bureau also conducts the American Housing Survey every other year, which tracks changes in the nation's housing stock and thereby generates data on residential mobility (changing residence regardless of how long or short the distance) within the country. Furthermore, the Census Bureau has an arrangement with the Internal Revenue Service that allows the Bureau to periodically examine the address changes reported by people on tax returns, and that drill provides yet another way of tracking migration flows within the country.

Measuring Migration

Migration is measured with rates similar to those constructed for fertility and mortality. These rates can be used to measure internal or international migration, depending on the focus of your analysis and the data you have at your disposal.

The crude or gross rate of in-migration (IMigR) is the ratio of all people who moved into the region (the flow) during a given year relative to the total midyear population in that region:

$$IMigR = \frac{IM}{p} \times 1,000$$

The gross rate of in-migration is a little misleading because the midyear population refers to the people living in the area of destination, which is not the group of people at risk of moving in (indeed, they are precisely the people who are *not* at risk of moving in because they are already there). Nonetheless, the in-migration rate does provide a sense of the impact that in-migration has on the region in question, so it is useful for that reason alone.

Gross or total out-migration (*OM*) represents the flow of all people who leave a particular region during a given time period (usually a year), and the crude or gross rate of out-migration (*OMigR*) relates those people to the total midyear population (*p*) in the region (and then we multiply by 1,000):

$$OMigR = \frac{OM}{p} \times 1,000$$

The numerical difference between those who move in and those who move out is called net migration. If these numbers are the same, then net migration is zero, even if there has been a lot of migration activity. If there are more in-migrants than out-migrants, net migration is positive; if the out-migrants exceed the in-migrants, net migration is negative. The crude net migration rate (*CNMigR*) is thus the net number of migrants in a year per 1,000 people in a population and represents the difference between the net in- and out-migration rates. It is calculated as follows:

$$CNMigR = IMigR - OMigR$$

The total *volume* (flow) of migration may be of interest to people because it can have a substantial impact on a community even if the net rate is low. This is measured as the total or gross migration rate (*TMigR*)—also sometimes called the migration turnover rate—which is the sum of in-migrants and out-migrants divided by the midyear population, or more simply the in-migration rate plus the out-migration rate:

$$TMigR = IMigR + OMigR$$

Another way of viewing migration is through the concept of migration effectiveness (*E*), which measures how "effective" the total volume of migration is in redistributing the population (Plane and Rogerson 1994, Manson and Groop 2000). For example, if there were a total of 10 migrants in a region in a year and all

10 were in-migrants, the "effectiveness" of migration would be 10/10, or 100 percent; whereas if four were in-migrants and six were out-migrants, the effectiveness would be much lower: (4 − 6)/10, or −20 percent. In general, the rate of effectiveness (E) is as follows:

$$E = \frac{CNMigR}{TmigR} \times 100$$

There is no universally agreed-upon measure of migration that summarizes the overall levels in the same way that the total fertility rate summarizes fertility and life expectancy summarizes mortality. However, one way of measuring the contribution that migration makes to population growth is to calculate the ratio of net migration to natural increase (the difference between births and deaths); this is called the migration ratio (*MigRatio*):

$$MigRatio = \frac{IM - OM}{b - d}$$

For example, between July 1, 2017, and July 1, 2018, the U.S. Census Bureau (2018b) estimated that there was a net migration of 978,826 people into the country (the difference between immigrants and emigrants). During that same one-year period there were 3,855,500 births in the United States and 2,814,013 deaths, so the natural increase (births minus deaths) was 1,041,487. The ratio of the net migrants to natural increase was thus 978,826 to 1,041,487 or .94, indicating that migration was just slightly less important than natural increase in its contribution to that year's population growth in the United States. If we rearrange that equation a little, we can calculate the percentage of growth attributable to migration (MigPct), which in this case is 48 percent:

$$MigPct = \frac{IM - OM}{(IM - OM) + (b - d)} \times 100$$

Because we often do not have complete sets of data on the number of in- and out-migrants, we can "back into" the migration rate by solving the demographic balancing equation (which we discussed in Chapter 2) for migration. This is known as the components of change (or residual) method of estimating migration. The demographic balancing equation states that population growth between two dates is a result of the addition of births, the subtraction of deaths, and the net effect of migration (the number of in-migrants minus the number of out-migrants). If we know the amount of population growth between two dates (e.g., from consecutive censuses), and we also know the number of births and deaths (typically from a system of vital statistics), then by subtraction we can estimate the amount of net migration. Let me give you an example. Based on the 2000 census of the United States, we know that on April 1, 2000, there were 281,424,600 residents counted in the country. Between that date and April 1, 2010, there were 41,406,971 births and 24,316,206 deaths in the country. Thus on April 1, 2010, we should have expected the census to find 298,515,365 residents if no migration had occurred. However, the 2010 census counted 308,745,538 people. That difference of 10,230,173 people was estimated to be the result of migration (note that a small fraction of the difference could also be the result of differences in coverage error between the two censuses, as discussed in Chapter 2). Because the difference is equivalent to about one million net immigrants per year, we can see that the numbers make sense.

In an analogous way, we can also calculate intercensal net migration rates for specific age groups by gender. If we know the number of people at ages 15–24 in 2000, for example, and if we can calculate how many of them died between 2000 and 2010, then we know how many people aged 25–34 there should have been in 2010 in the absence of migration. Any difference between the observed and the expected number in 2010 can be attributed to migration. Typically, we use a life table (see Chapter 4) to calculate the proportion of people who will die between two different ages, and we call this whole procedure the forward survival (or residual) method of migration estimation. For example, in 2000 in the United States, there were 19,105,073 females aged 15–24. Life table values suggest that 99.6 percent of those women (or 19,031,697) should still have been alive at ages 25–34 in 2010 (the forward survival). In fact, Census 2010 counted 21,308,500 women in that age group, or 2,276,803 more than expected. We assume, then, that those "extra" women (the residual) were immigrants, so this is a measure of net migration.

Once again, we note that this assumption ignores any part of that difference that may have been due to differences in the coverage error in the two censuses. If one census undercounted the population more or less than the next census, this could account for at least part of the residual that is otherwise being attributed to migration. Conversely, if we knew the number of migrants, then the difference between the actual and expected number of migrants would tell us something about the accuracy of the census (and that *is* one of the ways of evaluating the census, as we discussed in Chapter 2).

The residual method is also the key to estimating the undocumented immigrant population in the United States. The Current Population Survey and the American Community Survey ask people in large random samples of households questions about their place of birth and their country of last residence, and these survey results provide estimates for the entire country, as we discussed above in reference to Table 6.1. The assumption is made that everyone who entered the country prior to 1980 is now a legal resident, given the opportunities afforded to them (Hoefer, Rytina, and Baker 2012). We know how many people have been granted legal permanent residence in the United States since 1980 and can create estimates of how many of them may have subsequently left the country by assuming that legal residents would most likely go back to their country of origin when they retire and start receiving their Social Security checks. The difference between the total number of foreign-born people estimated to be in the country and our estimate of how many of them are legal residents leaves us with an estimate of how many of the foreign-born are in the country without documentation. In 2016, the estimate was that there were 10.7 million such persons, lower than the peak of 12.2 million in 2007, just before the Great Recession (Krogstad, Passel, and Cohn 2018).

Why Do People Migrate?

The theory of demographic change and response (see Chapter 3) suggested that migration is a ready adaptation that humans (or other animals, for that matter) can make to relieve the pressure put on local resources by population increase. If some people are willing (or are forced) to move, the pressure is reduced. And when people do move, they generally don't move at random—they tend to go where they believe opportunity exists. Because the demographic transition occurred historically in the context of economic development, which involved especially the centralization of economic functions in cities, migrants have been drawn to cities, and the urban transition is a central part of the migration transition, as we will discuss in the next chapter. Yet the mere existence of a migration transition does not explain why people move, who moves, and where they go. We need to dig deeper for those explanations.

Migration Selectivity

As we noted above, not everyone migrates, or even moves, in their life, and Everett Lee (1966) observed that two of the more enduring generalizations that can be made about migration are:

1. Migration is selective (that is, not everyone migrates, only a selected portion of the population).
2. The heightened propensity to migrate at certain stages of the life cycle is important in the selection of migrants.

One particular stage of life disproportionately associated with migration is that of reaching adulthood. Young adults are much more likely to migrate than anyone else. This is the age at which the demand or desire for obtaining more education tends to peak, along with the process of finding a job or establishing a career, and getting married. Furthermore, as you know from the discussion about the health and mortality transition, it is also the time of life when people are most healthy and thus capable of moving.

Selectivity by Age   The idea that young adults are more likely to migrate than anyone else is about as close as we can get to a biological component to migration. If there is such a thing as a "law of migration," this is it. As an example of this, the data in Figure 6.2 show the age pattern of intercounty migrants in the United States in 2016, using data from the American Community Survey. As you can see, young adults were much more mobile than people of other ages, and this same pattern has a long history in the United States and holds true in other countries as well.

The young adult ages, 20–29, are clearly those at which migration predominates, and this is true for both internal and international migration. From there the percentage of people who migrate drops off steeply, with a small rise at the older ages as people are moving to warmer climates and/or closer to their children

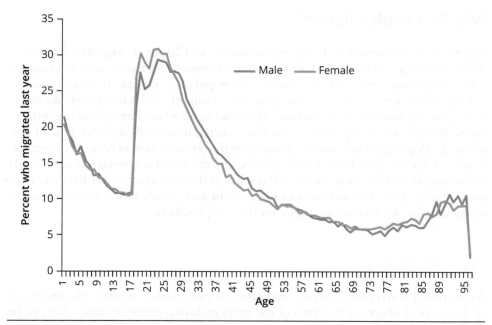

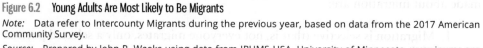

Figure 6.2   Young Adults Are Most Likely to Be Migrants

Note: Data refer to Intercounty Migrants during the previous year, based on data from the 2017 American Community Survey.

Source: Prepared by John R. Weeks using data from IPUMS-USA, University of Minnesota, www.ipums.org (Ruggles et al. 2018).

for old-age support. At ages younger than 20, children typically are just following their parents, so it is not surprising that younger children (who have the youngest parents) move more than older children. We can see, then, that age is an important determinant of migration because it is related to life-cycle changes that affect most humans in most societies.

Selectivity by Gender Older models of household decision-making about migration took for granted that it is the male of the household who will be making the migration decision (Cerrutti and Massey 2001). Any generalization about gender and migration is likely to be misleading, however. Like almost all aspects of migration, this one is complicated by cultural norms about the role of women in society. In the United States, for example, women have virtually the same rates of internal migration as do men, with an identical age pattern, as you can see in Figure 6.2. Furthermore, there are now actually more female than male legal immigrants to the United States, reflecting the general rise in gender equity. Women are increasingly apt to migrate on their own, rather than to move only because they are trailing a husband.

In so-called traditional societies, the role of women is assumed to be at home caring for children and other family members, and under such circumstances migration will likely be undertaken more by males than by females. Thus, men are more likely to outnumber women among migrants in those areas of the world where the status of women is lowest—Africa and Asia—whereas women are as likely or even more likely to be migrants in Europe, North America, Latin America, and the Caribbean (United Nations Population Division 2013).

The Push-Pull Theory

Over time, the most frequently heard explanation for migration has been the so-called push-pull theory, which echoes common sense by saying that some people move because they are pushed out of their former location, whereas others move because they have been pulled or attracted to someplace else. This idea was first put forward by Ernst Georg Ravenstein (1889), a German-English geographer who analyzed migration in England using data from the 1881 census of England and Wales. He concluded that pull factors were more important than push factors: "Bad or oppressive laws, heavy taxation, an unattractive climate, uncongenial social surroundings, and even compulsion (slave trade, transportation), all have produced and are still producing currents of migration, but none of these currents can compare in volume with that which arises from the desire inherent in most men to 'better' themselves in material respects" (p. 286). Thus Ravenstein is saying that it is the desire to get ahead more than the desire to escape an unpleasant situation that is most responsible for the voluntary migration of people, at least in late-nineteenth-century England.

In everyday language, we could label the factors that might push a person to migrate as stress or strain. However, it is probably rare for people to respond to stress by voluntarily migrating unless they feel there is some reasonably attractive alternative, which we could call a pull factor. The social science model conjures up an image of the rational decision maker computing a cost-benefit analysis of the situation. The potential migrant weighs the push and pull factors and moves if the benefits of doing so exceed the costs. For example, if you lost your job, it could benefit you to move if there are no other jobs available where you live now, unemployment compensation and welfare benefits have expired, and there is a possibility of a job at another location. Or, to be more sanguine about your employability, the process may start, for example, when you are offered an excellent executive spot in a large firm in another city. Will the added income and prestige exceed the costs of uprooting the family and leaving the familiar house, community, and friends behind?

A Conceptual Model of Migration Decision Making

In truth, whether or not you migrate will likely depend on a more complicated set of circumstances than the push-pull theory might suggest. The decision to move usually develops over a fairly long period of time, proceeding from a desire to move, to the expectation of moving, to the actual fact of migrating. Between the desire to move and the actual decision to do so there may also be intervening obstacles (Lee 1966). The distance of the expected destination, the cost of getting there, poor health, and other such factors may inhibit migration. These obstacles are hard to predict on any wide scale, however, so we tend to lump them together with the overall "costs" of moving and concentrate our attention on explaining the desire to move. Economic variables dominate most explanations of why people migrate. If it is assumed that people spend much of their life pursuing various goals, then migration may be seen as a possible means—an implementing strategy—whereby goals associated with different stages in the life cycle (such as more education, a better job, a nicer house, a more pleasant environment, and so on) might be attained.

Figure 6.3 provides an overview of the major aspects of the migration process that require explanation, adapted from a conceptual model devised by Gordon De Jong and James Fawcett (1981) and revised by De Jong (2000). These are analogous in certain respects to the three preconditions for a fertility decline. The migration process can be thought of as having three major stages (not unlike "ready," "willing," and "able" as we discussed for fertility) including: (1) the propensity to migrate in general, (2) the motivation to migrate to a specific location, and (3) the actual decision to migrate.

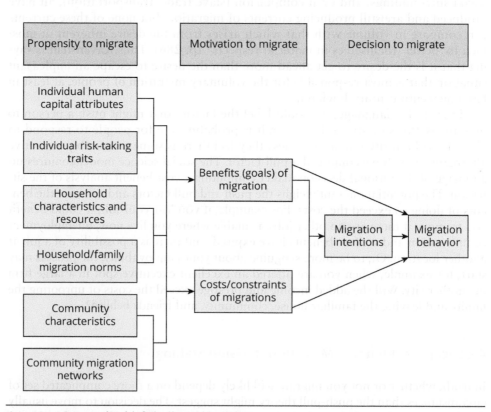

Figure 6.3   A Conceptual Model of Migration Decision Making

Source: Adapted by John R. Weeks from Gordon De Jong and James Fawcett, 1981, "Motivations for Migration: An Assessment and a Value-Expectancy Research Model," in G. De Jong and R. Gardner (eds.), *Migration Decision Making* (New York: Pergamon Press), Figure 2.2; and Gordon De Jong, 2000, "Expectations, Gender, and Norms in Migration Decision-Making," *Population Studies* 54:307–319, Figure 1.

The migration process begins with individuals and household members in the context of a given culture and society, represented by the community in which they live. The decision about who will migrate and when and to where may often be part of a household strategy for improving the group's quality of life—consistent with the perspective of demographic change and response. Furthermore, the household decision is not made in a vacuum; it is influenced by the sociocultural environment in which the household members live. Individual and household characteristics are important because of the selectivity of migrants—households with no young adults are less likely to contemplate migration. Social and cultural norms are important because they provide the context in which people might think consciously of migration as a necessary or desirable thing to do. Social norms can play a role in discouraging migration by emphasizing the importance of place and community or, on the other hand, political and economic instability may cause people to rethink their commitment to an area.

Personal traits are important because some people are greater risk takers than others. In the United States, the "average" person can expect to move 11.7 times in his or her lifetime (U.S. Census Bureau 2012). Nonetheless, an average like that hides a lot of variability. Some people account for a disproportionate amount of migration by migrating frequently, whereas others rarely or never move.

Demographic characteristics combine with societal and cultural norms about migration to shape the values people hold with respect to migration—the benefits they hope to gain by migrating. Such benefits represent clusters of motivations to move, including the desires for wealth, status, comfort (better living or working conditions), stimulation (including entertainment and recreation), autonomy (personal freedom), affiliation (joining family or friends), and morality (especially religious beliefs). At the same time, personal traits (such as being a risk-taking person) combine with the opportunity structure within the household and the community to affect the costs and constraints that might keep a person from migrating. All of these personal and social environmental factors combine to affect a person's expectation of actually achieving the goals they have in mind that might be facilitated by migration.

The amount of information a person has about the comparative advantages of moving also contributes to the expectation of attaining migration values or goals—that balancing of the likelihood of obtaining the benefits with the perceived costs involved in migrating. If the benefits appear to outweigh the costs, then the person is more likely to decide to migrate. Given the intention to move, a person may discover that by making adjustments in his or her current situation, personal or family goals can actually be achieved without having to move. "Such adjustments might include a change in occupation, alterations to the physical structure of the house, a change in daily and friendship patterns, or lifestyle changes" (De Jong and Fawcett 1981:56). Finally, the intention to move (or to stay) leads ultimately to the act of moving (or staying) itself, although unanticipated events may still affect that decision. Indeed, events may overtake a person in something akin to the diffusion model, so that even though there was no original intention to migrate, the person migrates anyway. We have all been swept up in situations and done things that we wouldn't necessarily have done had we given them more thought.

Explaining International Migration

Though immigration may be the sincerest form of flattery, few countries encourage it. Migration between countries is fraught with the potential for conflict among people of different cultural backgrounds and, as technology has eased the constraints of transportation and communication, migration has become easier than ever. This has brought the issues surrounding international migration into sharper focus. This is certainly nowhere more true than in the United States, where international immigration has been a way of life since the country's founding and toward which a substantial fraction of the annual volume of the world's international migrants still heads.

Referring back to Figure 6.3, we can make the general statement that internal migration is more strongly influenced by individual characteristics of people; whereas international migrants are more apt to be influenced by the social and political climate and by the opportunity structure (especially barriers to migration, or lack thereof, that influence the costs and constraints of migration). The kinds of migration goals that internal migrants have are also likely to differ somewhat from those of international migrants. Douglas Massey and his associates (Massey et al. 1993; Massey and Espinosa 1997; Massey, Durand, and Malone 2002; Massey 2008) have reviewed and evaluated various theories that try to explain contemporary patterns of international migration, as we discuss below

Of the factors laid out in Figure 6.3, there are several of the elements that are most important in explaining migration in the modern world. The first of these is the creation of new opportunity structures for migration, which raise the benefit of migrating (pull factors) partly by undermining existing local relationships between people and resources (push factors). At the same time, cheaper and quicker transportation and communication can increase the information that people have about a potential new location (lowering the risks associated with migration by closing the gap between the anticipated benefits and the perceived likelihood of attaining those goals) while also making it easier to migrate and to return home if things do not work out.

Step migration and chain migration, two migration strategies that have stood out over time, help determine where migrants go. Step migration is a process whereby migrants attempt to reduce the risk of their decision by sort of inching away from home. The rural resident may go to a nearby city, and from there to a larger city, and perhaps eventually to a huge megalopolis. Chain migration reduces risk because it involves migrants in an established flow from a common origin to a predetermined destination where earlier migrants have already scoped out the situation and laid the groundwork for the new arrivals.

Chain migration also has a built-in multiplier effect that is the underlying source of the dramatic way in which immigration is changing the face of North America and Europe. The "pioneer" immigrant arrives in the new country and becomes established and then sends for other family members—family reunification. Once the family is in place, the second generation is born and one immigrant has created a group (Bin Yu 2008). This is a pattern that especially characterizes migration from Mexico and the Philippines to the United States, and it reminds us that the choice of *where* to move is a large component of *why* people decide to migrate internationally.

The major theories that exist to help explain various aspects of international migration, as originally outlined by Massey and his associates (1993, 1994), include first those that focus on the initiation of migration patterns: (1) neoclassical economics; (2) the new household economics of migration; (3) dual labor market theory; and (4) world systems theory. Then there are three perspectives that help to explain the perpetuation of migration, once started: (1) network theory; (2) institutional theory; and (3) cumulative causation. All of these perspectives are aimed at explaining the flow of migrants between countries, although of course they may also be applicable in some instances to internal migration, especially in developing nations.

Neoclassical Economics Approach   By applying the classic supply-and-demand paradigm to migration, the neoclassical economics approach argues that migration is a process of labor adjustment caused by geographic differences in the supply of and demand for labor. Countries with a growing economy and a scarce labor force have higher wages than a region with a less developed economy and a larger labor force. The differential in wages causes people to move from the lower-wage to the higher-wage region. This continues until the gap in wages is reduced merely to the costs of migration (both monetary and psychosocial). At the individual level, migration is viewed as an investment in human capital (investments in individuals that can improve their economic productivity and thus their overall standard of living).

This theory suggests that people choose to migrate to places where the greatest opportunities exist. This may not be where the average wages are currently the highest, but rather where the individual migrant believes that, in the long run, his or her own skills will earn the greatest income. These skills include education, experience, training, and language capabilities. This approach has been used to explain internal as well as international migration. It is also the principle that underlies Ravenstein's conceptualization of push factors (especially low wages in the region of origin) and pull factors (especially high wages in the destination region).

New Household Economics of Migration   The neoclassical approach assumes that the individual is the appropriate unit of analysis, but the new household economics of migration approach argues that decisions about migration are often made in the context of what is best for an entire family or household. This approach accepts the idea that people act collectively not only to maximize their expected income, but also to minimize risk. Thus migration is not just a way to get rid of people; it is also a way to diversify the family's sources of income. The idea is that migrating members of the household have their journey subsidized and then remit portions of their earnings back home. This cushions households against the risk inherent in societies with weak institutions. If there is no unemployment insurance, no welfare, no bank from which to borrow money or even in which to invest money safely, then the remittances from migrant family members can be cornerstones of a household's economic well-being. This has become a huge part of the international migration story and we will return to it at the end of the chapter.

Dual Labor Market Theory   The dual labor market theory offers a reason for the creation of opportunities for migration. It suggests that in developed regions of the world there are essentially two kinds of job markets: the primary sector, which employs well-educated people, pays them well, and offers them security and benefits; and the secondary labor market, characterized by low wages, unstable working conditions, and lack of reasonable prospects for advancement. It is easy enough to recruit people into the primary sector, but the secondary sector is not so attractive. Historically, women, teenagers, and racial and ethnic minorities in the richer countries were recruited into these jobs, but in the past few decades women and racial and ethnic minority groups have succeeded in moving increasingly into the primary sector, at the same time that the low birth rate has diminished the supply of teenagers available to work. Yet the lower echelon of jobs still needs to be filled, and so immigrants from developing countries are recruited—either actively (as in the case of agricultural workers) or passively (the diffusion of information that such jobs are available).

World Systems Theory   The world systems theory offers a different perspective on the emerging opportunity structure for migration in the contemporary world. The argument is that, since the sixteenth century (and then gaining traction as part of the Industrial Revolution in Europe), the world market has been developing and expanding into a set of core nations (those with capital and other forms of material wealth) and a set of peripheral countries (in essence, the rest of the world) that have become dependent on the core, as the core countries have entered the peripheral countries in search of land, raw materials, labor, and new consumer markets.

According to world systems theory, migration is a natural outgrowth of disruptions and dislocations that inevitably occur in the process of capitalist development. As capitalism has expanded outward from its core in Western Europe, North America, Oceania, and Japan, ever-larger portions of the globe and growing shares of the human population have been incorporated into the world market economy. As land, raw material, and labor within peripheral regions come under the influence and control of markets, migration flows are inevitably generated. Migration flows do not tend to be random, however. In particular, peripheral countries are most likely to send migrants (including refugees and asylees) to those core nations with which they have had the greatest contact, whether economic, political, or military.

Network Theory   Once migration has begun, it may well take on a life of its own, quite separate from the forces that got it going in the first place, in a process that is part of the chain migration concept mentioned above. Network theory argues that migrants establish interpersonal ties that "connect migrants, former migrants, and non-migrants in origin and destination areas through ties of kinship, friendship, and shared community origin. They increase the likelihood of international movement because they lower the costs and risks of movement and increase the expected net returns to migration" (Massey et al. 1993:449). Once started, migration sustains itself through the process of diffusion until everyone who wishes to migrate can do so. In developing countries, such migration eventually may become a rite of passage into adulthood for community members, having little to do with economic supply and demand.

Institutional Theory   Institutional theory argues that, once started, migration also may be perpetuated by institutions that develop precisely to facilitate (and profit from) the continued flow of immigrants (Agunias 2009). These organizations may provide a range of services, from humanitarian protection of exploited persons to more illicit operations such as smuggling people across borders and providing counterfeit documents, and might include more benign services such as arranging for lodging or credit in the receiving country. These organizations help perpetuate migration in the face of government attempts to limit the flow of migrants.

Cumulative Causation   The cumulative causation perspective recognizes that each act of migration changes the likelihood of subsequent decisions about migration because of the cascading impact on the social environments in both the sending and receiving regions. The sending back of remittances increases the income levels of migrants' families relative to others in the community of origin and in this way may contribute to an increase in the motivation of other households to send migrants. Migrants themselves may become part of a culture of migration and be more likely to move again, increasing the overall volume of migration. In the receiving country, the entry of immigrants into certain occupational sectors may label them as "immigrant" jobs, which reinforces the demand for immigrants to fill those jobs continually.

Data from Massey's Mexican Migration Project suggest that migration streams are much easier to start than to stop, because migration cumulatively begets more migration as community members in and from the sending area derive a real benefit (human capital) from migration and as expanded networks (social capital) make it increasingly easier to migrate (Massey and Espinosa 1997).

Which Theories Are Best?   Massey and his associates (1994) attempted to evaluate the adequacy of each of the just-discussed theories in explaining contemporary patterns of international migration. Their conclusion was that each of the theories is supported in some way or another by the available evidence and, in particular, none of the theories is specifically refuted. Most of the research on migration since the mid-1990s has specifically tested one or another of these theories, with the same conclusion that each of them helps explain an important part of this complex phenomenon. Though no single theory seems able to capture all of its nuances, all the previous perspectives add something to our understanding of migration. Recognizing that the reasons for migrating are numerous and complex, we also must bear in mind that when people migrate, the impact is felt deeply at both individual and societal levels.

International migration is much more problematic than internal migration and is subject to political pressures and interventions that rarely exist for internal migrants. It is for that reason that most of our discussion in this chapter focuses on international migration. However, most migrants in the world are moving within their own country, not between countries, so in the next section we review what is happening with respect to internal migration in the United States, as a good example of what may be happening on a smaller scale elsewhere in the world.

Migration Within the United States

The United States is quite literally a nation on the move, and it always has been. Data from the Current Population Survey show that 32 million Americans (10 percent of the population) aged one and older in 2018 were living in a different house than in the year before. Some of these people had undoubtedly moved more than once during that period, so that represents a probable minimum level of mobility. Of those movers, 11 million crossed county lines and would thus be considered migrants. An additional 1 million persons moved in from outside the United States during the previous year—a number that is consistent with other estimates of the annual net immigration to the United States.

Data from the American Housing Surveys and the Current Population Surveys suggest that about one in five internal migrants in the United States is involved in a job transfer, strongly implying that the choice of destination may have been in someone else's hands. An additional one in ten migrants was moving closer to relatives, and obviously the location of the family member fixes the migrant's destination. Of course, the fact that they had to move to be near relatives is itself a function of somebody having previously moved—otherwise the relatives would still all be together.

Population movements are part and parcel of American life, and so the country continues to evolve demographically as a consequence of emerging patterns of migration in and between urban areas. There were several decades when migration was in the direction of the industrializing centers in the Northeastern and North Central states and to the rich farmland and industry in the Midwest. But the strongest of the directional movements was the one westward. At first, this meant that the mountain valley areas west of the Atlantic seacoast were migration destinations; then the Plains states were settled; and after the end of World War II, the Pacific Coast states became popular destinations.

From World War I through the 1960s, both White and Black migrants had also been heading out of the Southern states and into the Northeastern and North Central states, a phenomenon that has been called the Great Migration (Tolnay et al. 2005; Eichenlaub, Tolnay, and Alexander 2010). This generally represented rural-to-urban migration out of the economically depressed rural South into the industrialized cities of the North. In the 1970s, this pattern of net out-migration from the South reversed itself and the Northeastern and North Central states found themselves increasingly to be migration origins rather than destinations, as migrants headed not only west, but also back to the South, the "New Great Migration," as William Frey (2004b) called it.

This pattern has continued into the twenty-first century, as Americans have moved from the "Rust Belt" or "Snow Belt" states into the "Sun Belt" states, especially in the South and Southeast. Indeed, Frey (2009) called the first decade of the twenty-first century a "rollercoaster decade" for migration within the United States. In 2005, Hurricane Katrina led to a substantial forced outmigration from the New Orleans area. At the same time, the housing bubble was encouraging migration to more inland areas of the West and Southeast, in particular, where new homes were being built that were affordable largely because of the now infamous sub-prime lending practices of major banks. The ensuing bursting of that housing bubble and the Great Recession that followed in its wake rather dramatically slowed migration throughout the country (as well as into the country). But even as migration slowed, the Sunbelt states of Florida, Arizona, Texas and North Carolina, where housing is relatively less expensive, were taking in more people than other states, while New York and California (with high housing costs) were the country's biggest losers.

The "winners" and "losers" in terms of net internal migrants by state in 2018 are shown in Table 6.2. The states are ordered in the table according to the net numbers of migrants. Again, you can see that New York and California (with high housing costs) were the country's biggest losers. Florida and Arizona were the biggest winners, attracting the growing population of aging baby boomers to the sunshine.

Table 6.2   Net Internal Migration by State, United States, 2018

State	Net Internal (Domestic) Migration	Population 2018	Total Population Change 2017–2018	Natural Increase	Net International Migration
Florida	132,602	21,299,325	322,513	13,323	175,670
Arizona	83,240	7,171,646	122,770	24,744	14,335
Texas	82,569	28,701,845	379,128	190,951	104,976
North Carolina	66,991	10,383,620	112,820	25,724	20,035
South Carolina	50,775	5,084,127	62,908	6,462	5,490
Nevada	47,596	3,034,392	61,987	11,001	3,100
Washington	46,549	7,535,591	110,159	32,927	30,557
Colorado	43,293	5,695,564	79,662	27,882	8,207
Georgia	41,914	10,519,475	106,420	42,761	21,786
Tennessee	39,952	6,770,010	61,216	12,215	8,994
Oregon	26,819	4,190,713	44,121	9,114	8,177
Idaho	24,095	1,754,208	35,304	9,423	1,681
Utah	16,052	3,161,105	57,987	32,968	8,967
Delaware	6,858	967,171	10,093	1,402	1,820
Minnesota	6,769	5,611,179	43,024	25,770	10,718
Montana	5,987	1,062,305	9,215	2,324	889
Alabama	5,718	4,887,871	12,751	3,791	3,344
Maine	4,469	1,338,404	3,341	−1,641	570
New Hampshire	3,928	1,356,458	6,691	214	2,606
Indiana	3,555	6,691,878	31,796	19,211	9,227
Arkansas	2,475	3,013,825	10,828	6,098	2,260
Kentucky	798	4,468,402	14,528	8,025	5,816

(continued)

Table 6.2   Net Internal Migration by State, United States, 2018 (*Continued*)

State	Net Internal (Domestic) Migration	Population 2018	Total Population Change 2017–2018	Natural Increase	Net International Migration
South Dakota	638	882,235	8,949	4,650	3,659
Vermont	−62	626,299	1,774	12	1,850
District of Columbia	−936	702,455	6,764	4,104	3,592
Wisconsin	−1,011	5,813,568	21,517	14,656	8,051
North Dakota	−2,379	760,077	4,901	4,656	2,597
Rhode Island	−2,639	1,057,315	829	745	2,755
Missouri	−2,790	6,126,452	17,840	12,683	8,077
Iowa	−2,886	3,156,145	12,508	9,614	5,828
Nebraska	−3,314	1,929,268	11,693	10,334	4,705
Wyoming	−3,686	577,737	−1,197	1,893	597
Oklahoma	−4,474	3,943,079	10,439	10,728	4,272
New Mexico	−5,851	2,095,428	2,033	5,605	2,342
West Virginia	−7,029	1,805,832	−11,216	−4,541	386
Virginia	−9,831	8,517,685	52,478	30,750	31,641
Alaska	−10,752	737,438	−2,348	5,955	2,401
Mississippi	−10,818	2,986,530	−3,133	4,963	2,749
Ohio	−12,146	11,689,442	25,313	17,375	20,514
Hawaii	−12,430	1,420,491	−3,712	4,666	4,075
Kansas	−12,564	2,911,505	816	11,365	2,057
Michigan	−16,766	9,995,915	19,468	15,062	21,415
Pennsylvania	−20,463	12,807,060	16,613	2,343	35,377
Connecticut	−21,509	3,572,665	−1,215	3,736	16,494
Maryland	−24,518	6,042,718	17,827	19,845	22,575
Massachusetts	−25,755	6,902,149	38,903	11,791	53,013
Louisiana	−27,914	4,659,978	−10,840	14,085	3,012
New Jersey	−50,591	8,908,520	19,977	23,856	46,660
Illinois	−114,154	12,741,080	−45,116	38,025	30,735
California	−156,068	39,557,045	157,696	196,471	117,797
New York	−180,306	19,542,209	−48,510	61,371	70,375

Source: Prepared by John R. Weeks; data are from the U.S. Census Bureau (2018a).

North Carolina and Texas were third and fourth among the winners, due especially to the ability of these states to attract businesses away from places like California and New York, and the jobs and people followed the businesses.

Global Patterns of Migration

The Current Situation

The United Nations Population Division estimates that in 2017 (the most recent year for which data were available as of this writing) there were 258 million people who were long-term migrants, living in a country different from where they were born. This number is up considerably from the 153 million migrants estimated for 1990 (United Nations Population Division 2017). Table 6.2 shows you the top 20 countries of origin and destination. These data refer to the stock of migrants, but of course they also offer clues about the flow. That number, though large, is only 3 percent of the world's total population, but as we have noted, migrants have social, economic, political, and demographic impacts that are far larger than these large numbers might suggest.

There are more migrants in the world from India than from any other country, followed by Mexico, the Russian Federation and China. You can see in Table 6.3 that the top 20 countries account for 49 percent of migrants globally. You can also see that the United States clearly dominates the number of immigrants living within its borders from foreign countries. The 50 million immigrants in the United States account for one out of every five of the 258 million global migrants. Saudi Arabia is second on the list of receiving countries (the reasons for which we discuss below), closely followed by Germany and the Russian Federation. The top 20 receiving countries account for two out of every three (67 percent) migrants in the world.

There are lots of stories that could be told from the data in Table 6.3. For example, Germany has long had a substantial population of Turkish origin, and it also recently accepted a large number of Syrian refugees, as that country collapsed into a civil war. The backlash against the influx of refugees into Germany nearly led to a collapse of Angela Merkel's government as anti-immigrant groups gained political strength. In response, the EU granted Turkey a large sum of money to hold Syrian refugees in camps in Turkey, rather than allowing them to head to Europe.

Russia saw a lot of its citizens leave when the Soviet Union collapsed, only to be replaced over time by immigrants from former Soviet Republics like Azerbaijan, Belarus, Kazakhstan, Kyrgyzstan, Tajikistan, Turkmenistan, and Uzbekistan. Indeed, for several of those former republics, the remittances back home from migrants in the Russian Federation are important contributions to the national economy. On the other hand, the world's most populous country, China, has sent a lot of its citizens abroad, especially to Europe and North America, to be educated and to work in high-tech occupations, whereas it is all but closed to immigrants.

Over time, labor shortages in northern and western Europe, in the United States and Canada, and in Japan and Australia—the more developed societies with

Table 6.3   Top 20 Countries of Origin and Destination of International Migrant Stock, 2017

Rank	Sending Country	Migrants from Sending Countries	Receiving Country	Migrants in Receiving Countries
1	India	16,587,720	United States of America	49,776,970
2	Mexico	12,964,882	Saudi Arabia	12,185,284
3	Russian Federation	10,635,994	Germany	12,165,083
4	China	9,962,058	Russian Federation	11,651,509
5	Bangladesh	7,499,919	United Kingdom	8,841,717
6	Syrian Arab Republic	6,864,445	United Arab Emirates	8,312,524
7	Pakistan	5,978,635	France	7,902,783
8	Ukraine	5,941,653	Canada	7,861,226
9	Philippines	5,680,682	Australia	7,035,560
10	United Kingdom	4,921,309	Spain	5,947,106
11	Afghanistan	4,826,464	Italy	5,907,461
12	Poland	4,701,465	India	5,188,550
13	Indonesia	4,233,973	Ukraine	4,964,293
14	Germany	4,208,083	Turkey	4,881,966
15	Kazakhstan	4,074,446	South Africa	4,036,696
16	State of Palestine	3,803,893	Kazakhstan	3,635,168
17	Romania	3,578,504	Thailand	3,588,873
18	Turkey	3,418,932	Pakistan	3,398,154
19	Egypt	3,412,957	Jordan	3,233,553
20	Italy	3,029,168	Kuwait	3,123,431
	Total in Top 20	126,325,182		173,637,907
	Percent of all migrants	49		67

Source: Prepared by John R. Weeks; data are from the United Nations Population Division (2017).

aging populations—have created opportunities for workers from Africa, Western and Southern Asia, Latin America and, within Europe, from Eastern Europe. At the same time, the regional ebb and flow of economies stimulates movements of large numbers of people among the less developed nations themselves.

Guest labor programs helped to spark the migration from Mexico to the United States, as we discuss in the essay accompanying this chapter. They also flourished in post–World War II Europe, and they have been very popular in the Middle East and North Africa (Castles, de Haas, and Miller 2013). The Arab oil-producing nations became centers of rapid immigration in the late 1970s and early 1980s as they benefited economically from the rise in oil prices. Saudi Arabia (the second country on the receiving end of immigrants, as you can see in Table 6.3) and the United Arab Emirates (the sixth country on the receiving end of immigrants), in particular, have become attractive destinations for a wide range of guest workers from India, Pakistan, Bangladesh, Egypt, Jordan, Lebanon, and Afghanistan, not to mention South Asian women, especially from the Philippines and Indonesia, who have been recruited to cook and clean houses. The idea behind guest labor programs has been that people would come to the host country, work under contract for a certain period of time, and then go back to their country of origin. However, like the proverbial brother-in-law sleeping on your living room couch, they do not necessarily leave willingly when their time is up.

A common way to deal with guest laborers who become permanent residents is a variation on the segmented assimilation model, which we discuss below. Many countries (including all of the oil-producing Gulf states) deny citizenship to those people who were not born in the country, and then deny it to their children because the children were not born to citizens. Thus, the workers and their offspring may have the legal right to live and work in their adopted country, but they will never be fully participating citizens. This also means that it is easier to get rid of them if they are not wanted, as Saudi Arabia did in 2013 when it expelled hundreds of thousands of workers.

The above theories and data fit with the idea that people typically migrate for job-related reasons. However, it very often happens that their family members follow them in a pattern of chain migration (discussed earlier in the chapter) that involves family reunification. The flow of labor can generally be explained by the supply-and-demand model, with people moving from places where there aren't enough jobs to places where there are jobs. That model tends to shape the "big picture" in the world right now. Improved communication and transportation technology have greatly facilitated a time-honored way of solving short-term labor shortages—the importation of workers from elsewhere. Population growth in less developed nations has put incredible pressure on their resources, while the declining rate of population growth in the more developed nations has, in many instances, heightened the demand for lower-cost workers. This is the "demographic fit" that facilitated migration from Mexico to the United States for several decades until Mexico's birthrate dropped to nearly replacement level (as we discussed in Chapter 5) and the economy improved enough that fewer people were feeling compelled to migrate north in search of a job (Weeks and Weeks 2010).

How Did We Get to This Point?

The massive waves of international migration that characterized the nineteenth and early twentieth centuries represented primarily the voluntary movement of people out of Europe into the "new" worlds of North and South America and Oceania. This period was followed by restrictive immigration laws throughout the world (not just in the United States) and the worldwide economic depression between World Wars I and II that severely limited international migration in the 1920s and 1930s. However, World War II unleashed a new cycle of European and Asian migration—this time a forced push of people out of war-torn countries as boundaries were realigned and ethnic groups were transferred between countries. Shortly after the end of the war, for example, the 1947 partition of the Indian subcontinent into India and Pakistan led to the transfer of more than 15 million people—Muslims into East and West Pakistan and Hindus into India. Meanwhile, in the Middle East, the partitioning of Palestine to create the new state of Israel produced 700,000 Palestinian refugees and an influx of a large proportion of the North African and Middle Eastern Jewish population into that area. Substantial migration into Israel from Europe, the Soviet Union, and other areas continued well into the 1960s. In the 1980s, the flow of migrants into Israel began to dry up, replaced by a small but steady stream of out-migrants, but this trend was quickly turned around again in the early 1990s following the Soviet Union's decision to allow Soviet Jews to emigrate. Those choosing to leave headed primarily for Israel and the United States.

Another unexpected, albeit related, political event in Eastern Europe in the late 1980s and early 1990s was the collapse of the Berlin Wall and the amazingly rapid reunification of Germany. Stimulated by Gorbachev's policy of openness in the Soviet Union (and by the former USSR's economic inability to continue subsidizing other Communist nations), the reunification of Germany turned the migration spigot back on. Between 1950 and 1988, more than 3 million East Germans had fled to the West, but most of those had done so before the Berlin Wall went up in 1961. Then, in 1989, East Germany relaxed its visa policies, allowing East Germans to visit West Germany, and Hungary relaxed the patrol of its border with Austria, allowing "vacationing" East Germans to escape to the West. Within weeks, migration from east to west was transformed from a trickle into a flash flood.

This east-west migration in Europe is in many respects a continuation of a pattern that has evolved over centuries. The Cold War, which cut off much of that flow, was simply a temporary aberration in a long-term trend. Between 1850 and 1913 (the start of World War I), more than 40 million Europeans moved from east to west to populate North America (Hatton and Williamson 1994), but as that was occurring Polish, Slavic, and Ukrainian workers were also migrating west to Germany and France. The collapse of the Soviet Union also led to the formation and then expansion of the European Union, allowing Europeans to travel and work freely in other EU countries. This migrant flow has, as you might expect, largely been an east to west movement.

To this trend has been added a mixture of other patterns: (1) south-north migration (particularly of migrant laborers from developing countries of the south to developed countries of the north); (2) a flow of migrant laborers from some of the poorer developing countries to some of the "emerging" economies, especially in south and southeast Asia; (3) a flow of workers into the Persian Gulf region from the non–oil-producing to the oil-producing nations; and (4) a flow of refugees within Africa and western Asia (especially Syria). We are surely in what Stephen Castles, Hein de Haas, and Mark Miller (2013) call "the age of migration." Saskia Sassen (2001) has argued that the globalization of migration is, in part at least, a consequence of economic globalization—economic connections lead inevitably to flows of people. Income differences between regions attract migrants from lower- to higher-income places, and globalization has helped both to increase the income differences and increase the chance that people will migrate in hopes of improving their economic situation.

To date, the success of attempts to limit immigration has been highly variable at best, consistent with what Douglas Massey (1996) calls his "perverse laws of inter- national migration":

1. Immigration is a lot easier to start than it is to stop.
2. Actions taken to restrict immigration often have the opposite effect.
3. The fundamental causes of immigration may be outside the control of policy makers.
4. Immigrants understand immigration better than do politicians and academicians.
5. Because they understand immigration better than policy makers, immigrants are often able to circumvent policies aimed at stopping them.

In the final analysis, most attempts to limit immigration are motivated less by a desire to limit population growth in general, and more by a desire to limit the entry of certain kinds of people into the country. No matter what country we are talking about, xenophobia (Greek for "fear of strangers"), is at work. For as long as human beings have existed, we have been distrustful of those from other places, especially if they do not share our language and/or religion and/or they have different physical features than ours. It is common for the distrust to lead to discrimination against the "strangers" who may, in particular, be viewed as somehow inferior to us, and the combination of lack of trust and sense of superiority has produced a lot of violence in world history (Pinker 2012).

America's Immigration Trends

The greater the social and cultural differences between receiving and sending societ- ies, the more likely it is that attempts will be made to slow down the pace of immi- gration. This is certainly what has happened over time in the United States. Prior to World War I, there were few restrictions on migration into the United States and Canada, so the number of immigrants was determined more by the desire of peo- ple to move than anything else. Particularly important as a stimulus to migration, of course, was the drop in the death rate in Europe during the nineteenth century, which launched a long period of population growth, with its attendant pressure on

Europe's economic resources. Economic opportunities in America looked very attractive to young Europeans who were competing with increasing numbers of other young people for jobs. Voluntary migration from Europe to the temperate zones of the world—especially the United States—represents one of the most significant movements of people across international boundaries in history. The social, cultural, economic, and demographic impacts of this migration have been truly enormous.

Historical Background of Migration and Immigration Laws

Immigration to the United States during most of the nineteenth century was dominated by people arriving from northern and western Europe (beginning with England, Ireland, Scotland, Sweden, and Denmark, then stretching to the south and east to draw immigrants from Germany, especially). There was a lull during the American Civil War, although it was during that period that Congress passed the Immigration Act of 1864 establishing a Commissioner of Immigration within the State Department (Migration Policy Institute 2013). This legislation correctly assumed that after the war the pace of immigration would resume. The opening up of new land in the United States in the middle of the nineteenth century coincided with a variety of political and economic problems in Europe, and that helped to generate a great deal of labor migration to the United States. In the period just after the end of the Civil War, the percent foreign-born was 14.4, as you can see from Figure 6.4, a number even higher than in 2018 (13.7 percent).

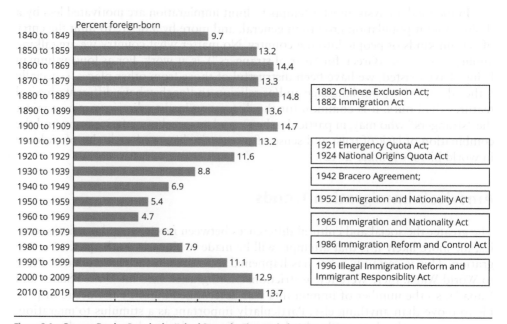

Figure 6.4   Percent Foreign-Born in the United States by Time Period, 1840 to 2019

Source: Prepared by John R. Weeks; percent foreign-born data are from the U.S. Census Bureau.

The United States responded in 1882 with two sets of immigration restrictions. The first of these was the Chinese Exclusion Act of 1882. The discovery of gold in California had prompted a demand for labor—for railroad building and farming—that had been met in part by the migration of indentured Chinese laborers. However, in 1869, after the completion of the transcontinental railroad, American workers moved west more readily and the Chinese showed up in the East on several occasions as strikebreakers. Resentment against the Chinese built to the point that in 1882 Congress was willing to break a recently signed treaty with China and suspend Chinese immigration for 10 years. But Congress was not through for the year. The 1882 Immigration Act levied a head tax of 50 cents on each immigrant, no matter where they came from, and blocked the entry of idiots, lunatics, convicts, and persons likely to become public charges (U.S. Immigration and Naturalization Service 1991).

The Chinese Exclusion Act was challenged unsuccessfully in the courts and, over time, restrictions on the Chinese, even those already residing in the United States, were tightened (indeed, the Chinese Exclusion Act passed in 1882 was not repealed until 1942). The exclusion of the Chinese led to an increase in Japanese immigration in the 1880s and 1890s, but by the turn of the century hostility was building against them, too (the Japanese Exclusion Act was passed in 1924), and against several other immigrant groups.

By the late nineteenth and early twentieth centuries, the immigrants from northern and western Europe were being augmented by people from southern and eastern Europe (Spain and Italy, then stretching farther east to Poland and Russia). In 1890, 86 percent of all foreign-born persons in the United States were of European origin, but only 2 percent were from southern Europe—almost exclusively Italy. Only 30 years later, in 1920, it was still true that 86 percent of the foreign-born were Europeans, but 14 percent were southern Europeans—a sevenfold increase.

The immigrant-processing center in New York City was moved to Ellis Island in 1892 to help screen people entering the United States from foreign countries, since the changing mix of ethnicity had led to public demands for greater control over who could enter the country. In 1891, Congress legislated that aliens were not to be allowed into the country if they suffered from "a loathsome or dangerous contagious disease" (Auerbach 1961:5) or if they were criminals. Tuberculosis was added to the unacceptable list in 1907, and then in 1917, a highly controversial provision was passed that established a literacy requirement, thus excluding aliens over age 16 who were unable to read.

Despite the new set of requirements, immigration to the United States (and Canada) reached a peak in the first decade of the twentieth century, when 1.6 million entered Canada and nearly 9 million entered the United States, accounting for more than one in ten of all Americans at that time. "They came thinking the streets were paved with gold, but found that the streets weren't paved at all and that they were expected to do the paving" (Leroux 1984).

This represents one of the most massive population shifts in history, and all of the theories of international migration discussed earlier in this chapter have something to offer by way of explanation. Compared to the United States, European wages were low and unemployment rates were high. Economies were very weak in some of the less developed areas of southern and eastern Europe. Eastern Europe was also undergoing tremendous social and political instability, and the Russian pogrom against Jews caused many people to flee the region.

Nor was all this emigration from Europe aimed at North America. Millions of Italians and Spaniards, as well as Austrians, Germans, and other Europeans, settled throughout Latin America during this period. Most notable among the destinations were Brazil and Argentina (Sanchez-Albornoz 1988). This wave of migration peaked at about the time of World War I, and Europe has never since experienced emigration of this magnitude, partly because wages rose in Europe, helping to keep people there (and encouraging some return migration from the Americas), compounded by the Great Depression of the 1930s (which also encouraged return migration to one's "roots").

Recognition of the problems created by still relatively free migration led to a new era of restrictions right after World War I, fueled by the belief that "millions of war-torn Europeans were about to descend on the United States—a veritable flood which would completely subvert the traditional American way of life" (Divine 1957:6). The United States and Canada both passed restrictive legislation in step with the eugenics movement that had gained popularity throughout Europe and North America in the 1920s (Boyd 1976). As applied to migration, the ideology was ethnic purity, and the sentiment of the time about migrants is perhaps best expressed as: Not too tired, not too poor, and not too many.

In 1921, Congress passed the first act in American history to put a numeric limit on immigrants. The Emergency Quota Law of 1921 "limited the number of aliens of any nationality to three percent of foreign-born persons of that nationality who lived in the U.S. in 1910" (Auerbach 1961:9). For example, in 1910, 11,498 people in the United States had been born in Bulgaria (U.S. Census Bureau 1975), so 3 percent of that number, or 345, would be permitted to enter each year from Bulgaria. Under the law, about 350,000 people could enter the United States each year as quota immigrants, although close relatives of American citizens and people in certain professions (for example, artists, nurses, professors, and domestic servants) were not affected by the quotas. The law of 1921 remained in effect only until 1924, when it was replaced by the Immigration Quota Act.

The 1924 law was even more restrictive than that of 1921, because public debate over immigration had unfortunately led to a popularization of racist theories claiming that "Nordics [people from northwestern Europe] were genetically superior to others" (Divine 1957:14). To avoid the charge that the immigration law was deliberately discriminatory, though, a new quota system—the National Origins Quota—was adopted in 1929. This was a complex scheme in which a special Quota Board took the percentage of each nationality group in the United States in 1790 (the first U.S. Census) and then traced "the additions to that number of subsequent immigration" (Divine 1957:28). The task was not an easy one because by and large, the necessary data did not exist, so a lot of arbitrary assumptions and questionable estimates were made in the process.

Once the national origins restriction had been established, the actual number of immigrants allowed from each country each year was calculated as a proportion of 150,000, which was established as the maximum number of all immigrants.

Thus if 60 percent of the population was of English origin, then 60 percent of the 150,000 immigrants, or 90,000, could be from England. The number turned out to be slightly more than 150,000 because every country was allowed a minimum of 100 visas. Furthermore, close relatives of American citizens continued to be exempt from the quotas, under the philosophy of family unification.

Congress, of course, retained the ability to override those quotas if the need arose, as it did during and after World War II, when refugees from Europe were accommodated. In 1952, in the middle of the anti-Communist McCarthy era, another attempt was made in the United States to control immigration by increasing the "compatibility" of migrants with established U.S. society. The McCarran-Walter Act (the Immigration and Naturalization Act of 1952) retained the system of national origin quotas while adding to it a system of preferences based largely on occupation (Keely 1971). The McCarran-Walter Act permitted up to 50 percent of the visas from each country to be taken by highly skilled persons whose services were urgently needed. Relatives of American citizens were ranked next, followed by people with no salable skills and no relatives who were citizens of the United States. Thus, the freedom of migration into the United States was severely restricted, even from those countries with an advantage according to the national origins quota system.

Canada passed similar legislation in the same year, just as it had previously enacted a national origins quota system (Boyd 1976). Canada had at least two reasons for echoing the immigration policies of the United States. In the first place, it shares much of the sociocultural heritage of the United States, and, second, of course, it shares a border with the United States. This cultural similarity and close proximity would have left Canada inundated with migrants excluded from the United States had Canada not passed its own restrictive laws.

These restrictive laws, coupled with the Great Depression and then World War II, effectively slowed migration to the United States and Canada to a trickle from the 1930s into the 1950s. To be sure, you can see in Figure 6.4 that the percent foreign-born bottomed out in the 1960 to 1969 period, just as the United States was transitioning to a new set of "origins and destinies" for immigrants to North America (Rumbaut 1994), embodied in the Immigration Act of 1965.

In the 1960s, the ethnically discriminatory aspects of North America's immigration policy ended, but its restrictive aspects were maintained. The Immigration Act of 1965 ended the nearly half-century of national origins as the principal determinant of who could enter this country from non–Western Hemisphere nations. Related changes had occurred in Canada ahead of this, in 1962. Although the criterion of national origins is gone, restrictions on the numbers of immigrants remain, including a limit on immigrants from Western Hemisphere as well as non–Western Hemisphere nations. A system of preference was retained, but modified to give first crack at immigration to relatives of American citizens. Parents of U.S. citizens could migrate regardless of the quota. In addition, a certification by the U.S. Labor Department is now required for occupational preference applicants to establish that their skills are required in the United States.

In 1976, the immigration law was amended so that parents of U.S. citizens had highest priority only if their child was at least 21 years old. The intent of that

Is Migration a Crime? Illegal Immigration in Global Context

Migration should be the most easily controlled of the three population processes, at least in theory. You cannot legislate against death (except for laws prohibiting homicide or suicide), and few countries outside China have dared try to legislate directly against having babies. But you can set up legal and even physical barriers to migration—keeping people in (as in the former Soviet Union) or out (as practiced by most countries in the world). In reality, of course, controlling migration can be very difficult if people are highly motivated to move. Undocumented migration from Mexico to the United States has been a leading example, although illegal or undocumented immigration is not a problem peculiar to the United States.

All over the globe, people without papers are moving in the millions. Is that a crime? Actually, that question could get us into a huge philosophical discussion since different cultures define crime in different ways, but in general, if a government passes a law and you violate that law, you have committed a crime. If a government says that only people with official permission may enter a country and reside permanently with full legal rights, and you enter that country without permission, then you have violated the law and, in that sense, you may have committed a crime. However, the usual penalty for being caught as an undocumented immigrant is to be returned to your country of origin, rather than serving time in jail (though, of course, you might temporarily be detained in a jail of some sort).

In fact, being undocumented (in legal terms, having a "lack of legal status") in the United States is a civil, not a criminal offense, which entails a completely different (and less severe) set of consequences (Seghetti, Viña, and Ester 2005). On the other hand, the penalty for being an illegal immigrant if you are not caught is that you may be exploited because unscrupulous employers know they can turn you in to authorities for deportation if you dare to complain. This can lead to people being forced to work in sweatshops, under near-slavery conditions, with little dignity and few legal rights (Ontiveras 2018).

The reason for the rise in undocumented immigration throughout the world is straightforward—there are more people who want to get into the more developed countries than the governments of more developed countries are willing to let in: So people sneak in. As Thomas Friedman (2019) put it: "People are moving out of the world of disorder into the world of order." And he argues that a key reason for "disorder" is, in fact, population growth.

In the United States, there were an estimated 10.7 million undocumented immigrants (the U.S. government uses "undocumented," "unauthorized," and "illegal" to describe this population) in 2016 (the most recent year available as of this writing), but that number is lower than the peak of 11.8 million in 2007 (Gonzalez-Barrera and Krogstad 2018). Mexico represents the single largest source of immigrants to the United States, with the 12 million immigrants from Mexico accounting for about one in four immigrants. Less than half (45 percent) of the immigrants from Mexico are undocumented, according to estimates prepared by the Pew Research Center in Washington, D.C., but they account for about half of the country's undocumented immigrant population.

Migration from Mexico to the United States began in earnest early in the twentieth century as a reaction to the Mexican Revolution, which started in 1910 and ended in the creation of the modern United Mexican States (the official name of the Republic of Mexico) in 1920. The migration northward from Mexico began to increase in the 1920s and 1930s. That flow was then halted by a combination of the Great Depression, which raised unemployment levels in the United States, and the concomitant discrimination against immigrants that surfaced during this period, leading to massive deportations of many immigrants (legal and otherwise), including many from Mexico.

Labor shortages in agriculture during World War II, however, led to a renewed invitation for Mexican workers to migrate to the United States. In 1942, the United States signed a treaty with the government of Mexico to create a system of contract labor whereby Mexican laborers ("braceros"—literally "those who work with their arms") would enter the United States for a specified period of time to work. After the war ended, the bracero program remained in place, but it was not until the early 1950s that the number of Mexican contract workers began to increase noticeably (Garcia y

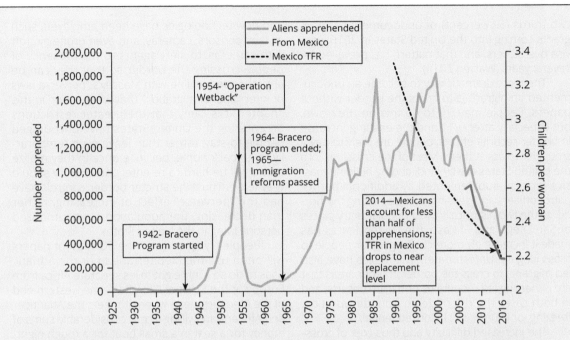

The Number of Apprehensions of Undocumented Immigrants Has Declined Steeply Since 2000, and Since 2014 Mexicans Are No Longer a Majority of Those Apprehended.

Source: Prepared by John R. Weeks; data are from United Nations Population Division (2017b); Total fertility rates for 2020 and 2050 are based on the medium projections.

Griego, Weeks and Ham-Chande 1990), as you can see in the accompanying graph. By the mid-1950s, the contract workers had been joined by many undocumented immigrants from Mexico, and the United States reacted in 1954 by deporting more than a million Mexicans (some later found to be U.S. citizens) in what was called "Operation Wetback."

The bracero program was ended formally in 1964, and in 1965 the new immigration act, which ended the national origins quota system, also put a numerical limit on the number of legal immigrants to the United States from countries in the Western Hemisphere. Neither action noticeably slowed the migration from Mexico, which was by then well entrenched because there was and still is a demand for immigrant labor. However, both of these government actions did jointly conspire to increase the number of immigrants classified as illegal or undocumented (U.S. Immigration and Naturalization Service 1991). This is a critical point with respect to undocumented immigration from Mexico: The flow from Mexico to the United States began because workers were needed and the government agreed to provide them with temporary work visas. Since the 1960s, however, the labor supply has continued to be needed, but the government has been less willing to provide documentation for the immigrants, so they "enter without inspection" (EWI—another way of describing people in this category). In other words, the flow of immigrant workers continued, but it came to be defined as illegal.

We should point out that there are two primary ways by which a person becomes an undocumented immigrant. A person may enter the country with a tourist or other visa and then overstay the visa. For example, you may arrive with a student visa, attend college in the United States, but then decide not to return home, at which point you become an illegal immigrant. Almost

(continued)

Is Migration a Crime? Illegal Immigration in Global Context (*Continued*)

two-thirds (62 percent) of undocumented immigrants coming into the United States in 2016 were visa overstayers, and that pattern has prevailed for several years (Warren 2019).

The more dramatic way to become an undocumented immigrant is to cross the border without papers. People may try to do this on their own, but especially after 9/11 and the ensuing increase in border security efforts, people are likely to pay a smuggler to assist them. Most of the crossings into the United States are by land, and by building massive fences—supplemented by additional border patrol officers and sensing devices—along the border at the two historically most popular entry places of San Diego and El Paso, the United States has made it increasingly more challenging for people to cross illegally. Unfortunately, the fences have also led migrants to cross the border in other areas that are either rugged mountains or barren deserts, and in both cases the risk of death from dehydration, freezing, or injury is not inconsequential.

The increased difficulty and thus cost of crossing the border, combined with the Great Recession and the lower birth rate in Mexico, have meant that the number of people apprehended along the U.S.-Mexico border has been declining since reaching a peak of 1.8 million persons in 2000. By 2016 that number had dropped to less than 600,000 (Baker 2017), as you can see in the accompanying graph. Even that number is likely too high since about 40 percent of those are people who are apprehended more than once (Weeks, Jankowski and Stoler 2011). When the U.S. Border Patrol apprehends undocumented aliens from Mexico, most are returned to Mexico, and we know from survey data in the United States and Mexico that most of them will keep trying to cross until they are successful, as most eventually are (Cornelius et al. 2008). Despite the historical importance of Mexicans crossing into the United States without papers, the pattern shifted rather dramatically starting in 2014 to one in which Mexican migrants were no longer the majority of those apprehended. Instead, the greatest number come from the "Northern Triangle" countries of Central America—Honduras, El Salvador, and Guatemala.

In the wake of 9/11, the number of agents patrolling the border was increased significantly and new technologies have been employed, such as land sensors, cameras, and even drone aircraft with cameras, to alert agents to the presence of people crossing the border so that they can be apprehended. In line with Massey's "perverse laws of international migration" that we mention in this chapter, it is likely that the greater restrictions on entering the United States have encouraged people to stay, rather than leave even temporarily to go back home, because once in they realize that it will be hard to re-enter the country should they leave. Thus, the stricter border controls have had the "perverse" effect of increasing, rather than decreasing, the population of unauthorized persons living in the United States.

People trying to enter the EU without papers will often use the Mediterranean or the Adriatic Seas to do so. Only eight miles separate Africa from Europe at the Strait of Gibraltar—the western end of the Mediterranean where it meets the Atlantic—and Africans are willing to pay considerable sums of money for a seat in a small boat for a rough nighttime journey from Morocco to Spain, across what is sometimes called the "Sea of Death" (Simons 2000). They may choose the longer and even more dangerous passage from Libya to Italy, or across the Mediterranean to the Aegean Sea to access Europe through Greece (UNHCR 2014). If they survive the journey and make it past Frontex (the EU's border control agency), they can move within the EU because countries within the EU no longer have border controls, although in recent years some countries have been policing their borders in order to apprehend undocumented immigrants. The big EU economy is, of course, attractive to workers outside of the EU. Because legal migration into EU countries is still quite limited, undocumented immigration has increased over time, pushed along by political unrest and economic uncertainty in the Middle East and North Africa (MENA) region after the Arab Spring, along with high rates of population growth in sub-Saharan Africa.

Undocumented immigration represents a true conundrum because it is a problem with no easy solution to which everyone can agree. There are those in the United States and Europe who argue that the solution is simple—fortify the borders ("build a wall") and do not let anyone in who has not been preapproved; immediately deport anyone who is found inside the country without papers; and do a better job of punishing those who knowingly hire undocumented immigrants (Simcox 2013). The latter issue was supposed to have been taken care of in the United States by the 1986 Immigration Reform and Control Act, but over time the continued demand for labor in the United States has not been met by legal immigrants, and in seeming recognition of this, the U.S. government has devoted very few resources to tracking down and fining these employers. This changing emphasis was reflected in the 1996 passage of the Illegal Immigration Reform and Immigrant Responsibility Act (IIRIRA), the main thrust of which was to focus Border Patrol attention on deterring, finding, and deporting illegal immigrants, rather than on penalizing employers of those immigrants.

Consensus in the United States is so difficult to achieve on this issue that, despite a variety of bills having been introduced in Congress to deal with immigration issues, nothing has been passed, at least not as of this writing. Inaction at the federal level has led many states and local governments to pass their own legislation aimed at punishing employers, arresting undocumented immigrants, or even penalizing landlords who rent to them. At the same time, a backlash to those policies has been legislation to create so-called sanctuary cities, where local governments protect immigrants from capture and deportation by the federal government. Because immigration policy has historically been the sole responsibility of the federal government, these initiatives are always challenged in federal courts.

So, the reality is that people continue to enter the United States without valid papers—once again, a civil offense—and this "crime" begets other genuinely serious crimes related to exploitation of the immigrants. The smugglers take advantage of the immigrants by failing to warn them of the dangers of crossing the desert without water, or of going into the mountains in winter without a jacket; and of course, the smugglers will leave the immigrants to fend for themselves at the first sign of trouble, sometimes simply leaving them to die. Once in the United States, the immigrants are, as we noted above, susceptible to many kinds of abuses from employers and others who know that the immigrants have few resources, legal or otherwise, to fight back. This set of circumstances leads many people to believe that illegal immigrants need to have some type of amnesty or "regularization" granted as soon as possible in order to provide a status that will protect their human rights.

Meanwhile, back in Europe, in 2008 the European Council (the governing body of the EU) approved the European Immigration and Asylum Pact, designed to provide guidance to member nations, who ultimately retain the power to decide for themselves how they wish to deal with immigrants. The pact was agreed to by the heads of state of all 27 members, so there is some high-level consensus, and the key element with respect to undocumented immigration is what might be called a zero-tolerance policy. The pact calls for all undocumented immigrants to be forced out of Europe, and it explicitly rejects the idea of a general amnesty for undocumented immigrants currently living in Europe.

At the opposite end of the spectrum from the idea of completely shutting down the border and throwing out all undocumented immigrants is that of an open border, which would allow people to come and go in quick response to changes in demand for their services. This idea generally appeals more to prospective employers, who would like to hire cheaper labor, though it has relatively little appeal to the currently employed, who do not relish the thought of increased competition for their jobs. This idea is not likely to be implemented in the near future because there is still a fair amount of anti-immigrant sentiment in the United States and in Europe. In the post-9/11 era, the idea of open borders has become even less popular, given the fact that terrorists could mingle with legitimate workers.

Discussion Questions: (1) If you lived in a developing country and thought you could have a better life by migrating to the United States even though you did not have U.S. government permission to do so, would you do it? Why or why not? **(2)** Do you think that richer countries should be less restrictive about legal immigration, more restrictive, or do you think the current situation does not require any change in policy? Explain your answer.

change was to eliminate what many people believed to be a fairly frequent ploy of a pregnant woman entering the country illegally, bearing her child in the United States (the child then being a U.S. citizen), and then applying for citizenship on the basis of being a parent of a U.S. citizen. Although there is little evidence to suggest that pregnant women now routinely cross the border illegally to have babies, there are many undocumented immigrant women in the United States who get pregnant and have a baby. These children are sometimes referred to as "anchor babies" because they provide an "anchor" for the family in the United States.

Current Immigration Trends

Since the change in immigration legislation in the 1960s, European immigrants to the United States have been replaced almost totally by those from Latin America (especially Mexico, but more recently from Guatemala, Honduras, and El Salvador), Asia (especially China, India, and the Philippines, as well as Vietnam and South Korea) and increasingly from Africa. The annual number of legal permanent immigrants peaked in 2006, at 1.2 million, not coincidentally at the same time that the housing bubble was peaking and the demand for labor was high. With the deep recession that followed the burst in that bubble, the annual number of immigrants dropped back to about 1 million per year.

Migration between Mexico and the United States represents the largest sustained flow of migrant workers over the last several decades, although it also took a hit with the global recession starting in 2007 and has diminished significantly since then both because the birth rate in Mexico has dropped nearly to replacement level, as we discussed in Chapter 5, and because the Mexican economy is now better able than in the past to absorb new entrants into the labor force. In fact, immigrants from Mexico are no longer the largest group from any given country into the United States. The number of legal immigrants has been surpassed by those from China and India, and the number of undocumented immigrants from Mexico has dropped precipitously since the beginning of the twenty-first century (Gonzalez-Barrera and Krogstad 2018). Data from the U.S. Census Bureau on the foreign-born population point to the shifts in immigration trends:

> The Census Bureau's figures for 2017 confirm a major shift in who is coming to the United States. For years newcomers tended to be from Latin America, but a Brookings Institution analysis of that data shows that 41 percent of the people who said they arrived since 2010 came from Asia. Just 39 percent were from Latin America. About 45 percent were college educated, the analysis found, compared with about 30 percent of those who came between 2000 and 2009.

> "This is quite different from what we had thought," said William H. Frey, the senior demographer at the Brookings Institution who conducted the analysis. "We think of immigrants as being low-skilled workers from Latin America, but for recent arrivals that's much less the case. People from Asia have overtaken people from Latin America." (Tavernise 2018)

Canada's Immigration Trends

Canada's immigration experience has been similar, but not identical, to the pattern in the United States, as we have already highlighted. Although Canada has historically had a high level of immigration, it also experienced considerable emigration (people leaving to return home, or entering the United States from Canada) until after World War II. Net migration jumped in the late 1980s and early 1990s as a result of immigration policy changes. Immigration slackened a bit in the first decade of the twenty-first century, but it took off again in 2016 to 2018. It is probably not a coincidence that the increase in the number of immigrants in Canada came just as the Trump administration was trying to hold back immigration into the United States.

The 2016 census data for Canada show that 21.9 percent of the population of 34 million was foreign-born in that year. As in the United States, recent immigrants to Canada are far less likely to have come from Europe than was true in the past. India, China, and the Philippines have become the three biggest contributors to the immigrant population, followed by the United Kingdom and the United States (Statistics Canada 2018). Immigration policy in Canada has three major prongs: (1) economic migrants who are admitted on a point system based on their education and skills, with the goal of matching immigrants to labor force needs; (2) family reunification for immigrants who have become Canadian citizens; and (3) acceptance of refugees. Family members typically are the single largest group of immigrants in any given year, followed by economic migrants, and then refugees.

Forced Migration

There are also unintended participants in the migration transition—people who may not have wanted to move but wound up being forced to do so anyway. A forced migrant is, as you might expect, someone who has been forced to leave his or her home because of a real or perceived threat to life and well-being (Reed, Haaga, and Keely 1998). There are tens of millions of people alive at this moment who are in this situation. Many are internally displaced—still in their original country but not in their original residence. Many more have been forced into another country and so are refugees. A third category, and an historically important one, is the worst one of all—slavery.

Refugees and Internally Displaced Persons

There are more than 68 million "uprooted" people in the world, according to the United Nations High Commissioner for Refugees (2019). About 25 million of these are refugees, 3 million are asylum seekers, and 40 million are internally displaced people. Most of the world's internally displaced persons and refugees are in developing countries, with Syria being the biggest contributor as of this writing, followed by Afghanistan and South Sudan. It falls disproportionately on neighbors to shelter refugees, and Turkey and Lebanon (adjacent to Syria) are hosting the majority of

Syrian refugees; Iran and Pakistan (adjacent to Afghanistan) are hosting the majority of Afghan refugees; Uganda (adjacent to South Sudan) is hosting the majority of South Sudanese refugees; and Colombia (adjacent to Venezuela) is hosting a majority of Venezuelan refugees fleeing the repressive government of Nicolás Maduro. Keep in mind that Turkey has such a large population of refugees because in 2015 it agreed to be paid by the European Union to host them (largely in refugee camps), rather than allowing them to proceed on to Europe to seek asylum.

There are essentially three solutions to the problem of refugee populations, including: (1) repatriation to the country of origin; (2) resettlement in the country to which they have fled; and (3) resettlement in a third country. None of these is easy to accomplish, and the situation is complicated by the fact that birth rates tend to be high among refugee groups. The United Nations High Commissioner for Refugees prefers not to call refugees migrants, in order to argue that they should not be constrained by the same regulations that might be placed on "regular" legal migrants. But the demographic reality is that they are migrants and their movement from one place to another has consequences that cannot be shrugged off (Fitzgerald and Arar 2018).

Slavery

There can be no doubt that the most hideous of migratory movements are those endured by enslaved people. Slavery has existed within various human societies for millennia, and McDaniel (1995:11) has summarized the early historical situation as follows:

> The international slave trade in Africans began with the Arab conquests in northern and eastern Africa and the Mediterranean coast in the seventh century. From the seventh to the eleventh century, Arabs and Africans brought large numbers of European slaves into the North African ports of Tangier, Algiers, Tunis, Tripoli, and Fez. In fact, most of the slaves traded throughout the Mediterranean before the fall of Constantinople were European.

Between the thirteenth and fifteenth centuries Africans, along with Turks, Russians, Bulgarians, and Greeks, were slaves on the plantations of Cyprus. However, the most massive migration of slaves was that of the Atlantic slave trade, which transported an estimated 11 million African slaves to the Western Hemisphere between the end of the fifteenth century and the middle of the nineteenth century (Thomas 1997). The slaves came largely from the west coast of sub-Saharan Africa, from countries that now comprise Senegal, Sierra Leone, the Ivory Coast, Dahomey, Benin, Cameroon, Gabon, Ghana, the Congo, and Nigeria. In fact, the northern part of Nigeria has been described as one of the largest slave societies in modern times (Lovejoy and Hogendorn 1993), and this is still a region in which human rights are routinely trampled (Kara 2017). "The preponderance of Africans who were sold into slavery were taken by force. Some were taken directly by Arab or European slave traders, but most were sold into slavery by the elite Africans who had captured them in warfare or who were holding them either for their own use as slaves or to be traded as slaves later" (McDaniel 1995:14).

The destinations were largely the sugar and coffee plantations of the Caribbean and Brazil, but hundreds of thousands were also sold in the United States to serve as laborers on cotton and tobacco plantations. The slave traders themselves were initially Portuguese and Spanish, but the French, Dutch, and especially the British were active later on. It was eventually the British, however, who pushed for a worldwide abolition of slavery. Slavery was abolished throughout the British Empire, including Canada, in 1833, although Canada had *never tolerated* slavery, and the impact of slavery on Canada was primarily that it was a place of refuge for those seeking to escape the United States. Similarly, there is little history of slavery in Mexico, which in 1827 declared that no person could be born a slave in Mexico. In the United States, it was not until 1865 (in the context of the Civil War) that the Thirteenth Amendment to the Constitution finally abolished slavery.

Even today slavery has not been abolished globally, at least not if we define it more generally in terms of involuntary servitude (Kara 2017; Patterson and Zhuo 2018). In 2013, the Walk Free Foundation in Australia published its first Global Slavery Index (Walk Free Foundation 2013), and since then they have been collaborating with the International Labour Office (ILO), which is affiliated with the United Nations, to update the number of affected human beings. They define slavery as the following: "Modern slavery includes slavery, slavery-like practices (such as debt bondage, forced marriage and sale or exploitation of children), human trafficking and forced labour, and other practices described in key international treaties, voluntarily ratified by nearly every country in the world." The ILO data for 2016 (the latest estimates at this writing) suggest that 40 million people (predominantly women) were in servitude in 2016, including 15 million in forced marriages, and 25 million in forced labor (Walk Free Foundation 2018).

Impact of Migration on Society

Why does migration matter? By now you know the drill: It has the potential to influence the lives of the people who move, whether forced or not, the people they leave behind, and the people with whom they interact at their destination. And, depending on the size of the migration flow over time, it has the potential to alter the demographic structure of a community in dramatic ways and within a very short period of time. It can also alter the social structure subtly, but importantly, as the immigrant stock adds its children to the societal recipe, and changes its flavor.

Although migrants typically move in order to improve their lives (or to save their lives, in the case of refugees), we must recognize that for the individual migrant relocation may nonetheless produce anxiety and stress as a new social environment has to be negotiated. Part of that negotiation process may be to deal with discrimination (possibly including violence) that is often the result of xenophobia, fear and mistrust of strangers on the part of people already residing in the place to which the migrant has moved. One of the ways in which migrants cope with a new environment is to seek out others who share their cultural and geographic backgrounds (sometimes called co-ethnics). This is often aided or even forced by the existence of an enclave (a place in a larger community within which members of a particular subgroup tend to concentrate) of recent and former migrants from the same or similar areas. In fact, the development of an enclave may facilitate migration since it reduces fear of the unknown, as discussed above in the network theory of migration. The enclave in the host area provides guides to the new environment—former migrants who have made the adaptation and stand ready to aid in the social adjustment and integration of new migrants. Ethnic ties may also provide entrepreneurial newcomers with access to working capital, protected markets, and a pool of labor to help get a business started (Portes and Rumbaut 2014).

Although finding people of similar background may ease the coping burden for a new migrant, there is some evidence to suggest that the long-run social consequences of "flocking together" (especially among relatives) in a closed society of other immigrants will retard the migrant's adjustment to and assimilation into the new setting. John F. Kennedy's comment that "the way out of the ghetto lies not with muscle, but with the mastery of English" is more than a facile phrase. It points to a key to educational success and labor force entry, especially for the children of immigrants (Kasinitz et al. 2008).

Immigrants undergo a process of adaptation to the new environment, in which they adjust to the new physical and social environment and learn how best to negotiate everyday life. Some immigrants never go beyond this, but most proceed to some level of acculturation, in which they adopt the host language, bring their diet more in line with the host culture, listen to the music and read the newspapers, magazines, and books of the host culture, and make friends outside of their immigrant group. This may be more likely to happen if the immigrant has children, because children often are exposed to the new culture more intensively than are adults. Language use is frequently employed as an indicator of acculturation, and the United States has been called a "graveyard" for languages because an immigrant's native language is unlikely to last much beyond his or her own generation (Rumbaut, Massey, and Bean 2006). Many migrants never go beyond linguistic acculturation, but some migrants (and especially their children raised in the host culture) assimilate, in which they take on not just the outer trappings of the host culture, but also assume the behaviors and attitudes of members of the host culture (Alba and Nee 1997; Rumbaut 1997). Intermarriage with a member of the host society is often used as an index of assimilation, although that does not necessarily mean that a person has abandoned the identification with their immigrant ethnic background (Feliciano and Rumbaut 2018).

These individual adjustments to a receiving society assume an open society and assume that immigrants are considered on an individual basis. In fact, nations rarely are open with regard to immigrants, and because immigration occurs regularly in clumps (with groups of refugees, or new guest workers arriving nearly *en masse*), immigrants often are treated stereotypically, leading to discrimination. Although assimilation is one model by which a society might incorporate immigrants into its midst, there are at least three other types of incorporation: integration (mutual accommodation); exclusion (in which immigrants are kept separate from most members of the host society and are maintained in separate enclaves or ghettos);

and multiculturalism or *pluralism* (in which immigrants retain their ethnic communities but share the same legal rights as other members of the host society).

Multiculturalism, in particular, is enhanced by the transnational migrant, who sets roots in the host society while still maintaining strong linkages to the donor society. Such individuals have also been called "skilled transients" (Findlay 1995)—relatively skilled workers moving internationally on assignment and, in the process, having an impact on the area of destination while always intending to return to the area of origin. In parts of sub-Saharan Africa, a type of transnationalism has been institutionalized into the social structure among migratory laborers, and there is evidence that elsewhere in the world less-skilled workers are adopting this strategy of living dual lives—working in one environment but maintaining familial ties in another (Levitt, DeWind, and Vertovec 2003).

Most of the explanations about how immigrants deal with their new society focus on adult immigrants who were raised in one country and are now adapting and adjusting to another. The children born to them in the new country (the second generation) will have the task of growing up mainly (or only) knowing the new country, but having to deal with immigrant parents. Note, however, that the youngest immigrants (those who are prepubescent, approximately 12 or younger) are actually in that same situation—too young for the country of origin to have had a strong impact on their own development, and growing up in the new country almost as though they had been born there. This is sometimes known as the 1.5 generation—halfway between the first generation (the immigrants), and the second generation (the children of immigrants) (Perlmann 2005; Rumbaut 1997).

The path that receiving societies often have in mind for the children of immigrants is a straight-line process of assimilation from the country of their parents' origin into the country of their own birth. You are already primed for the idea, however, that when it comes to migration, life is never going to be so simple. Research suggests that children of immigrants (including those who migrated as children) alter their view of their role in society as they move through the life course (a concept we discuss in more detail in Chapters 8 and 9). For example, Cynthia Feliciano and Rubén Rumbaut (2018:42) found in their analysis that:

> . . . ethnic identity formations among the second generation in middle adulthood are complex and varied. Although for some, attachments to an ethnic identity remain strong into their late thirties, for many, ethnic identity attachments begin to wane through the life course, as their social identities as parents, workers, or spouses become more central. Moreover, ethnic identities relate to political and social views and behaviors in complex, and often modest, ways.

Although the consequences of migration for the individual are of considerable interest (especially to the one uprooted), a more pervasive aspect of the social consequences of migration is the impact on the demographic composition and social structure of both the donor and host areas. The demographic composition is influenced by the selective nature of migration, particularly selectivity by age. The donor area typically loses people from its young adult population, as those people are then added to the host area. Many small towns in Latin America, for example, are left with older adults and children whose parents are abroad, a situation that carries with it a host of economic and psychological challenges. Further, because it is at the young adult ages that the bulk of reproduction occurs, the host area has its level of natural increase augmented at the expense of the donor area. This natural-increase effect of migration is further enhanced by the relatively low probability of death of young adults compared with the higher probability in the older portion of a population. This is the story of the demise of rural villages throughout the world.

The selective nature of migration, when combined with its high volume, such as in the examples of the United States and Canada, helps to alter the patterns of social relationships and social organization in both the host and donor communities. Extended kinship relations are altered, and local economic, political, and educational institutions have to adjust to shifts in the number and characteristics of people serviced by each.

Overall, then, migration has the greatest short-run impact on society of any of the three demographic processes. It is a selective process that always requires changes and adjustments on the part of the individual migrant, and these changes reverberate throughout society. It carries significant consequences for the social, cultural, and economic structure of both donor and host regions. Because of these potential consequences, patterns of migration are harbingers of social change in a society.

Summary and Conclusion

Migration is any permanent change of residence of sufficient distance to change your whole round of daily activities. In the modern world, this typically involves crossing administrative boundaries within a country (such as moving to a different county or state), or moving to a different country. It is the most complex of the three population processes because we have to account for the wide variety in the number of times people may move, the vast array of places migrants may go, and the incredible diversity of reasons there may be for who goes where, and when. Of importance to demographers is the fact that the migration transition is an inevitable consequence of the mortality transition, which lowers the death rate prior to the initiation of the fertility transition. This unleashes population growth in rural areas that cannot be accommodated by agricultural economies, pushing people (usually young adults) to migrate to where the jobs are—usually cities within their own country, but sometimes to other countries.

For decades, migration theory advanced little beyond the basic idea of push and pull factors operating in the context of migration selectivity. More recently, conceptual models have developed that are very reminiscent of the explanations of the fertility transition. To begin with, we need a model of how the migration decision is arrived at (not unlike the first precondition for a fertility decline—the acceptance of the idea that you are empowered to act). Then, most importantly for the study of migration, we need to understand what might motivate a person to migrate. A variety of theoretical perspectives has been offered, including the neoclassical approach, the new household economics of migration approach, the theory of the dual labor market, and world systems theory. Finally, the means available to migrate represent those things that "grease the skids," making it easy to migrate once a person is motivated to do so. These include not only improved transportation and communication but also the development of social networks and institutions that facilitate the migration process.

Voluntary migration on a massive global scale did not begin in earnest until the mid-nineteenth century, and it was primarily a movement of Europeans to the Americas. As the volume increased and the cultural mix changed, the United States began to put up hurdles to slow things down. This led in the 1920s to a set of very restrictive immigration policies that effectively choked off immigration for more than a generation. In the 1960s immigration laws were liberalized, and when President Lyndon Johnson signed the Immigration and Nationality Act of 1965, he argued that it was largely symbolic and would not really have an impact on immigration levels. He could not have been more wrong, and the United States has been adjusting to a new reality of immigration ever since.

Throughout the world, population growth has induced an increase in the volume of migration, both legal and undocumented. "Temporary" labor migration has also increased throughout the world as jobs have become more available in the aging, more developed societies for the burgeoning number of younger workers from less developed countries. Understandably, guest workers are often reluctant to leave higher-income countries, even when the economies in those places slow down and pressure builds for foreigners to go home. Such people are only a few steps away from the unhappily large fraction of the world's migrants who are refugees, seeking residence in other countries after being forced out of their own.

Migration has dynamic consequences for the migrants themselves, for the areas from which they came, and for the places to which they go. Some of these consequences are fairly predictable if we know the characteristics of the migrants. If immigrants are well-educated young adults, for example, they will be looking for well-paying jobs, they may add to the economic prosperity of an area, and they will probably be establishing families, which will further add to the area's population and increase the demand for services. Although it is not always apparent, the quality of our everyday life is greatly affected by the process of migration, for even if we ourselves never move, we will spend a good part of our lifetime adjusting to people who have migrated into our lives and to the loss of people who have moved away.

Main Points

1. Migration is the process of changing residence far enough and for long enough that you move your whole round of social activities from one place to another.

2. The migration transition is the shift from an historical pattern of a small fraction of people making rural to rural moves, to a larger fraction of a population moving especially from rural to urban areas, altering the demographic and social structure of societies in the process.

3. Migration can be assessed in terms of flows (the movement of people) or stocks (the characteristics of people according to their migration status).

4. Explanations of why people move typically begin with the push-pull theory, first formulated in the late nineteenth century.

5. Migration is selective and is associated especially with age, giving rise to the idea that migration is an implementing strategy—a means to a desired end associated especially with stages in the life cycle.

6. Migration within and between countries tends to be for economic reasons, although many of the migrants are family members following the person who is moving for job-related reasons.

7. Major theories offered to explain international migration include neoclassical economics, the new household economics of migration, the dual labor market theory, world systems theory, network theory, institutional theory, and cumulative causation.

8. The United States accepts more migrants (legal and undocumented) than any other country in the world, and for more than a century the U.S. government has implemented numerous complex and politically-charged efforts to control the number and characteristics of people entering the country.

9. Migration of all kinds, whether forced or voluntary, demands adjustment to a new environment on the part of the migrant, and sets in motion a societal response to the immigrant on the part of the receiving society.

10. Ross Baker once suggested that the "First Law of Demographic Directionality" is that a body that has headed west remains at west, and that is still generally an accurate statement for the world.

Questions for Review

1. Discuss the way in which the theory of demographic change and response (introduced in Chapter 3) provides a conceptual framework for understanding the migration transition. How does that framework help us understand future demographic changes in the developing nations?

2. Discuss the differences between migration stocks and flow, and then show how the two are interrelated in terms of their impact on both receiving and sending societies.

3. Describe your own lifetime experiences with migration and relate them to the decision-making model shown in Figure 6.3.

4. What do you think the migration policy of the United States should be? Defend your answer and explain what would be the consequences, intended and unintended, of your proposed policy.

5. Evaluate the way in which the timing of demographic transitions in other parts of the world has helped to explain the patterns of migration to the United States over the past 200 years.

CHAPTER 7
The Urban Transition

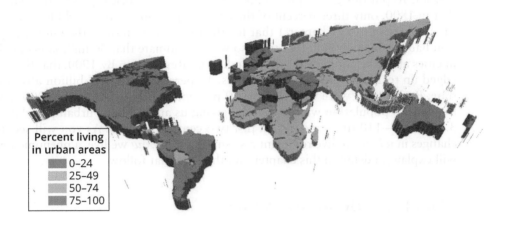

Percent living in urban areas
- 0–24
- 25–49
- 50–74
- 75–100

Figure 7.1   Percent Living in Urban Areas, as Estimated for 2020
Source: Adapted by John R. Weeks using data from United Nations Population Division (2018a).

What Is the Urban Transition?

Defining Urban Places

The Historical Pattern of the Urban Transition

The Proximate Determinants of the Urban Transition
Internal Rural-to-Urban Migration
Natural Increase
Mortality
Fertility
International Urbanward Migration
Reclassification
An Illustration from Mexico
An Illustration from China

The Urban Hierarchy
Defining the Metropolis
City Systems

The Urban Evolution That Accompanies the Urban Transition
Urban Crowding
Slums
Suburbanization
Residential Segregation
Urban Sprawl
Gentrification

Summary and Conclusion

Main Points

Questions for Review

ESSAY: *Cities as Sustainable Environments*

For most of human history almost no one lived in cities—they were small islands in a sea of rurality. Then, in an historical blink of the eye, we find more than half of us are living in urban places. Furthermore, that fraction is projected to increase to more than two-thirds by the middle of this century (United Nations Population Division 2018c). To put this geographic transformation into historical perspective, consider that in 1800, only three percent of the entire population of the world lived in cities. You will recall from Chapter 1 that for the first time in history the human population had hit one billion at that time, so we can estimate that 30 million people lived in cities at the beginning edge of the Industrial Revolution. By 1900, that figure had edged up to 224 million urban dwellers, 14 percent of the 1.6 billion alive at the time. By 2000 we were very close to 50 percent, which we then hit in 2007, when the world's population was 6.6 billion, giving us an estimated urban population of 3.3 billion—110 times more than just two centuries earlier. As you will see, these changes in *where* we live represent a seismic shift in *how* we live, a phenomenon we will explain in detail in this chapter and the ones that follow.

What Is the Urban Transition?

The urban transition represents the reorganization of human society from being predominantly rural and agricultural to being predominantly urban and nonagricultural—a genuinely revolutionary shift in society. Leonard Reissman (1964:154) described it this way:

> Urbanization is social change on a vast scale. It means deep and irrevocable changes that alter all sectors of a society. In our own history [the United States] the shift from an agricultural to an industrial society has altered every aspect of social life . . . the whole institutional structure was affected as a consequence of our urban development. Apparently, the process is irreversible once begun. The impetus of urbanization upon society is such that society gives way to urban institutions, urban values, and urban demands.

The vast majority of Americans are now living in—indeed were born in—cities, and almost everyone in the richer countries of the world shares that urban experience, as do an increasing fraction of people in developing nations. Most of us take the city for granted, some curse it, some find its attractions irresistible, but no one denies that urban life is the center of modern civilization. Cities, of course, are nothing new, and their influence on society is not a uniquely modern feature of life. However, the widespread emergence of urban life—the explosive growth of the urban population—is very much a recent feature of human existence. This urban transition is one of the most significant demographic movements in world history, and it is intimately tied to population growth and all aspects of the demographic transition. We can reasonably say that in the world today, population growth is originating in the countryside but showing up in the cities.

Cities are implicated in a wide range of problems, issues, and triumphs in all societies, but our intention here is not to review what life is like in a city. That is increasingly the story of human life in general, and it is well beyond the scope of this book. Rather, we want to provide you with a demographic perspective on the urban transition. First we examine the drivers of the urban transition—the reasons why urban places have become so popular. From there we will examine the more proximate determinants of the urban transition—the demographic mechanisms by which the transition is accomplished. Then we look at some of the more important ways in which the urban transition becomes an evolutionary process, as people constantly readjust to life in urban places. In the chapter's essay, we also examine the extent to which cities are sustainable. What is it that allows most humans to effectively disassociate themselves from living on the land, growing food, and being close to nature?

Defining Urban Places

What exactly is an urban place, you might well ask. We tend to know it when we see it, but how do we define it? An urban place can be thought of as a *spatial concentration* of people whose lives are organized around *nonagricultural activities*. The essential characteristic here is that urban means high density and nonagricultural, whereas rural means any place that is not urban. A farming village of 5,000 people should not be called urban, whereas a tourist spa or an artist colony of 2,500 people may well be correctly designated as an urban place. You can appreciate, then, that "urban" is a fairly complex concept. It is a function of (1) population size, (2) space (land area), (3) the ratio of population to space (density or concentration), and (4) economic and social organization.

As the number and fraction of people living in urban places has increased, the impact of urban life obviously becomes increasingly important. The study of human society is more and more the study of *urban* society, and the variability across space and time in the urban environment is a crucial part of the changes occurring all over the world. Keep in mind that the urban environment is a combination of the *social environment* (the people with whom we interact and share our lives) and the *built environment* (the physical buildings/infrastructure and landscapes in which life takes place).

Unfortunately, the definitions of *urban* used in most demographic research rarely encompass the more complex ingredients of what an urban place is really all about. Due to limitations in available data and sometimes simply for expediency, researchers (and government bureaucrats as well) typically define urban places on the basis of population size within a given defined area, implying that density is the major criterion. Thus, for most research purposes all places with a population of 2,000; 5,000; 10,000 or more (the lower limit varies) might be considered urban for research purposes. The United Nations Population Division, for example, has to deal with this national variability in urban definitions as it regularly puts together the estimates and projections of the urban and rural populations throughout the world that we will be discussing throughout this chapter (United Nations Population Division 2018b).

Although the difference between rural and urban areas may at first appear to be a dichotomy, it is really a continuum in which we might find an aboriginal hunter-gatherer near one end and an apartment dweller in Manhattan near the other. In between will be varying shades of difference, what we can call an urban gradient (Weeks 2004, 2010; Benza et al. 2017). The next time you drive from the city to the country (or the other way around), you might ask yourself where you would arbitrarily make a dividing line between the two. In the United States in the nineteenth and early twentieth centuries, rural turned into urban when you reached streets laid out in a grid. Today, such clearly defined transitions are rare, and besides, even living in a rural area no longer precludes your participation in urban life if you have access to the internet, as an increasing fraction of humans do. The flexibility of the automobile combined with the power of telecommunications puts most people in touch with as much of urban life (and what is left of rural life) as they might want. Rural villagers can now be knowledgeable about urban life, even if they have never seen it in person.

Ever since Census 2000, the U.S. Census Bureau has been using the power of geographic information systems (GIS—see Chapter 2 for details) to refine its definition of what is urban in the United States. To be urban by the Census Bureau standard, you start with a core census block or block group (an area that is part of a census tract—again, see Chapter 2 for those definitions) that has a population density of at least 1,000 persons per square mile, and then add any contiguous areas that have at least 500 persons per square mile. As long as the total population of this combined area is at least 2,500 people, the area is defined as urban, and any smaller place within that urban area is also called urban. Any place that is not within an urban area or urban cluster is defined as rural.

Canada defines an urban place in a similar but not identical fashion. An *urban place* or *urban area*, as defined by Statistics Canada, has a population of at least 1,000 concentrated within a continuously built-up area, at a density of at least 400 per square kilometer (equivalent to about 1,000 persons per square mile). However, starting with the 2011 census, Statistics Canada has implemented its own version of the urban gradient by dividing urban areas into three classes of population centers (or "centres," as they call them), based on population size: (1) small population centres, with a population of between 1,000 and 29,999; (2) medium population centres, with a population of between 30,000 and 99,999; and (3) large urban population centres, consisting of a population of 100,000 and over (Statistics Canada 2011). Mexico has traditionally defined *urban* as being any locality that has at least 2,500 inhabitants (INEGI 2010), although Mexico, like Canada, typically defines a *city* (i.e., large urban population centre in Canadian terms) as a place that has at least 100,000 inhabitants.

You can see that the United States and Canada use a combination of population size and density to define urban, whereas Mexico relies largely on population size alone. None of the three gives consideration to the economic and social characteristics of a place. Yet an essential ingredient of being urban is economic and social life organized around nonagricultural activities. You should thus keep in mind that there is a discontinuity between the *concept* of urban and the *definition* of urban as we turn now to a discussion of the demographic aspects of the process whereby a society is transformed from rural to urban.

The Historical Pattern of the Urban Transition

In its most basic form, the urban transition is the same concept as *urbanization* and refers to the change in the proportion of a population living in urban places. It is a relative measure ranging from 0 percent, if a population is entirely rural or agricultural, to 100 percent, if a population is entirely urban. The earliest cities were not very large because most of them were not demographically self-sustaining. The ancient city of Babylon (about 50 miles south of modern Baghdad, Iraq) might have had 50,000 people, Athens possibly 80,000, and Rome as many as 500,000; but they represented a tiny fragment of the total population of the region in which they were located. They were symbols of civilization, visible centers that were written about, discussed by travelers, and densely enough settled to be dug up later by archaeologists. Our view of ancient history is colored by the fact that our knowledge of societal detail is limited primarily to the cities, although we can be sure that most people actually lived in the countryside.

Early cities were not demographically self-sustaining because they had higher death rates and lower birth rates than the countryside did, which usually resulted in an annual excess of deaths over births, as we discussed in Chapter 4, and so they had to be constantly replenished by migrants from the hinterlands. Modern cities, by contrast, have lower death rates than rural areas, so they do not need migrants for replenishment. Rather, they need migrants to fill the jobs they are creating.

The economically self-sustaining character of modern urban areas began with the transformation of economies based on agriculture (a rural activity) to those based on manufactured goods (typically an urban activity) and has expanded to those based on servicing the rest of the economy (also typically an urban activity). Control of the economy made it far easier for cities to dominate rural areas politically and thus ensure their own continued existence in economic terms.

A crucial transition in this process came between about 1500 and 1800 with the European discovery of "new" lands, the rise of mercantilistic states (that is, based on goods rather than landholdings, as we discussed in Chapter 3), and the inception of the Industrial Revolution. These events were inextricably intertwined, and they added up to a diversity of trade that gave a powerful stimulus to the European economy. This was a period of building a base for subsequent industrialization, but it was still a preindustrial and largely pre-urban era. During this time, for example, cities in England were growing at only a slightly higher rate than the total population, and thus the urban population was rising only slowly as a proportion of the total. Between 1600 and 1800, London grew from about 200,000 people to slightly less than a million (Wrigley 1987), in the process increasing from 2 percent of the total population of England to 10 percent. This made London the largest city in Europe (and it remained that way until the 1960s, when it was surpassed by Paris). Nonetheless, in 1801, only 18 percent of the population in England lived in cities of 30,000 people or more, and nearly two-thirds of those urban residents were concentrated in London. Thus, on the eve of the Industrial Revolution, Europe (like the rest of the world) was predominantly agrarian, even as some major cities like London were gaining strength.

It was in the nineteenth century that urbanization began in earnest, its timing closely tied to industrialization and the decline in mortality that triggered population growth. Believe it or not, there is evidence that the potato was a key factor in both the decline in mortality in Europe (as we mentioned in Chapter 1) and, at the same time, in the urban transition. The potato not only improved nutrition and thus lowered the death rate, it was also more productive than other crops, allowing more food to be grown with fewer workers—exactly what is required to free up labor to move to the cities (Nunn and Qian 2011).

Urban factory jobs were the classic magnets sucking young people out of the countryside in the nineteenth century. This happened earliest in England, and in Figure 7.2 you can see this rapid rise in urbanization in the United Kingdom in response to early industrialization. Japan and Russia entered the industrial world later than the United Kingdom or the United States, and you can see in Figure 7.2 that their patterns of urbanization were therefore delayed. Once started, however, you can also see that urbanization proceeded quickly in Japan and Russia.

Figure 7.1 at the beginning of the chapter maps the countries of the world according to the percentage of the population living in urban places as estimated by the United Nations for 2020, keeping in mind that the definition of urban varies somewhat from country to country. Globally, 56 percent of the population lives in a place defined as urban. As a species, then, we are now an urban majority. However, as of 2020, there were still 75 countries that were not yet urban-majority nations.

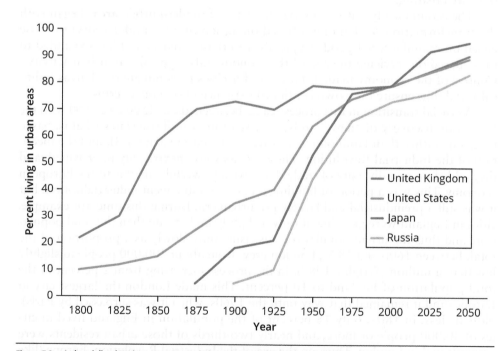

Figure 7.2   Industrialized Nations Have Passed Through Most of the Urban Transition

Sources: Prepared by John R. Weeks using data for 1800 through 1925 from Davis (1965); and data for 1950–2050 from United Nations Population Division (United Nations Population Division 2018a).

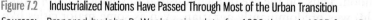

They are mainly found in South and Southeast Asia and sub-Saharan Africa. Prominent among these countries, as you can from Figure 7.1, are India, Pakistan, Bangladesh, Afghanistan, Sri Lanka, and the Philippines. Sub-Saharan Africa actually encompasses the places with the lowest percent urban, led by Burundi with only 14 percent. Looked at another way, though, almost every country in the world today (with only a handful of sub-Saharan nations as the exceptions) has a higher percent urban than England did at the start of the Industrial Revolution.

The pace of urbanization at the global level can be seen graphically in Figure 7.3. In 1950, 55 percent of the population in high-income countries of the world was already living in urban places, whereas only 9 percent of the population in the low-income nations was urban. Of special note is the rapid rise in the percent urban among countries that the United Nations Population Division labels as "upper-middle-income." They have soared from only 22 percent urban in 1950 to 68 percent in 2020 and are projected to nearly catch up with the high-income countries by 2050. Even the low-income countries are projected to reach 50 percent urban by 2050. The urban transition is very clear from these data.

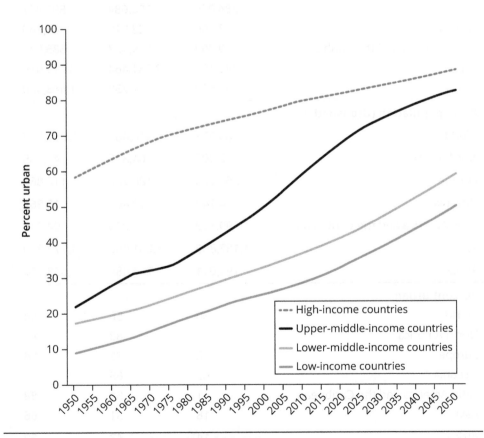

Figure 7.3   The World Has Urbanized at a Rapid Pace Since 1950

Sources: Adapted by John R. Weeks using data from United Nations Population Division (2018a).

Impressive as they are, the data in Figure 7.3 nonetheless understate the real growth in the urban population. Most of the world's population growth since 1950 has occurred in less developed/lower-income nations, so the increase in the *percentage* that is urban hides a staggering rise in the *number* of people living in urban places of those countries, as we mentioned earlier in the chapter. Table 7.1 summarizes the United Nations Population Division's estimates of the size of the urban and rural populations by the major geographic regions of the world. Especially noteworthy is Asia, which in 1950 had 246 million people in urban areas, increasing to more

Table 7.1   Asian, African, and Latin American Urban Populations Have Increased at a Staggering Rate Since 1950

	1950	2020	2050
Urban population (thousands)			
World	750,903	4,378,994	6,679,756
North America	110,300	304,761	386,690
Europe	284,085	556,684	598,857
Oceania	7,906	28,919	41,160
Latin America and the Caribbean	69,759	539,427	685,070
Asia	246,193	2,361,464	3,479,059
Africa	32,659	587,738	1,488,920
Rural population (thousands)			
World	1,785,372	3,416,488	3,092,067
North America	62,302	64,397	47,965
Europe	265,290	186,706	116,864
Oceania	4,742	13,465	15,961
Latin America and the Caribbean	99,159	125,046	94,771
Asia	1,157,869	2,261,990	1,777,869
Africa	196,011	764,884	1,038,637
Percent urban			
World	30	56	68
North America	64	83	89
Europe	52	75	84
Oceania	63	68	72
Latin America and the Caribbean	41	81	88
Asia	18	51	66
Africa	14	43	59

Source: Adapted by John R. Weeks from data in United Nations Population Division (2018a).

than 2 billion by 2020—a more than 10-fold increase since 1950—and expected to grow to 3.5 billion by 2050! In Africa, the urban population in 2020 was 18 times the size it had been in 1950. By contrast, in Latin America and the Caribbean, the urban population in 2020 was "only" 8 times what it had been in 1950 since these regions had urbanized earlier than Asia and Africa.

The United Nations expects the world's rural population in 2050 to be lower in number than in 2020 (3.1 billion in 2050 compared to 3.4 billion people in 2020), although that will still represent nearly twice as many rural people as there were in 1950 (1.8 billion). Only for Africa do the UN demographers project that the 2050 rural population will be greater in number than in 2020. Overall, the urban population of the world in 2050 (6.7 billion) is projected to be 52 percent larger than it was in 2020 (4.4 billion), and that would be nearly a nine-fold increase over the world's urban population of 1950 (which was 751 million).

As economic development has occurred over the past two centuries, cities have grown because they were economically efficient places. Commercial centers bring together in one place the buyers and sellers of goods and services. Likewise, industrial centers bring together raw materials, laborers, and the financial capital necessary for the profitable production of goods. They are efficient politically because they centralize power and thus make the administrative activities of the power base that supports them more efficient. In sum, cities perform most functions of society more efficiently than is possible when people are spatially spread out. The great urban historian Lewis Mumford said it well: "There is indeed no single urban activity that has not been performed successfully in isolated units in the open country. But there is one function that the city alone can perform, namely the synthesis and synergy of the many separate parts by continually bringing them together in a common meeting place where direct face-to-face intercourse is possible. The office of the city, then, is to increase the variety, the velocity, the extent, and the continuity of human intercourse" (1968:447).

Cities are efficient partly because they reduce costs by congregating together both producers and consumers of a variety of goods and services. By reducing costs, urban places increase the benefits accruing to business—meaning, naturally, higher profits. Those profits translate into higher standards of living, and that is why cities have flourished in the modern world.

The theory of the demographic transition was derived originally from the modernization theory (as you will recall from Chapter 3) that focused on the role played by cities. The basic thesis of modernization theory was that economic development is built on the efficiencies of cities. Cities are the engines of growth because of the concentration of capital (to build industry), labor (to perform the industrial tasks), and the financial, governmental, and administrative services necessary to manufacture, distribute, sell, and regulate the goods that comprise the essence of economic development. Once economic growth begins, the principle of cumulative causation (discussed in Chapter 6 with reference to migration) kicks in to promote further local development, often at the expense of other regions.

Modernization theory offers a generally good explanation of what happened in the now-developed countries, especially in the period up to World War II, as individual nation-building was taking place but transportation and communication still limited the amount of direct interaction between countries. But these theories, such as the often-quoted works of Gunnar Myrdal (1957) and Albert Hirschman (1958), refer to a time when urbanization in developing countries was still in its early stages. We now know that modernization theory tells only part of the story. The reality is that patterns of urbanization in different parts of the world may be determined not just by modernization, but by when a country entered the modern globalized economic system. The combination of modernization and globalization matters in the process of urbanization (Sassen 2012), creating new types of city systems and urban hierarchies, as we discuss later in the chapter.

The Proximate Determinants of the Urban Transition

As you watch the number and percentage of the population that is urban climb over time, you may assume that the explanation is very easy—people move out of rural areas into urban areas. That is a major part of the story, of course, but not the whole story. The urban transition occurs not only as a result of internal rural-to-urban migration, but also through natural increase, international urban migration, reclassification of places from rural to urban, and combinations of these processes. Another important thing to keep in mind is that the urban transition may end when nearly everybody is living in an urban area, but the urban *evolution*—changes taking place within urban areas—may continue forever, as we discuss later in the chapter.

Internal Rural-to-Urban Migration

The migration of people within a country from rural to urban places represents the classic definition of the urban transition because it is intuitively the most obvious way by which a population can be shifted from countryside to curbside. There is no question that in the developed countries, rural-to-urban migration was a major force in the process of urbanization. Over time, the agricultural population of these countries has tended to decline in absolute numbers, as well as in relative terms, even in the face of overall population growth. In less developed countries, though, rural-to-urban migration has been occurring in large absolute terms, but without a consequent depopulation of rural areas—although such a depopulation is projected for later in this century in most areas of the world, as you can see by looking back at Table 7.1. The reason, of course, is the difference in the rates of natural increase in less developed countries compared with rates in developed nations at a similar stage in the demographic transition.

Had it not been for migration, cities of the nineteenth century and earlier could not have grown in population size. In fact, in the absence of migration, the excess of deaths over births would actually have produced deurbanization. Of course, migration did occur because economic development created a demand for an urban population that was largely met by migrants from rural areas. Industrial cities drew the largest crowds, but commercial cities, even in nonindustrial countries, also generated a demand for jobs and created opportunities for people to move from agrarian to urban areas. The cities of most previously colonized countries bear witness to this fact. For example, migration accounted for 75–100 percent of the total growth of nineteenth-century cities in Latin America (Weller, Macisco, and Martine 1971).

Naturally, in the richer, highly urbanized countries, the agricultural population is now so small that cities (also nations) depend on the natural increase of urban areas, or immigrants from other countries, rather than migration from their own rural areas, for population growth. This helps to explain why Europe—one of the world's most urban regions—is facing depopulation: The low birth rate can no longer be compensated for by migrants coming in from the countryside, because the European countryside is emptied out of young people. As we discussed in the previous chapter, this is of course why migrants from Africa and Asia are heading to European cities, producing political backlashes in the process.

Natural Increase

The underlying source of urbanization throughout the world has historically been the rate of natural increase of the rural population. The decline in death rates in rural places, without a commensurate drop in the birth rate, has led to over-population in rural areas (too many people for the available number of jobs) and has caused people to seek employment elsewhere (the now-familiar tale of demo-graphic change and response). If there were no opportunities for rural-to-urban migration, the result might then simply be that the death rate would eventually rise again in rural areas to achieve a balance between population and resources (the "Malthusian" solution).

The speed of the urban transition—the number of years it takes to go from low-percentage urban to high-percentage urban—depends partly on the difference in the rates of natural increase between urban and rural areas. The rapid urban transition in China, for example, was made possible partly by the rapidly declining birth rate in cities (as we discussed in Chapter 5), which meant that migrants from the countryside were making a larger proportionate contribution to the shift in the percent urban.

Mortality

When the now-industrialized nations were urbanizing, death rates were higher in the city than in the countryside (Williams and Galley 1995; Szreter 2005), and this helped keep the rate of natural increase in the city lower than in rural areas. In turn, that meant that rural-to-urban migration was a more important factor influencing the urban percentage in a country. As an example, Kingsley Davis (1973) estimated that in the city of Stockholm Sweden, in 1861–1870, the average life expectancy at birth was only 28 years, whereas for the country as a whole at that time, life expectancy was 45 years. As we discussed in Chapter 4, the crowding of people into cities led initially to the spread of disease and higher death rates in cities than on the farms. These urban health crises helped to spur improvements in public health such as good sewerage, clean water, and then vaccinations against serious communicable disease. These innovations in the ability to resist death started in the cities and spread from there to the countryside. And, of course, over time they have been passed to the rest of the world by the industrialized nations.

For these reasons newer cities in developing countries do not have to experience a period of higher urban than rural mortality. For them, the health innovations were imported to the cities and diffused to the rural areas, with mortality being consistently lower in urban than in rural areas, as we can tell from the calculation of child mortality rates derived from the Demographic and Health Surveys (DHS) taken in developing countries around the world. Figure 7.4 shows the death rate to children under the age of five per 1,000 births (5q0) for urban and rural places, for a representative sample of recent surveys. The highest child mortality rates in Figure 7.4 are found in Africa, with Nigeria's rural child mortality rate at 149, which means that 14.9 percent of babies born were dying before their fifth birthday, based on data from the 2013 Nigeria DHS. This is one of the highest rates in the world, but at least it is lower (89) in urban areas. To put these numbers in perspective, by the way, the rate in the United States is 6 per 1,000 and in Norway it is 2 per 1,000.

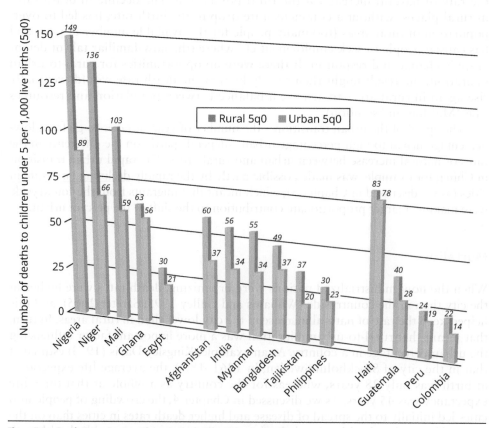

Figure 7.4   Death Rates Are Now Always Lower in Urban Than in Rural Areas

Source: Adapted by John R. Weeks using data from the DHS STATcompiler (2019).

The pattern of lower urban than rural mortality holds everywhere in the world today. The levels vary, as you can see in Figure 7.4, and sometimes the difference between urban and rural is not large (typically reflecting effective national programs to lower rural mortality levels), but it is still there. Of course, within cities you may encounter neighborhoods with rural-level death rates. Our research team working in Ghana, for example, has found that there are neighborhoods in Accra, the capital city of that country, where child mortality is as high as that experienced in many of the country's rural areas (Jankowska, Benza, and Weeks 2013). This is probably due to the very poor environmental conditions existing in urban slums of many cities of developing countries.

As a consequence of generally lower urban mortality, the process of urbanization in less developed countries is taking place in the context of historically high rates of urban natural increase. In the now higher-income countries, mortality declined as a response to economic development, and those same structural changes also lead to reduced fertility. But when death control is introduced independently of economic development—as it has been in almost all developing countries of the world—mortality and fertility declines lose their common source, and mortality decreases rather quickly whereas fertility takes longer to respond. This results in fertility levels being higher today in less developed countries (urban and rural places alike) than they were at a comparable stage of mortality decline in the currently advanced countries.

Fertility

We can usually anticipate that people residing in urban areas will have fairly distinctive ways of behaving compared with rural dwellers. So important and obvious are these differences demographically that urban and rural differentials in fertility are among the most well documented in the literature of demographic research. John Graunt, the seventeenth-century English demographer whom we first mentioned in Chapter 3, concluded that London marriages were less fruitful than those in the countryside because of "the intemperance in feeding, and especially the Adulteries and Fornications, supposed more frequent in London than elsewhere . . . and . . . the minds of men in London are more thoughtful and full of business than in the Country" (quoted by Eversley 1959:38). In rural areas, large families may be useful (for the labor power), but even if they are not, a family can "take care of" too many members by encouraging migration to the city. Once in the city, people have to cope more immediately with the problems that large families are apt to create for them. At the same time, the importance of the large family is challenged by the many alternatives to family life that cities offer compared to rural areas.

It is thus nearly axiomatic that urban fertility levels are lower than rural levels and this has probably been true throughout human history. Figure 7.5 provides urban and rural total fertility rates (TFR) for the same set of countries (from the same Demographic and Health Surveys) as in Figure 7.4. As was true with child mortality rates, the difference between urban and rural total fertility rates vary from fairly small in Asia (where family planning programs tend to have been in place for

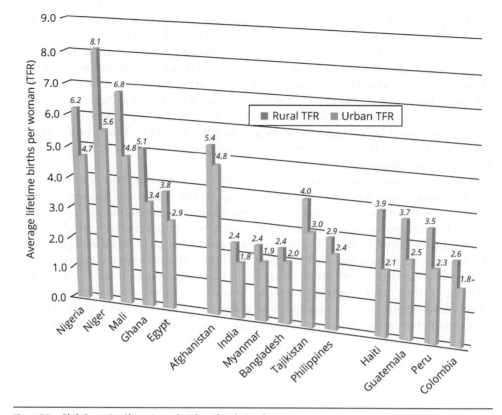

Figure 7.5   Birth Rates Are Always Lower in Urban Than in Rural Areas
Source: Adapted by John R. Weeks using data from the DHS STATcompiler (2019).

some time) to pretty large in Africa, where overall fertility levels are generally higher than anywhere else. And, just as was true for mortality, there can be very rural-like fertility levels within some parts of cities, as our research found in Cairo a few years ago (Weeks et al. 2004).

The emphasis in Figures 7.4 and 7.5 is on developing countries because they are the places in the world where both mortality and fertility tend to be high—in some cases still very high. Furthermore, the richer countries have very few people still residing in rural areas. For example, by the early 1990s, fewer than 2 percent of women in the United States of reproductive age were living on farms, and their fertility was only slightly higher than the other 98 percent of the population (Bachu 1993). Since the late 1990s, farm residence has not even been reported in the fertility data for the United States.

Urban fertility levels are also related to migration because migrants tend to be young adults of reproductive ages. Furthermore, migrants from rural areas typically wind up having levels of fertility lower than people in the rural areas they left, but they still have higher fertility levels than those in the urban areas to which they have moved (Kulu 2005). Migration rarely involves a simple move of people out of a rural area into the city and, as a result, lower fertility in urban areas may diffuse back to the countryside. The new urban dwellers are likely to go back for visits, bringing money and other things that aren't widely available in the countryside. They also bring back new ideas, new ambitions, and new motivations that can produce behavioral changes in the rural areas, including new ways of thinking about family size.

International Urbanward Migration

International migration also operates to increase the level of urbanization, because most international migrants almost always move to cities in the host area regardless of where they lived in the donor area. From the standpoint of the host area, then, the impact of international migration is to add to the urban population without adding significantly to the rural population, thereby shifting a greater proportion of the total to urban places. More than 95 percent of immigrants to the United States wind up as urban residents in big cities or their suburbs (U.S. Department of Homeland Security 2014), a fact driven home by data from the U.S. Census Bureau showing that several cities in the United States would have lost population between 2000 and 2009 had it not been for the influx of international migrants (U.S. Census Bureau 2010).

Reclassification

It is also possible for the urban transition to occur "in place." This happens when the absolute size of a place grows so large, whether by migration, natural increase, or both, that it reaches or exceeds the minimum size criterion used to distinguish urban from rural places. Note that reclassification is more of an administrative phenomenon than anything else and is based on a unidimensional (size-only) definition of urban places, rather than also incorporating any concept of economic and social activity. Of course, it is quite probable that as a place grows in absolute size it will at the same time diversify economically and socially, probably away from agricultural activities into more urban enterprises. This tends to be part of the social change that occurs everywhere in response to an increase in population size; an agricultural population can quickly become redundant and the lure of urban activities (such as industry, commerce, and services) may be strong under those conditions.

Another administrative trick that can lead to rapid city growth is annexation, either formally or simply through the spread of a city outward from its center. Urban growth rates can thus be misleading. For example, "The city of Houston grew 29 percent during the 1970s—one of the most rapidly growing large cities in the country. But the city also annexed a quarter of a million people. Without the annexation, the city would have grown only modestly" (Miller 2004:31). Throughout the world, this kind of phenomenon is associated with urban sprawl, which we discuss later in the chapter. In developing countries, reclassification is apt to be less formal but no less important. The greater metropolitan area of Cairo, Egypt, for example, encompasses a population of 21 million people. It has been swallowing up rural villages in its hinterland for several decades. As people move to Cairo they seek affordable housing, and existing villages near Cairo represent one set of opportunities. In the process, these villages become unintentionally, but inextricably, connected to Cairo (Rodenbeck 1999; Weeks, Larson, and Fugate 2005).

An Illustration from Mexico

The impact of population processes on the urban transition is well illustrated from the perspective of rural areas by what happened over time to people in one village in Mexico—Tzintzuntzan (which in the indigenous language means "the place of hummingbirds"), situated midway between Guadalajara and Mexico City in the state of Michoacán. Historically, the site was the capital of the Tarascan empire (Brandes 1990), but today it is a village of artisans, farmers, merchants, and teachers. For nearly 400 years, the population of Tzintzuntzan stayed right at about 1,000 people (Foster 1967). In the mid-1940s, as George Foster began studying the village, the population size was starting to climb slowly because death rates had started to decline in the late 1930s at about the time a government project gave the village electricity, running water, and a hard-surfaced highway connecting it to the outside world (Kemper and Foster 1975).

In 1940, the population was 1,077 and the death rate was about 30 per 1,000, while the birth rate of 47 per 1,000 was leading to a rate of natural increase of 17 per 1,000 (an implied doubling time of 40 years). For some time, there had been small-scale, local out-migration from the village to keep its population in balance with the limited local resources, but by 1950 the death rate was down to 17 per 1,000 and the birth rate had risen. Better medical care had reduced the incidence of miscarriage and stillbirth, and in 1950 the village had 1,336 people (Foster 1967). By 1970 the population had reached about 2,200 (twice the 1940 size); however, were it not for out-migration draining away virtually all of the natural increase of Tzintzuntzan, the population would again have doubled in about 20 years (Kemper and Foster 1975).

What, you ask, does growth in a small Mexican village have to do with the urban transition? The answer, of course, is that population growth meant that the local population was larger than the local economy could handle, so some of these villagers were forced to migrate out in search of work. The migrants headed for the cities, and therein lies the tale of the urban transition. Poverty is extensive in rural Mexico, and almost all of those people who leave Tzintzuntzan go to urban places where better opportunities exist—with Mexico City (230 miles away) having been the most popular destination (Kemper and Foster 1975). One of the easiest demographic responses that people can make to population pressure is migration, and in Mexico, as in most countries of the world, the city has been the receiving ground. Furthermore, the demographic characteristics of those who went to the city were what you would expect; they tended to be younger, slightly better educated, of higher occupational status, and more innovative than nonmigrants (Kemper 1977).

For Tzintzuntzeños, migration to Mexico City raised the standard of living of migrant families, altered the worldview of both adults and their children toward greater independence and achievement, and, indirectly, "urbanized" the village they left behind. This last effect is due to the fact that having friends and relatives in Mexico City was one factor that led the villagers to become aware of their participation in a wider world. This made it easier for each successive generation to make the move to Mexico City, because they knew what to expect when they arrived and they knew people who could help them.

Tzintzuntzeños have also been attracted to the United States, initially recruited through the bracero program (which we mentioned in Chapter 6), and the same patterns of mutual assistance encouraged the flow of money and ideas from cities in the United States to this small village in the interior of Mexico (Kemper 1996; Kemper and Adkins 2006). Remittances from international migrants can be an extremely important source of income in rural Mexico (Cornelius, Fitzgerald, and Fischer 2008), and over time migrants have also sent or brought back to the village many of the accoutrements of urban life, from new stoves and sewing machines to stereos, television sets, and mobile phones, in effect urbanizing what was once a remote village.

From a theoretical perspective, we can see that modernization was the key to the transformation of the lives of Tzintzuntzeños. However, the process of modernization was not endogenous—it sought the villagers out, rather than the other way around. In a very literal sense, the modernization of the village and its inhabitants depended on what was happening elsewhere. Government leaders in Mexico City (the core) made the decision to provide rural areas (the periphery) with health care, electricity, and paved highways. The rest, as they say, is history, because few villagers, when given the choice, turn down the opportunity for a higher standard of living (Critchfield 1994).

An Illustration from China

China is a very interesting case of urbanization because it is one of the few countries in the world where the government fairly successfully "kept them down on the farm." The Chinese Communist Party officially adopted an anti-urban policy when it came to power in 1949, believing that cities were a negative "Western" influence, and Chinese government policies in the 1960s and 1970s were designed to counteract the urban transition occurring in most of the rest of the world. These policies attempted to "promote wider income distribution, reduce regional inequalities, and create a more balanced urban hierarchy, which would lead to a greater decentralization of economic activities. In doing so, the intention was to slow population growth in the largest cities, while allowing continued increases in medium-sized and smaller urban centers" (as quoted in Bradshaw and Fraser 1989:989; Goldstein 1988).

As idyllic as that may sound, the basic policy has been enforced by a rigid household registration system initiated in 1958 called *hukou*, which created a type of occupational apartheid in China. "Anyone in a rural county is automatically registered as a farmer, anyone in a city as a non-farmer; and the distinction is near rigid. A city-dwelling woman (though not a man) who marries a farmer loses the right to urban life" (*The Economist* 1998:42). A person's status as rural or urban in 1958 was essentially passed on to children and grandchildren, and has been very difficult to change over time.

The problem with this system is that economic development in China has created a nearly classic demand for urban workers that has been met in part by "temporary" migrants from rural areas (Sun and Fan 2011). The rigidities of the household registration system, though, have created a situation whereby millions of Chinese are "illegal immigrants" in cities within their own country. "Even migrants who have lived in cities for many years, or the urban-born children of such migrants, are given far less access to government-funded health care and education than other city dwellers. This is because their rural *hukou* is often impossible to change" (*The Economist* 2014:30). The government announced in 2014 that it was loosening the policy and was beginning to grant urban status to some of the rural migrants to the cities. There are costs associated with this, however, because urban status then gives the migrants and their children access to government-funded schools and health care (Riley 2017).

Government policies in China thus prevented (or at least delayed) the high rate of natural increase in the rural areas from spilling over disproportionately into migration to urban areas, and the government located heavy industry in rural areas to help soak up the rural labor force (Hsu 1994). Of course, that did not mean that the urban population was not growing. Quite the contrary. Between 1953 and 1990, 326 new cities were created in China, and urban growth occurred especially in small to medium-sized places (Han and Wong 1994), just as the government had planned. Since, then, however, the economic changes that came about in conjunction with China's demographic dividend (a bulge of adults unencumbered by a lot of children due to the rapid decline in fertility—see Chapter 8 for more on this) have pulled people into cities at an increasing rate (Friedmann 2005; Riley 2017). At the time of the Communist revolution, China was just 12 percent urban, and by 1990 it had climbed to 26 percent, but by 2020 that had jumped to 61 percent, and the United Nations projects that China will be 80 percent urban by 2050.

The *hukou* system was successful administratively, in that it led to a much less varied urban hierarchy than exists in most modern nations (Fan 1999, 2008). The obvious examples are that Beijing is the politically most important city, Shanghai the most populous city, and Hong Kong the richest city (although it was already that way when China annexed it in 1997). Shanghai had an estimated 23 million people in 2015, while Beijing had 15.6 million, and an additional nine cities, including Hong Kong, had at least 7 million residents each. In Europe, by contrast, these three types of characteristics (power, population, and wealth) are often embodied in a single city (e.g., London or Paris).

The Urban Hierarchy

Defining the Metropolis

Anywhere you go in the world you will find cities that have grown so large and their influence extended so far that a distinction is often made between metropolitan and nonmetropolitan areas, definitions developed to refine the more traditional terms of urban and rural. This happened first in the richer countries such as the United States, and back in 1949 the U.S. Census Bureau developed the concept of a standard metropolitan area (SMA), consisting of a county with a core city of at least 50,000 people and a population density of at least 1,000 people per square mile. The concept proved useful in conjunction with the 1950 census and was subsequently renamed the standard metropolitan statistical area (SMSA), later shortened to be just an MSA (metropolitan statistical area). The basic idea of a metropolitan statistical area is that of an area containing a recognized population nucleus and adjacent communities that have a high degree of integration with that nucleus (U.S. Office of Management and Budget 2010). Thus, the spatial clustering of urban places creates an MSA.

Over time, modifications have been made to the definition and calculation of metropolitan areas, ordered always by the U.S. Office of Management and Budget (OMB), which uses these classifications for a variety of government purposes. The current set of definitions continues to use counties as the building blocks of a Core-Based Statistical Area (CBSA) classification scheme (Fitzsimmons and Ratcliffe 2004; U.S. Census Bureau 2018), which includes both metropolitan areas and the more recently added category of micropolitan areas. To be a metropolitan area, a CBSA must have a *core* urban area of at least 50,000 people, whereas a micropolitan area is an urban cluster of at least 10,000 people, but less than 50,000. Contiguous counties are then added to the CBSA if they meet specific criteria of connectivity: Either 25 percent or more of the employed residents of the county work in the central county of the CBSA or at least 25 percent of employment in the county is accounted for by workers who reside in the central county of the CBSA. Yes, this all seems a bit confusing, but remember that "urban" is not an easy concept to define in the first place, and in this case we are trying to refine the concept of urban to apply specifically to the most urban areas—the top end of the urban gradient.

In Canada, the definition of metropolitan is very similar, although not identical, to that in the United States. "A census metropolitan area (CMA) or a census agglomeration (CA) is formed by one or more adjacent municipalities centred on a population centre (known as the *core*). A CMA must have a total population of at least 100,000 of which 50,000 or more must live in the core. A CA must have a core population of at least 10,000. To be included in the CMA or CA, other adjacent municipalities must have a high degree of integration with the core, as measured by commuting flows derived from previous census place of work data" (Statistics Canada 2016). In Mexico, by contrast, government agencies have never defined metropolitan areas quite as precisely as have those in Canada and the United States.

Another level of aggregation is the urban agglomeration, a term used especially by the United Nations, and "refers to the population contained within the contours of a contiguous territory inhabited at urban density levels without regard to administrative boundaries. It usually incorporates the population in a city or town plus that in the suburban areas lying outside of, but being adjacent to, the city boundaries" (United Nations Population Division 2018b). The concept accepts a country's own definition of what is urban, and then puts together (agglomerates) all of the contiguous urban areas—another example of using spatial clustering to define large urban areas. As of 2018, the United Nations counted 1,859 urban agglomerations with more than 300,000 people, and it's a good guess that you can't name more than a few of them. The larger ones that you haven't heard of actually have the highest rates of population growth in the world. They have been called "black holes"—cities that are not part of a global network but are absorbing large numbers of people (Short 2004). How familiar are you, for example, with Haerbin, China (6 million people), Surabaya, Indonesia (3 million), or Srinagar, India (1.5 million)?

In general, the UN definitions of urban agglomerations are slightly more limited geographically than the metropolitan areas defined for the United States by the Census Bureau, but are nearly identical to those of the Canadian definitions. By UN definitions, Mexico City, with 21.8 million people, is more populous than the New York–Newark urban agglomeration (18.8 million). Toronto is Canada's most populous urban agglomeration with 7.1 million people, and its size would make it the sixth largest metro area in the United States and the second largest in Mexico.

As a further "refinement," an urban agglomeration with more than 10 million people is often identified as a mega-city. By this definition, there were 34 mega-cities in the world in 2020, and that number is projected to increase to 48 by 2035 (the end date of current projections). As you see in Table 7.2, in 1950 there were only two mega-cities in the world—New York and Tokyo. But, since then there has been a veritable explosion of mega-cities (a result of the global population explosion accompanied by the urban transition), almost all of them emerging in developing nations. Indeed, as of 2020, only 6 of the 34 mega-cities—Tokyo, Osaka, New York-Newark, Moscow, Los Angeles, and Paris—were in what in 1950 had been the world's richest countries. Today's big cities are found especially in the world's two most populous countries—China and India—where urbanization is occurring very rapidly (Ren 2018).

All of the definitions we have used so far rely on varying measures of urbanness and, as importantly, do not provide an index of the economic impact of the metropolitan areas that we are defining. Researchers have increasingly relied upon satellite imagery to help us in this task, using what Paul Sutton and colleagues (Sutton et al. 2001) once called a "census from heaven." By measuring the spatial extent and intensity of night-time lights collected from satellite sensors, it is possible to estimate both the size of the population in a metropolis, and its likely wealth, which can serve as a proxy for the city's global impact (see the essay accompanying this chapter for this kind of satellite image). Richard Florida and his colleagues (2012:184) did just that, identifying ". . . 681 global metropolitan areas with more than 500,000 people. These global metropolitan regions house 24 percent of the world's population but produce 60 percent of global output. We further find that Asia leads the way in global economic urbanization, followed by North America, the emerging economies, and Europe."

The rapid growth of cities in the context of continuing population growth in developing countries deserves considerable scrutiny on your part because it represents a potent source of social change with which each of these nations must cope. How they cope will almost certainly affect the rest of the world. On the positive side, successful coping will mean an increase in the standard of living of people in cities of developing nations, which would indirectly benefit the whole world through the increased potential for profitable interactions. The negative impacts have to do with the potential for the implosion of urban infrastructure under the weight of more people than can be sustained in these cities, leading

Table 7.2   The World's Largest Urban Agglomerations (Mega-Cities) Have Changed Dramatically over Time

1950		2020	
City	Population (millions)	City	Population (millions)
New York–Newark	12.3	Tokyo	37,393
Tokyo	11.3	Delhi	30,291
		Shanghai	27,058
		São Paulo	22,043
		Ciudad de México (Mexico City)	21,782
		Dhaka	21,006
		Al-Qahirah (Cairo)	20,901
		Beijing	20,463
		Mumbai (Bombay)	20,411
		Kinki M.M.A. (Osaka)	19,165
		New York-Newark	18,804
		Karachi	16,094
		Chongqing	15,872
		Istanbul	15,190
		Buenos Aires	15,154
		Kolkata (Calcutta)	14,850
		Lagos	14,368
		Kinshasa	14,342
		Manila	13,923
		Tianjin	13,589
		Rio de Janeiro	13,458
		Guangzhou, Guangdong	13,302
		Lahore	12,642
		Moskva (Moscow)	12,538
		Los Angeles-Long Beach-Santa Ana	12,447
		Shenzhen	12,357
		Bangalore	12,327
		Paris	11,017
		Bogotá	10,978
		Chennai (Madras)	10,971
		Jakarta	10,770
		Lima	10,719
		Krung Thep (Bangkok)	10,539
		Hyderabad	10,004

Source: Adapted by John R. Weeks using data from United Nations Population Division (2018a).

perhaps to the need for humanitarian relief measures, possibly even in the context of urban violence. In between these extremes lies an almost unlimited range of possibilities for cities, and neighborhoods within cities.

City Systems

In almost every nation of the world there is one city that stands out as the leading urban center and is noticeably more populous than other cities in the region. Such a place is called a primate city—a disproportionately large leading city holding a central place in the economy of the country. Looking at Table 7.2, for example, you can easily see that Tokyo is that place in Japan, while New York–Newark is that place in the United States. In the 1930s, Walter Christaller (1966) developed the concept of central place theory to describe why and how some cities were territorially central and thus in a position to control markets and the regional economy. Other cities are less important, although they may have their own pecking order.

Early empirical studies of city systems within countries suggested that a common pattern of cities by size could be expressed by the rank-size rule. As set out by George Zipf (1949), this says that the population size of a given city (P_i) within a country will be approximately equal to the population of the largest city (P_1) divided by the rank of city i by population size (R_i). Thus, the rank-size rule is:

$$P_i = P_1/R_i$$

So, if the largest city in a country has a population of five million, then the second largest city should have a population size of approximately 5/2, or 2.5 million, whereas the third largest city should have a population of 5/3, or 1.7 million people.

Despite its continued popularity, the only problem with the rank-size rule is that very few countries actually follow the formula very closely. In the U.S. example, the largest metropolitan area (New York–Newark) had a population in 2020 of 18.8 million (see Table 7.2). The second city, Los Angeles, should have had a population of about 9.2 million, and the third city, Chicago, should have been around 6.3 million. Instead, they were at 12.4 and 8.9 million, respectively. Thus, the U.S. cities are closer in population than predicted by the rank-size rule. Meanwhile, Canada's largest city is Toronto, with an estimated population in 2020 of 6.2 million. The rank-size rule would thus suggest that the country's second largest city, Montreal, should have a population of 3.1 million, and its third largest city, Vancouver, should check in with 2.1 million people. It turns out that Montreal has 4.2 million, and Vancouver has 2.6 million, so just as in the United States, the top three Canadian cities are a bit more clustered in population size than the rank-size rule would predict.

On the other hand, in Mexico, the largest city (Mexico City) has a population of 21.8 million people, so the rank-size rule would predict a population of 10.9 million, for the second largest city (Guadalajara) and a population of 7.2 million, for the third largest city (Monterrey). However, the estimated actual sizes of Guadalajara and Monterrey in 2020 were "only" 5.2 million and 4.9 million, respectively. Clearly, the urban hierarchy in Mexico also follows a different pattern than that expressed by the rank-size rule. Nonetheless, so compelling is the idea of the rank-size rule that people keep working to improve upon it by adding greater complexity (see, for example, Zengwang Xu and Harriss 2010).

Even though an empirical generalization such as the rank-size rule does not fit all countries, the importance of such ideas is that they led to the realization among scholars that most countries had a somewhat predictable system of cities that might be amenable to a consistent theoretical interpretation. An important set of such theoretical perspectives was the core-periphery model put forth by John Friedmann (1966). Prior to economic development, a series of independent cities may have existed in a region, but development tends to begin in, and will be concentrated in, one major site (the primate city). This is especially apt to happen in less developed countries that have a history of colonial domination, in which colonial functions were centralized in one city. Over time, the development process diffuses to other cities, but this happens unequally because the primate city (the core) controls the resources, and the smaller cities (the periphery) are dependent on the larger city. It was only a small step to apply these ideas of the core and periphery to a world system of countries and cities.

The world systems theory (which we discussed in Chapter 6 in relation to drivers of international migration) is based on the notion that inequality is part of the global economic structure and has been since at least the rise of capitalism 500 years ago (Wallerstein 1974). "Core" countries are defined as the highly developed nations that dominate the world economy and that were the former colonizers of much of the rest of the world. The "periphery" is composed of those countries that, in order to become a part of the global economic system (the alternative to which is to remain isolated and undeveloped), have been forced to be dependent on the core nations, which control the basic resources required for development and a higher standard of living.

Because countries tend to be dominated by cities, the world systems theory predicts that cities of core countries ("core cities") will control global resources, operating especially through multinational corporations headquartered in core cities (Chase-Dunn 2006); and cities in peripheral countries will be dependent on the core cities for their own growth and development (and, of course, that will filter down from the primate city to the other cities in a nation's own city system). These models suggest that the core cities are networked globally and emphasize services over manufacturing, whereas peripheral cities tend to be linked to more local markets and emphasize manufacturing over services.

As is so often the case, no single model seems capable of explaining all the complexity in the process of the urban transition. Several tests of modernization and world systems theories have suggested that variations of both contribute to our understanding of the real-world experience of urbanization (Firebaugh 2003). Part of the complexity is created by the fact that the sheer size of a city does not guarantee its importance in the system of world cities. To be a global city means to have economic power, which is often characterized by the presence of headquarters or major subsidiary locations of multinational corporations (Sassen 2012). Sheer size will be less important at the global scale than at the national or regional level, where the larger the city, the greater the economic opportunity is likely to be for

Cities as Sustainable Environments

For better or worse, human existence is increasingly tied to the city, which raises the key question of whether cities are sustainable places for humans to live. The answer seems to be that we have to make them so because we really have no other acceptable choice (Low et al. 2005). UN-Habitat is devoted to this task, and as of this writing, it has held three global gatherings on Housing and Sustainable Urban Development: Habitat I in 1976 in Vancouver, British Columbia; Habitat II in Istanbul, Turkey, in 1996; and Habitat III in 2016 in Quito, Ecuador. In between these official UN conferences, UN-Habitat hosts a World Urban Forum every two years. The goal of these meetings is largely to assess progress in dealing with each country's burgeoning urban population and to share best practices.

The opportunities that cities offer to rural peasants in less developed nations may seem meager to those of us raised in a wealthier society. Many developing country cities have outgrown their infrastructure and, as a result, drinkable water may be scarce (or available only in plastic sleeves sold by street vendors), sewage may not be properly disposed of, housing can be hard to find, transportation is probably inadequate, and electricity may be only sporadically available. This is not a pretty picture, but it is still an improvement on the level of living in the average rural village. Thus, "despite these problems, the flood of migrants to the cities continues apace. Why? The answer lies in the natural population increase in rural areas, limited rural economic development, and the decision-making calculus of urban migrants. . . . What this all means, of course, is that the primary cause of what some have termed 'overurbanization' (more urban residents than the economies of cities can sustain) is increasingly severe 'overruralization' (more rural residents than the economies of rural areas can sustain)" (Dogan and Kasarda 1988:19). You may think that quote from 1988 seems old, but it is still accurate. This is not a new issue—just a continually pressing one.

In the 1980s, Mexico City was the third most populous city in the world and many people projected it to continue growing almost forever.

However, the serious environmental problems in the Valley of Mexico created by population growth convinced the Mexican government to undertake a concerted effort to move industry out of the area and divert migrants to other metropolitan areas. The effort clearly paid off because the 1990 census counted fewer people in Mexico City than anticipated and, on that basis, the UN demographers revised their projections of population growth in Mexico City downward. Still, the 21.8 million people estimated to be living in Mexico City in 2020 was a huge increase from the 3.4 million in 1950, and the United Nations projects that the population of Mexico City will grow to 25 million by the year 2035, as it sprawls well beyond the older central city. Terrible smog, a dwindling water supply, and an increase in crime rates are all features of modern Mexico City—yet it offers more opportunity for the average rural peasant of Mexico than the countryside does, so people continue to move there.

Evaluations of the quality of life in the largest cities of the world reveal, not surprisingly, that the metropolitan areas of the richer countries are the preferred places to live. Every year, the Economist Intelligence Unit, based in London, creates a list of the most and least livable cities in the world. As of this writing, the most recent list ranked Vienna, Austria, as the world's "most livable city," followed by Melbourne, Australia (which had been at the top of the list for seven years in a row), and Vancouver, Canada. Six of the top ten most livable cities were in either Australia (Melbourne, Sydney, and Adelaide) or Canada (Calgary, Toronto, and Vancouver), two were in Europe (Vienna and Copenhagen), and two were in Japan (Osaka and Tokyo). None were in the United States. At the other end of the scale, Damascus, Syria, was the least livable city in the world as a result of several years of sectarian violence in that country. Indeed, cities with the greatest threat of conflict (e.g., Algiers, Algeria; Tripoli, Libya; and Karachi, Pakistan) and those with deepest levels of poverty (e.g., Lagos, Nigeria; and Harare, Zimbabwe) were the candidates to be on the least livable list.

We keep coming back to the same theme, however, that, as dismal as urban life is in developing

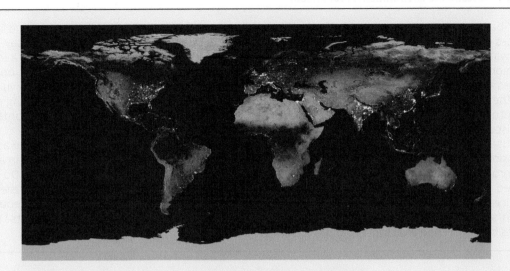

The Nighttime Lights from Satellite Images Show Where the Cities Are Located Globally
Note: The bright spots represent lights emitted from cities around the world.
Source: Adapted by John R. Weeks from imagery provided by NASA (2018).

countries, it is typically (although of course not always) a step up from life in rural areas. Cities are where economic development is occurring in the world, and it is where infrastructure and housing will continue to be built. The demand for housing itself is a function of the relationship between the population of young adults wanting to form their own family household and the number of people who are dying and thus presumably freeing up existing housing. The high rates of growth and attendant youthful age structures of the developing countries tell us that the worldwide demand for housing will be predominantly felt in the cities of less developed nations.

Along with housing, cities will also require infrastructure improvements, including safe water, adequate sewerage, electricity, roads, and public transportation. This is a daunting task, considering that the volume of housing and infrastructure needed is unprecedented in world history and, of course, we have not come even close to sheltering the current generation of people adequately. Furthermore, as we will discuss in more detail in Chapter 10, if the world is going to grow enough

food for the nearly 10 billion people that we expect by the middle of this century, we need machines to replace people on the world's farms. Large volumes of food need more "horsepower" than humans (or horses) can generate, so people are increasingly incidental to the main activities taking place in agriculture. The only other place for people is in the city, although of course, improving life for billions of people living in cities will use a tremendous amount of resources.

A related and very important cost of the urban transition is that as we gather ourselves into cities, we lose perspective about where our resources come from and where our waste goes. It seems like magic on both ends, but of course it is not. It is dangerous to forget our link to nature because there is a very real possibility that we have already overshot our capacity to sustain life for everybody in the world at a level even approaching that of the average urban resident of the United States, Canada, or Australia. We must learn how to deal successfully with the earth's limited resources because there are, in fact, no viable alternatives to the urban transition. This will require more

(continued)

plant-based diets, using solar and wind turbine sources of energy instead of fossil fuel, reusing our freshwater supplies, driving less (and using better and more efficient public transportation), consuming less and wasting less.

The link to nature is critically important for the future of cities. As you know already, and as we discuss in Chapter 10, global climate change is causing Arctic ice to melt and this is creating a noticeable rise in sea levels. As it turns out, a disproportionate share of the world's cities are located near oceans. This has been a deliberate practice to facilitate trade with other places since ocean shipping has been, and still is, a major means by which goods are sent around the world.

You can readily visualize this in the nighttime lights satellite image that accompanies this essay. The bright spots are large cities that put out a lot of light at night. As oceans rise, those cities on the coastlines are going to become increasingly vulnerable to flooding, and this will require moving people and infrastructure to higher ground in order to sustain life in these places.

Discussion Questions: (1) If you were asked to choose between living in a rural or urban area, which would you choose, and why? **(2)** Do you think that urban dwellers are likely to make the lifestyle changes that will almost certainly be required to maintain ourselves in our urban habitats? Why or why not?

its residents and the greater the attraction will be to potential migrants from other parts of the country. Empirical data show that cities in the United States are indeed rank-ordered with respect to the income of workers (Baum-Snow and Pavan 2013). In general, the more global a city, the higher the income, whereas the lower down in the ranking a city is, the higher the likelihood that its residents will be involved in low-income work (Elliott 1999).

The Urban Evolution That Accompanies the Urban Transition

As the richer countries approach a situation where almost everybody lives in urban places, it is important to remember that the end of the urban transition does not necessarily signal the end of the process of urban *evolution* (Pumain 2004). The mere fact that people are increasingly likely to live in places defined as urban does not mean that the urban environment itself stops changing and evolving across time and space. Indeed, there is probably more variability among urban places, and within the populations in urban places, than ever before in human history (Batty 2008). This is, of course, precisely why the definition of metropolitan areas keeps changing in the United States and elsewhere—it has to keep up with the evolution of those places.

Within cities, people do not just live anywhere—they sort themselves into neighborhoods in such a way that people who are more similar to one another socially and economically are more likely to live closer to one another than are people who are not so alike. Neighborhoods differ also with respect to the built environment—the transformation of the physical and natural environment that humans undertake in order to create a place where they can and want to live. It includes the infrastructure for piped water and sewerage, electricity and other types of energy, roads, buildings, parks, and everything else that physically represents what we think of as a city. These neighborhoods represent the context in which much of life is played out for its residents, and this is an interactive process in which the people help to shape the social and physical fabric of a neighborhood and, at the same time, the nature of the neighborhood promotes or constrains the options that people have in life. This is an organic process—sometimes improving neighborhoods and the lives of its residents, and sometimes not. It is why "you can't go home again." Home is constantly evolving.

The benefits of cities, of course, are what make them attractive, and they at least partially explain the massive transformation of countries like the United States and Canada from predominantly rural to primarily urban nations within a few generations. But there are also costs involved in living in cities, and the evolution of cities is partly a result of people trying to mitigate the downside of city life, especially crowding. Indeed, most of the demographically oriented changes that we discuss below—slums, suburbs and exurbs, urban sprawl, gentrification, and residential segregation—deal in one way or another with the impact of crowding, which most humans find distasteful in some way or another. We are a social species, but we also like our space.

Urban Crowding

For centuries, the crowding of people into cities was doubtless harmful to existence. Packing people together in unsanitary houses in dirty cities raised death rates. Furthermore, as is so often the case, as cities grew to unprecedented sizes in nineteenth-century Europe, death struck unevenly within the urban population. Mortality went down faster for the better off, leaving the slums as the places where lower-income people were crowded into areas "with their sickening odor of disease, vice and crime" (Weber 1899:414).

When early students of the effects of urbanization such as Adna Weber and Jacques Bertillon discussed crowding and overcrowding, they had in mind a relatively simple concept of density—the number of people per room, per block, or per square mile. Thus Weber quotes the 1891 census of England, "regarding as overcrowded all the 'ordinary tenements that had more than two occupants to a room, bedrooms and sitting rooms included'" (1899:416). The prescription for the ill effects (literally) of overcrowding was fairly straightforward as far as Weber was concerned: "The requirement of a definite amount of air space to each occupant of a room will prevent some of the worst evils of overcrowding; plenty of water, good paving, drainage, etc. will render the sanitary conditions good." Crime and vice are also often believed to be linked to urban life and, as a matter of fact, crime rates are almost always higher in cities than in the countryside. But what is it about crowding that might lead to differences in social behavior between urban and rural people? To examine that question, we first have to go a bit beyond Weber's definition of crowding.

The simplest definition of crowding is essentially demographic and refers to density—the ratio of people to physical space. As more and more people occupy a given area, the density increases and it therefore becomes relatively more crowded.

Under these conditions, what changes in behavior can you expect? In a 1905 essay, Georg Simmel suggested that the result of crowding was an "intensification of nervous stimulation" (Simmel 1905:408), which produced stress and, in turn, was adapted to by people reacting with their heads rather than their hearts. "This means that urban dwellers tend to become intellectual, rational, calculating, and emotionally distant from one another" (Fischer 1976:30). Here were the early murmurs of the urbanism concept—that the crowding of people into cities changes behavior—a concept often expressed with negative overtones.

Perhaps the most famous expression of the negative consequences of the city is Louis Wirth's paper "Urbanism as a Way of Life" (1938), in which he argued that urbanism will result in isolation and the disorganization of social life. Density, Wirth argued, encourages impersonality and leads to people exploiting each other. For two decades, there was little questioning of Wirth's thesis and, as Amos Hawley put it, "In one short paper, Wirth determined the interpretation of density for an entire generation of social scientists" (Hawley 1972:524). The idea that increased population density had harmful side effects lay idle for a while, but it was revived with considerable enthusiasm in the 1960s following a report by John Calhoun on the behavior of rats under crowded conditions.

Although he initiated his studies of crowding among rats in 1947, it was not until 1958 that Calhoun began his most famous experiments (which later helped inspire the popular stories and a movie about the rats of NIMH). In a barn in Rockville, Maryland, he designed a series of experiments in which rat populations could build up freely under conditions that would permit detailed observations without humans influencing the behavior of the rats relating to each other (Calhoun 1962). He built four pens, each with all the accoutrements for normal rat life and divided by electrified partitions. Initially, eight young rats were placed in each pen, and when they reached maturity, Calhoun installed ramps between each pen. At that point, the experiment took its own course in terms of the effects of population growth in a limited area.

Normally, rats have a fairly simple form of social organization, characterized by groups of 10 to 12 hierarchically ranked rats defending their common territory. There is usually one male dominating the group, and status is indicated by the amount of territory open to an individual. As Calhoun's rat population grew from the original 32 to 60, one dominant male took over each of the two end pens and established harems of 8 to 10 females. The remaining rats were congregated in the two middle pens, where problems developed over congestion at the feeding hoppers. As the population grew from 60 to 80, behavior patterns developed into what Calhoun called a "behavioral sink"—gross distortions of behavior resulting from animal crowding. Behavior remained fairly normal in the two end pens, where each dominant male defended his territory by sleeping at the end of the ramp, but in the two middle pens there were severe changes in sexual, nesting, and territorial behavior. Some of the males became sexually passive; others became sexually hyperactive, chasing females mercilessly; and still another group of males was observed mounting other males, as well as females. Females became disorganized in their nesting habits, building very poor nests, getting litters mixed up, and losing track of their young. Infant mortality rose significantly. Finally, males appeared to alter their concept of territoriality. With no space to defend, the males in the two middle pens substituted time for territory, and three times a day, the males fought at the eating bin.

Calhoun's study can be summarized by noting that, among his rats, crowding (an increase in the number of rats within a fixed amount of space) led to the disruption of important social functions and to social disorganization. Related to these changes in social behavior were signs of physiological stress, such as changes in their hormonal systems that made it difficult for females to bring pregnancies to term and care for their young. Other studies have shown that not only rats, but also monkeys, hares, shrews, fish, elephants, and house mice tend to respond to higher density by reducing their fertility (Galle, Gove, and McPherson 1972).

Although the severe distortions of behavior that Calhoun witnessed among rats have never been replicated among humans, research has suggested that at the macro (group) level, there may be some fairly predictable consequences of increasing population density (mainly as a result of increases in population size). For example, it has been argued that violent interaction can be expected to increase as population size increases: "The opportunity structure for murder, robbery, and aggravated assault increases at an increasing rate with aggregate size" (Mayhew and Levinger 1976:98). There are more people with whom to have conflict, and an increasingly small proportion of people over whom we exercise direct social control (which would lessen the likelihood of conflict leading to violence). Increasing size leads to greater superficiality and to more transitory human interaction—that is, greater anonymity. Bruce Mayhew and Roger Levinger (1976:100) point out that "since humans are by nature finite organisms with a finite amount of time to devote to the total stream of incoming signals, it is necessarily the case that the average amount of time they can devote to the increasing volume of contacts . . . is a decreasing function of aggregate size. This will occur by chance alone."

Because no person has the time to develop deeply personal relationships (primary relations) with more than a few people, the more people there are entering a person's life, the smaller the proportion one can deal with in depth. This leads to the appearance that people in cities are more estranged from each other than in rural settings. Claude Fischer (1981), however, offered evidence that in all settings, people are distrustful of strangers (xenophobia)—we just encounter more of them in the city. This may lead to personal stress as people try to sort out the vast array of human contacts since the more people there are, the greater the variety of both expectations others have of you and obligations you have toward others. The problems of not enough time to go around and of contradictory expectations lead to "role strain"—a perceived difficulty in fulfilling role obligations. On a more positive note, data from the General Social Survey of the National Opinion Research Center have been used to suggest that moving to a big city increases your tolerance for other human beings, rather than the other way around (Wilson 1991). Indeed, subsequent research by Fischer (2011) showed that family and friends are just as important as ever in the United States, despite the fact that Americans are now predominantly city dwellers.

It might be fair to say that the most reasonable reaction to the negative aspects of city life is to figure out how best to cope with them and minimize them. The most common response has been to get as far away from high-density city life as possible, while also staying close enough to it so that you can participate in its benefits. This is probably the underlying reason for the evolution in urban places. Most people do not really prefer to be packed together with others, and the increasing sophistication of transportation and information technologies has made it increasingly easy to spread out, at least in the richer countries. In cities in poorer countries, however, many people are struggling just to get by and find themselves living in densely settled slums because they have no other choice.

Slums

European and American cities had to begin dealing with slums in the late nineteenth and early twentieth centuries, as cities bulged with migrants who overran the local infrastructure. That process of rapid growth is now taking place in the cities of developing countries, so it is not surprising that today the slums in the world tend to be concentrated there. The United Nations Human Settlements Programme known as UN-Habitat defines slums as places that lack one or more of the following: (1) access to potable water, (2) access to piped sewerage, (3) housing of adequate space, (4) housing of adequate durability, and (5) security of tenure (UN-Habitat 2014a)—a definition that is not very different from Weber's ideas about London slums in the nineteenth century.

Nearly one billion people (one in eight human beings) was estimated by the United Nations to be living in a slum as of 2014 (UN-Habitat 2016). Nearly all of today's slum-dwellers live in developing countries, and the regional pattern is shown in Figure 7.6. You can see clearly that sub-Saharan Africa dominates the list—nearly

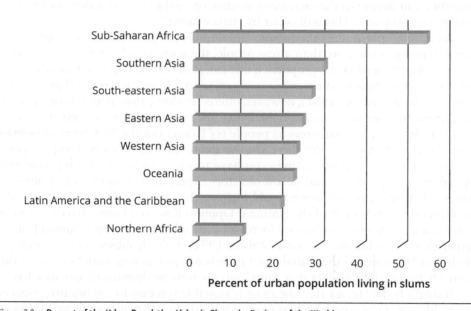

Figure 7.6   Percent of the Urban Population Living in Slums, by Regions of the World

Source: Adapted by John R. Weeks from data downloaded from UN-Habitat (2016); data refer to estimates for 2014.

half of all urban dwellers in that part of the world live in a slum. Mike Davis (2007) described the area in West Africa between Lagos, Nigeria, and Accra, Ghana, as a conurbation that may have "the single biggest footprint of poverty in the world" (p. 6). Furthermore, there is no immediate sign of relief, as evidenced by the UN-Habitat's report on African cities in 2014 (UN-Habitat 2014b:7):

> Ubiquitous urban poverty and urban slum proliferation, so characteristic of Africa's large cities, is likely to become an even more widespread phenomenon under current urban development trajectories, especially given the continuing and significant shortfalls in urban institutional capacities. Since the bulk of the urban population increases are now being absorbed by Africa's secondary and smaller cities, the sheer lack of urban governance capacities in these settlements is likely to cause slum proliferation processes that replicate those of Africa's larger cities.

The existence of slums signals that the urban population is growing more quickly than the local government can afford to build urban infrastructure. This is illustrated by the fact that UN-Habitat estimates that the percentage of people in sub-Saharan Africa who live in slums was lower in 2014 (56 percent) than in 1990 (70 percent). That's the good news. The bad news is that the urban population in sub-Saharan Africa was growing so fast during that time that more than twice as many were living in slums in 2014 (201 million) than in 1970 (93 million). If people are poor, and governments themselves have little money, then urban residents are forced to deal with life informally. These informal settlements are not likely to be the healthiest environments in which to live (Montgomery 2009), but at the same time, the health of residents in these places may still be better, or at least no worse, than if they were living in the countryside.

There is no better example of this than access to clean water. Even in rural areas of many developing countries, the streams and underground aquifers from which water is drawn may be polluted, and unless people have proper water treatment and storage capabilities, they will not have a good supply of drinking water. This can lead to diarrhea and other digestive problems, not to mention the threat of cholera and other water-borne diseases. In urban areas, the problem is increasingly being dealt with by packaged water. Bottled water is too expensive for most residents, so a cheaper solution has been to package clean water in plastic sleeves (called "sachets" in West Africa) that are sold by street vendors. Use of this source of water has been shown to be associated with better health among children in slum neighborhoods (Stoler et al. 2011). There is, to be sure, a downside to this source of water since the proliferation of discarded plastic sleeves clogs the city's system of open drains and generally increases the amount of nondegradable waste on the planet.

If there is such a thing as a positive aspect to the perspective that urban slums may not be any worse than life in rural areas, it is that in moving into the city people bring their poverty with them to a place where it is exposed to public view. As a consequence, it is more apt to be acted upon by governments and nongovernmental organizations (NGOs). This is likely to be small comfort to the people involved, however.

Suburbanization

Being crowded into a slum is probably the worst aspect of city life. This and other negative impacts of the urban transition on the human condition represent the set of unintended consequences that may prevent the city from being as attractive as it might otherwise be. The efficiencies of the city have generally been translated into higher incomes for city dwellers than for farmers and, as we mentioned earlier, the larger the city, the higher the wages tend to be. Wage differentials undoubtedly have been and continue to be a prime motivation for individuals to move to cities and stay there. But so-called "urban amenities" are also important, especially for the young adults who represent the majority of rural-to-urban migrants in cities of developing nations. Cities offer not only opportunity, but also entertainment and excitement that are rarely present in the countryside.

Throughout American history, the sins and foibles of urban life have been decried, and life in the city is often compared unfavorably with a pastoral existence. Fuguitt and Zuiches (1975) found that public opinion polls in the 1950s and 1960s showed consistently that a vast majority of Americans had a preference for living in rural areas or small cities and towns. However, in the 1970s, when for the first time they asked a survey question about the desire to be near a large city, those rural preferences became geographically more specific. Their data showed that among people who preferred living in rural areas or in small cities, 61 percent also wanted to be within 30 miles of a central city. A replication of the survey twenty years later revealed a remarkable consistency over time in those residential preferences (Fuguitt and Brown 1990)—rural, but not too rural.

People thus like it both ways. They aspire to the freedom of space in the country but also prefer the economic and social advantages of the city. The compromise, of course, is the suburb. More than a century has passed since Adna Weber (1899) noted that American cities were beginning to suburbanize—to grow in the outlying rings of the city. It was not until the 1920s, however, that suburbanization really took off. Amos Hawley (1972) calculated that between 1900 and 1920, people were still concentrating in the centers of cities, but after 1920, the suburbs began regularly to grow in population at a faster pace than the central cities. Two factors related to suburbanization are people's desire to live in the less-crowded environment of the outlying areas and their ability to do so—a result of increasing wealth and the availability of transportation, especially automobiles. Such transportation has added an element of geographic flexibility not possible when the early suburbanites depended on fixed-rail trolleys to transport them between home in the suburbs and work in the central city.

From the 1920s through the 1960s, the process of suburbanization continued almost unabated in the United States (as indeed in most cities of the world). Admittedly, the process was hurried along by automobile manufacturers and tire companies that bought local trolley lines in order to dismantle them and force people to rely on gasoline-powered buses (Kunstler 1993). Nonetheless, the advantages of the automobile are numerous and it was inevitable that cars would influence the shape of urban areas. According to the 2017 American Community Survey, 76 percent of all workers get to work by driving alone in their automobile (car, truck, or van)—a higher fraction than in 1990—and an additional 9 percent car-pooled to work in an automobile, meaning that altogether 85 percent of American workers get to work by driving. Only a small fraction of Americans (5 percent) use public transportation, and the remaining 10 percent walk or bike or scooter to work, or they work at home.

Furthermore, the commute may not be the classic suburb-to-city drive, but rather from one suburb to another because as the population has suburbanized, so have businesses, and this has led to a fading of the original distinction between urban and suburban (Frey 2004). The rest of the world is generally headed in the same direction. Tourists to Paris, London, or Tokyo may spend most of their time near the older "cultural" center of the city, but most of the people in these global cities now live and work out in the suburbs.

Suburbanization is also associated with two other trends worth commenting on (1) the western and southern tilt to urbanization in the United States has facilitated suburbanization through the creation of new places, as people migrate out of the older industrial cities of the Northeast and upper Midwest; and (2) many of those new places are edge cities within the suburbs, replacing the functions of the old central city. Let us examine both of these in a bit more detail, remembering that, although the comments refer primarily at the United States, many of these same trends are being seen all over the world.

The western United States, the land of open spaces, had become the most highly metropolitanized area of the country by the 1980s and a higher fraction of residents now lives in metropolitan areas in the West than in any other part of the country. This has happened because the flow of migration in the United States has been consistently westward, especially since the end of World War II, and migration in the modern world is almost always toward or between urban places. People and jobs have been moving west, and increasingly south as well—definitely toward the warmer climates (although climate is not necessarily the most important factor). In 1960, 25 percent of all Fortune 500 firms were headquartered in New York City, but by 2018 that had declined to 13 percent (Sauter and Stebbins 2018). Many companies are now in Sunbelt cities, led by Dallas, Houston, and San Francisco, but not necessarily in the central parts of those cities. The suburbs have become the new sites of company headquarters, congregating near major highways and regional airports. It is perhaps a sign of the times that the second-richest person in the United States (Bill Gates) founded a company (Microsoft) located in the suburbs (Redmond, Washington) of a Western city (Seattle).

Increasing suburbanization has meant greater metropolitan complexity, as new areas have sprung up on the edges of cities, competing with each other for jobs and amenities (Frey 2004). Joel Garreau (1991) coined the term "edge city" to describe the suburban entities that have emerged in the rings and beltways of metropolitan areas and are replicating, if not replacing, the functions of older central cities. Some of the edge cities are actually within the same city limits as the central city, but are distinct from it. Furthermore, larger metropolitan areas may have several edge cities, each with its own pattern of dominance over specific economic functions (such as high technology or financial services) in conjunction with a full range of retail shops and dining and entertainment establishments.

The growth of edge cities and the increasing economic and social complexity of the suburbs help to explain the shift in commuting patterns in the United States. In essence, the flexibility of the automobile allows people to live and work almost anywhere within the same general area. The number of commuters going from one suburban area to another far exceeds the number of commuters going from the suburbs to the central city. As noted above, those cars on the freeway in the morning are not all headed downtown—they are headed every which way.

As suburbs have become home to a majority of Americans, the issues that were once associated with inner cities have taken root in the suburbs. Poverty has spread to the suburbs, along with concentrations of immigrants, and residential segregation (which we discuss below) has taken root in many suburban communities (Lacy 2016). These changes have become associated with what Elizabeth Delmelle (2019) refers to as the "increasing sociospatial fragmentation of urban America."

Residential Segregation

Although suburbia has become a legendary part of American society and is a major force of urban evolution, suburbanization is a residential transformation that disproportionately involved whites in the United States until the 1970s. For example, in 1970 in 15 large metropolitan areas studied by Reynolds Farley (1976), 58 percent of whites lived in the suburbs compared with 17 percent of nonwhites. Beginning in the 1930s, the proportion of whites living in central cities declined steadily and the proportion of African Americans rose steeply (Schnore, Andre, and Sharp 1976). The African American population was undergoing a very rapid urbanization (the Great Migration that we mentioned in Chapter 6) at the same time that whites were suburbanizing.

During the period 1910–1930, there was a substantial movement of African Americans out of the South headed for the cities of the North and the West. The urban population of blacks grew by more than 3 percent per year during that 20-year period, whereas the rural population declined not only relatively but in absolute terms as well. The reasons for migration out of rural areas were primarily economic. The decline in the world demand for southern agricultural products provided the push out of the South and, at the same time, there were concurrent pull factors in the form of demands in northern and western cities for labor, which could be met cheaply by blacks moving from the South (Farley 1970; Tolnay et al. 2005). The Depression brought a slowdown in the urbanization of African Americans, but by the beginning of World War II half of the nation's blacks lived in cities, reaching that level 30 years later than whites had.

After World War II, the urban transition of blacks resumed at an even higher level than after World War I, and by 1960 the African American population was 58 percent urban in the South and 95 percent urban in the North and West. Urbanization was associated not only with the economic recovery after the war but also with severely restricted international migration, which, until the law was changed in 1965, meant that foreigners no longer were entering the labor force to take newly created jobs, thus providing a market for African American labor. An important consequence of the urban transition of blacks, accompanied by suburbanization of whites, was the segregation of black and white populations within metropolitan areas (Massey and Denton 1993; Massey 1996).

The segregation of people into different neighborhoods on the basis of different social characteristics (such as ethnicity, occupation, or income) is a fairly common feature of human society. However, in the United States residential segregation by race is much more intense than segregation by any other measurable category. Residential segregation of blacks in the United States has been called an "American apartheid system" (Massey and Denton 1993), and the maintenance of this pattern over time has been due especially to the following factors: (1) mortgage lending policies were discriminatory; (2) suburbs developed strategies for keeping African Americans out; and (3) federally sponsored public housing encouraged segregation in many cities (Farley and Frey 1994; Iceland and Nelson 2008).

Specific action has been taken over time to try to mitigate the most egregious causes of residential segregation while, at the same time, patterns of residential segregation have been impacted by the 1965 changes in the Immigration Act. Immigrants have diversified the ethnic structure of the country, and data suggest that Asians and Hispanics have a greater propensity or ability to suburbanize than do blacks, who remain residentially more segregated than other groups (Logan, Alba, and Zhang 2002; Iceland and Nelson 2008).

From the standpoint of demographic characteristics, the suburbs and exurbs are composed especially of more highly educated, higher-income, married-couple families (Berube and Thacher 2004; Berube et al. 2006)—a pattern that disproportionately works against blacks who have lower levels of education, lower incomes, and lower marriage rates than whites. But demographic components of suburbanization do not explain residential segregation, they merely point to its existence. The explanations are essentially social in nature. One of the long-standing ideas is that "status rankings are operationalized in society through the imposition of social distance" (Berry et al. 1976:249). In race relations, the social status of blacks has been historically lower than that of whites. That status ranking used to be maintained symbolically by such devices as uniforms, separate facilities, and so forth, which were obvious enough to allow social distance even though blacks and whites lived in close proximity to each other. However, as African Americans left the South and moved into industrial urban settings, many of those negative status symbols were also left behind. As a result, spatial segregation has served as a means of maintaining social distance. Thus as blacks have improved in education, income, and occupational status, whites have maintained social distance by means of residential segregation facilitated by suburbanization.

Differential suburbanization by race has done more than just keep whites separate from blacks. It has also separated blacks from job opportunities. Jobs have followed the population to the suburbs, making it increasingly difficult for people living in the central city—who may have inadequate access to transportation—to find employment. This "spatial mismatch" has been shown to be associated with higher unemployment rates for blacks living in Detroit and Chicago (Mouw 2000), as well as in other American cities (Wagmiller 2007).

However, there is some evidence that a trend toward desegregation does exist. As you know, immigration to the United States has increasingly involved people from Latin America and Asia, and almost all immigrants wind up in urban areas, as we discussed above. This increasing diversity of the U.S. population has combined with increasing suburbanization to create a more variegated and integrated suburban population, and blacks have been incorporated into these increasingly complex trends (Crowder, Pais, and South 2012; Holloway, Wright, and Ellis 2012; Fowler, Lee, and Matthews 2016). This process has been encouraged by the spreading out of Asians from the Pacific Coast, Hispanics out of the Southwest, and by the flow of many blacks to a "new" South whose economy is based on growth in higher-income service industries rather than agriculture (Frey 2006). Nonetheless, census data suggest that blacks are still segregated more from whites than are either Asians or Hispanics (Iceland and Nelson 2008).

European cities are also characterized by a certain amount of residential segregation, largely with respect to the ethnic minority groups that have comprised the immigrant populations (Andersson et al. 2018). However, in many parts of Europe a large segment of the housing market for working-class families is subsidized and controlled by the government, and this has limited the scope of residential segregation compared to the United States (Bulpett 2002; Maloutas 2004; Agnew 2010).

Urban Sprawl

Another alternative to the increasingly dense suburbanization has been to head even farther out of town, to what sometimes are called the exurbs—the suburbs of the suburbs. Another term for this is the peri-urban region—the periphery of the urban zone that may seem rural to the naked eye because of its low density, but which houses people whose social and economic life is tied to urban areas. "The peri-urban region is a distinctive zone that spans the landscape between contiguous urban development and the rural countryside" (Ford 1999:298).

Where will suburbanization and exurbanization end? How far away from a city's center are people willing to live? Does the concept of a city center even mean much anymore? These are the kinds of questions that are inspired by urban sprawl—"the straggling expansion of an urban area into the adjoining countryside" (Brown 1993:3002). Urban lives are increasingly complicated by multiple-earner households and by greater movement of people from job to job within the same area, often leading to long commutes (McKenzie and Rapino 2011). But the underlying cause of urban sprawl is almost certainly the desire of people to live in a low-density area yet be part of the urban scene. Trying to have it both ways has produced the phenomena of NIMBY and BNANA.

NIMBY, which stands for Not In My Back Yard, refers to the idea that whatever is proposed to be built should be built somewhere else besides your neighborhood. You do not mind that it (whatever it is) is built (you understand that urban places need these things), you just don't want it near you. BNANA, which stands for Build Nothing Anywhere Near Anyone, is more extreme. This represents a generalized antigrowth attitude expressed by people who essentially want to close the urban door behind them and let nothing and no one else in. The problem with both attitudes is that there is worldwide pressure for an increase in urban areas—the urban transition is an inevitable consequence of population growth everywhere in the world. So, if new homes and businesses are not built near you, they will nonetheless be built somewhere else near the urban area, in a rural area that will soon become part of the urban area (no matter how hard the BNANAs may protest) and that will contribute to urban sprawl, which in turn contributes to the demise of the countryside, widespread traffic gridlock, and a lowering of the perceived quality of life.

Since sprawl occurs especially in the absence of regional planning, even in the presence of protests, planning movements have arisen in metropolitan areas around the world to create "smart growth," the basic principles of which are as follows: (1) create a mix of land uses; (2) take advantage of compact building design; (3) create a range of housing opportunities and choices; (4) create walkable neighborhoods; (5) foster distinctive, attractive communities with a strong sense of place; (6) preserve open space, farmland, natural beauty, and critical environmental areas; (7) strengthen and direct development towards existing communities; (8) provide a variety of transportation choices; (9) make development decisions predictable, fair, and cost effective; and (10) encourage community and stakeholder collaboration in development decisions (U.S. Environmental Protection Agency 2019).

Smart growth is especially about containing growth spatially. This implies higher population densities, but within a context in which communities are rethought and well thought-out. Higher, but smarter, densities might mean improved public transportation, more small but well-planned urban open spaces, and the creation of urban villages that attempt to recreate the (largely mythical) atmosphere of small towns in the past.

Two important aspects of American public policy have contributed to urban sprawl and are addressed by smart growth policies: (1) massive public spending on highways and (2) local government authority over land use and taxation. If the government is willing to help subsidize the building of highways, then people can keep living farther from the central city without a huge jump in commute time. Of course, they can only do that if there are places to live farther out. The building of homes in the exurbs is aided by the ability and willingness of local governments to zone land for urban-residential uses, often as a way of increasing local tax revenue—which may then be used to improve local infrastructure (water, sewerage, electricity, communications, etc.), which of course stimulates even more urban development. On the other hand, if a state or other regional authority is able to draw an urban boundary or limit line, beyond which urban uses are very limited, then smart growth might have a chance—although the issues are extremely complex.

As is true with any movement, there is apt to be a counter-movement. In the case of urban sprawl, the argument has been made that sprawl is part of the long history of people wanting to be part of the city without having to endure its crowds, crime, and crud. Thus, rather than being a policy failure, sprawl is an inevitable part of urban life, at least in some places, and not necessarily a bad part. Smart growth for some areas may refer to the creation of densely settled, amenity-rich, and very walkable urban neighborhoods, but many people have been voting with their automobiles, so to speak, in the opposite direction.

Gentrification

Urban sprawl has tended to leave the central cities with a daytime population of "suits" who commute downtown to work at various service companies (especially government administration and financial services industries) that have remained in the central city. At the same time, shopping centers, corporate headquarters, many new high-technology industries, and traffic gridlock have all relocated to the suburbs, leaving a void in the old central cities.

Into that void have come some of the baby boomers and even Gen Xers. They grew up in the suburbs to a greater extent than earlier cohorts, but as they reached an age to buy homes, baby boomers and Gen Xers found themselves caught in the midst of spiraling housing costs amid increasing density in the suburbs. An alternative for some people has been to reverse the suburbanization trend and move back into the central city, where gentrification of buildings and of whole neighborhoods has been taking place in some, although not all, older cities of developed nations. This process has the controversial potential to remove the lower-income population that had settled into the areas previously abandoned by higher-income households, and may dramatically alter the social structure of the surrounding area, although this is not an inevitable result of gentrification (McKinnish, Walsh, and White 2010). Because these innovative renovators tend to be white and upwardly mobile (and often without children), they have been likened to the gentry moving back into the city, thus the term gentrification, referring to the restoration and habitation of older homes in central city areas by urban or suburban elites.

The popularity of downtown living has expanded the scope of renovation in an increasing number of cities to include tearing down entire blocks of older buildings and erecting new high-rise, high-priced condominiums (Ford 2003), in what has been called "new-build gentrification" (Rérat, Söderström, and Piguet 2009). Some of this development immediately preceded the burst in the housing bubble, and so progress has slowed since 2007.

Summary and Conclusion

The urban transition describes the process whereby a society shifts from being largely bound to the country to being bound by the city, and is a process that has been historically the close companion of economic development and an integral part of the demographic transition. The urban transition is associated with increasing differentiation among cities, leading to identifiable urban hierarchies throughout the world. Every country has its own rank-ordering of cities, and there is also a world ranking based on a combination of population size and global economic importance.

More than half of the human population now resides in urban places, and that percentage is climbing steadily. Although rural-to-urban migration is a major contributor to the urban transition, mortality and fertility are also importantly associated as both causes and consequences of the urban transition. Population pressures created by declining mortality in rural areas, combined with the economic opportunities offered by cities, have been historically linked to urbanization. On the other hand, mortality is now almost always lower in cities than in rural areas, which permits higher rates of urban natural increase than in the past. Urban life helps generate or ignite the perception of advantages to small families, and so fertility is always lower in urban than in rural areas. Nonetheless, in the cities of less developed nations urban fertility is still typically higher than in cities of the developed world. As a result, cities in less developed nations are the most rapidly growing places on earth.

As richer countries reach the point where almost everyone is residing in urban places (which we might define as the end of the urban transition), a new set of urban evolution processes are taking place. Most of these changes are attempts to deal somehow or another with the effects of crowding in urban places—the worst example of which is found in slums. Solutions to the crowding problem include especially suburbanization, which is now a worldwide phenomenon, but other trends such as exurbanization and gentrification are all part of the process as well. Other aspects of the urban evolution relate to the city's ability to support diversity among humans. The complexity of life in urban places is part and parcel of the overall demographic complexity of life in the modern world. Urban places are where mortality is lowest, fertility is lowest, the age structure is the most variable, and people of all different kinds of backgrounds can mingle together with deliberate anonymity or closeness. The demography of urban places is different from that of rural places, and that shows up most readily in the distribution of the population by age. The age transition is, indeed, an incredibly important part of the overall demographic transition, and we turn to it in the next chapter.

Main Points

1. The world is at the point at which more than one of every two people lives in an urban area; by the middle of this century, nearly two out of three will be there.

2. The urban transition reflects the process whereby human society moves (quite literally) from being predominantly rural to being largely urban.

3. One of the most striking features of urbanization is its recency in world history, because it depends heavily on all of the other changes that comprise the demographic transition—highly urban nations like England and the United States were almost entirely agricultural at the beginning of the nineteenth century.

4. Cities are centerpieces of the development process associated with demographic transitions because they are centers of economic efficiency.

5. Cities throughout the world are arranged in urban hierarchies that are often described in terms of the core and periphery model.

6. Until the twentieth century, death rates in cities were so high and fertility was low enough that cities could not have grown had it not been for migration of people from the countryside, but that is no longer true.

7. In virtually every society, fertility levels are lower in cities than in rural areas, yet cities in less developed nations almost always have higher fertility levels than cities in more developed nations.

8. The urban transition is morphing into the urban evolution, as urban places become increasingly spread out and complex.

9. Urbanization in the United States has now turned into suburbanization, with most Americans living in suburbs—a trend that we increasingly see all over the world.

10. Population growth in cities has given rise to fears about the potential harmful effects of crowding, and especially to concerns about the environmental sustainability of cities.

Questions for Review

1. Compare the positive and negative qualities of urban places with the positive and negative qualities of rural places. Which do you prefer, and why?

2. What are the characteristics of a city that would make it a global city, rather than just a city? Would you prefer to live in a global (core) city or one that is less connected to the rest of the world? Explain your choice.

3. Discuss the ways in which the different levels of mortality and fertility between urban and rural places wind up making an important contribution to the urban transition.

4. How does the longtime concern with the ill effects of urban crowding square with the movement for smart growth that aims to increase urban density?

5. Are slums an inevitable part of the urban transition? Why or why not?

PART THREE

USING THE DEMOGRAPHIC PERSPECTIVE

CHAPTER 8
The Age Transition and the Life Course

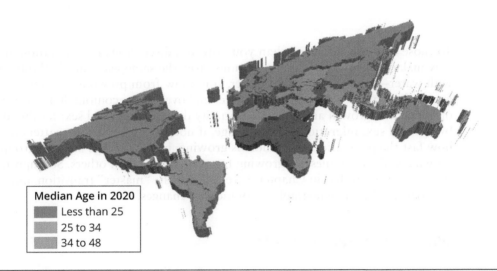

Figure 8.1 Countries of the World by Median Age as of 2020

Source: Adapted by John R. Weeks using data from the United Nations Population Division (2018a).

Note: Younger median ages tend to be associated with greater conflict and less democratic governments.

What Is the Age Transition?

The Concepts of Age and Sex
Age Stratification
Age Cohorts and Cohort Flow
Gender and Sex Ratios
The Feminization of Old Age

Demographic Drivers of the Age Transition
The Impact of Declining Mortality
The Impact of Declining Fertility
Where Does Migration Fit In?

Demographic Dividends—Age Transitions
    at Work
Measuring the Age Structure
The Progression from a Young to an
    Old Age Structure
Youth Bulge—Dead End or Dividend?

China's Demographic Dividend
What Happened to India's Demographic
    Dividend?
Demographic Dividends in the United States
    and Mexico

The Life Course and Population Aging
What Is Old?
The Third Age (Young-Old) and Fourth
    Age (Old-Old)
Centenarians—The Oldest of the Old-Old

Reading the Future from the Age Structure
Population Projections
    Extrapolation
    Components of Growth
    Cohort Component Method
Backward or Inverse Projections

Population Momentum

Summary and Conclusion

Main Points

Questions for Review

ESSAY: *The Age Transition Force Is With Us*

To those less well-informed than you now are, discussions of population growth may make it seem as though populations grow the same way your bathtub fills up with water—evenly all over. However, you know from previous chapters that the issues of age and sex rear their heads over and over again, confounding every aspect of population growth and change. Mortality differs by age and sex; fertility differs by age and sex; migration differs by age, if not always by sex. It matters not just how fast the population as a whole is growing, but *which* age and sex groups are growing and which ones are growing faster or slower than others. So important is the age transition that in Chapter 3 we called it the "master" transition and driver of broader cultural demographic evolutionary changes.

What Is the Age Transition?

The age transition represents a *shift over time* in the age and sex structure from a very young population, in which there are slightly more males than females, to an older population in which there are more females than males. In between, bumps and dents in the age and sex structure represent powerful forces for social, economic, and political change. In general, it is the interaction of fertility, mortality, and migration that produces the age and sex structure, which at any given time can be viewed as a key to the life of a social group—a record of past history and a portent of the future. Population processes not only produce changes in the age and sex structure but are, in turn, affected by it—yet another example of the complexity of the world when seen through your demographic "eye." In fact, it would not be exaggerating too much to say that changes in the age and sex structure affect all social institutions. In this chapter, we escort you through that complexity by first defining the concepts of age and sex as they relate to population dynamics, and then by examining the dynamics of the age transition at both the societal level and at the personal level of your own life course.

The Concepts of Age and Sex

The concepts of age and sex influence the way a society works (as well as your place in it) in important ways because society assigns social roles and frequently organizes people into groups on the basis of their age and gender (the social component of sex). Age is a biological characteristic, and of course your own age is constantly changing; whereas sex is also biological in nature, but it does not change (except by human intervention in rare cases). *Gender* roles can and do change, however, so the social side of sex (you know what we mean here!) is clearly dynamic. The changing nature of age imposes itself on society because younger people are treated differently from older people, and different kinds of behavior are expected of people as they move through different ages. At the same time, biological changes inherent in the life course influence what societies expect of people which, in turn, influences how people behave.

Age Stratification

The idea that societies have separate sets of expected roles and obligations for people of different ages is captured by the concept of age stratification. Kingsley Davis noted in 1949 that "all societies recognize age as a basis of status, but some of them emphasize it more than others" (Davis 1949:104). The age stratification theory begins with the proposition that age is a basis of social differentiation in a manner analogous to stratification by social class. The term stratification implies a set of inequalities, and in this case it refers to the fact that societies distribute resources unequally by age. These resources include not only economic goods, but also such crucial intangibles as social approval, acceptance, and respect. This theory goes beyond a mere description of status, however, as it introduces a dynamic element by recognizing that aging is a process of social mobility. Anne Foner noted that as we age we are actually moving within a social hierarchy, going from one set of age-related social roles to another, and each of these different roles comes with its own set of rights and obligations. Contrasted to other forms of social mobility, however, which may rely on merit, luck, or accident of birth, social mobility in the age hierarchy is "inevitable, universal and unidirectional in that the individual can never grow younger" (Foner 1975:156).

What aspects of life are influenced by age (and in some instances by sex or gender as well)? Table 8.1 lists just a few of the important variables that differ by age in most human societies. As the number and percentage of people at each age and sex change, the distribution of these characteristics will therefore also change and provide the impetus for social, economic, and political change. For example, a very young population will have a relatively small fraction of its population in the labor force unless, as happens in poorer countries, children are put to work at a young age. In such a society, of course, those younger workers will have lower-status occupations. It typically takes time and experience (including education and other training) to reach the higher occupational strata. Since income is closely related to occupation, it is the older (albeit not necessarily the oldest) adults who tend to have the highest incomes, and it is the maintenance of those higher incomes for several years that increases the chance that people will accumulate wealth. Thus, all other things being equal, we would expect that a population with a high proportion of middle-aged adults would have more people in the labor force, with higher incomes and more wealth, than a population with a high proportion of children.

For most activities in life, your exact age is less important than an age range or stratum. Thus, even though you cannot vote until age 18, society is typically less interested in the number of 18-year-olds than in the number of people aged, say,

Table 8.1   Aspects of Human Society That Vary by Age and Sex (or Gender)

Category	Characteristic or Activity
Demographic	Being sick and having restricted activities of daily living
	Dying
	Being sexually active
	Having a baby
	Moving or migrating
Social	Getting married/divorced
	Being involved in religious organizations and activity
	Being involved in political organizations and activity
	School enrollment
	Level of educational attainment
	Being involved in criminal or other socially disapproved behavior
Economic	Being in the labor force
	Occupation within the labor force
	Current income
	Level of accumulated wealth

18 to 29, who might be identified as "young adults." Such age strata are not viewed as fixed and unchanging, however. The assumption is that the number of age strata, and the prestige and power associated with each, are influenced by the needs of society and by characteristics of people at each age (their numbers and sociodemographic characteristics). European society of a few hundred years ago seems to have been characterized by three age strata—infancy, adulthood, and old age (Aries 1962); and power (highest status) seems to have been concentrated in the hands of older people (Simmons 1960). Modern Western societies appear to have at least seven strata—infancy, childhood, adolescence, young adulthood, middle age, young-old, and old-old, with power typically concentrated in the hands of the middle-aged and the young-old.

As we age from birth to death, we are allocated to social statuses (your relative position or standing in society) and social roles (the set of obligations and expectations that characterize your particular position in society) considered appropriate to your age. Thus, children and adolescents are typically allocated to appropriate educational statuses, adults to appropriate positions of power and prestige, and the older population to positions of retirement and waning influence. We all learn the roles that society deems appropriate to our age, and we reward each other for fulfilling those roles and tend to cast disapproval on those who do not fulfill the societal expectation. But bear in mind that neither the allocation process nor the overall socialization process (learning the behavior appropriate to particular social roles) is static. They are in constant flux as changing cohorts alter social conditions and as social conditions, in turn, alter the characteristics of age cohorts. All of this leads us to the concept of cohort flow.

Age Cohorts and Cohort Flow

In population studies, a *cohort* refers to a group of people born during the same time period, and *cohort flow* captures the notion that at each age we are influenced by the historical circumstances that similarly affect other people who are the same age in the same society. As Matilda White Riley (1976:194–195) pointed out:

> Each cohort starts out with a given size which, save for additions from immigration, is the maximum size it can ever attain. Over the life course of the cohort, some portion of its members survive, while others move away or die until the entire cohort is destroyed.
>
> Each cohort starts out also with a given composition; it consists of members born with certain characteristics and dispositions. Over the life course of the individual, some of these characteristics are relatively stable (a person's sex, color, genetic makeup, country of birth, or—at entry into adulthood in our society—the level of educational attainment are unlikely to change). . . . When successive cohorts are compared, they resemble each other in certain respects, but differ markedly in other respects: in initial size and composition, in age-specific patterns of survival (or longevity), and in the period of history covered by their respective life span.

At any given moment, a cross section of all cohorts defines the current age strata in a society. Figure 8.2 displays a Lexis diagram, a tool often used in population studies to help us discern the difference between period data (the cross-sectional snapshot of all ages at one time) and cohorts (of which there are many at any point

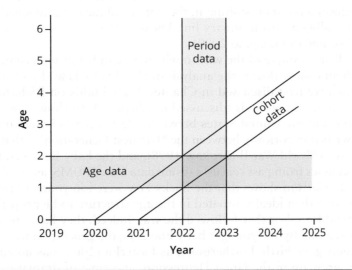

Figure 8.2   Lexis Diagram Visualizes the Relationship Between Cohorts and Period Data

in time). The diagram is named for a German demographer, Wilhelm Lexis (1875), who helped develop it in the nineteenth century as an aid for analyzing life table data (Vandeschrick 2001). Age is shown on the vertical axis, and time (the year of birth) is shown along the horizontal axis. Then we can look at a cohort of people, for example, people born in 2020, who "advance through life along a 45° line" (Preston, Heuveline, and Guillot 2001:31), which is represented by the area labeled "Cohort data" in Figure 8.2.

The period data, crosscutting many cohorts, are illustrated by the shaded area labeled "Period data" in the diagram, whereas comparing people at the same age across many cohorts over time would be done with data shaded as "Age data." Researchers use the Lexis diagram to calculate age-period-cohort (*APC*) rates that disentangle the combined influences of things specific to a particular age (the age effect), things unique to a time in history (the period effect), and things unique to specific birth cohorts (the cohort flow effect). Lung cancer, for example, is most likely to kill people at older ages (the age effect), but death rates from it will depend partly on when in history a person was diagnosed (the period effect influenced by the timing of new treatments for the disease), and partly on cohort effects (cohorts born from the 1920s through the 1940s were more heavily into cigarette smoking than earlier or later cohorts).

As cohorts flow through time, their respective sizes and characteristics may alter the allocation of status and thus their socialization into various age-related roles, because members of each cohort are moving through history together; whereas each separate cohort moves through moments in history at a different age (and thus with a different potential effect) than every other cohort. As cohorts move through time, their characteristics may change in response to changing social and economic conditions (such as wars, famines, and economic prosperity), and those changing conditions will influence the formation of new cohorts. This continual feedback between the dynamics of successive cohorts and the dynamics of other changes in society produces a constant shifting in the status and meaning attached to each age stratum, providing an evolutionary link between the age structure and the social structure (Gordon and Longino 2000).

An excellent example of the way in which we can better understand society by knowing about cohort flow is the analysis of the "Lucky Few" by Elwood Carlson (2008), which we first discussed in Chapter 2. He builds on Richard Easterlin's relative cohort size hypothesis (discussed in Chapter 3) to show how the fortunes of people born in the United States between 1929 and 1945 were influenced by being sandwiched historically between the "Greatest Generation"—that cohort that fought and won World War II (Brokaw 1998), and the baby boomers. Drawing on microdata samples from past censuses (using data from IPUMS, as we also discussed in Chapter 2), Carlson shows that the Lucky Few were too young to fight in World War II, but were then ideally situated in the age structure to be propelled forward by the demand for labor that followed the war. Indeed, they have spent their lives being pushed along by the younger baby boomers, the generation to which they as parents largely gave birth. Furthermore, as Easterlin (2008) has noted, the Lucky Few cohort grew up in the Great Depression, at a time of dramatically lowered expectations in life. Thus, they were more readily able to achieve their own goals in life, both in terms of family size and economic well-being, than either the prior or subsequent cohorts. They have also managed to move into the retirement years just ahead of the fiscal crisis that looms as the baby boomers retire, as we discuss in the essay accompanying this chapter.

Gender and Sex Ratios

One of the important trends in the modern world has been increasing gender equity, first in the richer nations, and now progressing, albeit unevenly, on a global scale. Note that we use the term sex when referring to the biological differences between males and females, reserving the term gender for the social differences. There is enough overlap between biology and the social world, however, that this distinction is often pretty fuzzy. Sorting out which is which is still important, though, because though we may not be able to do very much about biological differences, we can do something about the fact that women are still treated differently from men in most societies and different kinds of behavior are often expected from each. Women have been what Simone de Beauvoir (1953, although first published in French in 1949) called "The Second Sex," in a book that helped to spark feminism in the twentieth century:

> One is not born, but rather becomes a woman. No biological, psychological, or economic fate determines the figure that the human female presents in society; it is civilization as a whole that determines this creature (quoted by Clarke 2000:v).

In the more than half century since de Beauvoir made these comments, there has been a considerable amount of research that somewhat tempers her claim that civilization is the sole cause of gendered behavior. We mentioned sex dimorphism in Chapter 4 in connection with the apparent superiority of females with respect to longevity. The same concept has been applied to various aspects of human and other primate behavior in which hormones do seem to underlie certain kinds of behavior (for a review, see Udry 2000). The social environment is clearly the strongest influence on gendered behavior, but the biological differences between males and females cannot be ignored, partly because they have a direct effect on both fertility and mortality, and because of that they affect the age structure as well.

It is a common assumption, for example, that there are the same numbers of males and females at each age—actually, this is rarely the case. Migration, mortality, and fertility operate differently to create inequalities in the ratio of males to females (known as the sex ratio):

$$\text{sex ratio} = \frac{\text{number of males}}{\text{number of females}} \times 100$$

A sex ratio greater than 100 thus means that there are more males than females, whereas a value of less than 100 indicates there are more females than males. The ratio can obviously be calculated for the entire population or for specific age groups.

Fertility has the most predictable impact on the sex ratio because in virtually every known human society, more boys are born than girls. Sex ratios at birth are typically between 103 (the average among East African countries) and 110 (the average among Asian countries), with 105 generally considered to be the average for human societies. The United States, Canada, and Mexico all have the same sex ratio at birth (105), whereas India (111) and China (114) have among the highest rates in the world to date. Historically, they both have had sex ratios at birth that were slightly higher than average, probably due to the practice of female infanticide at the time of birth. It is perhaps telling that the rate rose significantly in both countries once selective abortion became possible as a result of ultrasound technology that can identify the sex of a fetus fairly early in a pregnancy.

Many years ago, Charles Westoff and Ronald Rindfuss (1974) argued that if these sex-identification methods ever enjoyed widespread acceptance, there would be a short-run rise in the sex ratio at birth, since a preference for sons as first children (and for more total sons than daughters) is fairly common throughout the world, as discussed in Chapter 5. Westoff and Rindfuss also concluded that after an initial transition period, the sex ratio at birth would probably revert to the natural level of about 105 males per 100 females, because the disadvantage of too many or too few of either sex would be controlled by a shift to the other sex. There is some evidence that this drop back to a lower sex ratio at birth is finally happening in Asia (Yoo, Hayford, and Agadjanian 2017), although China, in particular, continues to have a very high ratio. This is strong, even if indirect, evidence of continued gender inequality in that part of the world, since there is no evidence of a biological basis for these sex ratio differences from one country to another.

Despite these societal differences in the sex ratio at birth, there is still a fairly predictable pattern in the sex ratio by age as a population moves through the demographic transition. These patterns are observable in Figure 8.3, where I have plotted the sex ratios at each age group for three countries representing different cultural patterns with respect to the sex ratio: China, the United States, and Pakistan. China and the United States show the general pattern of the sex ratio declining with increasing age, but in Pakistan, the low social status of women puts them at higher risk of death than men at every single age. In fact, as you can see in Figure 8.3, the data from the United Nations Population Division suggest that the sex ratio in Pakistan actually goes *up* at the older ages, not down.

The Feminization of Old Age

Pakistan is a major exception to the general pattern of women living longer than men, which means that women tend disproportionately to populate the older ages, as you can see from the other two examples (China and the United States) in Figure 8.3. As recently as 1930 in the United States, there were equal numbers of males and females at age 65 and older (partly a result of the earlier influx of immigrant males) (Siegel 1993), but by 2020 there were only 81 males for every 100 females at the older ages (65+). In the United States, the ratio of males to

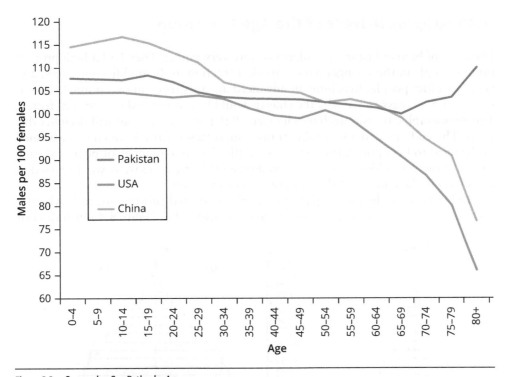

Figure 8.3   Comparing Sex Ratios by Age

Source: Adapted by John R. Weeks using data from United Nations Population Division (2018a); data are medium variant projections for 2020.

females aged 65–74 declined steeply between 1950 and 1970, leveled off, and has risen a bit since 1980 as men have begun to close the gender gap in life expectancy. Both United Nations and U.S. Census Bureau projections assume that life expectancy gains will be greater for males than females (a reversal of historical trends, probably due to the effects of smoking catching up with women, rather than a lot of positive things happening to men), and that will help push up the ratio of men to women in this generation as time goes by, changing the social dynamics at older ages. At age 75 and older, the higher mortality of males really has taken its toll: In 1950, there were 83 males per 100 females at that age in the United States, but this declined to only 54 males per 100 females by the 1990 census, with a rise since then to 72 in 2020, probably a result of changing smoking habits, as noted above.

The general pattern in the sex ratio at older ages has been similar in Canada and the United States, but the actual level of the sex ratio is consistently higher (albeit not by much) in Canada. This is probably due to the joint effects of immigration (immigrants account for a higher fraction of the Canadian than of the U.S. population), and the fact that the gender difference in life expectancy has been slightly less in Canada than in the United States. In Mexico, the feminization of old age is very apparent, especially in urban areas where death rates are lowest.

Demographic Drivers of the Age Transition

For most of human history, populations were very young. They had a high proportion of people in the younger ages, a modest fraction in the middle adult ages, and very few older people. Reaching an advanced age was truly an exceptional circumstance, and it is easy to see why the elderly would be revered and maybe even feared. The demographic transitions have changed all that in complex but still decipherable ways. The end of the demographic transition, if there really is an end, is assumed in the ideal to be a population with essentially the same number of people at each age until the very older ages when people die off fairly quickly, as we discussed in Chapter 4 in the context of the compression of mortality.

In between the historical pattern and this expected future pattern is where it gets messy, and that's just where we are in the world today. Figure 8.4 illustrates our

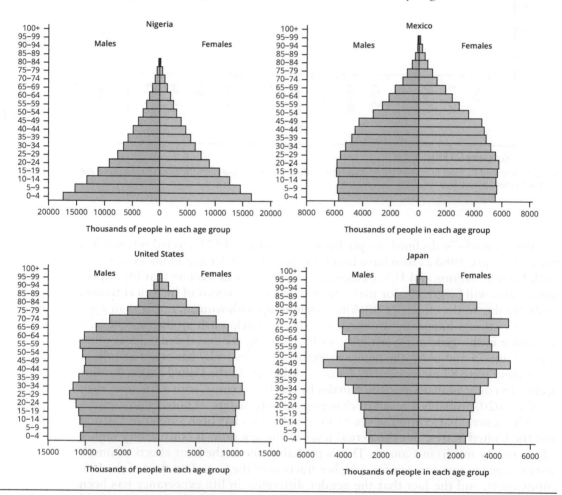

Figure 8.4   Population Pyramids for Countries Illustrating the Range from Very Young Populations to Old Populations

Source: Adapted by John R. Weeks using data from the United Nations Population Division (2018a); data are estimates for 2020.

current situation with examples from four countries—Nigeria, Mexico, the United States, and Japan, estimated for 2020. The graphs themselves are called population (or age) pyramids. They are called *pyramids* because the "classic" picture is of a high-fertility, high-mortality society with a broad base built of numerous births, rapidly tapering to the top (the older ages) because of high death rates in combination with the high birth rate.

Figure 8.1, at the beginning of the chapter, shows each country by its median age (the age at which half are above and half are below that age), and by that measure Nigeria is one of the world's youngest countries, with a median age of only 18.1 years. Mexico has a median age that is 11 years older than that, at 29.3. The United States is 9 years older than Mexico, at 38.3, and Japan is the currently the oldest population on the planet, with an average age of 48.2.

Because of its very young average age, Nigeria's age and sex structure reflects the classic look of the population pyramids, as you can see in Figure 8.4. There are progressively more people at each younger age, and the older ages are sparsely populated. At the other extreme is Japan, where every age under 45–49 has progressively fewer people, and there are more people in each group from 45–49 up through age 70–74 than there are at any age younger than 45–49. Remember, by the way, that no matter the shape, we still call the graph a population (or age) pyramid. You can also see that at the older ages in Japan there are clearly more females than males, despite the general pattern of lower status for females in that country. Once again, it is likely that smoking is the explanation. For several decades Japanese men were among the most avid smokers in the world, giving women a health advantage over men in old age.

In between the extremes of Nigeria and Japan are Mexico and the United States. At ages 20–24 and older, the age pyramid for Mexico is fairly similar to that of Nigeria, but at the younger ages you can readily see the impact of the fertility decline, as the number of people at the youngest ages is smaller than at ages 20–24. This is why the number of migrants from Mexico to the United States has been steadily going down, as we discussed in Chapter 6. The age pyramid for the United States is more complicated, reflecting the fertility boom and bust cycles that we discussed in Chapter 5. Most notable in comparison to Japan, however, is that the age structure in the United States is not caving in at the younger ages, as it does in Japan. This is why the United States is projected to continue to grow in number (owing to immigration), while Japan is projected to decline in population.

Figure 8.5 puts all of the countries together to give us a view of the age pyramid for the entire world population of nearly eight billion people as estimated for 2020. The median age for the world is 30.9 years, which is just slightly higher than Mexico's 29.3. So it is not too surprising that the age pyramid in Figure 8.4 that looks most similar to the world is the one for Mexico. The major difference is that the world still has more children at each successive age group below 20–24, reflecting the fact that the fertility decline being experienced by Mexico is not yet universal around the world.

The population pyramids shown in Figures 8.4 and 8.5 do not happen by chance, of course, since each of the three population processes of mortality, fertility, and migration has predictable impacts on the age structure. We have alluded to this

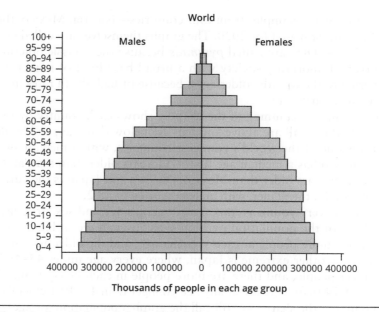

Figure 8.5   Population Pyramids for the Entire World Population

Source: Adapted by John R. Weeks using data from the United Nations Population Division (2018a); data are estimates for 2020.

before, but now let us be more systematic, looking at the impact of each population process in the order in which we introduced them to you in the previous chapters.

The Impact of Declining Mortality

Though mortality declines affect all ages and both sexes, it is a fact that in every society it is the very youngest and the very oldest who are *most* susceptible to death. You will recall from Chapter 4 that the early stages of the health and mortality transition are characterized by bringing communicable diseases under control, which tends to affect infants and children more than any other age. As a result, the early drop in mortality increases the proportion of children who survive and thus serves to increase the fraction of the population at the younger ages.

We can use data from stable population models to demonstrate the impact on an age structure as life expectancy increases. A stable population is a formal demographic model in which neither the age-specific birth rates nor the age-specific death rates have changed for a long time. Thus, a stable population is stable in the sense that the percentages of people at each age and sex do not change over time. A stable population could be growing at a constant rate (that is, the birth rate is higher than the death rate), it could be declining at a constant rate (the birth rate is lower than the death rate), or it could be unchanging (the birth rate equals the death rate). The latter is the case of zero population growth (ZPG), and if this situation prevails, we call it a stationary population.

Thus, a stationary population is a special case of a stable population—all stationary populations are stable, but not all stable populations are stationary. The life table (discussed in Chapter 4) is one type of stationary population model. For analytical purposes, a stable population is usually assumed to be closed to migration. Since 1760, when Leonhard Euler first devised the idea of a stable population, demographers have used the concept to explore the exact influence of differing levels of mortality and fertility on the age/sex structure. Such analyses are possible using a stable population model because it smooths out those dents and bumps in the age structure created by migration and by shifts in the death rate or the birth rate. Thus, if demographers were forced to study only real populations, we would be unable to ferret out all of the kinds of relationships we are interested in examining.

Stable population models reveal that as mortality declines without any change in fertility, the age structure actually becomes more pyramidal than it was before, as a result of the greater survivability of children, which means that the younger population is growing faster than the population at the older ages. In other words, the impact of declining mortality is largely to make a population younger than it was before (see, for example, Lee and Zhou 2017). This may sound counterintuitive since there is so much talk these days about aging populations. However, as we will discuss later in the chapter, the impact of declining mortality on you, as an individual, is to allow you to live to an older age than would have been possible in earlier times. At the same time, the most important societal impact is that there are more people alive at all ages, but especially at the younger ages.

In the short run, then, a decrease in mortality levels in all but already low-mortality societies will substantially increase the number of young people, and one of the best studies of this effect was by Eduardo Arriaga (1970) in his analysis of Latin American countries. He examined data from eleven countries for which information was available on the mortality decline from 1930 to the 1960s. He discovered that "of the 27 million people alive in all the eleven countries in the 1960s who would not have been alive if there had not been a mortality decline since the 1930s, 16 million—59 percent—were under 15" (1970:103). In relative terms, a lowering of mortality in Latin America noticeably raised the proportion of people at young ages, slightly elevated the proportion at old ages, and lowered the *proportion* at the middle ages (14–64). However, in absolute terms, the *number* of people at all ages increased.

Declining mortality had an impact similar to that of a rise in fertility, while also making a contribution to higher fertility. The appearance of higher fertility is, of course, produced by the greater proportion of children surviving through each age of childhood. It is as though women were bearing more children, thereby broadening the base of the age structure. The actual contribution to higher fertility is generated by the higher probabilities of women (and their spouses) surviving through the reproductive ages since under conditions of high mortality, a certain percentage of women will die before giving birth to as many children as they might have. When death rates go down, a higher percentage of women live to give birth to more children, assuming that social changes are not producing motivations for limiting fertility.

Note that the only time a change in mortality generates a change in the percentage of the population at each age is when the mortality shifts are different at different ages. If there is a change in the probability of survival from one age to the next that is exactly equal for all ages and for both sexes, then the age and sex structure will remain unchanged in percentage terms. On the other hand, in a low-mortality society such as the United States, where the vast majority of all deaths occur at ages 65 or older, a drop in mortality will age the population largely because the death rates are now so low at the younger ages that it is very hard, albeit not impossible, to improve on them. So, at the later stages of the health and mortality transition, continued declines in mortality will age the population, assuming there is no change in fertility or migration. This effect will be relatively small, however, and it is when we turn to the influence of declining fertility that we see the more dramatic drivers of the age transition.

The Impact of Declining Fertility

Both migration and mortality can affect all ages and differentially affect each sex. However, the impact of fertility is a bit more complicated and actually tends to have the most dramatic *long-term* impact on the age structure (migration has the biggest *short-term* impact, as we discuss below). It is a given that fertility adds people only at age zero, and so, for example, if the birth rate were to drop suddenly in one year, then as those people get older there will always be fewer of them than there are people of surrounding ages—a cohort flow effect. One example of this is the "Lucky Few" generation (Carlson 2008), that we discussed earlier. Another famous example is what happens during Japan's Year of "Hinoeuma," the Fire Horse, which occurs every 60 years. The last one occurred in 1966, and in that year the birth rate made a sudden one-year dip. According to a widely held Japanese superstition, girls born in the Year of the Fire Horse will have troublesome characters, such as a propensity to murder their husbands (no, we're not making this up!). Thus, girls born in that year are hard to marry off, and many couples avoided having children in 1966, creating a permanent dent in the Japanese age structure. Overall, there were only about two-thirds as many babies born in 1966 as there were in either the year before or the year after.

Figure 8.6 provides a way of comparing the relative impact of mortality and fertility on the age structure. It has age structures representing two different levels of fertility, as measured by the total fertility rate (TFR—discussed in more detail later in the chapter): high = 7.1 children per woman, and low = 2.1 children. Each level of fertility is paired up with two different levels of life expectancy. The low life expectancy of 40 years for females represents the high level of mortality that prevailed in the United States and Europe in the late eighteenth and early nineteenth centuries. The high life expectancy of 80 years for females, by contrast, is very close to the current level in the United States. You can see that when fertility is high, the age distribution is pyramidal in shape, regardless of whether life expectancy is low (an expectation of life at birth of 40) or high (life expectancy of 80). Conversely, when fertility is low, the age distribution is more barrel-shaped, regardless of whether mortality is high or low. Mortality does have some impact, of course, which is why the age distributions are slightly different at each fertility level, but fertility is having the greatest level of influence.

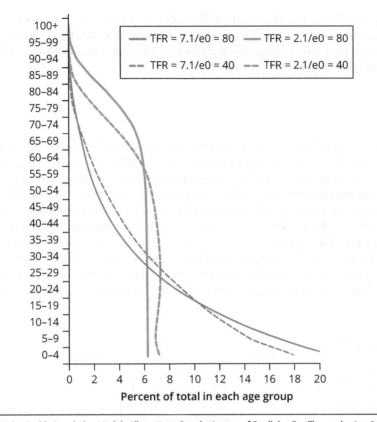

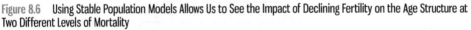

Figure 8.6   Using Stable Population Models Allows Us to See the Impact of Declining Fertility on the Age Structure at Two Different Levels of Mortality

Source: Calculations by John R. Weeks.

The impact of fertility levels is so important that with exactly the same level of mortality, just altering the level of fertility in a population can produce age structures that run the gamut from those that might characterize primitive cultures to those that are highly developed. Though the data in Figure 8.6 come from stable population models rather than the real world, they help show us what to look for.

For example, let us suppose we are looking at two countries with reasonably high female life expectancies of 78 years (such as Algeria and Russia). However, one country (Algeria) still has higher than average fertility (a TFR of 3.1 in 2018), whereas the other (Russia) has very low fertility (a TFR of only 1.6 in 2018) (Population Reference Bureau 2018). The respective age distributions of these two nations are very different because Algeria has had high fertility for a long time, whereas Russia has had low fertility for some time now. In Algeria, 29 percent of the population was under age 15 in 2018, compared with only 18 percent of the Russian population. By contrast, in Algeria, only 6 percent of the population was 65 or older, compared to 14 percent in Russia. What you now know is that when fertility drops to below replacement level in Algeria, as it currently is in Russia, the Algerian age structure will assume the barrel shape that currently characterizes Russia: its average age will rise, and the young will decline as a fraction of the total, while the old will increase as a fraction. This is the age transition at work in conjunction with the fertility transition shaping the parameters of a society as it moves through it own particular demographic transition.

Where Does Migration Fit In?

A population experiencing net in- or out-migration (and virtually all populations except the world as a whole experience one or the other) will almost certainly have its age and sex structure altered as a consequence. Since immigration has been especially important throughout the history of the United States, it provides a good beginning for our analysis. We can assess the impact of international migrants into the United States by looking at the age and sex distribution of legal permanent immigrants into the country in 2017 (the most recent data as of this writing), as compiled by the U.S. Department of Homeland Security (2018). You can see in Figure 8.7 that men outnumber women only at the youngest ages, and then from age 25 on, there are more female than male legal immigrants at each age. However,

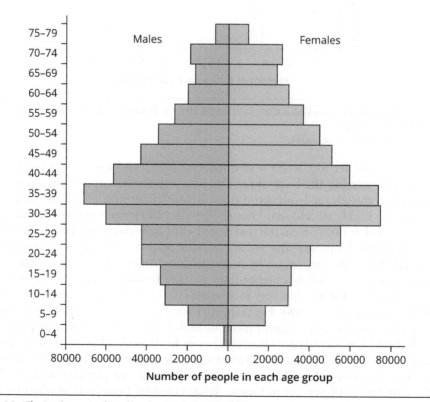

Figure 8.7   The Age Structure of Legal Immigrants to the United States

Source: Adapted by John R. Weeks from data in U.S. Department of Homeland Security (2018): Table 8.

the most significant part of the picture is that both male and female migrants are most likely to be younger adults. More than half of all legal immigrants are between the ages of 20 and 44—the prime reproductive ages.

In the short run, then, immigration adds people especially into the young adult ages in the host area, and of course those young people have been taken out of the age structure in the donor area. In the long run, the impact of migration is also felt indirectly through its influence on reproduction because these young adult immigrants are of prime reproductive ages, as we just noted. For example, it is estimated that there were 180,335 immigrants from other countries entering the state of California during 2018 (California Department of Finance 2018), and these people represented less than one percent of the total population of California (39.8 million) in that year. So, the arrival of immigrants in any given year is nearly undetectable in California's overall demographic structure. They add up over time, however, and the American Community Survey data show that 27 percent of California's population was foreign-born in 2017 and half of them were of reproductive age. It is therefore not too surprising to see that among 472,000 births in California in 2017, an estimated 38 percent were to women who were born outside the United States (Camarota, Zeigler, and Richwine 2018).

Having discussed the way in which the age and sex structure is built on the foundation of mortality, fertility, and migration rates, it is time now to see how the changing age structure influences life in human societies.

Demographic Dividends—Age Transitions at Work

As age cohorts flow through time, they can be a force to be reckoned with. That can be a challenge or an opportunity. A high birth rate does not simply mean more people, it means more kids entering school in a few years and more new job hopefuls and college freshmen 18 years down the road. At the other end of the spectrum, the very low birth rates in Europe and East Asia do not imply just that there will be fewer people in the future, they mean that schools will be closing, jobs will go begging, businesses will close, houses will be vacant, and life will be very different than it once was. Those are challenges with which the affected societies must cope. The opportunities arise especially during a time when fertility has just dropped quickly, and so there are fewer dependent children than before, there are still not many dependent older people, and a higher than average proportion of people are of working age. This is what we call a **demographic dividend.** Before we discuss it in more detail, however, we need to briefly show how we can go about measuring it.

Measuring the Age Structure

The age structure is not quite as easily summarized as is mortality (for which we often use life expectancy as a measure) or fertility (for which we often use the total fertility rate as a measure). One way to summarize the age distribution is to calculate a population's median age—the age at which half of people are above it and half are below (see Figure 8.1 earlier in this chapter for the global distribution of this measure). Young populations have a low median age, and older populations have a high median age. But the average age tells us very little about the variability in cohort size that might lead, for example, to a demographic dividend. We typically measure that with the dependency ratio—the ratio of the dependent-age population (the young and the old) to the working-age population. The higher this ratio, the more people each potential worker has to support; conversely, the lower it is, the fewer the people dependent on each worker:

$$\text{dependency ratio} = \frac{(\text{population } 0\text{–}14) + (\text{population } 65+)}{\text{population } 15\text{–}64}$$

It is conventional to use people under age 15 and those 65 and older to represent the "dependent" populations, which means those people who are unlikely to be in the labor force and are therefore having to rely on others (either family members or society in general) to provide the basics of food, shelter, and clothing. The reality is that over time, younger members of society have tended to increase the amount of time they are dependent. This may now be all the way up to graduation from college (typically age 22), or even beyond. At the other end of the age spectrum, the official ages at retirement have also been going up as people live much longer into old age. Indeed, most people reading this book in the United States won't be able to collect full Social Security until they reach age 67, and there have been multiple bills floating around Congress for years now that would increase that to an even higher age.

The Progression from a Young to an Old Age Structure

At the beginning of the demographic transition, every population had a young age structure with a characteristic pyramidal shape, exemplified even now by Nigeria, as shown in Figure 8.4. If the end of the demographic transition is associated with homeostasis (a stationary population), every population will then have an old age structure, with a characteristic barrel shape, as shown in Figure 8.6 when life expectancy for females is 80 years and the average female is having 2.1 children. In between those extremes, the age structure will undergo a period of time when it caves in at the younger ages as fertility declines, and there will be a bulge in the younger adult ages. Keep in mind that, as we noted in Chapter 3, it may be that there will be no real end to the demographic transition—it may continue to evolve in new cycles of change, especially of fertility and migration, to which societies must constantly adapt.

Youth Bulge—Dead End or Dividend?

We mentioned youth bulges in Chapter 1 as a potentially incendiary demographic phenomenon, especially in the Middle East but also in sub-Saharan Africa and South Asia. The size and timing of a youth bulge in any given country, along with that country's response to it, will help tell the tale of how dramatic the changes will be in the context of the age transition and whether those changes will be used for good or evil. The "good" reaction relates especially to the use of the young population to spur economic development and lift people out of poverty. This is the idea behind the demographic dividend. The "evil" reaction relates to the use of young people to promote violence and terrorism.

A quick drop in fertility that occurs fairly early in the mortality transition (and thus before too many people are surviving into the older ages) has the most dramatic and potentially positive impact on a society, increasing the economic productivity of the adult population because they have few children to deal with and also few older people to worry about. A slower transition to an older age, though socially and economically less disruptive than a very sudden change, may not be as conducive to the kind of positive evolutionary change a struggling economy needs in the face of the population growth that ensues as mortality declines and the demographic transition takes hold.

Many years ago, Edward Crenshaw and his associates (1997) examined the pattern of age-specific growth rates and economic development for the period 1965–1990 and concluded that an increase in the child population (the impact of declining mortality in a high-fertility society) clearly hindered economic progress in less developed nations. On the other hand, an increase in the adult population relative to other ages (the delayed effect of a decline in fertility) fosters economic development, producing what they call a "demographic windfall effect whereby the demographic transition allows a massive, one-time boost in economic development as rapid labor force growth occurs in the absence of burgeoning youth dependency" (Crenshaw et al. 1997:974). As you well know by now, the demographic "windfall" has also been called the "demographic dividend" (Bloom, Canning, and Sevilla 2003; Bloom, Kuhn, and Prettner 2017), the "demographic bonus" and the "window of opportunity" (Adioetomo et al. 2005), and China has been the poster child.

China's Demographic Dividend

In 1955, China had a population of 611 million and was plagued by high mortality (a life expectancy of 44 years for both sexes combined) and high fertility (a total fertility rate of six children per woman), although fertility was starting to decline, as you know from Chapter 5. Its age structure exhibited the classic pyramidal shape, reflecting a high proportion of the population in the very young ages, as you can see in Figure 8.8, with an overall dependency ratio of 71 people of dependent age (both young and old) per 100 of working age. These numbers are summarized in Table 8.2.

By 1995, 40 years later, China had transformed itself. Its population had doubled to 1.24 billion, due especially to declining mortality built on the very young age structure of 1955. During that same time period fertility had declined very dramatically, as you already know from Chapter 5, producing the youth bulge that you can see in Figure 8.8. In 1995, the total fertility rate was below replacement level (1.9 children per woman), and life expectancy had rocketed up to 70 years, while the dependency ratio had dropped to 51. This was a very good age structure for an

Table 8.2   Demographic Summaries of China's Age Pyramids, as Shown in Figure 8.8

	1955	1995	2035	2075
Population (in millions)	611	1,240	1,431	1,172
TFR	6.0	1.9	1.7	1.8
Life expectancy at birth (both sexes combined)	44	70	79	85
Median age	22.3	27.3	45.4	49.5
Dependency ratio	71	51	55	78

Source: Adapted by John R. Weeks using data from United Nations Population Division (2017); data for 2035 and 2075 are from the medium variant projections.

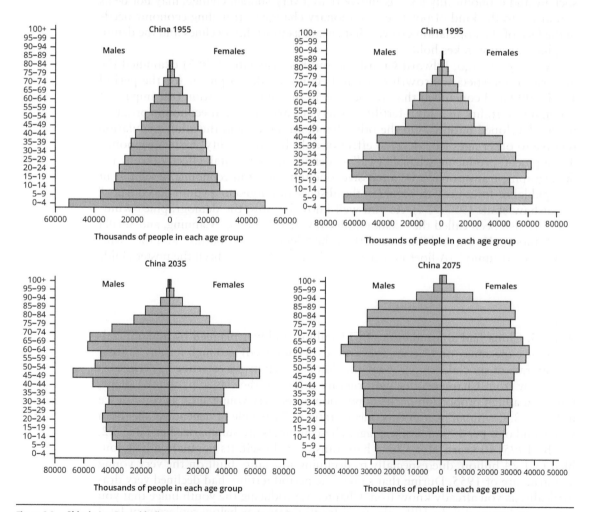

Figure 8.8   China's Age Pyramids Illustrate Its Demographic Dividend

Source: Adapted by John R. Weeks using data from United Nations Population Division (2017); data for 2035 and 2075 are from the medium variant projections.

economy trying to take off because it was loaded with people of working age and was not burdened by a lot of old and young people. The demographic dividend kicked in for China, pushing the economy forward in a society that emphasized education and in which the government enacted a variety of policies to promote capitalist-style businesses making goods that were being exported all over the world. This was the same kind of age structure that helped accelerate the economic reforms that created the East Asian economic miracle, not only in China, but also in Taiwan and South Korea, following the experience of Japan, which had enjoyed an earlier such demographic dividend after World War II ended.

All good things must come to an end, however, and the demographic momentum of the age transition in China will increasingly act as a brake on economic growth in that country. A similar age transition is certainly one of the reasons why the Japanese economy has been in the doldrums for some time now, but Japan grew rich before it grew old, whereas China might not. The Chinese government knows this and understands that it needs to maximize its advantage from this window of opportunity, which helps to explain the aggressiveness with which China is pursuing its current global economic expansion.

The United Nations projects that by 2035, the population of China will have peaked at about 1.4 billion and will be on the verge of decline. By this time, the bulge in the age structure will have moved into the middle adult ages, where productivity gains may be less than at the younger ages, but where consumption patterns tend to peak (see Figure 8.8). Overall, by 2035 the population of China will be weighted toward the older ages, with a median age that is twice what it was in 1955, and the country will face important policy issues arising from a rapidly aging population. The medium variant projection of the United Nations Population Division suggests that China's population in 2075 could be considerably older than it had been in 2035, as you can see in Figure 8.8. Indeed, China is already facing internal pressures to increase the birth rate in order to create a pool of new workers whose infusion of resources into the population at younger ages will keep the economy growing and help to support the older population. As we noted in Chapter 5, the government has effectively dropped the one-child policy, but to date, there has been no evidence that this had yet influenced couples to have more children. The government has also been working on policies to raise the age at retirement, given the nation's projected increases in life expectancy.

What Happened to India's Demographic Dividend?

In 1955 India had a population of 409 million, almost 200 million fewer than China at that time, although India was still the second most populous country in the world. By 2035 the United Nations projects that India will have nearly 1.6 billion, which would be 200 million *more* than are projected for China in that year, pushing it to the top of the population list. In between, however, it has not experienced the same kind of demographic windfall that has helped catapult China to economic power. This is because India's fertility decline has been slower and has not yet reached such a low level as in China, so its age structure has not delivered that "tipping point" into rapid economic change.

In 1955, India had a total fertility rate and a dependency ratio that were nearly identical to China's, so the two countries were starting from similar demographic situations. But by 1995, when China's demographic dividend was kicking in, women in India were having 3.8 children each, compared to only 1.9 in China, and India's dependency ratio of 69 in 1995 was almost the same as it had been 40 years earlier, compared to China's drop to 51.

Demographic Dividends in the United States and Mexico

The United States also had a youth bulge in the 1950s and 1960s, as you well know. The U.S. population was 186 million people in 1960, and the age structure for that year is noticeable for the effect of the baby boom generation at the younger ages, as seen in Figure 8.9, which graphs the age distribution for the total population, rather than as an age pyramid (simply to make the comparisons more obvious). Between 1960 and 2000, the population grew from 186 million to 288 million, but fertility levels then declined significantly (even if not as dramatically as in China)—the total fertility rate dropping from 3.6 children per woman in 1960 down to 2.0 children per woman in 2000, where it has pretty much stayed since then.

Just as we noted above for China, the rapid drop in fertility produced a demographic windfall in the age structure that coincided nicely with the economic expansion of the 1990s and the first half decade of the twenty-first century. As you can see in Figure 8.9, the U.S. age structure in 2000 bulged at the adult working

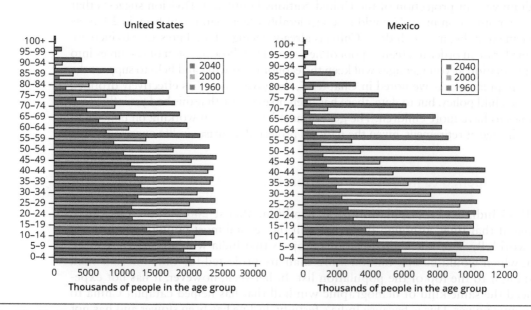

Figure 8.9   The Age Transition in the United States and Mexico

Source: Adapted by John R. Weeks using data from United Nations Population Division (2017); data for 2040 are from the medium variant projections.

ages, without the burden of huge numbers of either older or younger people. The picture for 2040 in the United States (Figure 8.9), however, is not quite like that for China in 2035 (see Figure 8.8). China's age structure begins to cave in at the young ages from the continuation of very low fertility, whereas the U.S. population straightens out a bit into a more classic barrel shape. Even though the U.S. population is expected to increase to 367 million by 2040, and the big bulge in the age structure will be transitioning toward the older, higher-consuming years, the number of younger people will be leveling off, rather than declining as in China. This is due to continued immigration into the United States and, as noted earlier, to the children of those immigrants.

Many of those immigrants currently living in the United States are, of course, from Mexico. In 1960, Mexico had 39 million people and a classic pyramidal age structure, and fertility in Mexico was higher that year (almost 7 children per woman!) than in either the United States or China. Mortality has been steadily declining over time in Mexico, as has fertility since the mid-1970s, as we discussed in Chapter 5. You can see in Figure 8.9 that by 2000, the younger ages had been reduced in size by the fertility decline in Mexico. But you can also see that the slowness of the fertility decline and its more recent start in Mexico than in either China or the United States meant that there was no bulge of population in the young adult ages—no demographic windfall to spur on an economy that was trying hard to grow but was being weighed down by the demographic burden of its youth bulge. The good news is that since 2000 the drop in fertility has been beneficial to the age structure and to the Mexican economy, and you can see that the projections out to 2040 suggest the most favorable age structure that Mexico has ever seen in its history.

The Life Course and Population Aging

The natural consequence of the demographic transition is for the population to age—for there to be both higher *numbers* of older people (due to a decline in mortality) and a greater *fraction* of the population that is older (due to a decline in fertility). Population aging produces changes in the organization of society that are partly the result of the process of individual aging. People change biologically with age and societies react differently to older than to younger people, generating the social changes that we see accompanying population aging.

We have outlined these concepts in Figure 8.10, where you can see that the nature of the social changes will depend partly on the social context, including aspects of society such as cohort-specific historical events that have affected different cohorts differently throughout the life course, and also societal levels of sexism, ageism, and racism. The impact of population aging will also differ according to the proportion of people who are young-old (the "third" age of life—in which the impact of aging on society is more social), compared with the proportion who are old-old (the "fourth" age of life—in which society must cope more with the individual biological aspects of aging, including increasing disability).

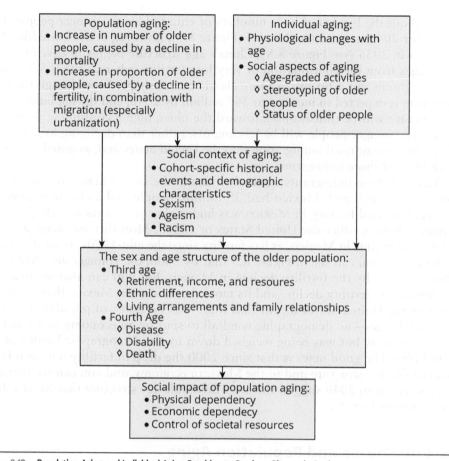

Figure 8.10   Population Aging and Individual Aging Combine to Produce Change in Society
Source: Prepared by John R. Weeks.

What Is Old?

Old age, as we usually think of it, is a social construct—something we talk about, define, and redefine on the basis of social categories, not purely biological ones. A good way to visualize this concept is to contemplate baseball legend Satchel Paige's famous question: "How old would you be, if you didn't know how old you was?" which illustrates the point that age takes on its meaning from our interaction with other people in the social world. If we are defined by others as being old, we may be treated like an old person regardless of our own feelings about whether or not we are, in fact, old.

We humans depend heavily on visual clues to assess the age of other people, and we instinctively understand that there are certain kinds of outward physical changes typically associated with aging—graying hair, wrinkling skin, muscle tone decline, and the changing body shape caused by the redistribution of fat. These are taken as signs of physical decline, and it is fair to say that most of us are, at best, ambivalent about the aging process—an attitude that is itself probably as old as human society (Warren 1998). Many people see themselves as being younger than their chronological age would suggest and that has led to the popular concept of your "real age." Some people also choose to hide or disguise the physical symptoms of aging (think of dyed hair, hair implants, Botox injections, face lifts, and liposuction).

Although there is no inherent chronological threshold to old age, in the United States and much of the world, old age has come to be defined as beginning at age 65. The number 65 assumes its almost mystical quality in the United States because that is the age at which important government-funded benefits such as Social Security (at least until recently) and Medicare become fully available. In 1935, when the present Social Security benefits were designed in the United States, the eligibility age was set at 65, "more because of custom than deliberate design. That age had become the normal retirement age under the few American pension plans then in existence and under the social insurance system in Germany" (Viscusi 1979:96). Keep in mind, however, that Congress has altered Social Security eligibility over time. For example, every person not yet 65 at the time you read this will have to be older than 65 to get full Social Security benefits. If you were born in 1960 or more recently, you cannot start collecting full Social Security until age 67. Every eligible person can start collecting as young as age 62, but your monthly benefit will be permanently reduced. On the other hand, if you wait until after your full retirement age, your monthly Social Security benefit will be permanently higher. Despite this tweaking of the system, we still think of 65 as somehow magical with respect to old age. Remember, though, that the number is arbitrary, and people obviously will not fit neatly into any senior citizen mold on reaching their 65th birthday. In fact, most people in low-mortality societies do not think of themselves as being old until well beyond that age, whereas most people in high-mortality societies would probably think of themselves as old well before age 65.

The Third Age (Young-Old) and Fourth Age (Old-Old)

Throughout most of human history, and still today in many less developed societies, old age was implicitly that age at which a person could no longer make a full economic contribution to the household economy due to one or more disabilities that would eventually (and sooner rather than later, in most cases) lead to death. The same wealth and application of science in the modern world that has lowered death rates has also made it possible to separate the decline in economic productivity from a decline in physical functioning.

Since you are reading this book, you are probably one of the lucky humans living in a place and time when you can take for granted both a long life and a comfortable income. You have grown up expecting, and almost certainly looking forward to, a time interval between the end of your work career and death—a time of leisurely retirement. This is a very recent invention. Less than 100 years ago, the older population in the United States was concentrated in the ages 65–74. High

The Age Transition Force Is With Us

According to UN estimates, there are more than 700 million people aged 65 and older in the world today (United Nations Population Division 2018a). If they all lived together under one flag, they would represent the third largest nation in the world. As a fraction of the total world population, they currently account for 9.4 percent, which is nearly double the percentage back in 1950 (5.1 percent). By 2050 it is projected to rise to 15.8 percent—three times what it was 100 years earlier. These percentages, of course, vary considerably from one part of the world to another, as you can see in the accompanying graph, and we have chosen several varying regions to illustrate the different age transitions underway, using data from the United Nations Population Division for several 30-year intervals.

Back in 1960, you can see in the graph that Northern Europe had the highest percent 65 and over because it was the area with the lowest levels of both mortality and fertility in the world at that time. That still held true in 1990, but by 2020, the rapid drop to very low fertility in Southern Europe had led to that region now having the world's highest percentage of older people, and this is projected to continue out to 2050. The most dramatic age transition, however, has taken place in Eastern Asia, including especially Japan, China, Taiwan, and South Korea. In 1960, all of the countries in the region except Japan had high mortality and high fertility with resulting low percentages of older people. However, by the 1990s, the entire region was experiencing rapidly declining mortality and fertility, and the result has been an unprecedented rise in the percentage of the population 65 and older.

In sub-Saharan Africa, mortality and fertility rates in 1960 were not much different from those in China or South Korea. However, over time as the death rates have declined, fertility has generally dropped quite slowly, and the result is that the older population remains a small fraction of the total population, even though it is expected to increase a bit by mid-century, as you can see from the graph, based on the assumption by UN demographers that fertility will continue to decline, even if not rapidly.

So, the increase in the percentage of the population that is older is largely a result of declining fertility, but the lower levels of mortality mean that people will increasingly live not just to old age, but to ever *older* ages, as we have emphasized throughout this chapter. In every middle and high-income society in the world today, old age is ideally thought of as a time of retirement from labor force activity. Indeed, when the Social Security Act was passed in the United States in the middle of the Great Depression in the 1930s, it was designed quite literally to encourage people to leave the labor force. At the time, the idea was to remove older workers from the workforce in order to replace them with younger workers, and thus lower the rate of unemployment among younger people. Most companies and government entities alike then turned age 65 into a mandatory age of retirement, forcing people out of the labor force whether or not they wanted to retire. People became increasingly interested in retiring before reaching age 65 if they could afford to do so, and the U.S. Congress facilitated this in the 1950s and 1960s by allowing reduced Social Security benefits to be available at age 62, which has been a popular option ever since.

In the 1950s the average man in the United States was almost 69 years old when he retired. By 2000, that had dropped down close to 62 (Gendell 2001), and since then it has dropped even a bit more, to 61, based on responses to the 2018 Gallup Poll (Brandon 2019). Notice the use of the term "man" in the previous sentence. Women of the baby boom generation are the first cohort to have been in the labor force in roughly the same way that men have been, but they are aging into an environment that looks different than it used to for potential retirees. "Longer life expectancy, improved health outcomes, and transformations in work driven by globalisation have produced greater diversity in when, why, and how people exit the labour force. Many boomer women are disadvantaged in later life by their histories of discontinuous employment and care-giving" (Sawyer and James 2018:1).

The idea behind retirement is that it is a time when you can leave the labor force and enjoy a life of leisure because you have enough money to live on in old age even if you are not working. There are two basic ways in which this can happen. Either you save enough money when you are younger

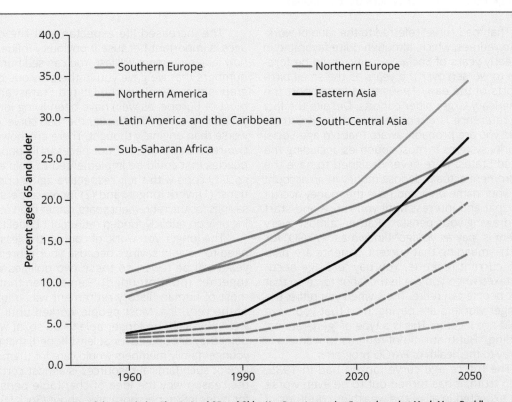

The Percentage of the Population That Is Aged 65 and Older Has Been Increasing Everywhere, but Much More Rapidly in Wealthier Regions of the World, Where Fertility Is Lowest.

Source: Prepared by John R. Weeks using data from United Nations (2018). Data for 2020 and 2050 are based on medium variant projections.

so you can draw on it for your retirement, and/or you have someone else pay your retirement check. "Someone else" could be your employer paying you a pension when you retire and/or it could be the government sending you a check each month. Where will that money really come from? For most countries, including the United States, the answer is that most of the money comes from people who are currently working.

Back in 1935, when President Franklin D. Roosevelt's Committee on Economic Security was putting the finishing touches on the Social Security legislation in the United States, two committee members met to discuss the projections that had been made for the program's expenditures for

1935 through 1980. Treasury Secretary Henry Morgenthau, Jr., and Harry Hopkins, head of the Federal Emergency Relief Administration, were aware of possible problems ahead, as is evidenced by their comments at the meeting (quoted in Graebner 1980:256):

Hopkins: Well, there are going to be twice as many old people thirty years from now, Henry, than there are now.

Morgenthau: Well, I've gotten a very good analysis of this thing . . . and I want to show them [other members of the committee] the bad curves.

Hopkins: That old age thing is a bad curve.

(continued)

The Age Transition Force Is With Us (Continued)

That "bad curve" referred to the ratio of workers to retirees, which, although quite favorable in the early years of Social Security, could be foreseen to worsen over the years as the small birth cohorts of the early 1930s tried to support the numerically larger older cohorts. Despite the fact that reference is often made to the term "trust fund," you are probably aware that old age Social Security systems in most countries, including the United States, were never designed to have the government actually deposit money in an account with your name on it and have the money accrue principal and interest until you retire and start withdrawing your pension. Rather, almost every system is "pay as you go" (known as "PAYGO" for short)—meaning that current benefits are paid from current revenue. You pay "old-age security" taxes when you are in the labor force so that older people can retire. Then, when you retire, the younger workers are paying in so that you have an old-age income. This is a type of "generational bonding." But that ratio of retirees to workers is the key to the health of PAYGO programs.

The future age curve looked bad in 1935, but in truth, it has turned out to be even worse than expected in all of the wealthier countries of the world: Life expectancy in the older ages has increased, and then the unexpected post–World War II baby boom in Europe and North America injected large cohorts that are now retiring. On top of all that, over time the U.S. Congress has considerably expanded Social Security coverage and raised benefits subsequent to the legislation's original passage in 1935.

The increased life expectancy at the older ages is important because it obviously influences how long retirement will last. You can see from the numbers that we gave you in the previous paragraphs that people in the United States (and in most of Europe, as well) have been living longer, yet retiring earlier. This makes the "bad curve" even worse than originally thought. There are, however, two reasonable (even if not necessarily popular) policies that could be implemented to help every society cope with their respective aging populations: (1) work longer, and (2) increase personal savings for the retirement years, rather than counting only on publicly-funded retirement benefits.

The longer you work, of course, the less you need to have in savings because your retirement years will be fewer, so these two policies work together (pun intended). Remember that for most of human history retirement was a luxury of the very rich. Most people worked until they were physically no longer able to do so, at which point they anticipated (or at least hoped) that their younger family members would care for them. The lack of such familial resources is almost certainly the reason why the idea of charitable pensions for older infirm persons came about (Social Security Administration 2019). However, the concept of widespread retirement when you are still healthy enough to work is pretty recent. How many years should that be if taxpayers are footing the bill for you? One idea is to use a life table (see Chapter 4) to find the age at which you have 15 years of expected life remaining (see, for example, Sanderson, Scherbov, and Gerland 2018) and use that as

mortality meant that people at that age were pretty close to death, and most continued to work for as long as they were physically able. As health has improved and mortality has declined, a greater fraction of people have survived into older ages, thus creating a new period between the traditional entrance into old age (e.g., age 65, as we discussed above) and the time when death begins to stalk us in earnest. We have taken advantage of this and have often been able to act on the old adage that "youth is wasted on the young" by giving ourselves a youth-like carefree period toward the end of life. This is the so-called Third Age (Laslett 1991), a time when we are still healthy enough to engage in all of the normal activities of daily life but are able also to be free of regular economic activity. There is a question, however, the age at which you qualify for benefits (unless, of course, a disability allows you to qualify at a younger age). For example, in the 1930s when the U.S. Social Security Act was being established, that age (for both sexes and the total population regardless of race/ethnicity) was 62 (Greville 1947), but by 2015 that age had increased to 72 (Arias and Xu 2018). Of course, 15 years is an arbitrary number, but the point is that we have been pushing up the age at which we might think about leaving the labor force.

Another important issue is that governments need to avoid retirement policies that fail to take the age transition into account. For example, as we look at the current huge influx of baby boom retirees in the United States, we should remember that when the baby boomers were younger, Congress felt generous about retirement benefits because the baby boom cohort was supplying an influx of new workers to pay taxes, and inflation was showering Social Security with unexpected revenue. In 1972, Congress boosted retirement benefits by 20 percent and built in an automatic adjustment to keep benefits increasing each year along with inflation. Back in the early 1980s, Robert Myers, former chief actuary of the Social Security Administration, worried that Congress would use the growing surplus of the 1990s to increase benefits, lower taxes, or pay off the national debt. Such a course of action could be disastrous, he felt, because the baby boom generation would really crunch the pension system. In fact, in 2001, the surplus was used to lower taxes, and the Social Security Trust Fund was significantly reduced, putting a greater burden on current workers to pay for retirees. That is pretty much where we are right now.

Bear in mind that, as critical as the situation is in the United States, it is even worse in most European nations. Throughout Europe, the benefit levels for retirees are higher than in the United States, whereas the retirement age is younger, and the more rapid drop in fertility has created an even greater imbalance between workers and retirees. Europeans are now facing up to the fact that the bad curve can be dealt with only by making some fundamental changes in society. Proposals for "replacement migration," which would bring in younger people from other countries to fill in the gaps created by the European baby bust, would not necessarily solve the problem in the long run unless it could be guaranteed that they were going to have above replacement-level fertility. In the short term, even the current smaller numbers of immigrants have created political issues for societies trying to cope with the inevitable cultural differences between older Europeans and younger immigrants who, by and large, are from countries in the Middle East, sub-Saharan Africa, and Asia.

And why do we have to think about all of these societal changes? The answer is simple: The age transition has forced us into it.

Discussion Questions: (1) Explain how a PAYGO system is affected both positively and negatively by the changing age structure. **(2)** One solution to the problem of dependency in old age would be to give up on the concept of retirement—would you be in favor of that or oppose it? Explain your answer.

about who is going to pay for our retirement in the Third Age, and we discuss that issue in the essay that accompanies this chapter.

The next step is the so-called Fourth Age—when the rest of our life will be increasingly consumed by coping with the health effects of old age. The distinguishing characteristic of this stage of life is an increasing susceptibility to senescence—increases in the incidence of chronic disease and associated disabilities and, of course, death. There is no clear age that defines the entrance to the Fourth Age, although 80 or even 85 are probably the ages in most demographers' minds when they think about this concept. Fortunately, this age keeps being pushed back to later and later in life. For the past several decades each group of people moving into old age has been healthier than the previous one, so if you have a few decades to go before you reach your 80s, you may well be healthier than today's octogenarians. You will have to work at it, though, because as we noted in Chapter 5, there are troubling signs that today's middle-aged population in both richer and poorer countries may move into old age with a new set of degenerative diseases associated especially with obesity and hypertension. The old mantra of "Watch your diet and keep exercising" is still important, it seems.

Centenarians—The Oldest of the Old-Old

Early in the twenty-first century, it has to be recognized that most people do not survive to be 100 years old. Nonetheless, this is one of the fastest-growing age groups in the population, reminding us that the life course in the future may be very different from what it was just a few decades ago. For instance, in 1911 there were only 100 centenarians (people who are least 100 years old) in England and Wales, and that had increased to only a few hundred by the end of World War II (Thatcher 2001); now there are more than 14,000, the vast majority of whom are women (U.K. Office for National Statistics 2018).

As the most populous low mortality country in the world, the United States has led in the number of probable centenarians (with "probable" reflecting the fact that not all ages can be verified). There were an estimated 2,300 centenarians in 1950, after adjusting for likely age exaggeration (Krach and Velkoff 1999). There were more than 53,000 counted in Census 2010, and the Census Bureau projections suggest that there will be 92,000 centenarians counted in the 2020 census (U.S. Census Bureau 2018a), and as in the United Kingdom, most of these are women. Projections from the United Nations Population Division suggest that by 2030, China's population of centenarians will have surpassed that of the United States (United Nations Population Division 2018b).

Reading the Future from the Age Structure

In a very real sense, the age and sex structure of a population forms a concise picture of its demographic history. Knowing what you do about the way in which mortality, fertility, and migration impact the age and sex structure, you should be able to look at a population pyramid and know what the past was like and what the future portends. We are, in fact, able to put all of the pieces together—mortality, fertility, migration, and the age-sex structure—to model the future course of a population. We do this with a very useful set of tools called *population projections*.

Population Projections

A population projection is the calculation of the number and composition of persons we can expect to be alive at a future date given the number now alive and given reasonable assumptions about age-specific mortality, fertility, and migration rates (Keyfitz 1968). By enabling us to see what the future size and composition of the population might be under varying assumptions about demographic trends, we can intelligently evaluate what the likely course of events will be many years from now. A word of caution, however, is in order. Population projections are always based on a conditional future—this is what will happen if a certain set of conditions are met.

Demographic theory is not now, nor is it likely ever to be, sophisticated enough to be able to *predict* future shifts in demographic processes, especially fertility and migration, over which we as individuals exercise considerable control. Thus we must distinguish projections from forecasts. A population forecast is a statement about what you *expect* the future population to be. This is subtly but importantly different from a projection, which is a statement about what the future population *could be under a given set of assumptions*. As Nathan Keyfitz (1982:746) observed many years ago, "Forecasts of weather and earthquakes, where the next few hours are the subject of interest, and of unemployment, where the next year or two is what counts, are difficult enough. Population forecasts, where one peers a generation or two ahead, are even more difficult."

Population projections are rarely right on the money, but in comparing past projections with subsequent censuses, the Panel on Population Projections of the National Research Council concluded that our ability to guess the future correctly is better over the short term than the long term, better for larger than for smaller countries, and better for more developed than for less developed nations (Bongaarts and Bulatao 2000). The U.S. Census Bureau has concluded that its projections are limited mainly by demographers' inability to predict turning points—those events, such as the baby boom, or the massive increase in immigration following the passage of the 1965 Immigration Act in the United States—that are nearly impossible to foresee but which have long term impacts on population growth and change (Mulder 2001). This is a reminder that we will do well to keep in mind the old adage: "Prediction is very difficult—especially with regard to the future."

There are several ways in which a demographer can go about projecting the population. These include: (1) extrapolation methods, (2) the components-of-growth method, and (3) the cohort component method. As you will see, given the importance of the age structure, the best method is the cohort component approach, which follows age cohorts through time, and in so doing allows us to assign probabilities to what we think are the most and least likely future scenarios. First, let's have a quick overview of all the usual methods of projection in order to see why we usually prefer to use a method that incorporates information about the age distribution.

Extrapolation   The easiest way to project a population is to extrapolate past trends into the future. This can be done using either a linear (straight-line) extrapolation or a logarithmic (curved-line) method. Both methods assume that we have total population counts or estimates at two different dates. If we know the rate of growth between two past dates, and if we assume that rate will continue into the future, then we can project what the population size will be at a given future date. In the year 2000, for example, 281,421,906 people were enumerated in the U.S. Census, and in 2010 the census counted 308,745,538. The average annual linear rate of growth (r_{lin}) between those two dates was 0.0097 or approximately 9.7 per thousand per year, which we can calculate using the following formula:

$$r_{lin} = \frac{\text{population at time 2} - \text{population at time 1}}{\text{population at time 1}}/n$$

In this example, the population at Time 1 is the census count in 2000, which we call the *base year;* the population at Time 2 is the census count in 2010, which we call the *launch year,* and *n* is the number of years (10) between the two censuses. You can plug in the above numbers to see that the average annual linear rate of growth turns out to be 0.0097.

Now, we use that rate of growth to extrapolate the population forward, for example, from our launch year (the beginning year of a population projection) of 2010 to a target year (the year to which we project a population forward in time) of 2050, using the following formula:

$$\text{target year population} = \text{launch year population} \times [1 + (r_{lin} \times n)]$$

In this formula, r_{lin} is the average annual linear rate of growth just calculated (0.0097) and *n* is the number of years (in this case, 40) between the launch year (2010) and the target year (2050). So, plugging in the numbers from above, the projected population in the year 2050 is:

$$308{,}745{,}538 \times [1 + (.0097 \times 40)] = 428{,}538{,}807$$

You know by now, however, that populations are typically thought to grow exponentially, not in a straight-line fashion. The formula that expresses the logarithmic growth of a population, assuming a constant rate of growth, is as follows:

$$\text{target year population} = \text{launch year population} \times e^{rn}$$

In this case, *r* represents the geometric or exponential rate of increase (r_{exp}), which is calculated with the following formula:

$$r_{exp} = \left[ln\left(\frac{\text{launch year population}}{\text{base year population}}\right) \right]/n$$

The term *ln* represents the natural logarithm of the ratio of the population at Time 2 (the launch year) to the population at Time 1 (the base year). It is one of the function buttons on most handheld calculators (including the one that comes with the iPhone and most other smart phones). Once again, *n* is the time between censuses. So, to calculate the exponential average annual rate of population growth between 2000 and 2010, we first find that the ratio of the population at those two dates (308,745,538/281,421,906) is 1.097. Then we find that the natural logarithm of that number is 0.0927, which is then divided by 10 to find that the rate of increase is 0.00927 (or 9.3 per thousand per year). Next, we plug this rate of growth

(0.00927) back into the formula for exponential or logarithmic growth (above) in order to project the population forward from the launch year of 2010 to the target year of 2050. The answer is:

$$308,745,538 \times e^{(.00927 \times 40)} = 447,339,331$$

This is, of course, a higher number than we found with the linear method of extrapolation, reminding us of the power of geometric growth (the power of doubling, as discussed in Chapter 1). But is this really what the future holds for the United States? Is the United States really expecting a huge increase in population between 2010 and 2050? Notice that these extrapolation methods of projection refer simply to total population size without taking into consideration the combination of births, deaths, or migration that would produce the projected population. If we have a way of projecting those details, then we can project the population to a target year using the components of growth method.

Components of Growth   The components of growth projection method is an adaptation of the demographic balancing equation mentioned earlier in the book. The population of the United States in the year 2050 will be equal to the population in 2010 plus all the births between 2010 and 2050, minus the deaths, plus the net migration between those two dates. But how will we figure out the number of births, deaths, and migrants that we might expect over those 40 years? We know that all of these population processes differ by age and sex, and we also know that as the population grows we cannot expect that the number of births and deaths will remain constant over time. A simple components of growth approach will work reasonably well for a short time period, but it is not very useful for a long time period such as that from 2010 to 2050. What is needed is a more sophisticated approach to figuring out what those components of growth are likely to be, since they are apt to change over time, especially as the age structure changes. This requires a method that takes the age structure into account, and we call this the *cohort component method.*

Cohort Component Method   To make a population projection using the cohort component method, we begin with a distribution of the population by age and sex (in absolute frequencies, not percentages) for a specific base year, which in this projection method will be the same as the launch year. Usually a base year is a year for which we have the most complete and accurate data—typically a census year. Besides the age and sex distributions, you need to have base-year age-specific mortality rates (that is, a base-year life table), base-year age-specific fertility rates, and, if possible, age-specific rates of in- and out-migration. Cohorts are usually arranged in five-year groups which facilitates projecting a population forward in time in five-year intervals. Of course, there is no reason why you can't project the population a year at a time if you have the data. Especially at the local level, planners may prefer to do that.

With the base-year data in hand and a target year in mind, we must next make some assumptions about the future course of each component of population growth between the base year and the target year. Will mortality continue to drop? If so, which ages will be more or less affected and how big will the changes be? Will fertility decline, remain stable, or possibly rise at some ages while dropping at others? If there is an expected change, how big will it be? Can we expect rates of in- and out-migration to change? Note that if our population is an entire country, our concern will be with international migration only, whereas if we are projecting the population of an area such as a state, county, or city, we will have to consider both internal and international migration.

The actual process of projecting a population involves several steps and is carried out for each five-year cohort (or single-year cohorts, if you are projecting year by year) between the base and target years. First, the age-specific mortality data are applied to each five-year age group in the base-year population to estimate the number of survivors in each cohort five years into the future. Since there were 10,571,823 females aged 20–24 in the United States in 2010 and the probability of a female surviving from age 20–24 to age 25–29 (derived from the life table, as discussed in Chapter 4) is 0.9976—see Table 4.3, then in 2015, we would have expected there to be 10,548,020 women surviving to age 25–29, before we make any adjustment for migration. This process of "surviving" a population forward through time is carried out for all age groups in the base-year population. The probabilities of migration (assuming that such data are available) are applied in the same way as are mortality data.

Fertility estimation is complicated by the fact that only women are at risk of having children, and of course those children are added into the population only at age zero. The tasks include (1) calculating the number of children likely to be born during the five-year intervals, and (2) calculating how many of those born will also die during those intervals. The number to be born is estimated by multiplying the appropriate age-specific fertility rate by the number of women in each of the childbearing ages. Then we add up the total number of children and apply to that number the probability of survival from birth to the end of the five-year interval.

Experience suggests that fertility behavior often changes more rapidly (both up and down) than demographers may expect, so population projectionists hedge their bets by producing a range of estimates from high to low, with a middle or medium projection that incorporates what the demographer thinks is the most likely scenario. The highest estimate reflects the demographer's estimate of the highest fertility trend possible in the future, along with the highest decline likely in mortality, and the likely maximum net immigration. Conversely, the lowest projection incorporates the most rapid decline in fertility, the least rapid drop in mortality, and the lowest probable level of net immigration. More sophisticated projection methods use statistical modeling to assign probabilities to the likelihood of one or another future course of demographic events (Lutz, Sanderson, and Scherbov 2008; Raftery et al. 2013).

The cohort component method is the most-often used projection technique, and it is the one used by the U.S. Census Bureau when preparing its series of population projections for the United States. Demographers at the Bureau, as at the United Nations, regularly revise their projections because new information comes along that alters some of the previous assumptions. The Census Bureau also uses single year of age cohorts, rather than five-year age groups, in order to produce as much detailed information as possible. Their projections are also done separately by race/ethnicity since different groups have somewhat different patterns of fertility, mortality, and migration. The projection begins with the age and sex structure as enumerated in the latest census. To this age structure are applied the age-specific birth rates among women, the age-sex-specific death rates for everyone, and the age-sex specific rates of net international migration. The process is repeated for each race/ethnic group for each year up to 2050. The total population for 2050, as projected using this method by the Census Bureau, is 389 million, which is considerably lower than the figures obtained by either of the extrapolation methods.

Backward or Inverse Projection

So, we know that population data are projected into the future in order to estimate what could happen down the road. Similar methods can be used to work backward to try to understand what happened in the past (Oeppen 1993; Smith 1992). The basic idea is to begin with census data that provide a reasonably accurate age and sex distribution for a given base year. Then, making various assumptions about the historical trends in fertility, mortality, and migration, you work back through time to "project" what earlier populations must have been like in terms of the number of people by age and sex. E. A. (Tony) Wrigley and Roger Schofield (1981) used this method to work backward from the 1871 census of England and Wales to reconstruct that region's population history. Thomas Whitmore (1992) used a complex backward projection model to show how it was possible for European contact to have led to a 90 percent depopulation of the indigenous peoples living in the Basin of Mexico at the time Hernán Cortés arrived.

Population Momentum

One important lesson to take away from population projections is that age structures carry with them the potential for substantial momentum of population growth. This is a concept not unlike the idea that a heavy freight train takes longer to stop than a light commuter train does, or that a Boeing 747 requires a longer runway for landing than a 737 does. The amount of momentum built into an age structure is determined by answering the following question: How much larger would the population eventually be, compared to now, if replacement fertility were instituted in the population right now (Kim and Schoen 1997)? Of course, we can turn this around, as Europeans are increasingly having to do, and ask about the momentum toward depopulation built into an older age structure.

You can figure out intuitively that if a population has a large fraction of women in their reproductive years, before the population stops growing these women will contribute many additional babies to the future population, even at replacement level. By contrast, an older population, with fewer women in their reproductive ages contributing fewer babies, will eventually stop growing. Most populations that now have above-replacement-level fertility will not immediately drop to replacement level. You know from Chapter 5 that the fertility transition does not normally work like that. So, researchers have devised formulas to calculate the momentum built into more gradual declines in fertility (Schoen and Kim 1998; Li and Tuljapurkar 1999; Espenshade, Olgiati, and Levin 2011). For example, Robert Schoen and Young Kim (1998) have devised formulas showing that a population growing at a rate of 2 percent per year (similar to Guatemala as of this writing) would be almost twice as large as it is now when it stopped growing if replacement-level fertility were achieved immediately. In Guatemala's case, that would require the TFR to drop instantaneously from the current level of 2.8 to 2.1, which is unlikely. More probable would be a decline over several decades. If the drop from 2.8 to 2.1 took 28 years, then their calculations suggest that the population would be 2.6 times larger when it stopped growing, and if it took as long as 56 years, the population would be 3.5 times larger when replacement level was finally reached (Schoen and Kim 1998).

Understanding population momentum allows you to appreciate that slowing down the rate of population growth requires both forethought and patience. The payoff, which is the demographic dividend that we discussed earlier in the chapter, is apt to be at least two decades down the road from the time that fertility begins to decline in earnest. The flip side is that if you are worried about the depopulating influence of an aging population, you cannot wait until it is happening to start doing something about it because it also takes a while to rebuild momentum once you lose it.

Summary and Conclusion

The age and sex structure of a society is a subtle, commonly overlooked aspect of the social structure, yet it is one of the most influential drivers of social change in human society. The number of people at each age and of each sex is a very important factor in how a society is organized and how it operates, and for this reason the age transition that accompanies the mortality and fertility transitions is a critical force for change. Age composition is determined completely by the interaction of the three demographic processes. Mortality declines initially produce more children in a society because the young are so vulnerable. Eventually, though, mortality declines lead to a larger group of older people because people keep staying alive. However, it is changes in fertility that tend to produce the biggest shifts in a society's age structure, regardless of the level of mortality. Falling fertility, for example, is the single most important driver of the increase in the *proportion* of the population that is in the older ages, even though declining mortality explains an increase in the *number* of older people. Migration can have a sizable impact because migrants tend to be concentrated among young adults, and thus they are likely to contribute not only themselves, but also their children, to a shifting age structure.

In all of the more developed societies in the world today, the fertility rate has been low for long enough that we may be approaching the end of the age transition, and population aging has become a major societal concern—not because we are afraid of old people, but rather because the demands on societal resources are very different for an older than for a younger population. "Life in an era of declining and ageing populations will be totally different from life in an era of rising and youthful populations. A new age calls for a new mind-set" (Wallace 2001:220).

Creating that mind-set is aided by the use of population projections, which allow us to chart the course of change implied by different age structures. There are some fairly predictable changes that occur to a population in the context of the age transition from a younger population at the beginning of the demographic transition to an older population at its end. The critical question is how quickly that transition occurs, because the distortions in the age structure that are part of the age transition can lead to changes in economic organization, political dominance, and social stability that must be dealt with by society—and they have the potential to be either positive or negative in their impact, depending on how society responds.

The aging of the population has enormous consequences for families, which are now coping with more older people and fewer children than at any time in human history. Lower fertility, lower mortality, and more migration (especially higher levels of urbanization) have all contributed to the age transition, and they are all important components of family demography, to which we turn in the next chapter.

Main Points

1. The age transition is a predictable shift from a predominantly younger population, when fertility is high (usually when mortality is also high), to a predominantly older population, when fertility is low (usually when mortality is also low).

2. The age composition of a society is a powerful stimulant to social change.

3. More male babies than females are generally born, but the age structure is further influenced by the fact that at almost every age more males than females die, and the sex ratio drops dramatically in the older ages in almost all societies.

4. Mortality has relatively little long-run impact on the age structure, although in the short run a decline in mortality typically makes the population younger in medium- to high-mortality societies, and a little older in lower-mortality societies; declining mortality mainly operates to increase population size, rather than dramatically affecting the age and sex structure.

5. Fertility is the most important determinant of the shape of the age/sex structure—high fertility produces a young age structure, whereas low fertility produces an older age structure.

6. Migration can have a very dramatic short-run impact on the age and sex structure of a society, especially in local areas.

7. Age transitions can provide a demographic dividend for countries experiencing a rapid fertility decline.

8. The end result of the age transition is a population with a higher fraction of people in the older ages.

9. The percentage of the population that is older is greatest in more developed countries because its increase largely depends on a decline in the birth rate in conjunction with declining mortality.

10. Population projections provide a way of using the age structure to read the future and are developed from applying the age and sex distribution for a base year to sets of age-specific mortality, fertility, and migration rates for the interval between the base year and the target year.

Questions for Review

1. It seems backward that fertility levels affect the age structure more than mortality levels do, especially given the importance of declining mortality to all of the transitions. Discuss this seeming paradox, and show why it makes sense after all.

2. The U.S. baby boom generation has sometimes been called "a pig in a python." Describe how that metaphor might help us to understand the age transitions associated with cohort flows.

3. The demographic dividend has been heralded as one of the more positive aspects of the age transition. Discuss exactly what that means, and what a society has to do in order to cash in on this dividend.

4. Discuss the way in which the health and mortality transition has helped to differentiate the older population into the third and fourth ages. What changes do you foresee in the older population by the time you get there, compared to the current situation?

5. Discuss how the changing age structure of the United States, as shown in Figure 8.9, has altered American society. What changes do you foresee if the age structure changes in the way suggested by the projection to 2040 in that graph? What might cause the actual age structure in 2040 to be different than projected?

CHAPTER 9
Family Demography and Life Chances

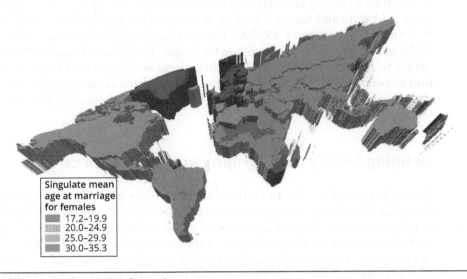

Figure 9.1 Singulate Mean Age at Marriage for Females

Source: Adapted by John R. Weeks from data in United Nations Population Division (2018); data are the most recent year available for each country.

Defining Family Demography and Life Chances
The Growing Diversity in Family Structure
    and Household Composition
Gender Equity and the Empowerment of Women

Proximate Determinants of Family
    and Household Changes
Delayed Marriage Accompanied by Leaving
    the Parental Nest
Cohabitation
Nonmarital Childbearing
Childlessness
Divorce
Widowhood
The Combination of These Determinants

Changing Life Chances
Education
Labor Force Participation
Occupation
Income
Poverty
Wealth
Race and Ethnicity
Religion

Summary and Conclusion

Main Points

Questions for Review

ESSAY: *Show Me the Money!*

Households used to be created by marriage and dissolved by death—in between there were children. Throughout the world today, however, this pattern has been transformed by the demographic transition which "is in essence a transition in family strategies: the reactive, largely biological family-building decision rules appropriate to highly uncertain environments come eventually to be supplanted by more deliberate and forward-looking strategies that require longer time horizons" (Cohen and Montgomery 1998:6). Put another way, the transition is from "family building by fate" to "family building by design" (Lloyd and Ivanov 1988:141). Our ability to control mortality and fertility, along with increased levels of urbanization associated with industrial and post-industrialized economies, has transformed and diversified family life all over the globe. Studying these changes is the work of family demography.

Defining Family Demography and Life Chances

Family demography seeks to understand the changes in family structure and family dynamics that are occurring everywhere in the world in the context of the demographic transition. Humans are inherently social beings and family life is an integral part of our existence, influencing and at the same time influenced by the life chances of family members. Life chances refer to demographic characteristics that influence how your life will turn out. These include especially education, labor force participation, occupation, and income, which in turn affect gender roles (the social roles considered appropriate for males or females) and marital status. All of these things have influenced the changing family and household structure, albeit differently for some cultural groups than others. Indeed, race and ethnicity, along with religion, mediate the impact of life chances in many human societies. The intersection of your population characteristics with your particular family and household structure is a crucial determinant of what life will be like for you. Similarly, at the societal level, the distribution of the population by different characteristics and by family and household structure will be influenced by where a society is in the demographic transition. Thus, by fitting all of these pieces together, we are in a position to say something about the future. To be sure, no social system could remain unchanged in the face of massive declines in mortality, followed by massive declines in fertility, accompanied by massive migration, especially to urban areas, along with a dramatic transition in the age structure occasioned especially by a decline in fertility—all of the changes we have discussed in the previous chapters.

The demographic transition promotes a diversity of family and household types because: (1) people are living longer, which means that they are more likely to be widowed, more likely to tire of the current spouse and seek a divorce, and less likely to feel pressure to marry early and begin childbearing; (2) this latter pressure is relieved by the decline in both mortality and fertility, which means that women, in particular, do not need to begin childbearing at such a young age, and both men and women have many years of life after the children are grown; and (3) an increasingly urban population is presented with many acceptable lifestyle options besides marriage and family-building.

In virtually every human society ever studied, people have organized their lives around a family unit. In a general sense, a family is any group of people who are related to one another by marriage, birth, or adoption. The nature of the family, then, is that it is a *kinship* unit. But it is also a mini-society, a micro-population that experiences births, deaths, and migration, as well as changing age structures as it goes through its own life course. The changes that occur in the broader population—the subject of this book in general—mainly occur within the context of the family unit, so the study of population necessitates that we study the family.

Implicit in the definition of a family is the fact that its members share a sense of social bonding: the mutual acceptance of reciprocal rights and obligations, and of responsibility for each other's well-being. We usually make a distinction between the nuclear family (at least one parent and their/his/her children) and the extended family, which can extend upward to other generations (add in grandparents and maybe even great-grandparents) and can also extend laterally to other people within each generation (aunts and uncles, cousins, and so forth).

So, where do these people live? Most often, people live in a housing unit, which is the physical space used as separate living quarters for people. It may be a house, an apartment, a mobile home or trailer, or even a single room or group of rooms. People who share a housing unit are said to have formed a household. The household is thus a *residential unit*, and a family household is a housing or residential unit occupied by people who are related to one another, although it may also include some non-family members, as well, such as friends, people renting a room, or people employed by the family. More specifically, we can say that a family household is a household in which the householder (defined by the U.S. Census Bureau as the person in whose name the house is owned or rented) is living with one or more persons related to him or her by birth, marriage, or adoption. On the other hand, a nonfamily household is considered by the Census Bureau to be a housing unit that includes only a person who lives alone, or consists of people living only with nonfamily co-residents, such as friends living together, a single householder who rents out rooms, or cohabiting couples. Note that many if not most people would consider cohabiting couples to be a family, and we adopt that approach in this chapter to the extent that data permit.

Especially important to the concept of the family household is that the family part of it makes it a kinship unit, as noted above, whereas the household part of it makes it a *consumption unit*. This means that when family members live in the same household some or all of them will be responsible for producing goods and services that are shared by, and for the mutual benefit of, the family members who live together. In sum, family members do not necessarily share a household, and household members are not necessarily family members. But when family members are sharing a housing unit, we have the most powerful kinship and consumer unit that we are likely to find in any society.

Families represent the *fusion* of people who were born into other families, and long before a family household dissolves, it is likely to have *fissured* into yet other families, as children born into the family grow up and leave the family household of their parents to create (fuse) their own households. With very few exceptions, humans grow up in, and typically live for all of their lives, in social groups that represent some sort of family, and our lives are shaped and bounded by our membership in the group. Clearly, we cannot understand the changes taking place elsewhere in society unless we connect those changes to what is happening to the family.

We can additionally describe a family in terms of its *geographic location* because where you are in the world will influence the kinds of social, cultural, economic, and physical resources that will be available to the family. We can also describe a family in terms of its *social location* (where it is positioned in the local social system) because that standing will influence the family's access to whatever local resources exist on which the family can draw. And, we can describe the family in terms of its own *social structure*, which refers to the number of people within the family, their age and gender, and their relationship to each other.

Each of these characteristics will influence the life chances of family members. Your own life chances refer, for example, to your probability of having a particular set of demographic characteristics, such as having a high-prestige job, lots of money, a stable marriage or not marrying at all, and a small family or no family at all. These differences in life chances, of course, are not necessarily a reflection of your worth as an individual, but they are reflections of the social and economic makeup of society—indicators of the demographic characteristics that help define what a society and its members are like.

We are born with certain ascribed characteristics, such as sex or gender and race and ethnicity, over which we have essentially no control (except in extreme cases). These characteristics affect life chances in very important ways because virtually every society uses such identifiable human attributes to the advantage of some people and the disadvantage of others. Religion is not exactly an ascribed characteristic, but worldwide it is typically a function of race or ethnicity (as well as location) and, as with ascribed characteristics, it is often a focal point for prejudice and discrimination, which influence life chances.

Life chances are also directly related to achieved characteristics or your personal human capital, those sociodemographic characteristics, such as education, occupation, labor force participation, income, and marital status, over which you do exercise some degree of control. For example, the better educated you are, the higher your occupational status is apt to be, and thus the higher your level of income will likely be. Indeed, income is a crass, but widely accepted, index of how your life is turning out. Ascribed characteristics affect your life chances primarily by affecting your access to achieved characteristics, which then become major ingredients of social status—education, occupation, and income. Population characteristics affect your own demographic behavior, especially family formation and fertility, although they also influence mortality and migration (especially urbanization), as we have already discussed in Chapters 4, 6, and 7, respectively.

The demographics of your family, in turn, affect life chances through the possession or acquisition of social capital—the ability to facilitate or retard your access to opportunities for higher education, a higher status occupation, or a better-paying job. All of these aspects of population characteristics and their influence on life chances converge to affect the kind of family we create and the type of household we form.

The Growing Diversity in Family Structure and Household Composition

The "traditional" family household of a married couple with children is no longer the statistical norm in North America and in many other parts of the world, even if it remains the ideal type of household in the minds of many people. Families headed by females, especially with no husband present, are now common, as are "non-traditional" households inhabited by unmarried people (including never-married, divorced, widowed, and cohabiting couples, who may represent opposite-sex or same-sex couples), by older adults raising their grandchildren, by married couples whose children are grown and out of the house, or by married couples who have not had or never will have children. You are, of course, keenly aware of these societal shifts through experiences of your own and/or of others you know. What may be less obvious is that these changes are closely linked to demographic trends.

The total number of households in the United States nearly doubled from 63 million in 1970 to 120 million in 2017 (the most recent detailed data available at this writing), but within that increase was a rather dramatic change in the composition of the American household, as Figure 9.2 illustrates. In 1970, the

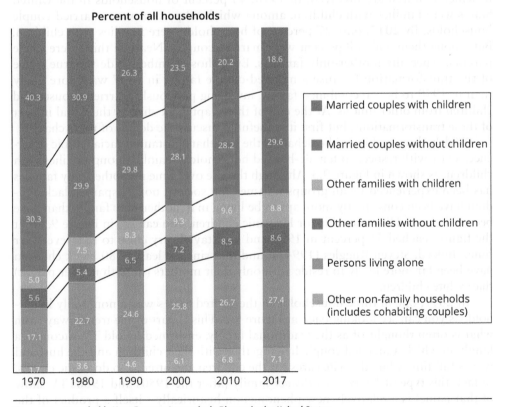

Percent of all households

	1970	1980	1990	2000	2010	2017
Married couples with children	40.3	30.9	26.3	23.5	20.2	18.6
Married couples without children	30.3	29.9	29.8	28.1	28.2	29.6
Other families with children	5.0	7.5	8.3	9.3	9.6	8.8
Other families without children	5.6	5.4	6.5	7.2	8.5	8.6
Persons living alone	17.1	22.7	24.6	25.8	26.7	27.4
Other non-family households (includes cohabiting couples)	1.7	3.6	4.6	6.1	6.8	7.1

Figure 9.2   Households Have Become Increasingly Diverse in the United States

Sources: Prepared by John R. Weeks: data for 1970 through 1990 are from Fields and Casper (2001), Figure 1; data for 2000 and 2010 are from Lofquist et al. (2012), Table 2; data for 2017 are from U.S. Census Bureau, American Community Survey 2017, 1-year data (accessed 2019).

classic "married with children" households already accounted for only 40 percent of all households in the United States. Married couples without children (either before building a family or after the kids were grown or those never having children) accounted for another 30 percent. So, in 1970, married-couple households accounted for 70 percent of all households. That was a drop from 76 percent back in 1940 when the Census Bureau first began to compile these data (Fields 2001). But look at the data for 2017, where less than 19 percent of households are married couples with children, while 30 percent are married couples without children. The latter percentage has remained essentially unchanged over time, but the total percent of all households that are comprised of married couples (with or without children) dropped to only 48 percent in 2017.

The phrase that best describes the changes in household composition as shown in Figure 9.2 is increased diversity or "pluralization" (meaning that no single category captures a majority of households). Although our focus here is on the United States, all of the other richer countries have experienced similar declines in the relative importance of households composed of a married couple with children. What is particularly noteworthy in Figure 9.2, though, is the shift in household composition in which children are involved. In 1970, 45 percent of households in the United States were families with children, among which 89 percent were married-couple households. By 2017, only 27 percent of households were families with children, but among them, only 68 percent were married couples. Nearly a third were single parents, especially mother-only families. Even those numbers hide the true scope of the transformation because a married-couple family in 2017 was more likely than in 1970 to be a recombined family, involving previously married spouses and children from other unions. At the end of this chapter, we discuss the social impact of these transformations, but first it is useful to discuss the details of these changes.

Widely discussed in public debate is the fact that substantial racial/ethnic differences exist with respect to female-headed households, mainly among families with children, as shown in Figure 9.3. Although the rise over time in mother-only families has been experienced by all groups in American society, non-Hispanic black children have been consistently more apt to be living in a mother-only family than have been either non-Hispanic white or Hispanic children. You can see in Figure 9.3 that the figure reached 51 percent in 1990 and has stayed very close to that level over time. Indeed, Steven Ruggles (1994) found that since at least 1880 black children have been far more likely to reside with only their mothers (or with neither parent) than white children.

In 2017, one in three households in the United States was a nonfamily household, as you can see looking back at Figure 9.2. This is part of the trend away from what is often thought of as the traditional family, enshrined by old TV sitcoms—a family in which a married couple live together with their children and the husband works full-time while the wife cares for the children and attends to domestic chores. In fact, this type of *Leave It to Beaver* family (after the 1950s and 1960s TV show of that name) is a relatively new phenomenon historically—itself a product of the demographic transition. High mortality alone (but especially when combined with high fertility and an agrarian economic environment) prevented this type of household from being the norm for most of human history. Let us explain.

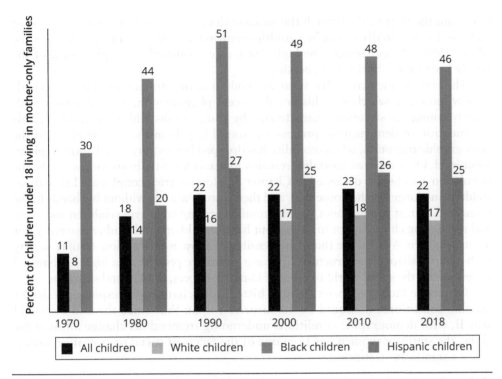

Figure 9.3   Racial/Ethnic Differences in the Percentage of Children Under Age 18 Living in Mother-Only Families, United States, 1970 to 2018

Sources: Adapted by John R. Weeks from data in U.S. Census Bureau, Current Population Survey, March and Annual Social and Economic Supplements (accessed 2019).

Human beings are by nature social animals. We prefer to live with others, and nearly all human economic activities are based on cooperation and collaboration with other humans. Our identity as individuals paradoxically depends on our inter- action with other people. We only know who we are by measuring the reaction of other people to us, and we depend on others to teach us how to behave and how to negotiate the physical and social worlds. Furthermore, humans are completely dependent creatures at birth, and every known society has organized itself into social units (households/families) to ensure the survival of children and the repro- duction of society. In high-mortality societies, the rules about who can and should be part of that social unit must be a bit flexible because death can take a mother, father, or any important household member at almost any time.

We referred in Chapter 4 to the Nuatl-speaking Mexican families in Morelos in the sixteenth century, who lived in a "demographic hell" where high mortality produced high rates of orphan- and widowhood. In response to these "vagaries of severe mortality," they developed a complex household structure that was "extremely fluid and in constant flux. Headship and household composition shifted rapidly because marriages and death occurred at what must have been a dizzying pace" (McCaa 1994:10). Similarly, data from Chinese genealogies show that from the thirteenth through the nineteenth centuries high mortality kept most Chinese from actually living in a multigenerational family at any particular time (Zhao 1994). As in Mexico, the high death rate produced a complex form of the family because of shifting membership.

The bottom line here is that what we think of as the "traditional" family depends on low mortality, which is an historically recent phenomenon, in combination with a fairly young age structure, characterized by young adults with their children. This combination of demographic processes is found largely in the middle phase of the demographic transition, when mortality has dropped but fertility is still above replacement level. Over time, as mortality remains low and fertility drops to low levels, the population ages (as we discussed in Chapter 8), older married couples are left without children any longer in the household, and then women are left without husbands in the household. But, at younger ages, people are still marrying and having children, marrying and not having children, not marrying but having children, and neither marrying nor having children. All of those things are possible in a low-mortality, low-fertility society with a barrel-shaped age structure. They are also more possible in a highly-urbanized society where the social world is a mix of family members, friends, and strangers.

Given the fact that societies have historically changed in response to demographic conditions, it should be no surprise to you that since the end of World War II, with demographic conditions undergoing tremendous change all over the globe, the status of women has been one of the facets of social organization undergoing a significant transition.

Gender Equity and the Empowerment of Women

The demographic transition does not inherently produce gender equity and the empowerment of women, but it creates the conditions under which they are much more likely to happen. The combination of longer life and lower fertility, even if achieved in an environment in which women are still oppressed, opens the eyes of society—including women themselves—to the fact that women are in a position to contribute in the same way that men do when not burdened by full-time parenting responsibility. And, as we have discussed earlier, the fact that this combination of low mortality and low fertility typically occurs in an urban setting means that women have many more opportunities than would exist in rural areas to achieve the same kind of economic and social independence that has been largely the province of men for much of human history.

To be sure, at no time in human history has there been a good justification for the domination of women by men, but the demographic conditions that prevailed for most of human history did at least facilitate that domination. Demographic conditions no longer provide that prop, and in most of the world the impediment to full social, economic, and political empowerment of women is simply the attitude of men, often aided by women who have grown up as "codependents" in the system of male domination. Thus, an important part of the demographic divide in the world is the gender divide or, as Ronald Inglehart and Pippa Norris (2003) called it—"the true clash of civilizations."

At the beginning of the twentieth century, it would have been unthinkable for a woman in America to go out to dinner without being accompanied by a man, and equally unthinkable for her to drive one of the cars that were making their first appearance at that time. At the beginning of the twenty-first century, those things were still unthinkable to most women in Saudi Arabia (one of the world's most gender-segregated societies), but just as demographic changes were occurring in the United States 100 years ago, so they are occurring in Saudi Arabia today, where women were finally in 2018 granted the right to drive a car. This was a small but still important step.

The changes under way in much of the world mean that the life chances for women are beginning to equal those of men, and thus women are in a better position to voluntarily head their own household if they want to, or to do so successfully even if forced into that position. It is certainly no coincidence that those countries still in the early to mid-stages of the demographic transition are also those where the rights of women are most trampled. In much of sub-Saharan Africa and South Asia, a woman's access to economic resources is restricted by severe limitations on their ability to inherit property and own land. India represents a classic example of a country where a woman's access to the formal labor market is much more limited than that of a man, so women disproportionately wind up in the informal sector, where they are far more likely to be economically exploited (Dunlop and Velkoff 1999; International Labour Organization 2013b). In Accra, the capital of Ghana, in West Africa, women are just as likely as men to be in the labor force, but nearly three-fourths of those women are in the informal sector, compared to about half of men (Weeks 2010).

Countries at the later stages of the demographic transition have generally discovered the benefits of unleashing the resources of the half of the population that had previously been excluded from full societal participation. Since 1979, the United Nations has been encouraging all countries to sign on to the Convention on the Elimination of All Forms of Discrimination against Women (CEDAW) and as of this writing, it had been ratified by 189 out of 194 countries. The United States has signed it, but has not ratified it, which is sort of a half-hearted endorsement.

The empowerment of women contributes to further change in society by expanding women's life chances, which, in turn, expand economic opportunity and enrich society and households. All of these transformations, of course, also contribute to the diversity of family and household structure. Let us now examine some of the direct proximate causes of the household structure transformation societies have been experiencing.

Proximate Determinants of Family and Household Changes

The increasing diversity in household structure is a result of several interdependent trends taking place in society, including especially delays in marriage, accompanied by young people leaving their parents' home (which in most more developed nations has increased the incidence of cohabitation), and an increase in divorce (which also contributes to cohabitation); whereas at the older ages, the greater survivability of women over men has increased the incidence of widowhood, which has an obvious impact on family and household structure. In between the younger and older ages, the smaller number of children in each family means that a much shorter period of time in each parent's life is devoted to activities directly related to childbearing. The life course of the family has thus been revolutionized.

Delayed Marriage Accompanied by Leaving the Parental Nest

One of the most important mechanisms preventing women from achieving equality with men is early marriage. When a girl is encouraged or even forced to marry at a young age, she is likely to be immediately drawn into a life of childbearing and family-building that makes it very difficult, if not impossible, for her to contemplate other options in life. This is one of the principal reasons why high fertility is so closely associated with low status for women. Figure 9.1 at the beginning of this chapter shows the world pattern in the average age at marriage for women. Since many countries do not actually keep statistics on this, the measure is technically called the *singulate mean age at marriage,* which uses age cohort data on marital status from censuses or surveys to estimate the average age at marriage. In all events, as you look at that map, you will not be surprised to notice that the highest percentage married at young ages occurs in those countries where fertility is highest and where the status of women is known to be low. By contrast, it is no coincidence that the age at marriage for women in the low-fertility regions of North America, Europe, and Oceania is high and the status of women is also higher than in other places in the world.

Even though women typically marry at young ages in high-fertility societies, men tend to be under less constraint on that score. This means that in those places where women are young when they marry, the chance is good that their husband is several years older. This further contributes to the ability of a man to dominate his spouse. "A girl with minimal education, raised to be submissive and subservient, married to an older man, has little ability to negotiate sexual activity, the number of children she will bear or how she spends her time" (Gupta 1998:22).

Table 9.1 shows that as the percentage of women who are married at ages 15–19 goes down, the difference in age between husband and wife also goes down. Thus, in those countries where less than 10 percent of women are married at ages 15–19, a man is on average 2.8 years older than the woman he marries. At the other end of the continuum, in those countries where 40 percent or more of women are married at ages 15–19, the average difference between bride and groom is 6.2 years. Although husbands tend to be older than their wives in the United States, data from the U.S. Census Bureau show that the average age at first marriage for men in 2018 was 29.8, just 2 years older than for women (U.S. Census Bureau 2018e). Demographic and Health Survey (DHS) data also indicate that the age at marriage has been on the rise in countries like Pakistan and Niger, signaling a potential change in fertility, female empowerment, and family change throughout the world. For example, the average age at first marriage among women interviewed in the 1990 Pakistan DHS was 18.6, and that had climbed to 20.4 in the

Table 9.1 The Average Difference in Age of Brides and Grooms Declines as The Percent of Women Married at Ages 15–19 Goes Down

Percent of Women Married at Ages 15–19	Average Difference in Age Between Bride and Groom	Number of Countries
40 or higher	6.2	5
30–39	5.4	3
20–29	4.8	21
10–19	3.6	41
Less than 10	2.8	92
Total	3.4	162

Source: Calculated by John R. Weeks from data in United Nations Population Division (2013b).

2017 survey. Even in Niger, one of the highest-fertility countries, the average age at first marriage has gone from 14.9 in 1992 to 15.7 in 2012—still very low, but moving in the right direction.

In the United States, as in many northern and western European countries, the early decline in fertility more than 100 years ago was accomplished especially by a delay in marriage. It is thus easy to understand that it was in these countries that some of the early feminist movements were able to take root. At a time when very few effective contraceptives were available, and when it was extremely difficult to get a divorce, postponement of marriage (and postponement of sexual intercourse, as well) was the principal route by which women were able to increase their options in life. In 1890 in the United States, more than one-third of all women aged 14 and older (34 percent) and close to one-half of all men (44 percent) were single.

The age at marriage stayed relatively high for both males and females until World War II and the post-war baby boom, when it dropped quickly and bottomed out between 1950 and 1960 (Elliott et al. 2012). Since then, people have once again been delaying marriage. By 1990 the age at marriage for both males and females in the United States had finally gone back up to the level of 1890. The difference this time around, of course, is that people can now more readily delay marriage without having also to delay sexual intercourse.

Thus, since the 1960s, the contraceptive revolution, especially the birth control pill, has allowed people to disconnect marriage from sexual intercourse, and it is not a coincidence that the rise in marriage age after 1960 was especially noticeable among women who reached maturity just as the pill was coming onto the market. Of course, people have known about and used birth control methods for a long time (refer to Chapter 5 if you need a review), but the failure rate of all of those pre-pill methods was significantly higher than that of the pill or the more recently introduced long-acting reversible contraceptive (LARC) methods, and a couple engaging in intercourse ran a clear risk of an unintended pregnancy. Prior to 1973 and the legalization of abortion in the United States, an American woman could end an unintended pregnancy only by flying to a country such as Sweden, where abortion was legal, or by seeking an illegal (and often dangerous) abortion. These unsafe abortions were often done in Mexico, even though abortion was illegal there (and still is everywhere except in Mexico City).

In more traditional societies (including the United States and Canada until the 1960s), an unintended pregnancy was most apt to lead to marriage, although a woman might also bear the child quietly and give it up for adoption. Illegitimacy was widely stigmatized and having a child out of wedlock was the course of last resort. Marriage was the only genuinely acceptable route to regular sexual activity, and only married couples were routinely granted access to available methods of birth control. That situation still prevails today in most of the world's predominantly Muslim nations.

In the late nineteenth century, the older age at marriage already alluded to in North America and Europe had been accompanied by a delay in the onset of regular sexual activity—the Malthusian approach to life. Intercourse was delayed until marriage, and in this way nuptiality was the main determinant of the birth rate: early marriage meant a higher birth rate, and delayed marriage meant a lower one. A variety of social and economic conditions might discourage an early marriage. The societal expectation that a man should be able to provide economic support for his wife and children tended to delay marriage for men until those expectations could be met. Under conditions of rising material expectations, as was the case in the late nineteenth century, marriage had to be delayed even a bit longer than in previous generations because the economic bar had been raised higher than before.

Delayed marriage typically meant that young people stayed with their parents in order to save enough money to get ahead financially and thus be able to afford marriage. Staying with parents also minimized the opportunities for younger people to be able to engage in premarital sexual intercourse, which might lead to an unintended pregnancy and destroy plans for the future. These behaviors are especially prevalent when societal norms forbid cohabitation. Thus, prior to the latter half of the twentieth century, delayed marriage did not typically lead younger people to leave home and set up their own independent household prior to marriage.

In the early post–World War II period, economic robustness meant that jobs were readily available for young people, allowing them to leave the parental home at an earlier age without an economic penalty and, since the risk of pregnancy meant that intercourse was still tied closely to marriage, the age at marriage reached historic lows in the United States and Europe. In discussing the situation in Germany, Hans-Peter Blossfeld and Alessandra de Rose (1992) suggest that from the end of World War II through the late 1960s, "the opportunity for children to leave their parental home had increased remarkably because of the improvement of economic conditions. But the social norm requiring that they be married if they wanted to live together with a partner of the opposite sex was still valid, so that age at entry into marriage was decreasing until the end of the 1960s" (p. 75). Similar arguments apply to the United States and other European countries, even for a country like Spain, where out-of-wedlock births accounted for only 2 percent of births in 1975, but had jumped to 30 percent by 2007 (Castro-Martín 2010).

Modern contraception has allowed sex to be disconnected from marriage and this has encouraged young people to leave their parental home before marriage, even while delaying marriage. Data from the 2012 Current Population Survey in the

United States show that among people aged 18–24, only 12 percent had been married (and 72 percent of those were living with their spouse). Slightly more than half (54 percent) were living with their parents, leaving more than one third (34 percent) living on their own, usually with one or more other non-family members, including cohabiting couples (U.S. Census Bureau 2013b).

Cohabitation

The delay in marriage has not necessarily meant that young people have been avoiding a family-like situation, nor that they have necessarily avoided having children out of wedlock, as we already mentioned. When leaving the parental home, young people may set up an independent household either by living alone (a very small percentage); moving into non-household group quarters such as a college dormitory; or sharing a household with nonfamily members. Within the latter group is the option of cohabitation, which can be defined as the sharing of a household by unmarried persons who have a sexual relationship (Cherlin 2013). As this trend was unfolding in the 1970s in the United States, the Census Bureau began asking more direct questions about unmarried partners in a household and now describes cohabitation as one of several types of living arrangements, recognizing as well that it may include persons of the opposite sex or of the same sex.

In 1970, when 64 percent of women aged 20–24 had been married at least once (Fields and Casper 2001), there were about 500,000 cohabiting couples in the United States, representing a ratio of about 1 cohabiting couple per 100 married couples. By 2012, when only 19 percent of women that age had ever been married, the number of cohabiting couples had increased to 7.8 million and the ratio of cohabiting to married couples had climbed to 14 per 100 (U.S. Census Bureau 2013a). Snapshot numbers like these almost certainly underestimate the importance of cohabitation, however, because it has become a widely accepted part of the life course in many low-fertility societies. Rather than being an alternative to marriage (a "poor person's marriage"), it has become a stepping-stone to marriage for many, as well as a step back from marriage after a divorce for others. Although a relatively small, yet obviously growing, fraction of couples are cohabiting at any one time, the data for the United States suggest that more than half of women between the ages of 19 and 44 have cohabited at least once, and that about 40 percent of children have experienced time in a cohabiting family by the time they are 12 years old (Kennedy and Bumpass 2008). Similar rapid increases have been observed elsewhere. For example, survey data from France suggest that in 1965 only 8 percent of couples cohabited before marriage, but by 1995 that figure had jumped to 90 percent (Toulemon 1997), where it has stayed since (Perelli-Harris et al. 2012).

Nonmarital Childbearing

The delay in marriage accompanied by high rates of premarital sexual activity (aided by the fact that many young people have been getting out of the parental home before marriage) means that the United States and some of the other low-fertility nations have been experiencing an increase in the proportion of nonmarital births. This is an event, of course, that immediately transforms a woman living alone, or an unmarried couple, from a nonfamily to a family household. In France, the percentage of first births occurring outside of marriage increased from 20 percent in 1974–1985 to 51 percent in 1995–2004 (Perelli-Harris et al. 2012). Between 1970 and 2012, the proportion of babies in the United States who were born outside of marriage increased from 11 percent to 41 percent (Martin et al. 2003; Martin et al. 2013).

Data from the American Community Survey provide information about the numbers and characteristics of women who are bearing a child outside of marriage. There are two ways to look at these data. The first perspective is to ask about the *percentage* of births to women in a given demographic category (e.g., age or educational level) that are taking place outside of marriage, whereas the second perspective asks which groups of women are having the greatest *number* of nonmarital births. With respect to the first perspective, certain groups have stood out for many years: (1) nearly 90 percent of births to girls under age 20, and nearly two-thirds of births to women aged 20–24 are nonmarital; and (2) more than two-thirds of births to African American women of all ages are outside of marriage.

Among younger women in the United States, the nonuse of contraception and the increasing lack of local access to abortion in many states pushes up the likelihood of young women getting pregnant and bearing a child. To be sure, the United States is more restrictive than most low-fertility societies in providing teenagers with easy and inexpensive access to methods of fertility limitation. Prior to the 1970s, most young women conceiving out-of-wedlock would have married prior to the baby's birth (Bachu 1999), so the ratio of nonmarital births to all births would have been much lower, even with the same level of premarital conceptions.

Blacks account for a disproportionate share of younger women bearing children outside of marriage, as we pointed out in Figure 9.3. It is not clear why this pattern exists, but even in the 1930s, when only 6 percent of white women in the United States were having a baby out-of-wedlock, the percentage among blacks was 31 (Bachu 1999). Since birth rates overall are nearly as low for blacks as they are for whites in the United States, the proportion of nonmarital births represents a different pattern of childbearing, not a different overall level of childbearing. The pattern is to have children at a younger age than the rest of the population does, and then to stop having them at a younger age as well. Thus, in 2017, the age-specific birth rates for black women were quite a bit higher than for whites at ages younger than 25, essentially the same at ages 25–29, but then lower than for whites at ages 30 and higher (Martin, Hamilton, and Osterman 2018).

The second perspective on nonmarital childbearing asks about which groups of women account for the greatest *number* of such births? Of 1.5 million U.S. nonmarital births in 2017, only 25 percent were to non-Hispanic blacks, whereas 37 percent were to non-Hispanic whites, and 31 percent were to Hispanics (Martin, Hamilton, and Osterman 2018). Thus, black women accounted for only one in four nonmarital births, despite the much higher fraction of black babies born outside of marriage than is true for the other groups. Similarly, it turns out that 62 percent of nonmarital births were to women aged 20–29 in 2017, while only 11 percent were to teenagers, despite the much higher percentage of teenage births that are outside of marriage.

We must also recognize that a significant fraction of children born to unmarried women are in a two-parent family, albeit in one in which the parents are cohabiting, not married. Data from the 2006–2010 round of the National Survey of Family Growth suggest that 57 percent of births to unmarried women are to cohabiting women, accounting for about one in four children born overall in the United States (Payne, Manning, and Brown 2012). That is tempered, however, by the fact that data from the National Survey of Family Growth suggest that "[c]ompared with those who were married or unmarried and not cohabiting, cohabiting women and men were more likely to have no high school diploma or GED. Both cohabiters and unmarried, noncohabiting individuals reported lower household incomes than married persons" (Nugent and Daugherty 2018:1).

To be sure, the principal societal concern about nonmarital childbearing is that both the mother and her child (or children) will have more limited life chances than would otherwise be the case. Isabel Sawhill (2014) argues that young women who "drift" into unplanned pregnancy and parenthood are creating lifelong problems for themselves and their children. They are in contrast to the "planners" who make more deliberate decisions about when and under what circumstances to have a child. Her underlying argument is that more attention needs to be paid to providing teenage and young adult women with easy access to effective contraception. Nonmarital childbearing increases the likelihood of living in poverty and data from the longitudinal Panel Study of Income Dynamics have demonstrated that poverty in childhood is generally associated with lower levels of income and well-being in adulthood (Duncan, Magnuson, and Votruba-Drzal 2017). Indeed, a congressionally-funded study by the National Research Council concluded in 2019 that "the weight of the causal evidence does indeed indicate that poverty itself causes negative child outcomes, especially when poverty occurs in early childhood or persists throughout a large portion of childhood (National Academy of Sciences 2019:S-2).

Childlessness

Some women choose not to bear a child, and some are unable to do so either because they and/or their partner(s) are infertile, as we discussed in Chapter 5. In the 1970s, data from the Current Population Survey suggested that about ten percent of women were reaching ages 40–44 without having had a child. At that time, it seems likely that most of those were unable to have a child. However, childlessness has slowly but steadily been increasing, reaching 15 percent according to data from the 2011–2015 National Survey of Family Growth (Martinez, Daniels, and Febo-Vazquez 2018). The rise is probably due to women choosing not to have a child. Some may have drifted toward childlessness by continually postponing the first child, which may also involve postponing marriage, until finally a woman is past her ability to conceive and bear a child. However, many almost certainly made the consciously planned decision not to have children (Hayford 2013).

An important consequence of gender equality is that there is less pressure on a woman to have children, even if she is married, particularly if she has a rewarding career that she doesn't want to interrupt or, as certainly happens in some cases, she and her husband simply prefer a life without children. In its turn, childlessness promotes household diversity by increasing the percentage of households represented either by someone living alone, or a married couple with no children of their own, or a cohabiting couple with no children, or a multiple-person nonfamily adult-only household.

Divorce

Not only has marriage been increasingly pushed to a later age, but once accomplished, marriages are also more likely to end in divorce than at any previous time in history. This trend reflects many things. An obvious reason is that changes in divorce laws since the 1970s have made it easier for either partner to end the marriage at any time for any reason (Waite 2000). Why were legislators motivated to make those changes? For answers, we can look to the loosening hold of men over women and the longer lives we are leading, both of which may produce greater conflict within marriage. In 1857 in the United States, there was only a 27 percent chance that a husband aged 25 and a wife aged 22 would both still be alive when the wife reached 65, but for couples marrying in the early twenty-first century, the chances have rocketed to 60 percent. Conversely, only about five percent of marriages contracted in 1867 ended in divorce (Ruggles 1997), whereas it has been estimated that almost half of the marriages contracted since the 1970s will end in divorce (Kreider and Fields 2002; Raley and Bumpass 2003; Schoen and Canudas-Romo 2006). That probability seems to have stabilized since the 1990s, however, which suggests that we may have passed the period of rising divorce rates (Lundberg and Pollak 2013).

Of course, the United States is not unique in having experienced an increase in divorce probabilities. William Goode (1993) compiled data showing that throughout Europe the percentage of marriages ending in divorce doubled between 1970 and the mid-1980s. For example, in Germany in 1970, it was estimated that 16 percent of marriages would end in divorce, increasing to 30 percent in 1985. In France, the increase went from 12 percent to 31 percent during that same time period. After that rapid rise, the divorce rate appears more recently to have plateaued in Europe, just as has happened in the United States.

Andrew Cherlin (2013) summarizes the major risk factors for divorce as including low income for the couple (which causes stresses and tension), early age at marriage, spouse's lack of similarity (this kind of similarity is known as *homogamy*, which refers to the fact that people who are more similar to one another are more likely to get along with each other or, conversely, those who are less similar will be more likely to divorce), and parental divorce (the copycat phenomenon, in which people whose parents divorced are more likely themselves to divorce). Keep in mind that there are probably as many reasons for divorce as there are divorces, but these are statistically the biggies.

Another key to the rise in divorce, as we noted earlier, is that many marriages that in earlier days would have been dissolved by death are now dissolved by divorce. This seems apparent from the fact that the annual combined rate of marital dissolution from both the death of one spouse and divorce remained remarkably constant for more than a century—essentially unchanged between 1860 and 1970 (Davis 1972). As widowhood declined, divorce rose proportionately. Only with the rapid increase in divorce during the 1970s did that pattern begin to diverge. So dramatic was the rise in divorce in the 1970s that in the mid-1960s not allowing people to divorce would have added an additional 6.7 years to the average marriage, whereas by the mid-1970s, banning divorce would have added 17.2 years (Goldman 1984).

Widowhood

As death has receded to older ages, the incidence of widowhood has steadily been pushed to the older years as well. Divorce is a more important cause of not being married than is widowhood up to age 65, beyond which widowhood increases geometrically because of the higher death rate of men, undoubtedly compounded by the tendency of divorced women to change their status to widow upon the death of a former husband. A person whose spouse has died may, of course, remarry, or cohabit with another person, just as would be the case for someone whose marriage ended in divorce.

The Combination of These Determinants

So now we know that as the demographic transition has unfolded people have been waiting longer to marry, although often cohabiting in the meantime, and when they do marry, their marriage is more likely to end in divorce than in widowhood. Robert Schoen and Nicola Standish (2001) used life table methodology to try to quantify the relative importance of these changes in family demography. Their results showed that between 1970 and 1995, for example, the proportion of women who could expect ever to marry declined from 96 percent to 89 percent. At the same time, the average age at marriage was increasing, the percentage of marriages ending in divorce was increasing, and the percentage of marriages ending in widowhood was declining. Furthermore, as life expectancy increases while the average duration of a marriage shortens, and the percentage of divorced people remarrying goes down, the percentage of a person's life spent being married obviously declines, thus adding to the individual diversity of household types in which a person might live during an entire lifetime.

Having described the key features of the transformation of families and households, let us now turn to how they have been influenced by changing life chances and how, in turn, life chances interact with family formation and dynamics.

Changing Life Chances

The leading explanations for the shift in household structure in western nations combine elements of the demographic transition perspective with the life course perspective. The demographic transition perspective relates changing demographic conditions (especially declining mortality, declining fertility, and urbanization) to the rise in women's status. This is aided especially by delayed marriage, which encourages higher levels of educational attainment. In turn, this has increased a woman's ability to enter the labor force and earn sufficient income to have the economic and social freedom to choose her own pattern of living. All of these changes have, of course, altered the life chances for males, as well as females. Throughout the world, increases in education, occupational status, and income have benefitted men and women alike. However, women's improving life chances have contributed in very special ways to the transformation of families and households. Again, we emphasize that these demographic conditions are probably necessary, but not sufficient, to initiate the current rise in the status of women in industrialized societies. What is also required is some change in circumstance to act as a catalyst for the underlying demographic factors. This is where the life course perspective comes in, because women who have grown up in a different demographic and social milieu, and thus see the world differently than did earlier generations of women, have the potential to generate new and innovative changes in society. It is easy to know where to begin the discussion of changes in life chances, because nothing is more important than education.

Education

Becoming educated is probably the most dramatic and significant change you can make in your life. It is the locomotive that drives much of the world's economic development, and it is a vehicle for personal success used by generation after generation of people in the highly developed nations of the world. Still, the relative recency with which advanced education has taken root in American society can be seen in Table 9.2. In 1940, less than one in four Americans aged 25 or older had

Table 9.2   U.S. Educational Attainment Has Increased Significantly over Time in the Population Ages 25 and Older

| Year | Males | | Females | |
	% High School Graduate or More	% College Graduate	% High School Graduate or More	% College Graduate
2017	87.3	31.3	88.6	32.6
2000	84.2	27.8	84.0	23.6
1990	77.7	24.4	77.5	18.4
1980	69.2	20.9	68.1	13.6
1970	55.0	14.1	55.4	8.2
1960	39.4	9.6	42.5	5.8
1950	31.5	7.1	35.1	5.0
1940	22.3	5.4	25.9	3.7

Sources: Data for 1940 to 1990 are from U.S. Census Bureau (2010), Table 1; data for 2017 are from U.S. Census Bureau (2018a).

graduated from high school, although women were more likely than men to have done so. Rural young men, in particular, were likely in those days to be drawn into agricultural or mining jobs before finishing high school. At that same time, slightly more than five percent of men and less than four percent of women were college graduates. An historically short six decades later, in 2000, 84 percent of both men and women were high school graduates and about one in four Americans had graduated from college—with men still being more likely than women to have accomplished that milestone. By 2017, data from the American Community Survey show that women aged 25 and older had surpassed men in terms of both high school graduation (88.6 percent to 87.3 percent) and a bachelor's degree or higher (32.6 percent to 31.3 percent) (U.S. Census Bureau 2018a).

The world as a whole has been experiencing an increasing equalization of education between males and females—an important component in raising the global status of women and, in its turn, encouraging smaller family sizes (Courbage and Todd 2011; Rees 2019). The ratio of females per males attending secondary school has been steadily increasing worldwide since at least the 1970s, according to World Bank estimates. Even in sub-Saharan Africa and southern Asia, as well as in northern Africa and western Asia, where the status of women has been notably low and where education for girls continues to lag behind that of boys, there have nonetheless been notable improvements in the ratio of girls to boys attending school. Philippe Fargues (1995) noted that in the middle of the twentieth century most of the countries of northern Africa and western Asia had gender equity with respect to education in the sense that most people—males and females alike—were illiterate. Education was extended first to young men, creating for a while both a gender and a generation gap in education. Now, as more generations of children have been educated, and as education has been offered to girls as well as boys, both of those gaps are closing, and this will certainly help accelerate the process of social and economic development (Grant and Behrman 2010).

The comments about closing the gap should not be taken to mean that we are galloping toward gender equity in education everywhere on the planet. Table 9.3 lists the 22 countries in the world (representing 11 percent of the world's population) as of 2017 in which the literacy rate among young women (aged 15–24) was at least 10 percentage points lower than that for males in the same age range. All of the countries are in either sub-Saharan Africa or South Asia, with Afghanistan having the greatest gender gap.

Our interest in education lies especially in the fact that by altering your worldview, education tends to influence nearly every aspect of your demographic behavior, as we have discussed to varying degrees in the previous chapters. Data from censuses and from sources such as the Demographic and Health Surveys show that nearly anywhere you go in the world, the more educated a woman is, the fewer children she will have. Not that education is inherently antinatalist; rather, it opens up new vistas—new opportunities and alternative approaches to life, other than simply building a family—and in so doing it delays the onset of childbearing, which is a crucial influence on how people view childbearing. In short, education tends to lower fertility, or to keep it lower than it might otherwise be, and this contributes to the variety of household and family structures we now observe all over the world.

Table 9.3   World Educational "Hot Spots": Countries Where the Literacy Rate Among Young (Aged 15–24) Women Is at Least 10 Percentage Points Lower Than for Young Men, circa 2017

Country	Region	Percent of Males 15–24 Who Are Literate	Percent of Females 15–24 Who Are Literate	Excess of Male Over Female Literacy
Afghanistan	South Asia	62	32	30
Benin	Sub-Saharan Africa	64	41	23
Central African Republic	Sub-Saharan Africa	49	27	22
Mali	Sub-Saharan Africa	61	39	22
Guinea-Bissau	Sub-Saharan Africa	71	50	21
Guinea	Sub-Saharan Africa	57	37	20
Chad	Sub-Saharan Africa	41	22	19
Nigeria	Sub-Saharan Africa	76	58	18
Niger	Sub-Saharan Africa	49	32	17
Mozambique	Sub-Saharan Africa	79	63	16
Angola	Sub-Saharan Africa	85	71	14
Pakistan	South Asia	80	66	14
Sierra Leone	Sub-Saharan Africa	65	51	14
South Sudan	Sub-Saharan Africa	44	30	14
Burkina Faso	Sub-Saharan Africa	57	44	13
Cote d'Ivoire	Sub-Saharan Africa	59	47	12
Senegal	Sub-Saharan Africa	76	64	12
Togo	Sub-Saharan Africa	90	78	12
Congo, Dem. Rep.	Sub-Saharan Africa	91	80	11
Burundi	Sub-Saharan Africa	85	75	10
Gambia, The	Sub-Saharan Africa	66	56	10
Nepal	South Asia	90	80	10

Source: Adapted by John R. Weeks from data in World Bank (2019b), Table 2.10; note that countries are listed in rank-order based on the percent of male over female literacy.

The fact that education alters the way you view the world also has implications for the marriage market. For example, in the United States until a few decades ago a major concern in choosing a marriage partner was to pick someone who shared your religious background (social scientists call this "religious homogamy"). Over time, however, the salience of religion has given way to "educational homogamy"—people want to marry someone with similar amounts of education, thus education has been replacing religion as an especially important factor in spouse selection (Schwartz and Mare 2005; Mare 2016). This trend is almost certainly related to gender equity. When men were generally more educated than women—a difference arising from the more traditional kind of society that also places a higher emphasis on religion—well-educated men, in particular, were less likely to find women with a level of education similar to their own. But as women caught up with men in terms of education—due to the modernization of society—men and women began to sort themselves into marriage with a similarly educated mate.

Gender equity, combined with the greater proportion of people going to college, has altered the lifestyles of many young Americans. It has been accompanied by delayed marriage, delayed and diminished childbearing and, consequently, higher per-person income among young adult householders. Table 9.4 uses data from the 2017 Current Population Survey to show that although women consistently earn less than men, for both men and women the more education you have, the higher your income will likely be. These data are for full-time, year-round workers, so we have controlled for the possibility that some people might be unemployed or only working part-time. In 2017, people with a graduate or professional degree were earning more than twice as much per year as those who were only high school graduates. This has become known as the "college premium," and its existence has almost certainly contributed to increased education (investment in human capital) and increased economic productivity. Although the college premium is the same for males and females in relative terms, you can also see that at each educational level women are earning only about three-fourths of what men earn. We may be headed toward gender equity, but we are not there yet.

Why is there a differential in income by gender? The obvious answer is that there has been a history of discriminating against women in the labor market in terms of what kinds of jobs they are hired for and what pay they receive (Marini and Fan 1997). This is true almost everywhere you go in the world. It has been

Table 9.4   Better-Educated Workers in the United States Had Higher Median Incomes in 2017, but Women Lagged Behind in Pay

People Aged 25 and Over Who Are Full-Time, Year-Round Workers	Males	Females	Ratio of Female Income to Male Income
Not high school graduate	$34,622	$25,454	0.74
High school graduate	$42,440	$32,243	0.76
Some college or associate's degree	$53,333	$38,450	0.72
Bachelor's degree	$71,991	$52,439	0.73
Graduate or professional degree	$101,363	$74,429	0.73

Source: Adapted by John R. Weeks from U.S. Census Bureau (2018b), Table PINC-03.

quipped that "Japan is the land of the rising sun, but only the son rises." In East Germany right up to the period before the Berlin Wall collapsed, communism was supposed to guarantee gender equality. Yet women with the same education as men, working at the same jobs as men, were receiving less pay than men (Sörenson and Trappe 1995).

Labor Force Participation

As education increases, so does the chance of being in the labor force. Among both males and females in the United States, the higher the level of education attainment among people aged 25–64, the higher the percentage of people who were currently in the labor force. Women are less likely than men to be in the labor force at any given level of education, but it is nonetheless true that the clear pattern over time has been for women to be working more. Prior to the 1970s, for example, women who worked typically did so only before they married or became pregnant. Thus, the labor force participation rates by age peaked in the early 20s and declined after that. That is still a common pattern in many less developed countries, but it no longer characterizes women in the richer nations, where labor force participation rates by age are now very similar for males and females.

Keep in mind as we talk about labor force participation rates that most countries include unemployed persons as being in the labor force. Thus, if you are looking for work, even though you are not actually working or even if you have never before held a job, you are considered to be in the labor force. Unemployment rates are strongly related to age—the older the age, the lower the rate. At younger ages, considerable numbers of people are looking for work even if they haven't found it yet, whereas at older ages, people are more likely to give up on employment and seek a retirement pension as soon as it is available if they experience difficulty finding a job, which may happen as a result of age discrimination.

By far the biggest gain in employment over the past half century has been the movement of baby boom women, especially married women, into the labor market (and then into retirement, as we discussed in Chapter 8). They literally burst their way into the workforce in the 1970s. In 1960, just before the baby boomers came of age, the labor force participation rate among married women aged 35–44 in the United States was 37 percent—well below the 83 percent for single women that year (U.S. Census Bureau 2012). By the mid-1990s, as the baby boomers had reached those ages, the participation rates for married women hit 75 percent, where they have stayed since.

Working, as we have mentioned before, cuts down on fertility under normal circumstances, and this is one of the ways in which working has an effect on the family and household structure. It is certainly no coincidence that the birth rate in the United States began to drop at about the same time that labor force participation rates for married women began to rise. Overall, the highest levels of fertility in the United States are found among poor women who do not work, whereas the lowest levels of fertility are among those women who do work and are well paid. This is one reason, of course, why child poverty is such a critical issue needing a solution—a disproportionate share of children are born to women with low incomes.

When women are able to combine having a family, even if only a small one, with a career, they are likely to choose both. This seems to be the combination that typically generates replacement-level fertility. However, in European countries such as Italy and Spain, where family values discourage that combination, women seem to choose career over family, contributing to the very low levels of fertility that are part of the "second demographic transition" that we discussed in Chapter 3. The pattern that has emerged in the richer countries is that a high proportion of women work before marriage, remain working after marriage, and adjust their fertility downward to accommodate their working. How far down they adjust may depend on how much familial and societal support they receive in making that accommodation. If child care is readily available and if husbands share domestic chores, we may well expect that fertility will be closer to replacement level, rather than well below it.

Women in the western world are able to operate in society independently of a husband or other male patriarch or protector, but they may not have the same ability to have an equal relationship at home with a husband. Nonetheless, an international comparison of data for 31 countries revealed that there was more within-marriage task-sharing in countries that have a longer history of maternal employment (Treas and Tai 2012). The data generally suggest that the higher the level of education a woman has, the more likely it is that her husband will be well-educated (and enlightened) and will share in child care and household chores (Grossbard and Stancenelli 2010).

We have already discussed the new household economics as an approach to explaining why fertility is kept low in developed societies and why households might encourage family members to migrate. Now, we can call on it again to explain why the rise in the status of women and increased female labor force participation might generate the household transformations we have been reviewing in this chapter. One idea is that "the rises in women's employment opportunities and earning power have reduced the benefits of marriage and made divorce and single life more attractive. Though marriage still offers women the benefits associated with sharing income and household costs with spouses, for some women these benefits do not outweigh other costs, whatever these may be" (McLanahan and Casper 1995:33). Yet another perspective is that the benefits of marriage for women have shifted from being largely economic (e.g., having a higher income household) to be more related to the investment in children (e.g., having more household resources to help propel children forward in life). "Marriage is the commitment mechanism that supports high levels of investment in children and is hence more valuable for parents adopting a high-investment strategy for their children" (Lundberg and Pollak 2013:1). Regardless of the reasons for deciding to marry or not, the key element is that women increasingly are in a position to make that choice for themselves.

Although mortality and fertility have been declining since the nineteenth century in the United States, and urbanization has been occurring throughout that time, it was during World War II that the particular combination of demographic and economic circumstances arose to provide the leading edge of a shift toward labor force equality of males and females. The demand for armaments and other goods of war in the early 1940s came at the same time that men were moving out of civilian jobs into the military, and there was an increasing demand for civilian labor of almost every type.

Earlier in American history, the demand for labor would have been met by foreign workers migrating into the country, but the Immigration Act passed in the 1920s (see Chapter 6) had set up national quotas that severely limited immigration. The only quotas large enough to have made a difference were those for immigrants from countries also involved in the war and thus not a potential source of labor. With neither males nor immigrants to meet the labor demand, women were called into the labor force. Indeed, not just women per se, but more significantly married women, and even more specifically married women with children. Single women had been consistently employable and employed since at least the beginning of the century, as each year 45–50 percent of them had been economically active, as we pointed out earlier. But in the early 1940s there were not enough young single women to meet labor needs, partly because the improved economy was also making it easier for young couples to get married and start a family. It was older women, including those past their childbearing years, who were particularly responsive to making up the deficit in the labor force during this historically crucial time (Oppenheimer 1967, 1994).

These were the women who broke new ground in female employment in America, with the biggest increase in labor force participation between 1940 and 1950 coming from women aged 45–54, and because more than 92 percent of those women were married, this obviously represented a break with the past. Who were these women? They were the mothers of the Depression, mothers who had sacrificed the larger families they wanted (and thus created the "Lucky Few" generation) to scrape by during one of America's worst economic crises. They were women who had smaller families than their mothers and thus were more easily able to participate in the labor force. However, the ideal family size remained more than three children, and the improved economy permitted the low fertility of the 1930s to give way to higher levels in the 1940s and 1950s. Women with small families from the Depression opened the door to employment for married women even though younger women were not yet ready to respond to those opportunities in large numbers. Indeed, after the end of World War II the labor force activity rates of women aged 25–34 actually declined for a short while as couples reunited after the war and started giving birth to the "boomers."

Things changed though, as you know, and since 1950 the number and proportion of American women in the labor force and earning independent incomes has increased substantially. In 1950, for example, there were 29 female, year-round, full-time workers for every 100 males in that category; by 2017, there were 74 females working full-time, year-round per 100 male workers. This increase in labor force activity was accomplished initially by younger women, especially those aged 25–34, whose children tended to be in school.

Getting a job is one thing, of course, but the kind of job you get—your occupation—depends heavily on education and is also influenced by factors such as gender and race/ethnicity.

Occupation

Occupation is without question one of the most defining aspects of a person's social identity in an industrialized society. It is a clue to education, income, and residence—

in general, a clue to lifestyle and an indicator of social status, pointing to a person's position in the social hierarchy. From a social point of view, occupation is so important that it is often the first (and occasionally the only) question a stranger may ask about you. It provides information about what kind of behavior can be expected from you, as well as how others will be expected to behave toward you. Although such a comment may offend you if you believe that "people are people," it is nonetheless true that there is no society in which all people are actually treated equally.

Since there are literally thousands of different occupations in every country, we need a way of fitting occupations into a few slots. Organizations like the U.S. Census Bureau and the International Labour Organization (ILO), a specialized agency within the United Nations, have devised classification schemes to divide occupations into several mutually exclusive categories. In Table 9.5, we have listed the occupational distribution of employed males and females 20 years of age and older in the United States as measured in the Current Population Survey in 2018. These categories form a rough status ranking, with the higher status occupations at the top of the table, and the lower status occupations on the bottom. You can see that women are more likely (45 percent) than men (38 percent) to be in the top two categories that include the management and professional occupations, with a clearly higher percentage of women in the professions. This may seem a little confusing, given the lower pay among women. The problem here is that women are more likely to be in the lower rungs of these positions—more likely to be a middle manager than the boss; more likely to be a nurse than a physician. Women are also more likely to be in service, sales and office occupations, which tend to be "white collar," but not necessarily high paying. Almost no one works in farming these days and

Table 9.5   U.S. Occupational Distributions Are Different for Males and Females

Employed Civilians 16 and Older	Percentage Distribution by Occupational Category—2018	
	Males	Females
TOTAL	100	100
Management, business, and financial occupations	18	16
Professional and related occupations	20	29
Service occupations	13	20
Sales and office occupations	15	28
Natural resources, construction, and maintenance occupations	17	1
Production, transportation, and material moving occupations	17	6

Source: Adapted by John R. Weeks from data in U.S. Bureau of Labor Statistics (2018), Table 9.

that is now subsumed under the category of natural resources, construction, and maintenance occupations. Almost all workers in this category are men. Similarly, men are much more likely than women to be in the other set of "blue-collar" occupations of production, transportation, and material moving.

As different as these occupational distributions look for men and women, they are considerably less different than they used to be. The index of dissimilarity (sometimes also known as the Gini coefficient) for the data in Table 9.5 is 30, but it was 43 in 1970. We would interpret that to mean that in 2018, you would had to have moved 30 percent of women into other occupational categories to achieve exactly the same distribution as for men, compared to having to move 43 percent of women back in 1970.

There is a global tendency for women not to be in the best jobs, and there are three important issues that the ILO sees as still needing considerable improvement in order to achieve gender equality in the workplace: (1) the "global glass ceiling" (women being less likely than men to make it to top management); (2) the gender pay gap (worldwide, women earn an average of about two-thirds what men earn); and (3) the "sticky floor" (women tend to get stuck in the lowest-paid jobs) (International Labour Organization 2013a).

People holding the higher status occupations are more likely to think of themselves as having a career as opposed to just a job, and they are apt to derive more intrinsic satisfaction from their work. They are also less likely to be working in what Arne Kalleberg (2018) has labeled as "precarious jobs." These are jobs in which there are no guarantees of continuous employment and for which the benefits may be scarce or non-existent. Unfortunately, they represent an increasing share of jobs in the richer countries of the world, as companies have sought ways to reduce costs in an increasingly globalized economy. Kalleberg (2018:5) argues that precarious work "has widespread consequences not only for the quantity and quality of jobs, but also for many other outcomes," including "delayed entry into marriage and having children." The kind of job you have, then, and the income you earn from it, will be your keys to economic and social independence.

Income

Even after the disastrous Great Recession of 2007–2008, the average chief executive officer (CEO) at the 500 biggest companies in the United States made $8 million in 2009, including salary, bonuses, and stock gains (DeCarlo 2010). This works out to about $30,000 per workday, so if we assume a normal workday, this average CEO had already made $7,000 by the time the bagels and cream cheese arrived for his (yes, "his") morning coffee break (only 3 percent of those CEOs were women). The CEO's average daily salary, by the way, was nearly equivalent to the entire annual income for a female year-round worker with a high school education, as you see by looking back at Table 9.4. There is a good deal of controversy about whether the average CEO is worth that kind of money, but there is no doubt that income is at least partially a consequence of the way in which we have parlayed a good education into a good job.

Occupation may be the primary clue that people have about our social standing, partly because it is considered by most people to be a proxy for our income level. People are too polite to ask you how much you make, but by knowing your occupation, they will have important clues about your income level. Little has changed since the late 1970s, when Richard Coleman and Lee Rainwater (1978:29) concluded that "money, far more than anything else, is what Americans associate with the idea of social class." It is not just having the money, rather it is how you spend it that signals to others where you stand in society. The principal indicators of having money, of course, include the kind of house you live in, the way your home is furnished, the car or cars you drive, the clothes you wear, the vacations and recreations (the "toys") you can afford, and even the charities you support.

Some of the best demographic predictors of high or low family income are things we have discussed in some detail already such as age, educational attainment, and marital status. Data for the United States for 2017 are shown in Figure 9.4, where you can see that incomes tend to rise from young adulthood into middle age, and then decline after that. At the same time, there is a huge gap between incomes for people with a bachelor's degree or higher (with family income peaking at age 51 at $125,500 per year) and those with only a high school diploma or less (peaking at age 54 at $54,877). If we add marital status into the mix, the gaps widen even more. A married person with a spouse present who had a college degree had a peak family income of $151,153 at age 52, compared to only $70,305 at that age for a college graduate who was not married and living with their spouse. Naturally, the more good earners there are in the family, the more money there is to go around.

A very poor situation to be in is to have no more than a high school diploma and not be married and living with your spouse. Those people actually had peak income at age 40 of only 40,400 and by age 52, when income for the better educated folks was peaking, the less well-educated people without a spouse were earning only $33,355, scarcely 20 percent of the family income of college graduate married couple families. At the same time, those with no more than a high school education but who were in a married-couple family had a peak income of $74,048, which was slightly higher than a college graduate who was not in a married-couple family ($70,981).

It is no mystery that there is an uneven distribution of income in virtually every human society, and rising inequality in richer countries has become a topic of considerable debate. One of the key pieces of data igniting controversy was the revelation that the 85 richest people in the world have as much wealth as the poorest half of the world's population of 7 billion people (Oxfam International 2014). This is a staggering statistic, but inequality is becoming increasingly pervasive in richer countries (Piketty 2014; Alvaredo et al. 2018).

Data from the 2018 Current Population Survey show that in the United States, the richest 20 percent of families earned 50 percent of the nation's total income (in fact, the top 5 percent brought in 22 percent of the nation's total income), while the poorest 20 percent earned only 3 percent . There has clearly been a deterioration of the income distribution that had prevailed in the late 1960s, when the top 20 percent commanded "only" 43 percent, while the bottom 20 percent shared a little more than 4 percent of the nation's income. In fact, the trend toward inequality is

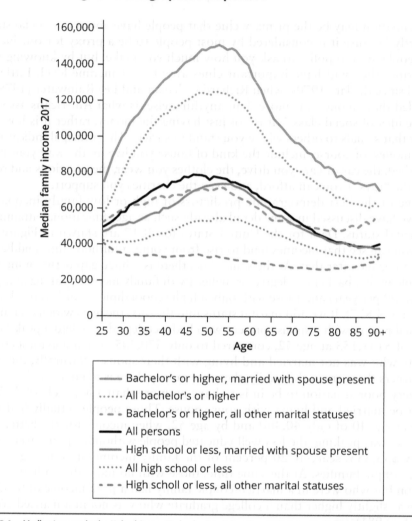

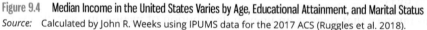

Figure 9.4   Median Income in the United States Varies by Age, Educational Attainment, and Marital Status
Source: Calculated by John R. Weeks using IPUMS data for the 2017 ACS (Ruggles et al. 2018).

perhaps even more stark than those numbers might suggest. Economist Emmanuel Saez calculates that this is not the first time we have had this kind of inequality—we last saw it in 1928, just before the Great Depression (Saez 2013).

The increase in inequality is argued to be at the root of the decline of the middle class in the United States, which is in turn almost certainly related to the rise in "precarious jobs" that we discussed earlier. A report by the Luxembourg Institute for Statistics in 2014 found that Canada's middle class had replaced the United States as the richest middle class in the world (Leonhardt and Qualy 2014). How did this happen? Three broad explanations have been offered for the increasing inequality in the United States: (1) public policy changes, such as tax "reforms" (largely tax breaks for the very wealthy) that benefit some groups more than others, coupled with a low minimum wage and diminished public support for education; (2) labor market changes (occurring throughout the world, not just in the United States), such as an increasing mismatch between the demands of jobs and the skills of the labor force, or a polarization of jobs into those that require high skills and those that require few skills, with little in between; and (3) changes in demographic structure, such as the increasing fraction of households headed by females. This latter point would not be an issue if females earned as much as men, but as you know from Table 9.4, this is not the case.

Family income rose steadily for American families during the 1950s and 1960s, leveled off a bit in the 1970s and early 1980s, and then rose, albeit unevenly, between the mid-1980s and the early 2000s, peaking just before the Great Recession and dropping after that. These patterns can be seen in Figure 9.5, which plots median household income, not the mean, thereby avoiding being affected by the very high top-end incomes. In 1947 (the first year for which such data are available from the Current Population Survey), a household headed by a white person in the United States had an income equivalent to $28,940 at constant 2017 prices; and it was

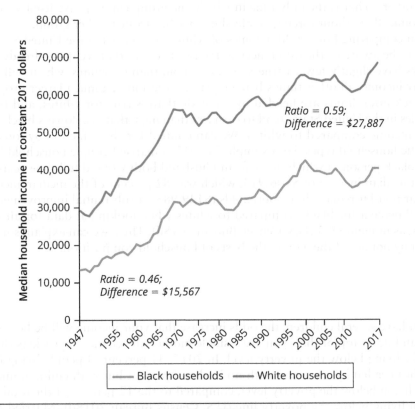

Figure 9.5   The Gap in Family Income of Whites and Blacks Has Widened over Time

Sources: Adapted by John R. Weeks from data in U.S. Bureau of the Census (1991), Table B-22; DeNavas-Walt Cleveland, and Webster (2003), Table 6; and Fontenot, Semega, and Kollar (2018), Table A1.

Note: Data are for households and are expressed in constant 2017 dollars.

2.4 times that—$68,145—in 2017 even in the aftermath of the Great Recession. Households headed by a black person have experienced a tripling of income since the end of World War II, from the equivalent of $13,373 in 1947 to $40,258 in 2017.

In relative terms, then, income for black households has grown slightly faster than that for white families. In 1947, black household income was less than half that of whites (a ratio of 0.46); that ratio peaked in the year 2000 at 0.65, but there has been some backsliding since then to a ratio of 0.59 in 2017. Despite the long-term rise in household income and a general narrowing of the income gap with whites in relative terms, black households were actually losing ground to whites in absolute terms. In 1947, the "dollar gap" between black and white households, as shown in Figure 9.4, had been $15,567, but by 2017 the gap in constant dollars had nearly doubled to $27,887.

Blacks have thus been in the peculiar position of having their incomes rise faster in percentage terms than whites, while in dollar terms (the actual money available to spend) they are falling further behind. This is one of the paradoxes that results from structural mobility—that situation in which an entire society is improving its situation economically, even though some groups may be gaining at a faster rate than others. That is the only time in which one group can improve itself socially or economically without forcing an absolute sacrifice from another group.

In comparing household incomes of whites and blacks in the United States, we need to be aware of the differences in family structure that we have already noted. Blacks have slightly fewer earners per household than do whites, which will reduce family income, all other things being equal. Furthermore, a much larger proportion of black households are headed by a female than is true for whites, and because females in the United States tend to earn less than men, that also lowers black household income compared to whites. We can control for these factors by looking at specific household types. For example, in 2017, a married-couple household headed by a black person in which the wife and husband both worked full-time year-round had a median income of $106,913, which was 82 percent of the median income of similar non-Hispanic white households ($129,983), a substantial improvement over the 59 percent for blacks compared to whites when looking at data for all households, as in Figure 9.5 (U.S. Census Bureau 2018d). Thus, we can explain some, but certainly not all, of the gap on the basis of household composition.

Poverty

If you have several children, the odds increase that your income will be below average, and if, on top of that, you are a single mother, the chance skyrockets that you will be living below the poverty level. In 2017, 41 percent of people living in U.S. families headed by a woman with no husband present but with children under 18 were living below the poverty level, compared to the 12 percent of the total population living below the poverty line (U.S. Census Bureau 2018d). Married-couple households have the lowest poverty rate at 5.7 percent, but even among married couples with children under age 18, the poverty rate of 8.4 percent is well below the national average 12 percent.

To imagine the struggle it is to manage successfully in the United States on so little money, it is necessary only to review the definition of the poverty level. The poverty index was devised initially in 1964 by Mollie Orshansky of the U.S. Social Security Administration. It was a measure of need based on the finding of a 1955 Department of Agriculture study showing that approximately one-third of a poor family's income was spent on food, and on a 1961 Department of Agriculture estimate of the cost of an "economy food plan"—a plan defined as a minimally nutritious diet for emergency or temporary use (Orshansky 1969). By calculating the cost of an economy food plan and multiplying it by 3, the poverty level was born. It has been revised along the way, but the idea has remained the same, and since 1964 it has been raised at the same rate as the consumer price index.

The poverty threshold for a single person under the age of 65 was $12,752 as of 2017 (Fontenot, Semega, and Kollar 2018). This was the equivalent of earning $6.13 an hour if you were a year-round, full-time worker, keeping in mind that the federal minimum wage in that year was $7.25. A single parent with two children under the age of 18 could be earning $19,749 per year and still be right at the poverty-level threshold. Between 1960 and 1973, the percentage of Americans living below the poverty level was cut in half, from 22 percent to 11 percent as a consequence of a variety of government programs aimed specifically at reducing poverty, and it remained that low until the Great Recession, after which it climbed to 15 percent, but it has since dropped back to 12 percent, as noted above.

Canada has adopted a strategy similar to that of the United States for measuring the lower end of the income scale. In 2017, they called it the "market basket measure," defined as the amount required to purchase a specific basket of goods and services in its community. It has since been redefined as the Official Poverty Line, and as of 2017, 9.5 percent of Canadians lived below that cut-off (Statistics Canada 2019).

On the basis of global comparisons, it might be argued that very few people in North America are poor in absolute terms—it is the relative deprivation that is socially and morally degrading. Organizations such as the ILO and the World Bank have adopted an international standard that defines poverty as an income of less than $1.90 per day—an astonishingly small amount of money on which to try to survive. If $1.90 seems like an odd number, it is only because the index started years ago at $1 per day and has since been adjusted upward for inflation. Using this definition, data from the World Bank produce the estimate that about 1 in 10 humans in the world lives in poverty, as shown in Table 9.6. Even in the United States the data suggest that 1 person in 100 lives at this level.

The good news is that this deep poverty rate used to be a lot higher, but the bad news is that the numbers are still striking for South Asia and sub-Saharan Africa, as you can see in Table 9.6. "We live not as we wish, but as we can" is how a southern Indian peasant once described life in that country (quoted by Hockings 1999:213). The precariousness of income in many parts of the world is illustrated by the additional World Bank data on the percent of the population living on less than $5.50 per day. These data are also shown in Table 9.6, where you can see that almost half of the world's population lives on less than that amount, as does a very high percentage of people in South Asia (e.g., 84 percent in India) and sub-Saharan Africa (e.g., 98 percent in the Democratic Republic of the Congo). To put that number in perspective, remember that

Table 9.6   A Relatively Small Percentage of People in Developing Countries Live on Less than $1.90 per Day, While a Large Percentage Live on Less than $5.50 per Day

Region	Selected Countries Within the Region	Poverty Rate (Percent Below)	
		$1.90/day	$5.50/day
East Asia and the Pacific		2	35
	China	1	27
	Indonesia	6	59
Europe and Central Asia		2	14
	Armenia	1	50
	Georgia	5	44
Latin America and Caribbean		4	26
	Mexico	3	35
	Haiti	25	79
Middle East and North Africa		4	42
	Egypt	1	62
	Yemen	19	82
South Asia		16	84
	India	21	87
	Pakistan	4	75
Sub-Saharan Africa		41	85
	Ghana	13	57
	Congo (Kinshasa)	77	98
Total		10	46

Source: Adapted by John R. Weeks from data in World Bank (World Bank 2019a); data are circa 2011–2017.

the poverty line in the United States in 2017 for a single person under the age of 65 was $12,752, which works out to be more than $35 per day—a fortune for a huge percentage of the world's population. At the same time, the data suggest that two 2 percent of Americans live on less than $5.50 per day, which amounts to only $2,000 per year.

Wealth

Poverty implies not only the lack of adequate income from any and all sources but also the lack of any other assets from which a person might draw sustenance. As people obtain and build assets, they create wealth. An asset is something that retains value or has the potential to increase in value over time. Every generation produces its share of self-made magnates such as Bill Gates of Microsoft, but his three children will inherit at least a part of that wealth, rather than have to produce it for themselves. Wealth and its attendant high income from assets are essentially ascribed characteristics for those born into families that own huge homes, large amounts of real estate, and tremendous interests in stocks and bonds or other business assets.

There are three basic ways to generate wealth: (1) inherit assets from your parents or other relatives (the easiest way), (2) save part of your income to purchase assets (the hardest way), and (3) borrow money to purchase assets (the riskiest way). For most people, a home is the most important asset they will acquire in a lifetime, but assets can also include personal property such as jewelry or other collectibles, stock in companies or mutual funds, savings accounts in banks, rental property, or ownership in a business venture. Typically, wealth is measured as net worth—the difference between the value of assets and the money owed on those assets. If your only asset is the house you just bought for $233,000 (the median sales price of a home in the United States in 2019), you are in the process of building wealth, but your net worth may be close to zero because you still probably owe as much on the mortgage as the house is worth.

Since most of us do not have fabulously wealthy parents, our ability to inherit enough from them (assuming that they have been able to accumulate at least some wealth) to build on to create our own wealth will, in fact, be determined importantly by two basic demographic characteristics: (1) how many siblings we have; and (2) how long our parents can expect to live. The fewer people with whom we have to share our parents' inheritance, the more there is for us to use ourselves, so those groups with the lowest fertility are likely to have a higher proportion of people who are able to accumulate wealth. The age of our parents, especially relative to our own age, will influence the likelihood that they will die and leave us something while we are still young enough to do something with it. In fact, as life expectancy continues to increase, the older generation has been hanging on to its money, as we discuss in the essay that accompanies this chapter.

The principal sources of data on the wealth of Americans are household surveys, such as the Survey of Income and Program Participation (SIPP) conducted every few years by the U.S. Census Bureau. At this writing, the most recent data are from 2014 (U.S. Census Bureau 2018c). These data show that net worth among Americans (including equity in homes) averages $81,850 per household (based on the median), but one in six households (16 percent) have zero or negative net worth.

Marriage is an important ingredient in accumulating wealth (as long as the couple stays married). This is consistent with the data in Figure 9.4 showing the differences in family income by married couple families compared with other family types. The data show that the highest level of net worth occurs among older (65 and older) married-couple households, whose net worth in 2014 of $331,200 was more than twice the net worth of unmarried male householders ($116,500) or unmarried female householders ($116,200) of that age (and notice that female net worth is nearly identical to male net worth—an improvement over previous years). Keep in mind that Figure 9.4 showed that income peaks in middle age and declines after that, so a key to accumulating wealth is to save and invest while you are in your peak earning years. Figure 9.6 also reminds you of the value of a college education.

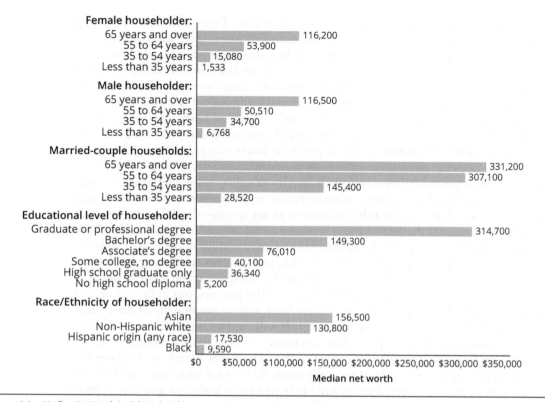

Figure 9.6   **Median Net Worth Is Highest for Older Married Couples in the United States**

Source: Adapted by John R. Weeks from data in U.S. Census Bureau (2018c), Table 1.

Among all householders, regardless of marital status, those with a graduate or professional degree had a net worth of $314,700, which was almost nine times the level of householders who had not gone beyond high school.

However, there can be little question that one of the more striking comparisons in Figure 9.6 is by race and ethnicity (including all marital statuses and all levels of educational attainment). The average household headed by a person whose self-reported race/ethnicity was Asian had the highest net worth at $156,500, followed by non-Hispanic white households at $130,800. However, the figures were only $17,530 for Hispanics and $9,590 for blacks. Some of this difference is due to differences in the age structure, especially among Hispanics who are relatively young, and some is due to differences in marital status and education; however, much of it is due to the greater difficulty that Hispanic and black household members have in generating enough income for long enough to be able to acquire higher levels of wealth. Note that Asians generally have high levels of education, high rates of marriage but low levels of fertility, almost no teenage pregnancies, and have the nation's lowest level of nonmarital births. These are important predictors of income and wealth, and what we don't know with certainty is the role that racial/ethnic discrimination plays in producing these differing life chance trajectories (Iceland 2019).

Race and Ethnicity

Not all countries encourage immigration, since it can create a range of difficult issues about how to fit new people into the existing society. The assimilation model of immigration, which we mentioned in Chapter 6, requires that a nation be like a melting pot where everyone eventually shares cultural values and norms, and where ultimately every person becomes pretty much like everyone else. This is sometimes referred to as the "North American Model" of race and ethnic relations, which is aimed at combating racial discrimination and ethnic inequality (Haug 2000). The multicultural model, on the other hand, assumes a salad bowl where everybody stays different but gets along just fine. European nations, with the notable exception of France, have tended to prefer this latter approach, and it has actually been adopted at least informally as the main U.S. model in the past few decades, encouraged by a positive governmental emphasis on diversity. The assimilation model assumes that distinctions of race and ethnicity will eventually be wiped out by intermarriage, whereas the multicultural model assumes not only that things won't work like that, but that people prefer to remain separate. The United States has historically fluctuated somewhere between those two extremes, but from the moment of the country's creation more than 200 years ago, the issue of race was on the table. It has been there ever since.

Recognizing that race and ethnicity are important issues in a society does not mean that they will be easy to measure (Glenn 2009). They are, in fact, not easy to measure because they are not easy to define, so measurement becomes more an art than a science. Indeed, the "science" part is scary because it can too easily lead us back to the eugenics movement at the beginning of the twentieth century in which people were trying to measure genetic differences among people for often nefarious reasons. Our cultural heritage, not our genetic heritage, distinguishes us, and that is very difficult to measure.

Race and ethnicity represent human differences that allow people to identify and be identified with a particular group. The characteristics may be physical in nature such as skin pigmentation, hair texture, shape of the eyes or nose (these would normally fall under the category of race), or they may be more behavioral, such as language, or identification with a particular ancestry and geographic place (these would normally fall under the category of ethnicity).

The history of racism in the world suggests that anything that distinguishes you can, and probably will, be used against you. Therefore, to be a member of a subordinate (not in political control) racial, ethnic, or religious group in any society is to be in jeopardy of impaired life chances. Blacks, Hispanics, Asians and Pacific Islanders, and American Indians and Alaska Natives in the United States are well aware of this, as are indigenous people in Mexico, Tamils in Sri Lanka, Muslims in Israel or India, Indians in Malaysia, and virtually any foreigner in Japan or China.

As you will recall from our discussion of census data in Chapter 2 (see, especially, Figure 2.2), in the United States, the Census Bureau asks two questions to allow people to report their race/ethnicity. The first of these is about "race" and the second is about your identity as "Hispanic." The Census Bureau has, over time, kept adding more detailed categories of "race" to which people can respond in

Show Me the Money!

Few would argue with the idea that people with the highest levels of income and wealth are apt to garner the highest levels of attention and respect in a society. Whether or not you think that society should operate in that way, it nonetheless tends to be true. In fact, *Forbes* magazine has tapped into this idea for many years, first by publishing a list of the 400 richest people in the United States, and more recently creating lists for the entire world and for other countries besides the United States. The three richest people in the world are Americans, and the general pattern among the richest 400 Americans is that they are college-educated older men.

The two youngest billionaires among the top 400 as of 2018 were the co-founders of Snapchat, Evan Spiegel (age 28) and Bobby Murphy (age 30), and the oldest, at age 95, were Alex Spanos (who made his money in real estate in California and who owns the Los Angeles Chargers football team), and Sumner Redstone (owner of a vast media empire). The youngest female billionaire was Lynsi Snyder, who at age 36 is the heiress of the In-N-Out Burger chain, while the oldest female billionaire was 87-year-old Doris Fisher, who co-founded The Gap clothing store chain with her now-deceased husband. Overall, 86 percent of the richest Americans are men, and their median age is 69, compared to a slightly younger median

age for women of 64. The accompanying table summarizes the age distribution of the *Forbes* 400 richest. Note, in particular, that 59 percent of the richest Americans are aged 65 and older, compared to only 15 percent of the total U.S. population of that age.

In the past, and still today in many less developed countries, the higher status of the elderly has been tied partly to the fact that as old age approached, they were situated in their own housing unit. Even if they lived with their children, it was likely that the children (typically a son with his wife and children) were actually living in the parental home, rather than the other way around (Kertzer 1995; United Nations Population Division 2005). The concept of filial piety, of respect for one's parents, has been a traditional value in most cultures, encouraging children to take care of their parents when the need arises, and this is facilitated by the children never leaving the parental home.

Of course, in high-mortality societies, the probability that parents would survive to old age (and the probability that their children would survive to help them) was low enough that relatively few people ever had to make good on that promise. For example, under a constant mortality regime of 40 years of life expectancy, a person aged 30 has less than one chance in four of having both parents still alive, and there is about one chance in

Age Distribution of the *Forbes* 400 Richest Americans Compared to the Total U.S. Population

	Forbes 400 Richest Americans						Total U.S. Population
	Male		**Female**		**Total**		
Age group	Number	Percent	Number	Percent	Number	Percent	Percent
Less than 20	0	0	0	0	0	0	26
20–44	22	6	1	2	23	6	33
45–64	113	33	30	55	143	36	26
65+	210	61	24	44	234	59	15
	345	100	55	100	400	100	100

Source: Adapted by John R. Weeks from data in Forbes (2018); data for the U.S. population are from the U.S. Census Bureau (2018a).

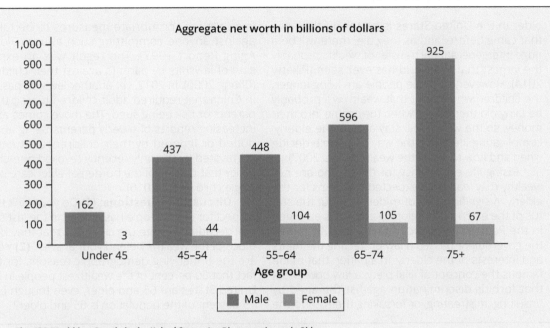

Aggregate net worth in billions of dollars

The 400 Wealthiest People in the United States Are Disproportionately Older
Source: Adapted by John R. Weeks from data in *Forbes* (2018).

two that one parent will still be alive. However, at a life expectancy of 70 years, nearly two out of every three adults aged 30 can expect to have both parents still alive, and nearly eight in 10 people aged 30 can expect to have at least one parent still alive. On the other hand, a high level of mortality increases the odds that a younger person will be able to inherit the family farm or business, or will be able to move into some other position in society being vacated by the relatively early deaths of other people.

The decline in mortality tends to throw a monkey wrench into these kinds of arrangements. Increasing survivability of people to old age increases the likelihood that a young or middle-aged adult will have surviving parents, and that these parents will be heading up the family household (Ruggles and Heggeness 2008). This pattern essentially clogs up familial and societal mobility because it means that family assets are not turned over as rapidly as would otherwise be the case. It also means, of course, that enough people are living long enough to accumulate a substantial portion of any society's resources.

The wealthy are disproportionately old, as you can see in the accompanying graph. Until very recently, it was the oldest members of this elite group who tended to have the greatest wealth. This changed just in the last few years as computer and internet technology generated new ways of creating wealth. For example, the richest man in America (and in the world) as of this writing is Jeff Bezos, even after his 2019 divorce settlement, and he was 54 in 2018 when this list was put together. Bill Gates, who only recently was overtaken by Bezos as the world's richest man, is 63, although his good friend Warren Buffett (the third-richest person in the world), is 88. Indeed, if we focus on the 10 wealthiest Americans in 2018, 5 of them are 65 or older. The cohort of people now aged 65 and

(continued)

older in the United States is better off than any that came before, and as they die, there will be a huge intergenerational transfer of wealth, probably the largest that the world has ever seen (Piketty 2014). However, because people are living longer, the children who inherit that wealth will probably be fairly old themselves when they come into their money, so the wealth will stay among the elderly, complicating life along the way as people decide when and how to share the wealth (Angel 2007).

Rising life expectancy for those who are not wealthy may lead to unexpected problems for the elderly. A significant bit of evidence about the status of the elderly in developing countries emerged in the People's Republic of China in 1997, when the government passed a law protecting the rights and interests of the elderly. In a nation that made famous the concept of filial piety, a law now exists that forbids discrimination against the aged by "insulting, mistreating, or forsaking them," and the

law calls for appropriate measures to be taken against anyone committing such abuse (Global Aging Report 1997). The result was an explosion of lawsuits by parents against their children (Chang 2000). In 2012, yet another law was passed in China that required adult children to visit their parents or risk being sued. The move comes after increasing reports of elderly parents being abandoned or ignored by their children, a situation aggravated by the only recently revoked one-child policy that puts all of the burden of elder care on a single child (Brant 2016).

Discussion Questions: (1) Do you think that respect for older people has eroded in the last several decades, despite the clear fact that they hold much of the wealth? Defend your answer. **(2)** What are the underlying demographic reasons for the fact that 60 percent of the wealthiest people in the United States are 65 and older, even though only 15 percent of the population is 65 and older?

the decennial census and the various other census surveys, including the American Community Survey and Current Population Survey. Of special note is that people are able to check more than one box, encouraging a recognition of diversity.

A person of "Hispanic, Latino, or Spanish" origin is defined as one who is "of Cuban, Mexican, Puerto Rican, South or Central American, or other Spanish culture or origin regardless of race." The relatively "indeterminate" concept of Hispanic (Idler 2007) is often confusing to those arriving in the United States from those origin countries because it is not used anywhere outside of the United States. Immigrants from Nicaragua, for example, will find themselves identified officially as Hispanic, while having a high probability of being thought of unofficially as Mexican. The majority of Hispanics in the United States are indeed from Mexico, and despite the discrimination that they have faced over time, they are less discriminated against than blacks. "Mexican Americans intermarry much more than do blacks, live in less segregated areas, and face less labor market discrimination. . . . In this sense, racial boundaries for Mexican Americans are clearly less rigid than for African Americans" (Telles and Ortiz 2008:264).

In the United States, blacks were the largest minority group for all of the nation's history—until recently. In 2005 the Hispanic or Latino population passed the black population in size, and Hispanics now account for 17 percent of the population, compared to 12 percent for blacks (see Table 9.7 below). However, it turns out that not being the numerically largest minority group in the country does not necessarily make life easier. Being of African origin in the United States is still associated with higher probabilities of earlier death, lower levels of education, lower

Table 9.7   Two Different Ways of Distributing the U.S. Population by Race/Ethnicity

	Hispanic Exclusive			Inclusive Identity	
	Number	**Share of Total Population**		**Number**	**Share of Total Population**
Non-Hispanic White alone	197,277,789	61.5%	All Whites	242,977,313	75.7%
Non-Hispanic Black or African American alone	39,445,495	12.3%	All Blacks	41,448,457	12.9%
Non-Hispanic American Indian and Alaska Native alone	2,098,763	0.7%	All American Indian and Alaska Native	2,639,609	0.8%
Non-Hispanic Asian, Native Hawaiian and Other Pacific Islander alone	17,505,062	5.5%	All Asian, Native Hawaiian and Other Pacific Islander	18,338,032	5.7%
Non-Hispanic some other race alone	715,432	0.2%	*not applicable*		
Non-Hispanic two or more races	7,451,295	2.3%	*not applicable*		
Hispanic or Latino (of any race)	56,510,571	17.6%	Hispanic or Latino (of any race)	56,510,571	17.6%
TOTAL POPULATION	**321,004,407**	**100.0%**	**TOTAL POPULATION**	**361,913,982**	**112.7%**

Source: Calculated by John R. Weeks using IPUMS data for the 2017 ACS (Ruggles et al. 2018).

levels of occupational status, lower incomes, and higher levels of marital disruption than for the non-Hispanic white population. Tufuku Zuberi (2001) has argued that the different life chances of whites and blacks in American society are due to racial stratification, which he defines as a socially constructed system that characterizes one or more groups as being distinctly different. Your membership in a group defined as different from the others then creates, in essence, a different social world for you than for those who are in other groups, and this affects your behavior and your life chances in society because there is no genuine societal expectation that you will be assimilated into the rest of the society.

In the 2017 American Community Survey (the most recent data available from the Census Bureau as of this writing), 97 percent of the population indicated that they belonged to only one racial category, keeping in mind that a separate question is asked if a person identifies as Hispanic or not, as we noted above. This single race response was the same percentage as the 2010 census, so these data are consistent over time. Those who chose "white" on the race question accounted for 73 percent of the population. This was, of course, a fairly substantial drop from 50 years prior to that, when 89 percent of the population was white—when "white" was not yet thought of as an ethnic category (Perry 2001). By the twenty-first century, the racial and ethnic changes have been so substantial that Anthony Perez and Charles Hirschman (2009) refer to the phenomenon of "emerging American identities," while William Frey (2018) labels it a "diversity explosion."

The "diversity explosion" has also created what we might call a "diversity confusion," because the data collected by the government can be organized in several different ways, each of which tells a somewhat different story (Prewitt 2018). The most common way to combine the race and ethnic Hispanic questions is to create a set of "Hispanic-Exclusive" categories. Everyone who says they are Hispanic are put into that category, regardless of race. Then those who say they are not Hispanic are divided up according to their response to the race question. The left side of Table 9.7 shows, for example, that in 2017, 61.5 percent of the population indicated that they were not Hispanic and that their only racial identification was "white." Similarly, 12.3 percent of the population indicated that they were not Hispanic and that their only racial identification was "black."

Is it appropriate to essentially force Hispanics into a single race/ethnic category of "Hispanic" while ignoring their separate race designation? As Dowell Myers and Morris Levy (2018:218) have argued: "At different moments the same person, such as an African American who is also Hispanic, might wish to be categorized with all African Americans or, alternatively, with all Hispanics. For some purposes, it clearly is desirable to count all people of a race rather than just the non-Hispanic remainder."

So is it also possible to add up the responses in a way that is more inclusive, rather than exclusive? The answer is yes, and the results are on the right side of Table 9.7 where you can see that if we employ an "inclusive identity" approach, then we find that 75.7 percent of all Americans considered themselves to be "white alone" or "white" in combination with one or more of the other racial categories. One of the major reasons for the higher percent white is that 66 percent of Hispanics consider their race to be white. Most Hispanics who do not consider themselves white choose the "other race" category. Indeed, Hispanics account for 95 percent of all people who say that their race is "other." This is clear evidence of the confusion between the census categories of race and ethnicity.

Overall, then, if we follow the Census Bureau's guidelines that Hispanic is an ethnicity, not a race, and if we accept the idea that many people of mixed race also include themselves as white, then we see that the Census Bureau estimated that in 2017, 76 percent of the U.S. population considered themselves to be white, compared to the non-Hispanic one-race only definition, by which 62 percent were white. Census Bureau population projections using the very restricted definition of white suggest that by 2045 whites would drop to slightly less than 50 percent of the population (Frey 2018). However, by the inclusive definition of whites, by 2060 (the end date for the current Census Bureau projections), whites are still 74 percent of the population (Myers and Levy 2018). To put it another way—the melting pot is working.

For better or worse, official statistics in the United States make extensive use of the racial and ethnic categories just discussed, but on an everyday basis people are also conscious of ethnicity in a broader context, as measured by the question about ancestry that has appeared in the last several U.S. censuses and is incorporated into the American Community Survey. Overall, the most-often-recorded ancestry in the 2010 American Community Survey was German (15 percent of the U.S. population—48 million people). Next most often listed was Irish (11 percent, or 35 million people), which is pretty remarkable when you consider that there are fewer than five million people living in Ireland, and not even all of them are Irish! English, American, and Italian round out the top five ancestries.

The United States does not have a corner on the racial and ethnic minority market, nor are demographic differences by race and ethnicity peculiar to the United States. As befits a multiracial, multiethnic, officially bilingual society, Canada also has several ways to measure diversity. What would be called "race" in the United States is labeled "visible minority" in Canada. The visible minority accounted for 19 percent of Canada's population in the 2011 census, up from 11 percent in 1996. The most populous group in 2011 was South Asians (largely from India), followed closely by Chinese and then African-origin blacks (albeit coming largely from the Caribbean). Ethnicity is essentially a geographic concept, based on a place with which you identify, similar to the concept of "ancestry" as measured by the U.S. Census. The single biggest ethnic group in Canada is—guess what—Canadian. However, the largest non-Canadian origin identified was the British Isles. Another identifier in Canada is whether or not you are a member of the aboriginal population, which accounts for just less than four percent of the country's total population and coincides with the U.S. ethnic identification of American Indian or Alaska Native. Language is the other major identifier in Canadian society, with English being listed most often as the language spoken at home (58 percent of the population), followed by French (18 percent, with the vast majority of French-speakers living in the province of Québec).

Language is a divisive-enough issue in Canada that in the 1990s it led the francophone (French-speaking) population in the eastern edge of the country (Québec) to attempt to secede from the anglophone (English-speaking) remainder of the country. Demographics played a role in defeating the referendum on separation held in 1995, however, because the traditionally Catholic francophone population now has very low levels of fertility—among the lowest anywhere in North America. French Canadians are not replacing themselves, and non-francophones (especially recent immigrants) generally did not support separation, leading Canadian demographers correctly to predict that separation would not be approved by the voters (Kaplan 1994, Samuel 1994). Still, the controversy over language in Canada, which continues to this day, underscores the power of society to turn any population characteristic into a sign of difference, from which prejudice and discrimination often follow.

Language is also an issue in Mexico, where the lowest stratum of society tends to be occupied by those who speak an indigenous language (linguistically related to Aztec and Mayan languages), rather than Spanish. According to the 2010 census, seven percent of Mexicans speak an indigenous language, but in Oaxaca it is 34 percent, followed by 30 percent in the Yucatán, and 27 percent in Chiapas. These are also the Mexican states where people are poorest and fertility is highest. Language minorities thus represent both the geographic and demographic extremes in North America, from francophone Québec in the northeast, with very low fertility, to Mayan-language Chiapas in the south, with very high fertility.

Religion

Virtually everyone is born into some kind of religious context, which is why religion is often thought of as an ascribed characteristic, closely affiliated with ethnicity. Yet people can willingly change their religious preference during their lifetime, so it is also akin to an achieved status. Despite the appearance of choice, however, most people do not alter religious affiliation, so it is a nearly permanent feature of their social world. People may become more or less religious within their particular group, but they are unlikely to change the major affiliation. Like race and ethnicity, religion sets people apart from one another and has historically been a common source of intergroup conflict throughout the world. Because it is an often-discussed sociodemographic characteristic, religion has regularly come under the demographer's microscope, with particular attention being paid to its potential influence on fertility, which is bound up with factors including gender equity and family and household structure.

America's history of religious pluralism, in which a wide variety of religious preferences have existed side by side, perhaps sensitized American demographers to the role of religion in influencing people's lives. A good deal of attention was focused over the years on the comparison between Protestants and Catholics. Until the late twentieth century, Catholics routinely had more children than did Protestants in the United States, and internationally it has been true that predominantly Protestant areas (such as the United States and northern Europe) experienced low fertility sooner than did predominantly Catholic areas (such as southern and eastern Europe). However, analyses of data from the U.S. National Survey of Family Growth revealed that in the mid-1960s, as the baby boom was ending, it was particularly noticeable that Catholics were increasing their use of modern contraception, even as the papal encyclical was trying to push them in the opposite direction (Westoff and Westoff 1971). This turned into a genuine revolution in birth control practices of U.S. Roman Catholics (Westoff and Rindfuss 1973), which shortly thereafter led to the end of 'Catholic' fertility in the United States (Westoff and Jones 1979).

In the middle of the twentieth century, no one could have imagined that Catholic fertility would ever drop to the level of non-Catholics in the United States, much less dip below those levels. Indeed, fertility is now lowest in Europe precisely in the most Catholic countries of Spain and Italy, as we have already discussed, and it is even below replacement level in predominantly Catholic Mexico City (INEGI 2013). Does this mean that religion is less important demographically than it used to be? Obviously, the relationship between religion and demographic behavior is not a simple one, but there are two major themes that run through the literature: (1) religion plays its most important role in the middle stage of the demographic transition; and (2) religiosity (how intensely you practice your religion) may be more important than religious belief.

With respect to the demographic impact of differences in religion, we turn to a classic study by Joseph Chamie (1981) of differentials in Lebanese fertility, in which he concluded that a major effect of religion may be to retard the adoption of more modern, lower-fertility attitudes during the transitional phase of the demographic revolution. Adherents to religious beliefs that have been traditionally associated with high fertility will be slower to give ground than will people whose religious beliefs are more flexible with respect to fertility. In the United States, for example, Jews have generally had lower fertility levels than the rest of the population. Trends in Jewish fertility have followed the American pattern (a decline in the Depression, a rise with the baby boom, a drop with the baby bust), but at a consistently lower level. Why? "Widespread secularization processes, upward social mobility, a value system emphasizing individual achievement, and awareness of minority status have all been indicated as factors that are both typical of American Jews and conducive to low fertility" (DellaPergola 1980:261). Indeed, it is not just Jews in America whose fertility has been low for a long time. Jewish communities in central and western Europe were characterized by low fertility as early as the second half of the nineteenth century, largely because contraception is readily accepted in the Jewish normative system (at least among non-Orthodox Jews) (DellaPergola 1980). And, as we noted in Chapter 5, fertility in the United States declined earliest in those areas dominated by more secularized religious groups (Leasure 1982). People who are more traditional in their religious beliefs tend to be less educated and have less income, and are thus more prone to higher fertility. Although Jews in Europe and the United States tend to be relatively secular and have low fertility, the ultra-orthodox (i.e., highly religious) Jewish population (the Israeli *haredim*) has one of the highest levels of fertility of any group in the world, at about 7 births per woman (DellaPergola, May, and Lynch 2014). This young and rapidly growing population within Israel is bound to shape the country's demographic and political future.

In the twenty-first century, Islam has emerged as the dominant religion in a large percentage of countries characterized by above-average levels of fertility. There are now an estimated 1.8 billion Muslims in the world, representing one in four people globally, and nations that are growing in population at rates above the world average are disproportionately those in which a majority of the population is Muslim (Hackett and McClenton 2017). The high fertility leads to the projection that by 2035 there will be more Muslim babies born each year than Christian babies (Pew Pesearch Center 2017). Nonetheless, there is considerable variability in fertility among the Muslim-majority countries, ranging from Iran, at below replacement level (2.0 births per woman), to Niger, at more than seven children per woman.

Will Muslims follow the pattern of Catholics and quickly lower fertility levels to replacement or below? If secularization is a key to low fertility, then it is not religion *per se* that matters, but how strongly one holds any given set of religious beliefs, which you will recall is known as *religiosity*. Regardless of the religion to which one adheres, research has consistently shown that higher levels of religiosity are associated with higher fertility, either directly by intention or indirectly through the non-use of methods to prevent pregnancy.

In terms of doctrine, Islam may not be any more pronatalist (expressing an attitude that favors high fertility) than other religions (McQuillan 2004), but the way in which Islam structures societies may promote a type of religiosity that lowers status for women relative to men in ways that will indirectly promote pronatalism. At the same time, the extent to which communities are structured in this way may well be regionally variable, reflecting underlying cultural attributes shared by all populations in a region, whether Muslim or not. Thus, Muslims in South Asia and sub-Saharan Africa tend to have higher fertility than Muslims in North Africa or Europe, at least partly because fertility levels are higher for everyone in South Asia and sub-Saharan Africa (Weeks and Westoff 2010).

Charles Westoff and Tomas Frejka (2007) have shown that even in Europe fertility is positively associated with religiosity; yet among the most religious, Muslim fertility is still higher, suggesting an interaction between religion and religiosity. Their analysis is consistent with other research showing that in general the strength of one's religious beliefs is predictive of fertility because the greater the level of religiosity, the more traditional are family values and the more oppressed are women. It is these factors that are especially influential in determining family size (Inglehart and Norris 2003; Norris and Inglehart 2004). This may be particularly important among Muslims because "Islam is not merely a religion of worship, but is also a pervasive social system" (Rashad and Eltigani 2005:186). Similarly, Calvin Goldscheider (2006), in discussing high fertility among Muslims in Israel, argues that "values that emphasize the subordinate role of women within households and gender hierarchies appear to be critical in sustaining high fertility levels" (p. 46). Youssef Courbage and Emmanuel Todd (2011) argue, however, that the critical change in Muslim societies, as elsewhere, will be an increase in educational attainment. As educational levels rise for both males and females, they foresee a convergence of low fertility levels among Muslim and non-Muslim countries.

Summary and Conclusion

The past few decades have witnessed a fundamental shift in household structure in the United States and other richer nations, and these changes are beginning to evolve all over the world as changes in family structure and composition take place in the context of the health and mortality, fertility, migration, urban, and age transitions. Married-couple households with children have become less common, being replaced by a combination of married couples without children, cohabiting couples with and without children, lone parents with children, people living alone, people living with nonfamily members, and just about any other combination you can think of. This greater diversity in household structure is a direct result of the trends in marriage and divorce, which are themselves influenced by trends in mortality and fertility and urban living. Marriage has been increasingly delayed (although most people do eventually marry), but people are leaving the parental nest to live independently by themselves, with friends, or in a cohabiting relationship prior to marriage, a pattern greatly facilitated by access to effective methods of contraception. Once married, there is a greater tendency than in the past to dissolve the marriage. Some of this is due to the fact that spouses are far less likely to die than in earlier times, and some is due to the fact that divorce laws have accommodated the changing relationships between men and women. Accompanying these trends has been a rise in the proportion of children born outside of marriage, contributing to the increased percentage of children who are living with only one parent.

Less directly, but no less importantly, the transformation of family and household structure has been a result of changing population characteristics, especially the improvement in women's life chances. Women have become less dependent on men as they have begun to live longer and spend more of their lives without children in an urban environment, where there are alternatives to childbearing and family life. Throughout the world, women are closing the education gap between themselves and men, entering the paid labor force, and moving up the occupational ladder.

These new opportunities to be more fully engaged in all aspects of social, economic, and political life have been simultaneously the cause and consequence of declining fertility and improved life expectancy. They have enabled women to delay marriage while becoming educated and establishing a career, choose marriage or not (most do), choose children or not (most choose at least one), and, if married, to choose to stay married (only about half do). Therein lie the principal explanations for the increased diversity of families and households.

Not all people have equal access to societal resources such as advanced education, a well-paying job, and other assets with which to build wealth. In the United States, blacks, Hispanics, and American Indians and Alaska Natives are less likely than others to be highly educated. This without doubt contributes to their relative social and economic disadvantage in American society, although racial prejudice and discrimination continue to play a role in lowering levels of educational attainment which, in turn, lowers lifetime incomes, keeping people from accumulating wealth. On the other hand, Asians tend to have higher levels of education than other groups, which helps account for their higher levels of income and wealth (as well as higher life expectancies). In most countries of the world, we find one or more groups who, for reasons of discrimination beyond their control, are disadvantaged compared to the dominant group.

The impact of the trends toward greater family and household diversity falls disproportionately on children. Growing up in a household that is not a two-parent family means lower household income, increased odds of health and social problems in childhood and young adulthood, and it generally increases the risk that your their life chances may be limited. However, another group also bears the brunt of dissolved marriages. Today's divorced or otherwise not married women could become the biggest group of elderly poor in the future. This is a trend we will have to watch over time, but it will be easier to track than in previous generations because most households with older people in industrialized nations are now in urban areas, where they may be more visible than the elderly poor in rural areas of less developed nations. The elderly poor stand in stark contrast to the richest people in the world who also tend to be older, rather than younger. The richest among us also tend to be well-educated, and rising education is a key trend shaping our demographic future.

Another trend we are watching with great trepidation is the overall degradation of our environment. As we try to improve the lives of a larger and increasingly diverse population in the world, our efforts have created serious questions about the sustainability of life as we have come to know it over the past two centuries, and we take a look at these issues in the next chapter.

Main Points

1. Married-couple households with children are declining as a fraction of all households, being replaced by a variety of other family and nonfamily household types.

2. The direct causes of these changes in household composition are a delay in marriage, an increase in cohabitation and nonmarital births, a rise in the propensity to divorce, and, to a lesser extent, widowhood in the older population.

3. The underlying indirect causes of these changes are the several other transitions associated with the overall demographic transition, including declining mortality, declining fertility, migration to urban areas, and the underlying age structure changes brought about over time by demographic change.

4. The transformation of families and households has accompanied improved life chances for women, including higher levels of education, labor force participation, occupation, and income.

5. Average educational attainment has increased substantially over time in most countries, and, especially in industrialized nations, women appear now to have closed the gender gap in education.

6. In the United States during World War II, a combination of demand for labor and too few traditional labor force entrants created an opening for married women to move into jobs previously denied them, and since 1940, the rates of labor force participation have risen for women, especially married women.

7. Over time in the United States, poverty has declined while at the same time Americans of almost all statuses have become wealthier in real absolute terms, but there have been only minor changes in the relative status of most groups.

8. Race may be just "a pigment of your imagination," but blacks, in particular, tend to be disadvantaged compared to whites in American society.

9. The diversity of households seems to have plateaued in richer nations but is on the rise in most of the rest of the world.

10. Family demographers can prove that the average person in Miami is born Cuban and dies Jewish.

Questions for Review

1. What is the difference between a kinship unit and a consumption unit, and why is the difference important to an understanding of the changes in family structure and composition?

2. Discuss the ways in which each of the other components of the demographic transition lead up to and help explain the changes taking place in families and households.

3. How do the differences in, or changes in, life chances for an individual affect the proximate determinants of his or her own family and household living arrangement? Pick one demographic characteristic such as education and discuss how different levels of that characteristic could affect the living arrangement choices that a person might make.

4. Why do you think that race and ethnicity affect life chances in so many different societies?

5. What is/are the most important reason(s) why we should care about the increasing diversity in family and household structure?

CHAPTER 10
Population, the Environment, and Global Sustainability

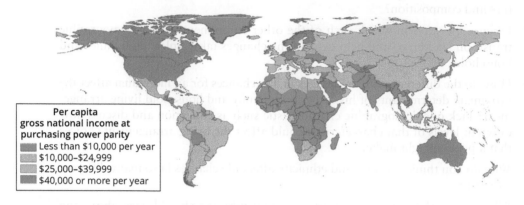

Per capita
gross national income at
purchasing power parity
- Less than $10,000 per year
- $10,000–$24,999
- $25,000–$39,999
- $40,000 or more per year

Figure 10.1   The Highest Per Capita Incomes Are Found in the Global North
Source: Adapted by John R. Weeks from data in World Bank (2019b).

The Use and Abuse of the Earth's Resources
Economic Growth and Development
Measuring GNI and Purchasing Power Parity

How Is Population Related to Economic
    Development?
Is Population Growth a Stimulus to Economic
    Development?
Does Demographic Overhead Explain the
    Relationship?
Are Demographic Dividends the Key to Economic
    Development?

Can Billions More Be Fed, Given Our
    Environmental Issues?
The History of Economic Development and Food
We Are at the Limit of Land to Be Used for
    Growing Food
Moving to a More Plant-Based Diet
Our History of Getting More Food from the Land

The Demand for Food Is Growing Faster Than
    the Population

The Environmental Constraints to Growing
    More Food
Water Supply Issues
Polluting the Ground
Air Pollution and Climate Change

Human Dimensions of Environmental Change
Assessing the Damage Attributable to
    Population Growth
Environmental Disasters Lead to Death and
    Dispersion

Sustainable Development—Possibility or
    Oxymoron?

Policies Aimed at Slowing Population Growth

Summary and Conclusion

Main Points

Questions for Review

ESSAY: *How Big Is Your Ecological Footprint?*

Two whole centuries have passed since Thomas Robert Malthus was stewing about population growth outstripping the food supply and sounding the clarion call for action. Was he Aesop's little boy who cried wolf? After all, global food production has actually outpaced population growth over the past 200 years. That sounds like Malthus was wrong. Right?

Those of us fortunate enough to rely on clean water from the tap and nutritious food from the grocery store or local takeout have so far had the privilege of dealing with the prospect of famine and drought pretty much on a theoretical level. Somewhere in the back of our minds we know intellectually that not all people on the planet can find a seat on the gravy train—we've seen images on television and even puddle up a little bit at the images, but history has taught us that the wonderful world of chemicals and modified crops will somehow prevail.

There are those who cling tenaciously to the theory that population growth stimulates economic development and point to the ever-increasing food yield as their star witness. These people are sometimes known as boomsters. The logical extension of their optimistic perspective is that somehow we will find the magical formula whereby everyone will be better off in the future and we can all live happily ever after. That is the promise of the obviously popular concept of sustainable development. It is elementary, my dear Watsons: We can grow it as we need it without destroying the ecosystem in the process.

However, as we peer a little more intently through the looking glass, the image that comes into focus is somewhat less rosy, even for people with the good fortune of living in wealthier nations. The clues increasingly point to the grim reality that we will all be paying a very heavy price for coaxing ever-higher yields of food and other resources from our increasingly overburdened planet. As anyone with even a passing interest in current events must have noticed, our efforts so far have led to polluting the land, changing our global climate and using up our finite supply of fresh water. The plot has taken a dastardly turn. Could it be that Malthus and the doomsters were right all along? Although the formula for ultimate disaster was more complicated than Malthus knew, critical resources such as land and water are, indeed, finite. At some point we will almost certainly exhaust the earth's capacity to produce.

One of the most influential of the neo-Malthusian doomsters is biologist Paul Ehrlich who, as we discussed in Chapter 3, has argued for decades that continued population growth will lead to certain economic and environmental collapse in a worldwide tragedy of the commons. For Ehrlich, the policy choices have always been clear: Population limitation must always be part of any sustainability strategy or everybody loses. Since his seminal work, *The Population Bomb,* was published in 1968, some believe his predictions have influenced governments and nongovernmental organizations (NGOs) to alter policies that have so far averted (or at least postponed) the collapse he foresaw.

But, not so fast, say the boomsters. This camp, most famously influenced by economist Julian Simon, claim that resources are economically indefinite. This is a cornucopian theory, a belief that humans will continuously innovate to deal with population growth and develop new resources. Simon argued for decades that population growth stimulates development rather than slowing it down. His book, *The Ultimate Resource,* published in 1981, sought to rebut Ehrlich's position and posits that development strategies should not deliberately slow down population growth because such growth is both a cause and a symptom of economic development. This boomster view recognizes that population cannot grow indefinitely, but the argument is that people will lower their fertility when they see an advantage from doing so. This feat entails lifting the masses out of poverty through free trade and globalization. These are the ingredients necessary to create sustainable development, a concept adopted by nearly all influential international agencies such as the United Nations and the World Bank. It must be noted that limiting population growth is a very politically sensitive issue that many influential agencies prefer not to address directly because it inevitably bumps up against the touchy issue of women's reproductive health.

Boomsters and doomsters have both been around a long time. Based on what you know now, are you leaning boomster or doomster, or maybe something in between? To help you decide for sure, read on as we review some key concepts.

The Use and Abuse of the Earth's Resources

Economic development represents a process by which a country may create growth in average income—a higher standard of living—usually defined as per capita (per person) income. A closely related idea is that economic development can be seen to be occurring when the output per worker is increasing. Since more output should logically lead to higher incomes in a fair society, you can appreciate that they are really two sides of the same coin. An important aspect of development more broadly defined, however, is that it is concerned with improving the overall welfare of human beings. It includes more than just increased productivity; it includes the resulting rise in the ability of people to consume (either buy or have available to them) the things they need to improve their level of living and, presumably, their enjoyment of life. Included in the list of improvements might be higher income, stable employment, more education, better health, consumption of more and healthier food, better housing, and increased public services such as water, sewerage, power, transportation, entertainment, and police and fire protection. Naturally, these improvements in human welfare, in turn, help increase economic productivity because the relationship is synergistic.

The starting point of economic development is an investment of capital, which we usually think of as money, but it more generally represents a stock of goods used for the production of other things rather than for immediate enjoyment. Think of it as anything we invest today to yield income tomorrow. In Chapter 9 we discussed this in terms of creating wealth at the personal level. Here, however, we are talking not just about individuals, but about the community or society more generally. Investments can be made in infrastructure (roads and bridges, communication networks, etc.) that make the economy more productive, as well as in things that make individuals more productive—more education, better health care, and, in general, the accumulation and application of knowledge. For an economy to grow, the level of capital investment of all kinds must grow.

Where the rubber meets the road demographically, though, is that the higher the rate of population growth, the higher the rate of investment must be. This is what Harvey Leibenstein (1957) called the "population hurdle." If a population is growing so fast that it overreaches the rate of investment, then it will be stuck in a vicious Malthusian cycle of poverty. Many of the countries at the lower end of the per capita income level are in this situation, as shown in the map (Figure 10.1) at the beginning of this chapter.

Crucial to our understanding of economic development and rising incomes is the fact that an increase in well-being typically requires that we use more of the earth's resources. How efficiently we are able to use these resources influences how widely they can be spread out among the entire (and still growing) population. At the same time, the use of every resource leads to waste products, and our efficiency in reducing waste and dealing with it effectively influences the extent to which we can minimize damage to the environment and thus sustain a larger population at a desired level of living. Exactly what level of living that should be is a matter of debate, as we discuss later in the chapter.

Economic Growth and Development

Economic growth refers to an increase in the total amount of productivity or income in a nation (or whatever your geographic unit of analysis might be) without regard to the total number of people, whereas economic development relates that amount of income to the number of people. The most commonly used index to measure a nation's income is the gross national income, or GNI (the term now preferred by the World Bank), replacing the previously used concept of *gross national product, or GNP*. The World Bank somewhat obscurely defines GNI as "the sum of value added by all resident producers plus any product taxes (less subsidies) not included in the valuation of output plus net receipts of primary income (compensation of employees and property income) from abroad" (World Bank 2019e).

Basically, if you add up the value of all of the paid work that goes on in a country, and then add in the money received from other countries, you have the measure of GNI. If you exclude the money from abroad and just include the income generated within a country's own geographic boundaries, you have gross domestic product (GDP). However, in today's world, the income from foreign companies and remittances sent back home from international migrants can be a substantial part of a nation's income, so it is important to include that. Figure 10.1 shows you the distribution of countries of the world according to their per person level of GNI.

Measuring GNI and Purchasing Power Parity

Though GNI is the most widely used measure of economic well-being in the world, it is important to keep in mind the things that GNI does not measure: (1) it does not take into account the depletion and degradation of natural resources (which is obviously a key issue when we start thinking about sustainability), so it may overstate how well the economy is doing; (2) it does not make any deduction for depreciation of manufactured assets such as infrastructure (i.e., future maintenance costs that will be required to keep the economy at its current level), again with the potential to overstate the economy's performance; (3) it does not measure the value of unpaid domestic labor such as that generated especially by women in developing nations (which, if assigned a value for its productivity, would increase the amount of income generated in that country); and (4) it does not necessarily account for regional or national differences in purchasing power (which means the numbers might not be comparable from one place to the next).

This latter limitation is one in which the World Bank has been particularly interested, at least partly because it is the easiest to deal with. Although GNI figures are usually expressed in terms of U.S. dollars, a dollar may go further in Ghana than it will in England, even when exchange rates have been taken into account. The United Nations and the World Bank have sponsored a number of household expenditure surveys in developing countries to try to estimate actual differences in the standard of living in order to produce more meaningful income comparisons. The wealthier nations have also been encouraged to conduct such surveys, along the lines of the Consumer Expenditure Survey of the U.S. Bureau of Labor Statistics.

The product of these efforts is a measure called purchasing power parity (PPP), defined as "a price which measures the number of units of country B's currency that are needed in country B to purchase the same quantity of an individual good or service as one unit of country A's currency will purchase in A" (World Bank 2019e). One way of expressing this concept is through the use of what *The Economist* calls its "Big Mac Index." McDonald's sells its hamburgers in nearly 120 countries, and in each country the sandwich must conform to essentially the same standards of ingredients and preparation. If the Big Mac costs an average of $5.58 in the United States (as it did in 2019), then it should cost the same in real terms anywhere else in the world. So, if you go to China and discover that you're paying only $3.04 at market exchange rates, that tells you roughly that the yuan was undervalued by 45 percent at that time (*The Economist* 2019).

By expressing GNI in terms of PPP (rather than official exchange rates), the result is the gross national income in purchasing power parity (GNI PPP). These are the numbers used to create Figure 10.1, and in Figure 10.2 they are summarized for the world's 20 largest economies as of 2018. In that year, the GNI in the United States was $20.7 trillion, which was less than China's $25.3 trillion GNI. The economies of those two countries are so large that together they account for 34 percent of the world's entire income. However, since China's population is so much larger than that of the United States, per person GNI in the United States is $55,000 per year, compared to only $15,000 in China. The top five economies (which adds in India, Japan, and Germany) represent almost exactly 50 percent of the entire economic product of the world and 43 percent of the world's population. The 20 countries shown in Figure 10.2 account for 75 percent of the world's economic output, but only 61 percent of the world's total population.

What are the sources of income that go into these measures? Much of it comes from the transformation of natural resources into things that are more useful to us—converting a tree into a house and furniture or paper; converting the "fruit" of cotton plants into shirts and dresses; converting minerals found in rocks into the steel body of an automobile; transforming a hidden pool of underground oil into

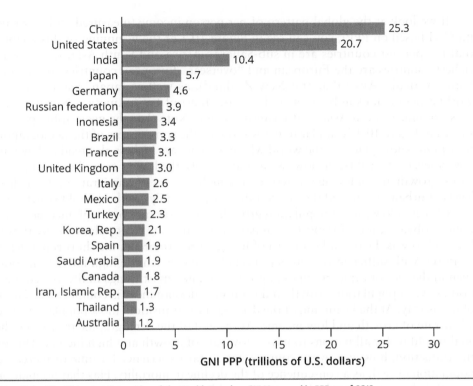

Figure 10.2   The 20 Largest Economies of the World, Based on GNI Measured in PPP, as of 2018
Source: Adapted by John R. Weeks using data from the World Bank (2019e).

fuel used by machines. These products must then be packaged, delivered, and sold. People or, increasingly, robots have to coordinate all of that and make sure that the infrastructure exists to do everything that needs to be done. So, in essence, we can divide the resources that go into producing income into two broad categories— natural resources (that which is given to us on the planet), and human resources (how clever and successful we are in making something of those natural resources). Together, this combination of resources can be thought of as the wealth of a nation.

How Is Population Related to Economic Development?

There is a nearly indisputable, albeit somewhat complex, statistical association between economic development and population growth; when one changes, the other also tends to change. As you no doubt already know, though, two things may be related to each other without one causing the other. Furthermore, the patterns of cause and effect can conceivably change over time. Does population growth promote economic development? Are population growth and economic development only coincidentally associated with each other? Or is population growth a hindrance to economic development? The problem is that the data presently available lend themselves to a variety of interpretations.

If we look at the global pattern of per person income (measured with per capita GNI based on PPP), you can see in Figure 10.1 at the beginning of this chapter that the poorest countries are in sub-Saharan Africa and South Asia, whereas the richest countries are the European and "overseas" European countries (the United States, Canada, Australia, and New Zealand), as well as Japan. The rest of the world generally falls in between and includes most of Latin America, North Africa, Western and Eastern Asia, and Eastern Europe. Note that the geographic pattern shown in Figure 10.1 is similar to maps showing the components of the demographic transition. Those places in the world where incomes are highest also tend to have the lowest levels of fertility, the lowest mortality levels, the lowest overall rates of population growth, the oldest age structures, the highest rates of immigration, the highest levels of urbanization, and the greatest diversity in family and household structure.

Clearly, a low rate of population growth is no assurance of a high income—that point is obvious, since for most of human history the rate of population growth was low and so was the overall standard of living. Furthermore, in the short run at least, countries with sufficient resources (especially oil) can achieve high levels of income even in the face of rapid population growth. So, like most things in life, the connection between population growth and economic development is complicated. Think of it this way: At the beginning of the demographic transition, most populations had a low rate of growth and low income. At the end of the demographic transition, the goal would be for all nations to have a low rate of growth and high income. During the transition, however, every country has so far experienced a time of increased population growth as a consequence of the decline in mortality. Has that population growth helped them (as the boomsters would suggest), or been a hindrance (as the doomsters would argue), or is it something more complicated than either of those two positions? Let's find out.

Is Population Growth a Stimulus to Economic Development?

An early proponent of the idea that population growth could be the trigger of economic development was the Danish economist Ester Boserup. In a set of extremely influential writings (see, especially, Boserup 1965, 1981), she advanced the idea that, in the long run, a growing population is more likely than either a non growing or a declining population to lead to economic development. The history of Europe shows that the Industrial Revolution and the increase in agricultural production were accompanied almost universally by population growth. Boserup's argument is based on the thesis that population growth is the motivating force that brings about the clearing of uncultivated land, the draining of swamps, and the development of new crops, fertilizers, and irrigation techniques, all of which are linked to revolutions in agriculture. The kernel of the argument has been well stated by British agricultural economist Colin Clark (1967: Preface):

> [Population growth] is the only force powerful enough to make such communities change their methods, and in the long run transforms them into much more advanced and productive societies. The world has immense physical resources for agriculture and

mineral production still unused. In industrial communities, the beneficial economic effects of large and expanding markets are abundantly clear. The principal problems created by population growth are not those of poverty, but of exceptionally rapid increase of wealth in certain favoured regions of growing population, their attraction of further population by migration, and the unmanageable spread of their cities.

The thesis that population growth is beneficial to economic development looks to Europe and the United States for evidence, where development was taking place in the context of population increase, whether caused by it or not. To be sure, some historians regard preindustrial declines in death rates in Europe, associated partly with the disappearance of the plague and the introduction of the potato, as the spark that set off the Industrial Revolution. The reasoning goes that the lowered death rates created a rise in the rate of population growth, which then created a demand for more resources.

The only problem with this line of reasoning is that it makes a big leap from population growth stimulated by an increase in agricultural productivity to the idea that population growth stimulated industrialization. In Chapter 3 we suggested that both phenomena were almost certainly the twin products of the Enlightenment, a point of view that embraced science and the innovations that can emerge from a less traditional way of viewing the world. On its own—outside of the context of a cultural change such as the Enlightenment—population growth may just as easily promote warfare as it will industrialization (Pinker 2012).

Although history may show that population growth was associated with development in the now highly industrialized nations (whether causally or not), statistics also reveal very important differences between the European/American experience and that of modern developing nations. Today's developing countries are not, in general, retracing the steps of the already developed nations. In particular, they are building from a base of much lower levels of living than those that prevailed in either Europe or the United States in the early phases of economic development. Furthermore, although the rate of economic growth in many low-income countries has recently been higher than at comparable periods in the history of developed nations, population growth is also significantly higher. These countries have experienced higher rates of population growth than European or American countries did, with the possible exception of America during the colonial period. In fact, over the past half century, the rates of population growth in the low-income world almost certainly have been unparalleled in human history.

Furthermore, today's developing nations do not seem to require any kind of internal stimulation to be innovative. They can see the fruits of economic development in the world around them, and quite naturally want to share in as many of those goodies as possible—a situation often referred to as "the revolution of rising expectations." Everyone now knows what economic development has created, and by studying the history of the highly industrialized nations, others can see at least how it used to be achievable.

It seems unlikely that a spark such as population growth is necessary any longer to stimulate economic development, if it ever was. Nonetheless, in the 1980s, Julian Simon popularized his still widely cited thesis that a growing human population is the "ultimate resource" in the search for economic improvement. Eschewing the Malthusian idea that resources are finite, Simon suggested that resources are limited only by our ability to invent them and that, in essence, such inventiveness increases in proportion to the number of brains trying to solve problems. This idea surfaced as recently as 2019, when Senator Mike Lee (R-Utah) suggested that the solution to climate change was to have more babies! (Itkowitz 2019). That's obviously nonsense. More and more people are unlikely to solve the energy use and climate change problems facing us.

From Simon's vantage point, innovation goes hand in hand with population growth, although he was quick to point out that moderate, rather than fast (or very slow), population growth is most conducive to an improvement in human welfare. Simon made another crucial assumption: To be beneficial, population growth must occur in an environment in which people are free to be expressive and creative. To him, that meant a free market or capitalist system.

There is, however, no direct evidence of a causal relationship between population growth and innovation. As Nathan Keyfitz pointed out, ". . . the England that produced Shakespeare and shortly after that Newton held in all 5 million people, and probably not more than one million of these could read or write. . . . The thought that with more people there will be more talent for politics, for administration, for enterprise, for technological advance, is best dismissed. . . . For the most part, innovation comes from those who are comfortably located and have plenty of resources at their disposal" (quoted in United Nations Population Fund 1987:16). Perhaps in response to this criticism, Simon later moved toward the position that population growth is far less important an issue in economic development than is the marketplace itself. He suggested that "...the key factor in a country's economic development is its economic and political system. . . . Misplaced attention to population growth has resulted in disastrously unsound economic advice being given to developing nations" (Simon 1992:xiii).

Promoting a free market as a way of stimulating the economy is still a major theme in international affairs. The demographic link is that the resulting economic development is expected then to lead automatically to a decline in the birth rate. Thus, the policy prescription is to take care of the economy and population will take care of itself.

Does Demographic Overhead Explain the Relationship?

Regardless of the reason for an economy starting to grow, that growth will not be translated into development unless the population is growing slower than the economy. An analogy can be made to business. A storekeeper will make a profit only if expenses (overhead) add up to less than gross sales. For an economy, the addition of people involves expenses (demographic overhead) in terms of feeding, clothing, sheltering, and providing education and other goods and services for those people, and if demographic overhead equals or exceeds national income, there will be no improvement (profit) in the overall standard of living. If overhead exceeds income, then a business (or a country) can avert disaster for a while by borrowing money, but eventually that money has to be repaid and if the loan is used simply to pay expenses, rather than being invested in human capital, it is unlikely that there will be money available to pay the loan when it comes due. So, the loan is extended or refinanced, and disaster is averted for just a little while longer.

Are Demographic Dividends the Key to Economic Development?

Another complication in the calculation is that the demographic overhead varies according to where a society happens to be in terms of its age transition. As we discussed in Chapter 8, the age transition can provide a demographic dividend for countries by creating a period of time when an increasingly larger fraction of the population is in the economically productive ages. Since this is a function largely of declining fertility, in the context of declining mortality, it is also usually accompanied by a delay in marriage and childbearing among women and, as we discussed in Chapter 9, this can lead to increased levels of education and labor force participation for women. The movement of women into the paid labor force may then have the effect of noticeably increasing the overall level of productivity, which contributes to economic development. This is the path to higher incomes taken by the successful east Asian societies of Japan, China, Taiwan, and South Korea.

Overall, then, the most important part of the discussion about population growth and the improvements in societal well-being is that the rate of total population growth is less important than is the rate of growth of different age groups (Headey and Hodge 2009). As we discussed in Chapter 8 in comparing the economic trajectories of China and India, China has benefited economically from rapid growth in the young to middle adult ages at the same time that it was experiencing declining rates at the younger ages and only slow increases at the older ages. Indeed, the nominally Marxist (but essentially capitalistic) government of China has found that there are three ingredients to economic development: (1) a rapid decline in fertility and thus in the rate of population growth; (2) implementing capitalism as the economic model; and (3) improving human capital, especially in terms of education.

We have also discussed the problem that all societies have in maintaining economic growth in the face of an aging population. As countries move through the health and mortality transition, and then the fertility transition, the age structure inevitably becomes older and, as Ronald Lee and Andrew Mason (2010) have pointed out, an older age structure may also be conducive to lower levels of saving, since in retirement people may be taking money out rather than putting it in. More importantly, as people leave the labor force at the older ages without being replaced by equal or greater numbers of younger people, economic productivity is bound to suffer, potentially lowering the overall standard of living. This implies that the end of the age transition (if there is such a thing—after all, fertility could rise again) may be associated with lower levels of economic productivity than the middle stages of the transition, at least to the extent that economic productivity is dependent on the number of people of working age in relation to the older more dependent population. Will robot workers be the substitutes for those working age people? Clearly we see that they already are taking over more and more jobs, and only time will tell where this will go.

If a country does not recognize that the demographic dividend is transitory rather than permanent, and does not implement long-term economic policies promoting sustainable productivity, the demographic change will not produce the hoped-for economic results. It will seem as though there was no relationship between population and economic development when, in reality, the demographic change generated an opportunity that was squandered.

No matter where a country currently stands in terms of the economic well-being of its population, the natural resources required to achieve a higher level of living continue to remind us of the underlying Malthusian dilemma: Are there enough resources in the world to sustain a larger population even if the standard of living is not increasing, much less for more people at a higher level? We have to look again at the same basic issue that bedeviled Malthus more than two hundred years ago. Can we feed the world?

Can Billions More Be Fed, Given Our Environmental Issues?

It is a fact of life that every transformation of natural resources has a cost associated with it. There will be waste products associated with it (pollution of the air, water, and land), along with the costs of restoring the resource itself, or of discovering replacements for that particular resource when it is gone. It should be intuitively obvious that more people consuming resources and leaving behind the detritus of the industrial world are detrimental to the long-term health of the planet. There has to be a balance between resources and people—that balance represents the earth's carrying capacity, which refers to the number of people that can be supported in an area given the available physical resources and the way people use them. For most of human history people used resources *extensively,* since hunting and gathering rely on nature's bounty without much human intervention. But a rise in our standard of living means using resources *intensively*, beginning slowly with the Agricultural Revolution 10,000 years ago and ramping up quickly with the industrial and post-industrial revolutions of the past two centuries.

So, we know the issue of just having enough food to sustain a large and growing population is a huge problem for the world, and we cannot simply assume that there will always be enough food to go around. The Food and Agriculture Organization (FAO) of the United Nations estimates that more than 800 million people in the world are undernourished (Food and Agriculture Organization 2019a)—nearly the number of all people alive when Malthus first wrote his *Essay on Population* in 1798. During the next minute, as you read this page, six children under the age of five will die of diseases related to malnutrition, although their places will be more than taken by the 266 babies who will be born during that same minute.

The good news is that the current number of undernourished humans (821 million) is less than it was in 1990, when it was one billion (Roser and Ritchie 2019b), but that is tempered by the apparent rise in undernourishment since 2015 (Food and Agriculture Organization 2019b). But the question remains: Can we increase the food supply enough to feed the two or three billion additional people projected to be joining us on the planet over the next few decades while also improving everyone's diet and health in the process? Almost certainly not, unless we go back to more plant-based diets. Do we have enough fresh water to support all those people and the food we are growing for them? Probably not, unless we can use renewable energy to convert salt water to fresh water, and keep our current supply of fresh water as clean as possible. Will global climate change undermine all of our efforts to feed more people? Yes, unless we change our ways. How did we get to this point, and what can we learn from the past that might help us in the future?

The History of Economic Development and Food

Roughly 10,000 years ago, humans began seriously to domesticate plants and animals, thereby making it possible to grow food and settle down in permanent villages. The domestication of plants, of course, hinged on the use of tools to work the ground near the settlement site, and the invention of those tools and their application to farming can be traced to many different areas of the world, as we pointed out in Chapter 1. Some of the earliest known sites are in the Dead Sea region of the Middle East, where the Agricultural Revolution apparently took place around 8000 BCE. From the eastern end of the Mediterranean, agricultural innovations spread slowly westward through Europe (being picked up in the British Isles around 3000 BCE) and east through Asia. Plants and animals were also domesticated in the western hemisphere several thousand years ago, resulting in an increase in the amount of food that could be produced per person.

The classic Malthusian view, of course, is that cultivating land caused population increase by lowering mortality and possibly raising fertility. This perspective suggests that the Agricultural Revolution "created an economy which, by . . . giving men a more reliable supply of food, permitted them to multiply to a hitherto unknown degree" (Sanchez-Albornoz 1974:24). By contrast, the Boserupian view is that independent increases in population size among hunter-gatherers, perhaps through a long-run excess of births over deaths, led to a need for more innovative ways of obtaining food, and so, of necessity, the revolution in agriculture gradually occurred. Seen from this perspective, the Agricultural Revolution was the result of a "resource crisis," in which population growth, slow though it may have been 10,000 years ago, generated more people than could be fed just by hunting and gathering. The crisis led to a revolution in human control over the environment—humans began to produce food deliberately, rather than just take what nature provided. In turn, this had the cumulative effect of sustaining slow but fairly steady population growth in most areas of the world for several thousand years preceding the Industrial Revolution.

Even in the modern world we can appreciate that there is a feedback loop, rather than a straight-line relationship, between the food supply and population growth. Increasing the food supply can lower the death rate and lead to population growth, but continued population growth then depends upon growing ever more food. Furthermore, even when the population stabilizes at a particular size, we have to continue growing enough food to keep the death rate from going back up. Needless to say, the huge increase in population over just the past 200 years has been associated with an equally gigantic rise in food production. That has consumed a lot of the earth's resources.

Industrialization and economic development in general require a massive increase in energy use. If everyone is consuming more, it is because production per person has increased, and that comes about by applying nonhuman energy to tasks previously done less efficiently by people, or not done at all because people could not do them. Wood served as the major energy source for most of human history, but in Europe a few hundred years ago, population growth and the beginnings of industrialization led inexorably to deforestation, producing an "energy crisis" (Harrison 1993). That crisis forced a new way of thinking about energy sources—a new way of controlling the environment that helped to spawn the Industrial Revolution.

Keep in mind that the Agricultural and Industrial Revolutions are inextricably linked. The Industrial Revolution of the nineteenth century was associated with important changes in agriculture that significantly improved output. Throughout most of human history, including the time during which Malthus was developing his view of the world, increases in the food supply depended largely on extensification of agriculture—putting more land under production. However, over time we have essentially run out of new land that can be farmed without great difficulty and considerable environmental harm. Thus, the modern rise in agricultural output has come about through something not foreseen by Malthus—the intensification of agriculture—getting more out of the land than we used to. In Europe and North America, the factors helping to increase agricultural productivity in a relatively short time included the mechanization of cultivating and harvesting processes, increased use of irrigation, fertilizers and pesticides, and the reorganization of land holdings so that farming could be more efficient.

The Industrial Revolution generated a host of mechanical devices, especially mechanical reapers, to greatly speed up harvesting. Drawn first by horses or oxen, reapers were pulled later by an even more efficient energy converter—the tractor. Like most early engines of industrialization, tractors were driven by steam, but something had to be burned to generate that steam. Their thirst for fuel was quenched by wood as long as it lasted, but the use of coal became necessary as a result of deforestation. The idea behind the steam engine, by the way, has been around for a long time, just waiting for the right moment to be adapted to something dramatically useful. In the ancient world, "Greek mechanics invented amusing steam-operated automata but never developed the steam engine; the crankshaft and connecting rod were not invented until the Middle Ages, and without a crankshaft it is impossible to transform longitudinal into circular motion" (Veyne 1987:137). Overall, the mechanization of agriculture vastly increased the number of acres that one person or a few people could farm, and also increased the amount of land that could be devoted to more than one crop per growing season, since land could be cultivated and harvested so much more easily.

Many agricultural innovations have also been made possible by reorganizing agricultural land and developing better policies for land use. Collecting farms into large units and using meadows and pastures for cultivation rather than extensive grazing have increased production, particularly in the United States and Europe, since large farms introduce economies of scale that permit investment in expensive tractors, harvesters, fertilizers, irrigation systems, and the like. In the United States, this process has a long history and is still continuing. For example, between 1950 and 2017, the number of small farms (less than 180 acres) in the United States decreased from 4.1 million to 1.4 million, a 66 percent decline (U.S. Department of Agriculture 2019). In the 1990s, the total number of farms in the United States dropped below 2 million for the first time since 1850, after reaching a peak of 6.8 million in 1935, although it has since risen back up to slightly more than 2 million as of 2017 (the latest data currently available). This does not mean that the number of acres under cultivation has declined much (it has changed very little), but rather that there is a trend toward large commercial farms and away from small family farms.

Although it may be intuitively obvious, it bears repeating that industrial expansion cannot occur unless agricultural production increases proportionately. As we discussed in Chapter 7, industrialization is typically associated with people migrating out of rural and into urban areas, naturally resulting in a shift of workers out of agriculture and into industry. Therefore, those rural workers left behind must be able to produce more—enough for themselves and also for the nonagricultural sector of the population. The flip side of that scenario is that as both the population and demand for food grow, the need to mechanize agriculture to increase production leads to a declining demand for agricultural workers as they are replaced by machines. Thus, you can see that the Industrial Revolution would have been impossible if agricultural production had not increased—and vice versa.

We Are at the Limit of Land to Be Used for Growing Food

Water covers about 71 percent of the earth's surface, leaving the remaining 29 percent for us to scratch out our respective livings. Only 12 percent of the world's land surface is readily suitable for crop production, and an additional 26 percent is devoted to permanent pasture. Forests and woodlands cover about 32 percent of the land surface, and the remaining 31 percent is too hot or too cold for any of those things, or is used for other purposes (such as cities and highways). Most of the land that could be fairly readily cultivated is already cultivated; the rest is covered by ice, or is too dry, too wet, too hot, too cold, or too steep, or has soil unsuitable for growing crops. To be sure, climate change could make some cold areas warm enough to be used for farming, but this would probably be offset by areas becoming too hot and dry to allow the continuation of farming.

In reaching the limits of readily cultivable land, we have been encroaching on land that supports plant and animal habitats that we really cannot do without, because we are dependent on biological diversity to a much greater extent than most people appreciate (Miller and Spoolman 2012; United Nations Environment Programme 2019). We threaten our environment as we search for more land on which to grow food and then modify that land in order to increase its productivity.

At the same time, it turns out that the total acreage of the very best farmland is actually in decline. In some parts of the world this is a result of soil erosion or desertification, whereas in many other places it is a consequence of urban sprawl.

Historically, most major cities have been located near abundant agricultural regions that could regularly provide fresh food to the city populations. Only recently have transportation and refrigeration and other forms of storage lessened (but not eliminated) that need. But the early days of those cities represented a time when the urban population was still a small fraction of the total. As cities have grown in size, nearby agricultural land has been increasingly graded and paved over to make room for higher-profit residential or business uses. So, at the same time that an increasing proportion of the population was moving to cities, some of the good nearby farmland was being converted to other uses, forcing farmers to clear other less desirable land in order to grow the food demanded by the city dwellers.

A potential alternative source of "land" is the sea—aquaculture. Farming the sea includes both fishing and harvesting kelp and algae for human consumption. The expense of growing kelp and other plants is so great that it does not yet appear to be an economically viable—or perhaps sufficiently taste-tempting—alternative to crops cultivated on land. On the other hand, farming fish (including shellfish) has been steadily increasing as a source of fish for food. It appears that we have reached the level of the ocean's sustainable fish catch, so any increase in fish production will of necessity be through aquaculture. Overall, it seems very doubtful that either extending agricultural land or farming the ocean will produce the amount of food needed by the world in the next century, given current world population projections. The output per acre of land under production must continue to increase if we are to feed billions more.

Moving to a More Plant-Based Diet

One of the single most important issues surrounding the productivity of farmland is the question of what crops are being grown and for whom? It may surprise you to learn that 77 percent of the earth's agricultural land is currently used for meat production (United Nations Environment Programme 2019). This includes land used for pasturing animals before they are slaughtered, and land used to grow food for them before they are killed. It is assuredly true that most people could eat less meat and still be well nourished, and there is increasing pressure in that direction for many reasons. For one, it takes several pounds of grain to produce just one pound of red meat, and there are other, more efficient ways to get protein (such as soybeans, peanuts, peas, and beans). Cutting back on animal protein could then free up the production of grain for human consumption.

So, who are the big meat eaters in the world? A report by the Paris-based Organisation for Economic Co-operation and Development (OECD 2018) shows that on a per capita basis, people in Argentina eat more beef and veal than anyone else, followed by Uruguay and Brazil, with the United States coming in fourth place. The Chinese consume the greatest amount of pork on a per person basis, followed by the residents of the European Union (collectively), South Korea, Vietnam, and then the United States. Poultry is consumed by people in Israel at a higher rate than anywhere else, following by the United States and Saudi Arabia. You can see, then, that the United States, in particular, does not top any of the lists, but it is high on all of them—unlike any other country. The Chinese are not the biggest meat-eaters in the world on a per-person basis, but the country has so many people that they actually are the biggest meat consumers in the world, and the overall consumption has been rising quickly along with the country's rising incomes.

The consumption of meat is not just an issue of how the land is used. Methane gas from the manure of animals is an important contributor to climate change. At the same time, farmers in places like Brazil have deforested swaths of jungle to create farmland to grow soy to be fed to pigs in China (Spring 2018). Keep in mind that deforestation is also a major contributor to climate change, as we discuss later in the chapter.

A relatively small, but growing, fraction of Americans and Europeans consider themselves to be vegetarian, but an increasing number appear to be "flexitarian"—people who want to reduce their consumption of meat without giving it up altogether (*The Economist* 2018; Ritchie 2019). In line with this trend, several major hamburger chains in the United States have now added meatless burgers to their menus, being provided these products by an increasing number of producers of "meatless meat," who now find it profitable. Before you say that it seems unlikely that a lot of people will eat less meat, remember that no one would have guessed 50 years ago that Catholics would today have among the lowest levels of fertility in North America and Europe, or that millions would actually stop smoking. Humans really can change their behavior, and that's a good thing.

Our History of Getting More Food from the Land

We have been feeding a growing population for many decades now, based on our ability to get more food from the same amount of land. There are several different ways to increase output from the land, and methods typically must be combined if substantial success is to be realized. Those methods include plant breeding, increased irrigation, fertilizers, and the careful use of pesticides. In combination, they add up to the Green Revolution. The Green Revolution is a term coined by the U.S. Agency for International Development (USAID) back in the 1960s, but it began quietly in the 1940s in Mexico at the Rockefeller Foundation's International Maize and Wheat Improvement Center. The goal was to provide a means to increase grain production and under the direction of Norman Borlaug (who received a Nobel Peace Prize for his work), new high-yield varieties (HYV) of wheat were developed. Known as *dwarf types,* they have shorter stems that produce more stalks than do most traditional varieties.

In the mid-1960s, these varieties of wheat were introduced into a number of countries, notably India and Pakistan, with spectacular early success—a result that had been anticipated after what the researchers had seen in Mexico (Chandler 1971). In 1954, the best wheat yields in Mexico had been about three metric tons per hectare, but the introduction of the HYV wheat (now used in almost all of Mexico's wheat land) raised yields to six or even eight tons per hectare if crops were carefully managed. A major difference was that more traditional varieties were too tall and tended to lodge (fall over) prior to harvest, thus raising the loss per acre, whereas the dwarf varieties (being shorter) prevented lodging. This is critical, because lodging can be devastating; it destroys some ears of grain and damages others. Furthermore, and very importantly, resistance to lodging makes it easier to apply the heavy fertilization and irrigation that are necessary for high yields.

The Green Revolution was not restricted to high-yield wheat and maize. In 1962, the Ford Foundation began a research program of rice breeding at the International Rice Research Institute in the Philippines. In a few short years, a high-yield variety of dwarf rice had been developed that, like HYV wheat, dramatically raised per-acre yields. Rice production increased in India and Pakistan, as well as in the Philippines, Indonesia, Vietnam, and several other less developed countries. China and India have also embraced the Green Revolution as a means for ensuring the food security of their people. Food security, by the way, is a United Nations term meaning that people have physical and economic access to the basic food they need in order to work and function normally; that is, the food is there, and they can afford to buy it.

There is, however, a huge set of costs attached to the Green Revolution— success requires more than simply planting a new type of seed. These plants require fertilizers, pesticides, and irrigation in rather large amounts, a problem compounded by the fact that fertilizer and pesticides are normally petroleum-based and the irrigation systems require fuel for pumping. These are expensive items and usually demand that large amounts of adjacent land be devoted to the same crops and the same methods of farming, which in turn often means using tractors and other farm machinery in place of less-efficient human labor. This is the true meaning of the revolution, and it is more than just a revolution in farming practices. Land ownership and management tend to be revolutionized in the process. This is because the Green Revolution is based on Western (especially American and Canadian) methods of farming, in which the emphasis is on using expensive supplies and equipment and on the high-risk, high-profit principle of economies of scale—plant one crop in high volume and do it well.

Reorganizing society in this way is not an easy thing to do and it takes time, assuming that people who own the land are willing to do it at all. The lure of large sums of money is often quite convincing and so we find that in several parts of the world, especially sub-Saharan Africa, farmers are being tempted by foreign companies to give over the rights to large tracts of land. The production from that land is then not aimed at the local population but rather at the global market. This has been called the "land grab" by which small farmers are essentially dispossessed of (albeit compensated for) their land in order for outsiders to come in and make the land agriculturally more efficient (McMichael 2012). This is obviously a politically sensitive issue, and there is considerable backlash against it. At the same time, it is not clear where the investment would otherwise come from to improve agricultural productivity in these regions, so the farms in these areas may remain in a state of relatively low output.

The plants involved in the Green Revolution, then, have principally been wheat, maize, and rice, but considerable research has also gone into the development of HYV soybeans, peanuts, and many other high-protein plants. Considerable attention has also been devoted to the spread of nutritious plants native to specific regions. There is certainly no better example of this than quinoa. The FAO designated 2013 as the International Year of Quinoa, noting: "Like the potato, quinoa was one of the main foods of the Andean peoples before the Incas. Traditionally, quinoa grains are roasted and then made into flour, with which different types of breads are baked. It can also be cooked, added to soups, used as a cereal, made into pasta and even fermented to make beer or chicha, the traditional drink of the Andes" (Food and Agriculture Organization 2013).

Another candidate for continued development is the winged bean (or goa bean), sometimes known as "a supermarket on a stalk" because the plant combines the desirable nutritional characteristics of the green bean, garden pea, spinach, mushroom, soybean, bean sprout, and potato—all in one plant that is almost entirely edible, save the stalk. It is becoming a staple in poorer regions of Africa and South Asia because it grows quickly in tropical areas, is disease resistant and high in protein.

At least as important as the nutritional aspect of plant breeding is the development of disease and pest resistance. The rapid change in pest populations requires constant surveillance and alteration of seed strains. Insects are very much our competitors for the world food supply and are a problem both before and after crops are harvested. Efforts to control pest damage have focused on designing seed varieties that are resistant to pests or that are hardy enough to tolerate pesticides and herbicides, so that these chemicals can be used on plants without destroying the plant itself. Thus far, there seems to have been considerable success in designing genetically engineered (GE) pest-resistant maize, cotton, and soybeans (Romeis et al. 2019).

However, in the United States and Europe, there has been a consumer backlash against these kinds of genetically modified seeds (GMOs—aka GE seeds), so food manufacturers have become cautious about using them and instead have chosen to charge premium prices for organic foods that have not had chemicals applied to them and have not been grown with GE seeds but which, as a consequence, will have lower average yields per acre. Organic foods, then, are becoming the equivalent of luxury goods in the food department. Keep in mind, though, that organic farming won't feed the entire world's population. No has pointed this out more succinctly than the Green Revolution's "founder," Norman Borlaug (2002:A16):

> I've spent the past 20 years trying to bring the Green Revolution to Africa—where the farmers use traditional seeds and the organic farming systems that some call "sustainable." But low-yield farming is only sustainable for people with high death rates, and thanks to better medical care, more babies are surviving. . . . Africa desperately needs the simple, effective high-yield farming systems that have made the First World's food supply safe and secure.

The Demand for Food Is Growing Faster Than the Population

The Green Revolution and the other changes in agricultural productivity have worked the miracle of not only providing food for an ever-growing population but of providing enough so that, despite continued malnutrition in some areas, the average human is consuming more food than ever before in history. Improved diets are one of the elements of an increase in life expectancy in developing countries, but this has gotten us into a vicious cycle from which it will not be easy to disentangle ourselves. Up to a point, at least, more food per person contributes to longer lives, which in turn increases the demand for food.

And, there is yet another twist to the story. The economist Robert Fogel received a Nobel Prize for his body of work that included research showing that improved nutrition brings with it not only healthier people, but also an increase in the size of the average human and in the number of daily calories used per person (Fogel and Helmchen 2002; Fogel 2004). Table 10.1 shows the change in daily caloric intake in the world in the years between 1961 (when FAO first began compiling such data) and 2016 (the most recent data as of this writing). You can see that there was a 29 percent increase in food intake per person in the world as a whole. So, the food capacity of the world was obviously outpacing population growth during this time period, because the average person was consuming nearly a third more food in 2016 than in 1961. Now, to be sure, 10 percent of the population is undernourished, as we mentioned previously, but a lot of people are eating more than they used to. Some of this caloric increase is excessive, as you almost certainly know, and contributes to the evidence we cited in Chapter 4 regarding the nutrition transition as people become potentially less healthy with a modern diet of more processed food, more meat, and fewer fresh fruits and vegetables.

You can see in Table 10.1 that there is considerable regional variability in the overall intake of food per day, and in the change over time. Europe and the Americas

Table 10.1   Differences in Per Person Daily Caloric Intake Over Time

	Calories per Day per Person		
	1961	2016*	Percent Increase
World	2,255	2,904	29
Regions:			
Europe	3,052	3,365	10
The Americas	2,226	3,265	47
Asia	1,803	2,824	57
Africa	2,061	2,593	26
Most Populous Countries:			
China	1,439	3,108	116
India	2,010	2,459	22
United States	2,880	3,682	28
Indonesia	1,824	2,777	52
Brazil	2,209	3,263	48
Nigeria	1,947	2,700	39
Pakistan	1,884	2,440	30

*Data for individual countries refer to 2013.

Source: Adapted by John R. Weeks from data in Food and Agriculture Organization (2019b), and Roser and Ritchie (2019a).

(which includes North America and Latin America) are the best-fed places on earth, while Africa has become the region with the lowest calorie intake as a result of the huge jump in consumption in Asia between 1961 and 2016, pushing the food intake above levels in Africa. The good news was that the African diet was also improving in terms of caloric intake, as you can see. The increase in Asia was driven especially by China, which vaulted from 1,439 calories per person per day in 1961 (just after the government-imposed famine in that country) to 3,108 (a 116 percent increase) in just over a half century. As the world's most populous country, that has had an obvious impact on the increasing demand for food.

More food, especially when young, means bigger people. The increase in body mass, at least up to a point, is a good thing for economic productivity—bigger, healthier people work better than smaller, sicklier people. However, the fact that the demand for food is increasing faster than the population is growing exacerbates the obvious question of whether or not it will be possible to grow enough food for a population that is increasing both in number and in body mass.

The Environmental Constraints to Growing More Food

It is also very troubling to realize that some of the techniques that have seemed to offer the greatest hope for increasing the food supply and improving standards of living may be changing the very ecosystem upon which food production depends. This raises the question: If we stay on our current course of environmental degradation, will we permanently lower the sustainable level of living on the planet? The answer is almost certainly yes. We are in the midst of what Paul Harrison (1993) many years ago called "the pollution crisis," and we will either work our way through this on a global scale or be faced with a major ecocatastrophe that could greatly diminish the quality of life for all of us. This is not a new issue, but we have been very slow to respond.

Water Supply Issues

Irrigation obviously requires a water source (typically a reservoir created by damming a river), an initial capital investment to dig canals and install pipes, and energy to drive the pumps. Each of these elements represents an expensive resource. Remember that we humans need clean water for our own health, and yet we compete with agriculture for that limited supply. This is such an important issue that targets for improving the availability of safe water for human consumption are built into the United Nations Sustainable Development Goals (which we discuss below), and in 2003 the United Nations created an initiative called UN-Water to focus on this specific topic. To give you some sense of the magnitude of the water issue, it takes about half a million gallons of water to grow an acre of rice, and irrigated agriculture accounts for about 70 percent of the water consumed worldwide (Food and Agriculture Organization 2009a). The tremendous expense of providing irrigation imposes serious limits to any sizable future increase in the amount of land being irrigated in developing nations.

Water is amazing. It covers 71 percent of the earth's surface, including most of the southern hemisphere and nearly half of the northern hemisphere. You are full of it—about 65 percent of your weight is water. Despite all that water everywhere, only a small fraction—3 percent—is the fresh water that humans, other animals, and plants need. Furthermore, most of that 3 percent is locked up as ice in the poles and glaciers or in extremely deep groundwater. So, only a very small fraction of the total volume of water is fresh water readily available to us in lakes, soil moisture, exploitable groundwater, atmospheric water vapor, and streams. Although fixed in amount, the water supply is constantly renewed in the hydrologic cycle of evaporation, condensation, and precipitation. The principal issues with respect to water have to do with its management (distributing it where it is needed), purity from disease (in order to be drinkable), and pollution. Since the amount of fresh water is fixed, but the population continues to grow, it is obvious that the amount of water available per person is steadily declining.

Within the ecosphere, salt water is converted to fresh water through the hydrologic cycle, but it is very expensive to mimic nature. In fact, it has been joked that the two most difficult things to get out of water are politics and salt. Most desalination plants are based on a process of distillation that imitates the water cycle by heating water to produce vapor that is then condensed to produce fresh, potable (drinkable) water. The problem is that it is very costly to heat the water and, as a result, desalinated water is typically several times more expensive than drinkable local water, and the resulting salt brine waste is environmentally damaging. The major producer of desalted water is Saudi Arabia, which is, for all intents and purposes, turning oil into water. Unless there is a technological breakthrough of the kind that boomsters typically expect, it seems unlikely that anything but naturally generated fresh water will be able to supply human needs for the foreseeable future, and we will have to survive by using that resource more efficiently than in the past. Thus, even if it is now widely recognized that the world is facing severe water shortages, not everyone realizes that "a future of water shortages will also be a future of food shortages" (Brown 2012:59). In 2018, UN-Water summarized the situation as follows: ". . . demand for water—from agriculture and industry as well as domestic use—is rapidly rising and water pollution and ecosystem degradation are being made worse by increasing amounts of untreated wastewater. And all of this is happening against a backdrop of climate change, which is playing havoc with the predictability of our most precious resource" (UN-Water 2018:1).

Ironically, among the main sources of water pollution are the chemicals we add to the soil to improve agricultural productivity. This is then aggravated by using irrigation, which increases the amount of water exposed to the chemicals. Irrigation requires dams, of course, and there has been a worldwide movement to stop the construction of dams as we learn more about the ecological damage caused upstream, downstream, and on the cropland itself by dams and the irrigation water, not to mention the displacement of millions of people around the world because their home would be underwater in the reservoir behind the dam. Most of the choice dam sites have already been taken, but not all. Asia has a higher percentage of its land under irrigation than any other area of the world, and China, in particular, is adding to the total. China built three major dams in the early 2000s, the largest and most famous of which is the Three Gorges Dam on the Yangtze River, which was designed to supply irrigation water and generate hydroelectric power (estimated at more than 10 percent of China's total), but which forced the migration/relocation of an estimated 1.3 million people.

Polluting the Ground

We survive on the thin crust of the earth's surface. Actually, as you learned earlier in this chapter, we live on only 29 percent of the surface. The rest is covered with water, especially the oceans, which we tend to treat as open sewers, and which we also exploit for the resources that are in the ground under that water. The land surface of the earth is where most things we humans are interested in grow, and the damage we do to this part of the environment has the very real potential to lower the ability of plants and animals to survive. We have been busy doing damage such as (1) soil erosion, (2) soil degradation from excess salts and water, (3) desertification, (4) deforestation, (5) loss of biodiversity, (6) strip mining for energy resources, and (7) dumping hazardous waste.

If not carefully managed, farming can lead to an actual destruction of the land (think of the Dust Bowl in the United States in the 1930s). For example, improper irrigation is one of several causes of soil erosion to which valuable farmland is lost every year. Even if cropland is not ruined, its productivity is lowered by erosion, because few good chemical additives exist that can adequately replace the nutrition of natural topsoil. Unfortunately, the push for greater yield per acre may lead a farmer to achieve short-term gains in productivity with little concern for the longer-term ability of the land to remain productive.

In many human cultures, agriculture is practiced as an extractive industry, in which the nutrition in the soil is sucked out by the repeated growing of crops, and soils are routinely degraded throughout the world. The conversion of land to agricultural purposes alters the entire ecosystem, and the resulting impact on soil structure and fertility, quality and quantity of both surface and groundwater and the biodiversity of both terrestrial and aquatic communities diminishes present and future productivity. Crop rotation and the application of livestock manure help to reduce soil erosion, but in some parts of the world the land is robbed of even cow dung by the need of growing populations for something to burn as fuel for cooking and staying warm. The eroded soil has to go somewhere, of course, and its usual destinations are riverbeds and lake bottoms, where it often causes secondary problems by choking reservoirs.

Desertification and deforestation are additional ecological crises associated with the pressure of population growth on the environment. At the dawn of human civilization, forests covered about half of the earth's land surface. Only about half of that forest is left today. Most, if not all, of that deforestation can be attributed to the impact of population growth, as people move into areas and clear forests to meet the economic demands for more resources made by growing populations around the world.

Of course, forests are also susceptible to the effects of air pollution, which can damage the vegetation and lessen plants' resistance to disease. In their turn, fewer

How Big Is Your Ecological Footprint?

Demographers are sometimes at a loss to explain why the relationship between population growth and environmental impact does not show up more clearly in the statistics of world development. It is intuitively obvious that more people consuming resources and leaving behind the debris of the industrial world are detrimental to the long-term health of the planet. But it is maddeningly difficult to show that population growth in Mexico, for example, is more or less damaging to the earth than population growth in Indonesia. One of the problems is that those of us in the highly industrialized countries don't always make the biggest mess where we live—we are able to get someone else somewhere else to make our mess for us, which means that they (usually in less developed nations) in turn have an environmental impact that really should not be directly attributed to them. The best way to visualize this is with the concept of the ecological footprint.

An ecological footprint has been defined as "the land and water area required to support indefinitely the material standard of living of a given human or human population, using prevailing technology" (quoted in United Nations Population Fund 1987:16). For most of human history, this was easy to figure out. If you farmed two hectares (about five acres) and all of your needs were met from the resources within those two hectares and all of your waste products were deposited within that acreage, then you did not influence life outside that zone in any demonstrable way. Your ecological footprint was 2.0 hectares. But urbanization changed all that because, of course, an urban population requires that someone else in the countryside grow their food, cut their wood, gather their sources of energy, get their water for them, and stow their trash and other waste. Thus, it is not easy to determine how big an impact an urban resident has on the resources of the earth, since the resources are drawn from multiple sources and the waste is spread out in multiple directions.

Urban areas are not sustainable on their own, as we discussed in Chapter 7. They must borrow their carrying capacity from elsewhere, and this is why it has been so important historically for cities to establish political and economic dominance over the countryside. Who are city residents borrowing from, and how much are they borrowing? Those are questions that William Rees of the University of British Columbia sought to answer back in the 1990s, in collaboration with Mathis Wackernagel, then one of his graduate students. "The simplest way to define ecological footprint would be to call it the impact of human activities measured in terms of the area of biologically productive land and water required to produce the goods consumed and to assimilate the wastes generated. More simply, it is the amount of the environment necessary to produce the goods and services necessary to support a particular lifestyle" (World Wide Fund for Nature 2019:1).

Cities are, of course, densely settled areas where people tend to use a disproportionate share of resources and generate a disproportionate amount of waste. This ensures that they will exceed the world average footprint. Rees calculated that the 472,000 residents of his home city of Vancouver, British Columbia, as of 1991 (it was 675,000 as of this writing), generated an average ecological footprint of more than four hectares per person, which meant that the city had a footprint of more than 2 million hectares. Vancouver itself comprises only 11,400 hectares, so Rees points out that "the ecological locations of cities no longer coincide with their locations on the map" (Rees 1996:2). A city like Tokyo, for example, has an ecological footprint that would cover a large section of Southeast Asia if it were aggregated all in one place. The same analysis can be applied to countries.

Of course, a large ecological footprint may not matter much if you have an equivalent or greater amount of biological capacity. If your footprint is smaller than your capacity, you are in good shape. However, if your footprint is larger than your biological capacity, you are exceeding your carrying capacity. Many wealthy countries exceed their own carrying capacity by borrowing ecological resources from other parts of the globe. In the long run, sustainability means that those countries that are running an ecological deficit (we might call

Ecological Footprints of Selected Nations in Hectares per Capita

Country	Ecological Footprint per Person Within the Nation	Available Biocapacity per Person Within the Nation	Ecological Reserve or Deficit (If Negative)
Qatar	14.41	1.00	−13.41
United States	8.10	3.65	−4.45
Canada	7.74	15.12	7.38
Denmark	6.80	4.17	−2.63
Australia	6.64	12.27	5.63
Norway	5.51	7.27	1.76
Russia	5.16	6.96	1.80
Germany	4.84	1.62	−3.22
New Zealand	4.74	9.34	4.60
Switzerland	4.64	1.00	−3.64
Japan	4.49	0.58	−3.91
France	4.45	2.38	−2.07
United Kingdom	4.37	1.09	−3.28
China	3.62	0.96	−2.66
Mexico	2.60	1.17	−1.43
Indonesia	1.69	1.28	−0.41
India	1.17	0.43	−0.74
Nigeria	1.09	0.69	0.40
Afghanistan	0.73	0.43	−0.30
WORLD	**2.75**	**1.63**	**−1.12**

Source: Adapted by John R. Weeks using data provided by Global Footprint Network (data.footprintnetwork.org); Data refer to 2016.

Note: A hectare is 10,000 m², or approximately 2.5 acres as measured in the United States; 1 acre is approximately the size of an American football field.

them the "exploiters") must be offset by those who have an ecological surplus. The numbers in the accompanying table summarize data for selected regions and countries of the world. It probably will not surprise you to learn that the average resident of the United States has one of the largest ecological footprints in the world, at 8.10 hectares per person, which is equivalent to using about 20 football fields per person to sustain the lifestyle of the average American. The vastness of

(continued)

How Big Is Your Ecological Footprint? (*Continued*)

the country's size and resources offers the average American a biocapacity of 3.65 hectares per person—more than twice the world average of 1.63. Yet, Americans still exceed that capacity by 4.45 hectares per person.

The highest footprint in the world belongs to the small oil-producing nation of Qatar (14.41), and three of the other top five are also small oil-producing nations—United Arab Emirates (8.92), Bahrain (8.63), and Kuwait (8.59). They are all living well beyond their ecological means. There are, however, rich countries that have an ecological surplus. Canadians, for example, have an ecological footprint of 7.74 hectares—a bit less than in the United States—but a biocapacity of 15.12 hectares per person, so they have one of the highest reserves in the world. Australia, New Zealand, Norway, Sweden, and Finland are other rich countries with substantial reserves. Of course, those reserves are essentially being "used" by others, i.e., those with a deficit. Near the very bottom in terms of ecological footprint is Afghanistan, with a value of only 0.73 hectares per person. Yet, even Afghanistan is running a deficit, since its estimated biocapacity is only 0.43 hectares per person.

The richer countries are obviously the ones that can afford to have the higher ecological footprints. The accompanying figure shows rather dramatically that North America, in particular, represents a vast area of higher-than-average ecological footprints. The contrast with Europe, however, is especially noteworthy because they are rich countries in which the footprint on the planet is less noticeable than in North America.

The bottom line of these data is that the average person in the world in 2016 (latest estimates as of this writing) required the constant production of 2.75 hectares (the global ecological footprint) in order to maintain his or her standard of living, whereas only 1.63 hectares were estimated to be available on a sustainable basis. If these data represent the real impact of humans on the environment, then we have already overshot our carrying capacity, not unlike people who continue to charge things on their credit card without knowing if or how they will pay back that indebtedness. Another way to think of this is to consider jumping off a 100-story building and at the 50th floor saying to yourself: So far so good!

Not everyone agrees with the concept of ecological footprints, since the calculations require assumptions that are not easily quantifiable. However, the principal argument against the implications of the ecological footprint is the belief by many people that somehow human ingenuity will solve the problem of our current overuse of resources, so someone may think that the world has exceeded its global carrying capacity, but we really have not. Put another way: Maybe something will turn up! For example, we hope to employ new sources of energy that are renewable and less harmful to the environment than our current reliance on fossil fuels. Solar and wind power are the obvious candidates to create electricity, and hydrogen has been offered as a substitute for gasoline to power motors for cars, trucks, boats, and planes. There is even still some interest in nuclear energy, despite its obvious safety concerns. The problem is not technology. The problem beyond sticky politics is the cost of creating and running the infrastructure for these new power sources all over the world. One or two generations (or more) will pay vastly higher prices for energy than we are currently paying in order to put these systems in place.

---

trees and less-healthy trees may alter the climate because the forests play a key role in the hydrologic cycle as well as in the carbon cycle. In the hydrologic cycle, water is being continuously converted from one status to another as it rotates from the ocean, the air, the land, through living organisms, and then back to the ocean. Solar energy causes evaporation of water from the oceans and from land, and it condenses into liquid as clouds, from whence come rain, sleet, and snow to return water to the ground. Trees are important in this cycle both directly, because water

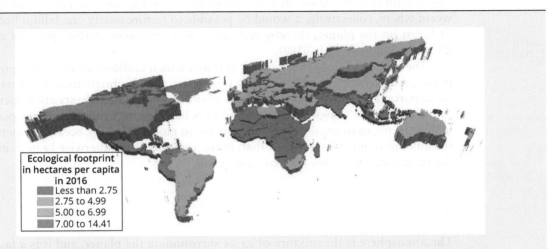

Ecological footprint
in hectares per capita
in 2016
■ Less than 2.75
■ 2.75 to 4.99
■ 5.00 to 6.99
■ 7.00 to 14.41

Source: Adapted by John R. Weeks using data provided by Global Footprint Network (data.footprintnetwork.org); Data refer to 2016.

Note: A hectare is 10,000 m², or approximately 2.5 acres as measured in the United States; 1 acre is approximately the size of an American football field.

We also consume a lot of energy by creating and using consumer products that are associated in most people's minds with a high standard of living: cars, iPads, video games, designer clothes—you can make your own list. A lot of labor also goes into the production of these goods. But we can afford them all in a way that previous generations could not because they are increasingly produced in developing countries using low-wage labor and employing energy sources for which the cost of reducing pollution is unlikely to be factored into the price of the product. If all these consumer products were made in the United States by well-paid workers working for companies that were minimizing the polluting effects of production, we couldn't afford nearly so many of them. Everyone's material standard of living would thus arguably be lower. Now ask yourself, what happens in a pie in the sky scenario in which all of those workers in the rest of the world are receiving high wages and working for companies that are trying to minimize the impact on the environment? For the most part, world economic policy leaders seem to prefer to believe that everybody needs more stuff, and we'll let the consequences fall where they may. Down the road something will have to give.

Discussion Questions: (1) How could you lower your personal ecological footprint in order to increase the chances of sustainability? **(2)** Given the large populations of both China and India, discuss the global consequences of those countries lowering the percentage of the population living in poverty.

transpires through the plants and is evaporated into the air, and indirectly, because the trees slow down the runoff and heighten the local land's absorption of the water. More than half of the moisture in the air above a forest comes from the forest itself (Miller and Spoolman 2012), so when the forest is gone, the local climate will become drier. These changes can mean that an area once covered by a lush and biologically diverse tropical forest can be converted into sparse grassland or even a desert. So important are trees that a widely cited study published in 2019 offered the opinion that, based on analyses of satellite imagery, there are places around the world where, collectively, it would be possible to restore nearly one billion hectares of forest on the planet, thereby reducing the atmospheric carbon pool by about 25 percent (Bastin et al. 2019).

The carbon cycle is that process through which carbons, central to life on the planet, are exchanged between living organisms and inanimate matter. Plants play an important role in this cycle through photosynthesis, and forests are sometimes called the earth's "lungs." Deforestation thus has the effect of reducing the planet's lung capacity, so to speak, which contributes to global warming because it increases the amount of greenhouse gases that, in the right number, otherwise keep us at just the right temperature for normal existence.

Air Pollution and Climate Change

The atmosphere is the mixture of gases surrounding the planet, and it is a layered affair (each layer being a "sphere"). We spend our life in the troposphere, that part of the atmosphere near the surface, where all the weather takes place. But other layers are of vital importance as well, such as the ozone in the stratosphere that protects us from the ultraviolet radiation from the sun. Most famous of the gases are the greenhouse gases (mainly carbon dioxide and water vapor, but also ozone, methane, nitrous oxide, and chlorofluorocarbons), which allow light and infrared radiation from the sun to pass through the troposphere and warm the earth's surface, from which it then rises back into the troposphere. Some of this heat just escapes back into space, but some of it is trapped by the greenhouse gases, and this has the effect of warming the air, which radiates the heat back to the earth. In general, the greenhouse effect is a good thing, because without it the average temperature on the planet would be 0°F (−18°C) and life would not exist in its present form, but too many greenhouse gases have the effect of global warming—an increase in the global temperature.

As you no doubt already know, global warming has the potential to change climatic zones, warm up and expand the oceans, and melt ice caps. The result is a rise in average sea level—inundating coastal areas (where a disproportionate share of humans live), and a shift in the zones of the world where agriculture is most productive. One estimate suggests that 20 million people in the United States could be affected by a rise in the sea level by 2030 (Curtis and Schneider 2011). These effects are, as you know, already taking place in various parts of the world. So important is this issue that the World Bank has a data set keeping track of how many people in each country live at an elevation less than 5 meters above sea level, since these are the places most vulnerable to being inundated. In truth, the number goes beyond coastal areas that are directly impacted and extends inland because of the migration networks that will influence where people will go in response to this change.

Population growth, the intensification of agriculture, and the overall increase in people's standard of living have all been made possible by substantial increases in the amount of energy we use. John Holdren, who was science advisor to President Barack Obama, estimated that in 1890, when the world's population was 1.5 billion, the annual world energy use was 1.0 terawatts. (A terawatt is equal to 5 billion barrels of oil.) One hundred years later, in 1990, when the world's population was at 5.3 billion, total world energy use had rocketed to 13.7 terawatts. This is an important number because *"energy supply accounts for a major share of human impact on the global environment"* (Holdren 1990:159, emphasis added). By 2013, the world's energy use was estimated to have gone up still more to 16 terawatts (U.S. Energy Information Administration 2013), while the population had increased to 7.1 billion, which would mean (assuming these energy estimates are correct) that less energy was used per person in 2013 than in 1990. The obvious good news is that energy use per person is down, but the bad news is that population growth means that more energy overall is being used than ever before in human history.

The by-products of our energy use (especially carbon dioxide and methane) wind up disproportionately in the atmosphere. As you can see in Table 10.2, the

Table 10.2   Emissions of Carbon Dioxide by Country

Top 20 Countries by Total Emissions	Total CO_2 Emissions in Metric Tons	Top 20 Countries with Population of 1 Million or More, by Per Person Emissions	Per Capita CO_2 Emissions (Metric Tons per Person)
China	10,291,927	Qatar	43.9
United States	5,254,279	Trinidad and Tobago	34.0
India	2,238,377	Kuwait	25.8
Russia	1,705,346	Bahrain	23.5
Japan	1,214,048	United Arab Emirates	22.9
Germany	719,883	Saudi Arabia	19.4
Iran	649,481	Luxembourg	17.4
Saudi Arabia	601,047	United States	16.5
South Korea	587,156	Australia	15.4
Canada	537,193	Oman	15.2
Brazil	529,808	Canada	15.2
South Africa	489,772	Estonia	14.8
Mexico	480,271	Kazakhstan	14.4
Indonesia	464,176	Turkmenistan	12.5
United Kingdom	419,820	Russia	11.9
Australia	361,262	South Korea	11.6
Turkey	345,981	Singapore	10.3
Italy	320,411	Netherlands	9.9
Thailand	316,213	Japan	9.5
France	303,276	Norway	9.3

Source: Adapted by John R. Weeks from data in World Bank (2019cb); Data refer to 2014.

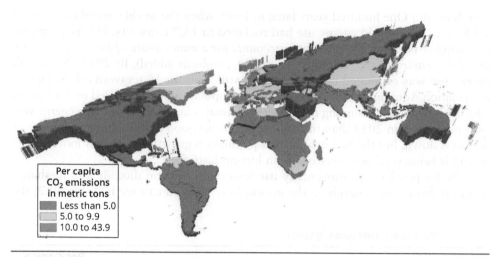

Per capita
CO₂ emissions
in metric tons
■ Less than 5.0
□ 5.0 to 9.9
■ 10.0 to 43.9

Figure 10.3   CO₂ Emissions Per Capita by Country

Source: Adapted by John R. Weeks from data in World Bank (2019c); Data refer to 2014.

United States is second to China as of 2014 (the most recent data available as of this writing) on the list of CO_2 producers in absolute terms. This is at least partly due to the fact China now manufactures many of the products sold in the United States (and elsewhere). We have offloaded that portion of our ecological footprint onto China (see the essay accompanying this chapter).

Because of their small size, it may be hard to see on the map in Figure 10.3 that four of the top five countries in terms of per person CO_2 emissions are the oil-producing and exporting countries in the Middle East (see the data in Table 10.2). Their high emissions, of course, represent the effect of the richer nations' demand for oil. Of the more populous industrialized countries, the United States, Australia, and Canada are high on the list with respect to per person carbon emissions. Russia and several other countries that were members of the former Soviet Union are also high on the pollution list, a reminder that those countries, like so many others, have tried to increase their standard of living with little concern for the environment.

The list of countries ranked by total CO_2 emissions per person is very similar to the list of the wealthiest countries of the world on a per person basis, as shown in Figure 10.1. This is no coincidence, of course, since emissions are directly related to energy use, which is directly related to levels of income. Indeed, the United States has 15 percent of the total income in the world and produces 15 percent of the world's CO_2 emissions. The top five countries on the list in Table 10.2 of total emissions (China, United States, Russia, India, and Japan) account for 46 percent of the world's population and 57 percent of all the world's carbon dioxide emissions. It is fair to say that the economically and demographically biggest countries make the biggest mess.

Human Dimensions of Environmental Change

As we discussed above, humans are clearly implicated in the degradation of the environment, although our impact depends on many variables. Furthermore, for most of us, the greatest concern about the implications of environmental damage is: What does this mean for me?

Assessing the Damage Attributable to Population Growth

The role of population in environmental degradation differs from place to place, from time to time, and depends on what type of degradation we are discussing. In general terms, however, environmental degradation can be seen as the combined result of population growth, the growth in production (transformation of products of the natural environment for human use) that we call economic development, and the technology applied to that transformation process. Ehrlich and Ehrlich (1990) summarized this relationship in their now-famous impact (IPAT) equation:

$$\text{Impact } (I) = \text{Population } (P) \times \text{Affluence } (A) \times \text{Technology } (T)$$

Impact refers to the amount of a particular kind of environmental degradation; *Population* refers to the absolute size of the population; *Affluence* refers to per person income; and *Technology* refers to the environmentally damaging properties of the particular techniques by which goods are produced (measured per unit of a good produced). "Technology is double-edged. An increase in the technical armoury sometimes increases environmental impact, sometimes decreases it. When throwaway cans replaced reusable bottles, technology change increased environmental impact. When fuel efficiency in cars was increased, impact was reduced" (Harrison 1993:237).

A major limitation of the IPAT formula is that it treats population size as a simple driver of environmental change. As you now know, some age groups have a different impact than others, so the age structure matters. Furthermore, urban populations use resources disproportionately, because they are the wealthier people and have different household structures that influence energy use. Everything is more complicated than it appears at first glance, but we can say that although those of us living in developed nations still consume a vastly disproportionate share of the earth's resources and thus contribute disproportionately to the pollution crisis, the rates of population growth and economic development in developing countries mean that the global impact is shifting increasingly in that direction. For example, the data in Table 10.2 show that China and India are among the five biggest CO_2 polluters in the world, despite fairly low per person rates in those two countries (neither is among the top 20 in terms of per person emissions). Second, notice that technological improvements (such as the use of solar and wind power) are already operating to dampen the environmentally degrading impact of consumption while, at the same, population growth has been exerting continual upward pressure on degradation.

You can see the dilemma here: Just to maintain the current impact on the environment, technology must completely counteract the impact of population growth and increasing affluence. It is a fact that much of the affluence in developed nations has come at the expense of the rest of the world—we have used resources without paying for them because the price of goods we purchased did not typically include the environmental costs associated with their production and consumption.

It is obvious that we cannot continue to draw down the "capital" of nature indefinitely to supplement our standard of living. The price of goods will increasingly have to include some measure of the cost of dealing with the environmental impact of making that product (the pollution from the manufacturing process) and the cost of getting rid of the product when it is used up (the pollution from waste). Measuring the cost of goods in this way may slow down the rate of development, measured in a purely economic way, but it should increase overall human well-being by balancing economic growth with its environmental impact.

Nowhere in this set of equations can it be concluded, however, that increased population is beneficial. Population growth is something that must be coped with at the same time that we continue to try to slow it down, because "rational people do not pursue collective doom; they organize to avoid it" (Stephen Sandford, quoted by Harrison 1993:264). In the world as a whole we expect there to be nearly 10 billion people by the middle of this century—all of whom will likely be hoping for a good diet and a reasonably high standard of living. Is it possible not only to provide that kind of development but to sustain it? Maybe. But only if we start making the adjustments right now!

Environmental Disasters Lead to Death and Dispersion

Keep in mind that since much of the world depends on rain-fed agriculture, the weather obviously remains of paramount importance in our food supply. Historical data for China and Europe suggest that, just as you would expect, bad weather contributes to poor harvests, higher mortality, and slower population growth, whereas good weather has the opposite effect (Galloway 1984). In the African Sahel, south of the Sahara, drought (a prolonged period of less-than-average rainfall) occurs with devastating predictability, and for the thousands of years that people have lived there, they have learned to combat the high mortality that drought exacerbates by having large families.

Drought is only one of several adverse weather conditions that can lead to famine—a situation of "complete lack of food access and/or other basic needs where mass starvation, death, and displacement are evident" (IPC Global Partners 2008:19). Famine periodically hits South Asia either as a result of a drought caused by the lack of monsoon rains or by flooding caused by over-heavy rains. Either extreme devastates crops and can lead to an increase in the death rate. As in Africa, the high death rates are typically compensated for by high birth rates, and the famine-struck regions of the world continue to increase in population size. That maintains the pressure on the agricultural sector to improve productivity all it can. Still, we always have to come back to the fact that in the long run, the only solution is to halt population growth; at some point, the finite limit to resources will close the gate on population growth.

Worldwide dependence on the weather is all the more troubling given the evidence that human-induced climate change is altering food production throughout the world. The United Nations Working Group II of the Intergovernmental Panel on Climate Change (IPCC) issued a report in 2014 that was very explicit: "Human interference with the climate system is occurring, and climate change poses risks for human and natural systems" (IPCC 2014:3). A warming planet is melting polar ice and the subsequent rise in sea level could devastate coastal areas in general and do cataclysmic damage to a country like Bangladesh. To be sure, the United Nations Population Division projections suggest that Bangladesh will lead the world in outmigration between 2020 and 2050. This is not a pleasant prospect for the country and its citizens, nor for the countries that will wind up making room for these environmental migrants.

Shortly after the IPCC report was released, a related report was published by the U.S. government-sponsored National Climate Assessment Committee tasked to figure out how climate change might affect the United States (National Climate Assessment Committee 2014). The conclusion was stark: Climate change is already happening in the United States and the goal is not just to try to stop it, but to adjust to its reality. The most negative side is the increased volatility of the weather—more rain, higher heat. There are some potential short-term benefits—a longer growing season in the Midwest and a longer shipping season on the Great Lakes. But, in the long term, volatile weather is likely to diminish the value of those benefits. In 2019, another United Nations report warned that a million species of plants and animals were on the verge of extinction, with clear threats to human health from their demise (IPBES 2019). The warming climate was listed as the major cause of the impending extinctions.

Rich country residents have greater resilience to deal with effects of climate change than do those in less developed nations, but everyone on the planet is being affected in some way or another. David López-Carr and his associates (2014) found that in sub-Saharan Africa there are hot spots (literally and figuratively) where levels of precipitation declined over the 30-year period from 1980 to 2010. Unfortunately, these also tend to be areas where the population is growing quickly and incomes are very low. They concluded, in particular, that the densely populated Lake Victoria basin, encompassing parts of Kenya, Uganda, Rwanda, and Tanzania, is an area with both a population and a climate burden exacerbated by recurrent droughts and flooding associated not only with a drop in precipitation but, at the same time, increasing rainfall variability. This will almost certainly lead to a combination of higher death rates, especially among children due to malaria and diarrhea, and increased migration out of the area.

The irony is that a significant fraction (10 to 12 percent) of the greenhouse emissions causing climate change is induced by our shift in agricultural practices designed to feed a growing population (Smith et al. 2007), and the 2014 IPCC report projected that between then and 2050 this shift could be one of the fastest growing contributors to global emissions. Much of the damage is due to the increase in methane gas associated with the increasingly industrialized methods of raising animals for food. Tony Weis (2013) called this our "ecological hoofprint," but as we discussed earlier in the chapter, this could be quickly modified by shifting to a flexitarian diet.

History is replete with examples of how humans have had to respond to catastrophes of one kind or another. Take, for example, the great Mesopotamian civilizations of Sumeria and Babylon that flourished in western Asia nearly 9,000 years ago. The region at the time was covered with productive forests and grasslands, but each generation over time made greater and greater modifications to the environment—deforesting the area and building great irrigation canals. Around 1900 BCE, it appears that the population peaked at a level that greatly exceeded the ecosystem's carrying capacity (Simmons 1993). A combination of environmental degradation, climate change, drought, and a series of invading armies led to a long-term decline in population in the region (Miller and Spoolman 2012), and the area became the barren desert that today makes up parts of Iran and Iraq.

In more recent history, the Mayan civilization in Central America reached a peak of population size about the year 800 CE, and the civilization then collapsed as the population overshot the region's agricultural capacities, perhaps aggravated by a severe drought (Hodell, Curtis, and Brenner 1995). These are only a few stories among many of premodern humans exceeding the carrying capacity of a region.

Earlier in the book we reminded you of the Irish potato famine, caused because the Irish put themselves at risk by developing a dietary dependency on one type of potato, which then was wiped out by a rogue imported fungus in the middle of the nineteenth century. The result was a permanent change in Irish society, and a concomitant change in the ethnic makeup of the United States. Many of the Irish died during the famine, but the long-term consequence was a dispersal of the Irish population, mainly to America.

The recent several year conflict in Syria has taken place in an environmentally stressed region (to be sure, in the same general area as ancient Mesopotamia). Thomas Friedman (2013) has argued that the severe drought that preceded Syria's violence was, in fact, one of the causes of violence because it unleashed a wave of refugees heading to cities with a government unable or unwilling to assist them, leading to a revolution: "This Syrian disaster is like a superstorm. It's what happens when an extreme weather event, the worst drought in Syria's modern history, combines with a fast-growing population and a repressive and corrupt regime and unleashes extreme sectarian and religious passions, fueled by money from rival outside powers—Iran and Hezbollah on one side, Saudi Arabia, Turkey and Qatar on the other, each of which have an extreme interest in its Syrian allies' defeating the other's allies" (p. 1).

Within the United States there have been multiple disasters to which the population has responded largely by dispersing to other parts of the country, including famously the Dust Bowl of the 1930s and the Katrina Hurricane disaster that hit New Orleans and the Gulf Coast in 2005, killing 1,800 people and displacing hundreds of thousands (Gutmann and Field 2010; VanLandingham 2017).

Earthquakes represent another type of natural disaster that affects the population directly through mortality and migration and then indirectly through the adjustments that have to be made in the aftermath of the disaster. Furthermore, the size of the impact is directly related to the density of population and buildings, along with how well protected the population is. Earthquake damage is largely driven by how well people are able to get out of harm's way, and on the resources that they have (their resilience) to bounce back after the disaster (Cutter, Mitchell, and Scott 2000; Rashed and Weeks 2003; Rashed et al. 2007). In 2004 an under-ocean earthquake triggered a tsunami tidal wave that killed 130,000 people in Aceh, Indonesia, who, unable to reach high ground, were drowned or crushed by the water. In 2010 a 7.0 magnitude earthquake hit Port-au-Prince, Haiti, killing an estimated 230,000 people—nearly 10 percent of the city's population—many of whom were crushed by falling buildings (Over and McCarthy 2010). Yet a few months later an even stronger 7.2 magnitude earthquake hit Mexicali, Mexico, but killed only two of its one million residents. The difference in the death toll between Port-au-Prince and Mexicali lay largely in how buildings were constructed in the two places.

In Chapter 1, we discussed the terrible governmentally imposed famine in China in 1959–1960 that led to the deaths of 30 million Chinese peasants. In that chapter we also mentioned the enormous consequences for Europe of the plague ("Black Death") over a several-century period. The major consequence was a rise in the death rate that essentially restructured European society. Earlier in European history, in 79 CE, Italy had experienced the eruption of Mt. Vesuvius, which wiped out the city of Pompeii and, in the process, buried alive a large fraction of its population. Note, by the way, that Mt. Vesuvius is still an active volcano and there are an estimated two to three million people living in its vicinity today.

All of these examples are meant to remind you of the two major direct human responses to specific environmental and other natural disasters—an increase in mortality and a high rate of out-migration (Lutz 2009; Hunter, Luna, and Norton 2015). The threat of death or at least poor health from environmental degradation is a real concern for the global community (United Nations Environment Programme 2019), and that is consistent with the importance of the health and mortality transition to our entire existence.

The migration of people vulnerable to ecological disasters may tell the entire story of why the earth is now covered with our fellow humans. As a species, we have spent millennia trying to find better and/or safer places to live, and the most widely anticipated reaction that demographers foresee from climate change is more of the same. But the political side of the equation now rears its head because we have spent the last 200 years fencing the planet off into nation-states. This limits the range of options readily open for people to respond to changes in the local environment. To deal with global climate change will mean reckoning with global social change as well, as people from different cultural groups reorganize themselves spatially. What could go wrong?

Sustainable Development—Possibility or Oxymoron?

In 1987, the United Nations World Commission on Environment and Development issued its extremely influential report "Our Common Future" (World Commission on Environment and Development 1987). This is usually called the report of the Brundtland Commission, named for its chair, Gro Harlem Brundtland, who was then prime minister of Norway and later became director of the World Health Organization. The commission defined the now-popular term sustainable development as "development that meets the needs of the present without compromising the ability of future generations to meet their own needs" (p. 43). At the same time, and for the first time in the world arena, the issue of environment and equity was laid on the table. It was made clear that part of the environmental problem is that some (rich) nations are consuming too much, while at the other end of the continuum, environmental problems are caused by people living in poverty who use the environment unsustainably because their own survival is otherwise at stake. Within the concept of sustainable development, the commission recommended that "overriding priority" should be given to the essential needs of the world's poor.

The Brundtland Commission defined sustainable development in a deliberately vague way. That has had the advantage of building a worldwide constituency for the concept, with the attendant disadvantage that everybody defines it the way they want to. One of the most popular ways to define sustainable development is to translate it to mean "let's sustain development," implying that economic growth is the best solution to all of the world's problems. In particular, economic growth is viewed as the way to salvation for the world's poor. Over time, the World Bank and the United Nations have taken up the theme of eliminating poverty as one of the world's important missions. The World Bank's Development Report for 2000/2001 was subtitled *Attacking Poverty* (World Bank 2000), and the World Bank and the United Nations collaborated to design a set of subsequently very influential Millennium Development Goals (MDGs) with the goal of reducing extreme poverty by 2015.

In 2015, the United Nations formulated a new set of Sustainable Development Goals (SDGs), which continued the global attack on poverty, while also incorporating a more specific set of goals aimed at protecting the environment at the same time that higher levels of human well-being were being promoted. "They recognize that ending poverty and other deprivations must go hand-in-hand with strategies that improve health and education, reduce inequality, and spur economic growth – all while tackling climate change and working to preserve our oceans and forests" (United Nations 2019a:1). These SDGs are listed for you in Table 10.3.

Though the goal of reducing poverty in developing nations is without question an important one, it sidesteps the issue that continues to *drive* poverty in developing nations—one that you now know so well—population growth and its aftermath (which is the impact of the age transition). Indeed, SDG 3 is aimed directly at improving health; certainly success with all 17 goals would almost undoubtedly improve human health—at least in the short term. To the extent that they succeed, the death rate will drop and the rate of population growth will, of course, be pushed up as a consequence. At the same time, two of the SDGs (4 and 5) should indirectly help to push the birth rate down, though there is no assurance that those forces will counteract the anticipated drop in the death rate. Will the combination of population growth for another several decades and our continuing quest for higher standards of living push us beyond the point of sustainability?

In animal populations, overshoot of the local carrying capacity occurs with a certain regularity in some ecosystems, and the consequence is a die-back of animals to a level consistent with resources, or at the extreme, a complete die-off in that area.

Table 10.3   United Nations Sustainable Development Goals (SDGs)

SDG #	Description
1	No poverty
2	Zero hunger
3	Good health and well-being
4	Quality education
5	Gender equality
6	Clean water and sanitation
7	Affordable and clean energy
8	Decent work and economic growth
9	Industry, innovation, and infrastructure
10	Reduced inequalities
11	Sustainable cities and communities
12	Responsible consumption and production
13	Climate action
14	Life below water
15	Life on land
16	Peace, justice, and strong institutions
17	Partnerships for the goals

Source: United Nations (2019b).

A good rain one winter may produce an abundance of food for one species, creating an abundance of food for its predators, and so on. In classic Malthusian fashion, each well-fed species breeds beyond the region's carrying capacity, and when normal rainfall returns the following season there is not enough food to go around, and the death rate goes up from one end of the food chain to the other. Biologists have been documenting such stories for a long time.

Premodern humans were susceptible to the same phenomena, as we mentioned above in reference to Mesopotamia and the Mayans. The apocryphal story is told of the goat that destroyed a civilization. A civilization existed that depended heavily on goats for meat and milk. "The goat population thrived, vegetation disappeared, erosion destroyed the arable land, sedimentation clogged what once had been a highly efficient irrigation system. The final result was no water to drink or food to eat. It did not happen overnight, but gradually the people had to leave to survive and the civilization perished" (Freeman 1992:3).

Carrying capacity is, to be sure, a moving target. We know that the carrying capacity of the earth is greater than Malthus thought because we have discovered that certain kinds of technological and organizational improvements can increase the productivity of the land. As you will recall, boomsters assume that human ingenuity will permit a continued expansion of carrying capacity up to the point at which the world's population stops growing of its own accord, which we expect to happen at the end of this century with a population somewhere close to 11 billion.

Let us assume that for all of human history up to the beginning of the nineteenth century, the carrying capacity of the globe was essentially fixed (even if it fluctuated over time from region to region) and was greater than the global population at any given time in the past, but that the gap between population and sustainable resources had been narrowing—the perception of which spurred Malthus to write his *Essay on Population*. The Industrial Revolution was associated with increasing population growth, of course, but also with innovations in agriculture that allowed food production to stay ahead of that population growth, as we discussed earlier. At least some of these innovations in growing food are certainly sustainable, so it is reasonable to assume (even if it cannot be proven) that the carrying capacity is greater today than it has ever been in history. Thus, the assumption is that since the dawn of the Industrial Revolution, both population size and the global carrying capacity have increased.

The problem is that we don't know whether or not we have now already exceeded the new and improved carrying capacity. This is partly because the global carrying capacity is a somewhat elusive concept. It is easy to know if a ship has exceeded its carrying capacity because it sinks. But we don't know for sure how big a load the earth can carry. If we have exceeded carrying capacity, then we are in a period of global overshoot and will face a catastrophe down the road.

There is strong evidence that we have, indeed, exceeded the global carrying capacity for sustaining more than about 2 billion people at the current North American standard of living (Cohen 1995; Pimentel et al. 1997; Chambers, Simmons, and Wackernagel 2002). If you and everyone else in the world were content to live at the level of the typical South Asian peasant, then the number of humans the world could carry would be considerably larger than if everyone were trying to live like the CEO of a Wall Street hedge fund. Indeed, it is improbable that the world has enough resources for our current crop of almost 8 billion people (much less 9 or 10 or 11 billion) ever to approach the standard of living of the average American. That implies that we are doomed to global inequality with respect to the consumption of resources, unless we in the highly developed world are willing (or are forced) to lower our standard of living dramatically. Christopher Chase-Dunn (1998:xxi) once put it this way: "If the Chinese try to eat as much meat and eggs and drive as many cars (per capita) as the Americans the biosphere will fry." More than two decades later, we are getting closer to that situation. When we think of sustainable development, we must think of development in qualitative, not quantitative terms. We need to think about improving the quality of our life in ways that put less burden on the earth's resources, rather than in ways that just use and abuse the earth.

Policies Aimed at Slowing Population Growth

As you look around the world and consider what you have learned about the demographic change taking place everywhere, you now understand that countries are not operating in a vacuum—people have strategized about population growth for a long time. Indeed, that is why Malthus is still relevant. Nearly a hundred years after his death—and with numerous references to him—the very first World Population Conference was held in Geneva in 1927, organized by Margaret Sanger who, as we noted in Chapter 5, was a pioneer in the family planning movement. In the aftermath of that conference the early ideas about the demographic transition began to take shape, although global concern about population waned as the Great Depression of the 1930s led to a rapid decline in fertility in the more developed countries, and high mortality continued to constrain population growth in the less developed nations.

However, after the end of World War II it became evident that population growth was going to be back on the global agenda, and in 1954 the United Nations organized a World Population Conference in Rome—the conference generally credited with alerting the world community to the very high rates of growth in less-developed nations (Harkavy 1995). This was followed by subsequent conferences in Belgrade, Yugoslavia, in 1965, after which the United Nations responded in 1969 with the creation of the United Nations Fund for Population Activities (UNFPA—now known more simply as the United Nations Population Fund). The UNFPA coordinates a wide range of population-related activities around the world, primarily in developing countries. Additional World Population Conferences were organized by the United Nations in Bucharest in 1974, Mexico City in 1984, and Cairo in 1994. The latter conference was officially known as the International Conference on Population and Development (ICPD), and it generated a "Programme of Action" that continues to guide international efforts to manage demographic change throughout the world, especially in the rapidly growing less developed nations that are projected to contribute the majority of the additional two or three billion people to the planet between now and the end of this century. Unfortunately, as you can from the SDGs shown in Table 10.3, the issue of directly confronting population growth issues is not currently on the global policy table.

The United Nations does provide policy advice to nations regarding their demographic trends, along with financial assistance to implement policy initiatives, and most nations now have a government agency devoted to gathering and analyzing population data and putting policies into action. These activities are often accomplished with the help of non-governmental organizations (NGOs). The value of NGOs is that they are not burdened by a government bureaucracy, and they typically have well-developed policy initiatives that can help set the agenda for a nation's population program. They also provide technical assistance that government personnel might otherwise lack, and they can fund demonstration projects to convince government leaders of the value of population programs. In some cases, NGOs are operating with their own philanthropic sources of money (e.g., the Bill and Melinda Gates Foundation), but many NGOs (e.g., John Snow, Inc.) receive funding from governments of richer countries, including the United States.

One of the constraints of being an NGO receiving money from a government is that strings may be attached. In the population field this has been an issue ever since the 1984 World Population Conference in Mexico City. At that meeting, the United States announced that any organization in the world that received money from the American government was prohibited from providing abortion, abortion counseling, or abortion-related services. This was called the "Mexico City Policy" and later dubbed the "Global Gag Rule." The Reagan administration, which had devised this policy, later decided that the UNFPA was in violation (despite repeated denials by the United Nations) and the Reagan and then the Bush administrations withheld all funding from the UNFPA from 1987 to 1992. Funding was reinstated by the Clinton administration in 1993, withheld again when George W. Bush took office in 2001, reinstated after Barack Obama was inaugurated in 2009, and then withheld yet again after Donald Trump was inaugurated in 2017. In fact, under the Trump administration the restrictions on spending money internationally on women's reproductive health issues have been so severe that the policy has been labeled the global gag rule "on steroids" (Goldberg 2017).

The government of the United States has, however, played a key role in explicitly encouraging governments of developing nations to slow down their rate of population growth, and it has provided a great deal of money to establish and maintain family planning programs all over the world. Peter Donaldson (1990) chronicled the growing American consciousness from the 1940s through the 1960s that rapid population growth in less-developed nations might not be good either for those nations specifically or for the United States more generally.

When President Kennedy established the Agency for International Development (USAID) within the Department of State in 1961, there was an early recognition that population was an important factor in development. By 1967, Congress had earmarked USAID funds for the purpose of providing demographically-related assistance along with economic assistance. For the next 18 years, the United States played a crucial part in helping to slow down the rate of population growth in the world—an effort that may have reduced the world population by nearly half a billion people compared to the growth that would have occurred in its absence (Bongaarts, Mauldin, and Phillips 1990). Even now, USAID remains one of the largest sources of international support for family planning programs, with most of the funding being provided to NGOs working in less developed nations. Other countries, especially Germany, Japan, and Norway, have also provided important sources of funding for these efforts.

Governments know that they do not have to "go it alone" when it comes to population policy, and the United Nations regularly queries national governments about their plans for trying to influence fertility, mortality, and migration, in order to achieve national goals for improving the lives of their citizens. This is an important source of information because it helps demographers at the United Nations (and other institutions) make decisions about the possible future trends in demographic change, given a government's apparent commitment to a particular course of action. If a country currently has above replacement level fertility, but the government is interested in actively working to lower fertility, we can obviously infer that lower fertility may be more apt to lie ahead than if the government has no interest in policy interventions.

Summary and Conclusion

Although most people seem to share the view that too much population growth is not good, it has been frustratingly difficult to prove a direct cause-and-effect relationship. Into this void of conclusions have leapt competing perspectives. The doomsters are neo-Malthusians who argue that population growth must slow down and stop or else the economic well-being of the planet will deteriorate over time. Boomsters are those who believe that population growth is a good thing—it stimulates development and is a sign of, rather than a threat to, well-being.

There can be little question that population growth creates long-term pressures on societal resources that must be dealt with. In the final analysis, each of the perspectives of the relationship between population growth and economic development has some merit—it is just that each is describing a different part of a complicated process, one that is unfolding differently for today's developing or emerging nations than it did historically for the already richer countries. Furthermore, we are all wrapped up in the global consequences of environmental degradation, especially as relates to the causes (human use of resources) and consequences (human and planetary health) of environmental degradation, especially global climate change.

We are now coping with the effects of the much more rapid rates of population growth among developing countries over the past few decades than were ever encountered in the history of wealthier nations. This creates more opportunities for commerce than might otherwise exist (more feet to be shod, more food to be processed, more people to buy cell phones and cars), but it also means that we have been consuming resources at an historically unprecedented rate. Rapid population growth has meant that we have been dipping into our capital—not just financial capital, but the resource base of the planet. We have been using up our environmental resources and changing the very nature of human (and other animal and plant) life in the process, and that raises some very legitimate concerns about how long we can sustain both development and increasing population size.

The world's still increasing population naturally requires an increase in food production, unless we dramatically alter what we eat (especially moving to a more plant-based diet), and how we waste food once produced. Since the world is essentially out of additional land that can be readily cultivated, increases in yield per acre offer the principal hope for the future. Indeed, that is what the Green Revolution has been all about—combining plant genetics with pesticides, fertilizer, irrigation, crop rotation, land reorganization, and multiple cropping to get more food out of each acre. At current levels of technology, it may be reasonable to suppose that the world's population could be fed for many years to come if food can be properly distributed, if farmers in less developed nations are able to reach their potential for production, and if environmental degradation and the consequent global climate change do not intervene to limit productivity. Whether that happens is more a political, social, and economic question than anything else. Indeed, this is what the SDGs are for—guidelines for a future that we have to design for ourselves collectively. What does seem clear is that it is almost inconceivable that all of the world's people will ever be able to have the lifestyle that Americans currently do. We have almost certainly exceeded the carrying capacity for that level of living.

Demographers, of course, cannot implement direct solutions to the problems of feeding the population or of halting environmental degradation, but they have wrestled mightily with what lies ahead for us as a consequence of population change. You will almost certainly spend the rest of your life doing the same.

Main Points

1. Economic development represents a process by which a country may create growth in average income—a higher standard of living—usually defined as per capita (per person) income.

2. Data for the world indicate that higher levels of average income are typically associated with lower rates of population growth; whereas higher rates of population growth generally are accompanied by lower levels of average income.

3. Neo-Malthusians express the "doomster" view that population growth is detrimental to economic development, whereas Ester Boserup and Julian Simon led the "boomster" argument that population growth serves as a stimulus for technological development and economic advancement.

4. The single best way to ensure the sustainability of our food supply is to cut back dramatically on our consumption of meat, which accounts for three-fourths of agricultural land use, and which also contributes to global warming.

5. Food production can be increased by increasing farmland or per-acre yield. The latter can be accomplished by continued plant breeding and increased use of irrigation, fertilizers, and pesticides, along with new patterns of land tenure.

6. It is often said that if you give a man a fish, he will eat for a day, but if you teach him how to fish, he will sit in a boat and drink beer all day.

7. It is estimated that the world cannot grow enough food for the entire population to eat an average American diet, yet it is perhaps within the realm of possibility that 11 billion people could be sustained with no increase in the death rate if food production and distribution worked far more efficiently and fairly and if environmental degradation did not intervene to lower agricultural productivity. Of course, those are big "ifs."

8. Environmental disasters are not new to human history, and they almost always end in some demographic combination of death and migration.

9. Achieving sustainable development will almost certainly require either a different definition of a desirable standard of living and/or acceptance of permanent inequalities in levels of living around the world. The latter seems more likely than the former.

10. The next time someone says that the population problem is "solved," remind them that more than 200,000 people are added to the world's population every 24 hours. That is the equivalent of nearly 500 full flights per day on a Boeing 747. Even if they are not landing near you, you will know about them soon enough.

Questions for Review

1. How would you describe economic development as it applies to your own life? Do you aspire to more material goods? Do you aspire to more cultural goods that use human rather than natural resources?

2. Thinking about the community in which you grew up, would you say that population growth was positively or negatively related to the local economy, or both, or not related at all? Defend your answer.

3. Would you be willing to give up or at least dramatically reduce your intake of meat in order to feed the planet and limit environmental damage? Why or why not?

4. Given the clear evidence that human-induced global climate change is occurring, what do you think might be the long-term consequences for the choices (voluntary or forced) that people will make about where to live in response to climate changes, especially in places where the population is continuing to increase? How will these choices impact the world community?

5. What is your perception of the strengths and weaknesses of the ecological footprint concept? How useful is the concept to you in helping you to understand your own impact on the earth?

GLOSSARY

This glossary contains words or terms that appeared in boldface type in the text, and which are central to an understanding of the study of population. The chapter notation in parentheses refers to the chapter(s) in which the term in discussed in detail, not necessarily the first time it is used in the text.

abortion the induced or spontaneous premature expulsion of a fetus (Chapter 5).

abridged life table a life table in which ages are grouped into categories (usually five-year age groupings) (Chapter 4). See also *life table*.

accidental or unintentional death loss of life unrelated to disease but attributable to the physical, social, or economic environment (Chapter 4).

acculturation a process undergone by immigrants in which they adopt the host language, bring their diet more into line with the host culture's diet, and participate in cultural activities of the host society (Chapter 6).

achieved characteristics those sociodemographic characteristics such as education, occupation, income, marital status, and labor force participation over which we have some degree of control (Chapter 9).

adaptation a process undergone by immigrants in which they adjust to the new physical and social environment of the host society (Chapter 6).

administrative data demographic information derived from administrative records, including tax returns, utility records, school enrollment, and participation in government programs (Chapter 2).

administrative records with respect to migration, this term refers to forms filled out for each person entering the U.S. from abroad that are then collected and tabulated by the U.S. Citizenship and Immigration Service (Chapter 2).

age and sex structure the number (or percentage) of people in a population distributed by age and sex (Chapter 8).

age pyramid a graph of the number (or percentage) of people in a population distributed by age and sex (Chapter 8).

age-sex-specific death rate (ASDR) the number of people of a given age and sex who died in a given year divided by the total (average midyear) number of people of that age and sex (Chapter 4).

age-specific fertility rate (ASFR) the number of children born to women of a given age divided by the total number of women that age (Chapter 5).

age stratification the assignment of social roles and social status on the basis of age (Chapter 8).

age structure the distribution of people in a population by age (Chapter 8).

age transition the shift from a predominantly younger to a predominantly older population as a society moves through the demographic transition (Chapter 8).

Agricultural Revolution a change that took place roughly 10,000 years ago when humans first began to domesticate plants and animals, thereby making it easier to live in permanent settlements (Chapter 1).

Alzheimer's disease a disease involving a change in the brain's neurons, producing behavioral shifts; a major cause of organic brain disorder among older persons (Chapter 4).

amenorrhea the temporary absence or suppression of menstruation (Chapter 5).

American Community Survey an ongoing "continuous measurement" survey conducted by the U.S. Census Bureau to track the detailed population characteristics of every American community; designed to allow the long form to be dropped from the decennial census in 2010 (Chapter 2).

anovulatory pertaining to a menstrual cycle in which no ovum (egg) is released (Chapter 5).

antinatalist based on an ideological position that discourages childbearing (Chapter 3).

applied demography see *demographics* (Chapter 1).

apportionment the use of Census data to determine the number of seats in the U.S. Congress that will be allocated to each state (Chapter 2).

aquaculture farming fish (including shellfish); a steadily increasing source of fish for food (Chapter 10).

arable land that is suitable for agricultural purposes (Chapter 10).

ascribed characteristics sociodemographic characteristics such as sex or gender, race, and ethnicity that we are born with and over which we have essentially no control (Chapter 9).

assimilate what immigrants do as they not only accept the outer trappings of the host culture, but also assume the behaviors and attitudes of the host culture (Chapter 6).

asylee a person who has been forced out of his or her country of nationality and who is seeking legal refuge (permanent residency) in the country to which he or she has moved (Chapter 6).

baby boom the dramatic rise in the birth rate following World War II. In the United States it refers to people born between 1946 and 1964; in Canada it refers to people born between 1947 and 1966 (Chapter 5).

boomsters a nickname given to people who believe that population growth stimulates economic development (Chapter 10).

built environment the physical transformation of the physical and natural environment that humans undertake in order to create a place where they can and want to live (Chapter 7).

capitalism an economic system in which the means of production, distribution, and exchange of wealth are maintained chiefly by private individuals or corporations, as contrasted to government ownership (Chapter 3).

carbon cycle a process through which carbon, central to life on the planet, is exchanged between living organisms and inanimate matter (Chapter 10).

cardiovascular disease a disease of the heart or blood vessels (Chapter 4).

carrying capacity the size of population that could theoretically be maintained indefinitely at a given level of living with a given type of economic system (Chapter 10).

census metropolitan area (CMA) a metropolitan areas as defined in Canada, including a core urban area with a population of at least 100,000 and adjacent urban and rural areas that have a high degree of economic and social integration with that core urban area (Chapter 7).

census of population an official enumeration of an entire population, usually with details as to age, sex, occupation, and other population characteristics; defined by the United Nations as "the total process of collecting, compiling and publishing demographic, economic and social data pertaining, at a specified time or times, to all persons in a country or delimited territory" (Chapter 2).

chain migration the process whereby migrants are part of an established flow from a common origin to a prepared destination where others have previously migrated (Chapter 6).

checks to growth factors that, according to Malthus, keep population from growing in size, including positive checks and preventive checks (Chapter 3).

child control the practice of controlling family size after the birth of children (postnatally), through the mechanisms of infanticide, fosterage, and orphanage (Chapter 5).

child–woman ratio a census-based measure of fertility, calculated as the ratio of children aged 0–4 to the number of women aged 15–49 (Chapter 5).

children ever born (CEB) births to date for a particular cohort of women at a particular point in time (Chapter 5).

co-ethnic a person who shares your ethnic heritage (Chapter 6).

cohabitation the sharing of a household by unmarried people who have a sexual relationship (Chapter 9).

cohort people who share something in common; in demography, this is most often the year (or grouped years) of birth (Chapters 3 and 8).

cohort component method of population projection a population projection made by applying age-specific survival rates, age-specific fertility rates, and age-specific measures of migration to the base year population in order to project the population to the target year (Chapter 8).

cohort flow the movement through time of a group of people born in the same year (Chapter 8).

cohort measures of fertility following the fertility of groups of women as they proceed through their childbearing years (Chapter 5).

Columbian Exchange the exchange of food, products, people, and diseases between Europe and the Americas as a result of explorations by Columbus and others (Chapter 3).

communicable disease a disease capable of being communicated or transmitted from person to person (Chapter 4). Also called *infectious disease*.

completed fertility rate (CFR) the cohort measure of fertility, calculated as the number of children ever born to women who have reached the end of their reproductive career (Chapter 5).

components of change or residual method of migration estimation a method of measuring net migration between two dates by comparing the estimate of total population with that which would have resulted solely from the components of birth and death, with the residual attributable to migration (Chapter 6).

components of growth a method of estimating and/or projecting population size by adding births, subtracting deaths, and adding net migration occurring in an interval of time, then adding the result to the population at the beginning of the interval (Chapter 8).

condom See *male condom* (Chapter 5).

consolidated metropolitan statistical areas (CMSAs) groupings of the very largest Metropolitan Statistical Areas in the United States (Chapter 7).

content error an inaccuracy in the data obtained in a census; possibly an error in reporting, editing, or tabulating (Chapter 2).

contraception the prevention of conception or impregnation by any of various techniques or devices (Chapter 5).

contraceptive device mechanical or chemical means of preventing conception (Chapter 5).

contraceptive prevalence the percentage of "at risk" women of reproductive age (15 to 44 or 15 to 49) who are using a method of contraception (Chapter 5).

Core-Based Statistical Area (CBSA) a method for identifying metropolitan areas adopted by the U.S. Office of Management and Budget in 2000 and implemented by the U.S. Census Bureau in connection with Census 2000 data (Chapter 7).

core-periphery model a model of city systems in which the primate city (the core) controls the resources, and the smaller cities (the periphery) depend on the larger city (Chapter 7).

cornucopians "boomsters" who believe that we can always grow enough food to feed whatever size population we have (Chapter 10).

coverage error the combination of undercount (the percentage of a particular group or total population that is inadvertently not counted in a census) and overcount (people who are counted more than once in the census) (Chapter 2).

crowding the gathering of a large number of people closely together; the number of people per space per unit of time (Chapter 7).

crude birth rate (CBR) the number of births in a given year divided by the total midyear population in that year (Chapter 5).

crude death rate (CDR) the number of deaths in a given year divided by the total midyear population in that year (Chapter 4).

crude net migration rate (CNMR) a measure of migration calculated as the number of in-migrants minus the number of out-migrants divided by the total midyear population (Chapter 6).

cumulated cohort fertility rate (CCFR) see *children ever born* (Chapter 5).

de facto population the people actually in a given territory on the census day (Chapter 2).

de jure population the people who legally "belong" in a given area whether or not they are there on census day (Chapter 2).

degeneration the biological deterioration of a body (Chapter 4).

demographic analysis (DA) a method of evaluating the accuracy of a census by estimating the demographic components of change since the previous census and comparing it with the new census count (Chapter 2).

demographic balancing equation the formula that shows that the population at time 2 is equal to the population at time 1, plus the births between time 1 and 2, minus the deaths between time 1 and 2, plus the in-migrants between time 1 and 2, minus the out-migrants between time 1 and 2 (Chapter 2).

demographic change and response the theory that the response made by individuals to population pressures is determined by the means available to them (Chapter 3).

demographic characteristics see *population characteristics* (Chapter 9).

demographic metabolism the ongoing replacement of people at each age in every society (Chapter 3).

demographic overhead the general cost of adding people to a population caused by the necessity of providing goods and services (Chapter 10).

demographic perspective a way of relating basic information to theories about how the world operates demographically (Chapter 3).

demographic processes see *population processes* (Chapter 1).

demographic transition the process whereby a country moves from high birth and high death rates to low birth and low death rates with an interstitial spurt in population growth, accompanied by a set of other transitions, including the migration transition, age transition, urban transition, and family and household transition (Chapter 3).

demographics the application of demographic science to practical problems; any applied use of population statistics (Chapter 2).

demography the scientific study of human populations (Chapter 1).

density the ratio of people to physical space (Chapter 7).

dependency ratio the ratio of people of dependent age (usually considered to be 0–14 and 65) to people of economically active ages (15–64) (Chapter 8).

diaphragm a barrier method of fertility control—a thin, dome-shaped device, usually of rubber, inserted in the vagina and worn over the uterine cervix to prevent conception during sexual intercourse (Chapter 5).

differential undercount the situation that occurs in a census when some groups of people are more likely to be underenumerated than other groups (Chapter 2).

disability-adjusted life year (DALY) a summary measure of the burden of disease that incorporates the number of years of life lost to a premature death plus the number of unhealthy years lived because of a specific cause of death (Chapter 4).

doctrine a principle laid down as true and beyond dispute (Chapter 3).

donor area the area from which migrants come (Chapter 6).

doomster   a nickname given to people who believe that population growth retards economic development (Chapter 10).

doubling time   the number of years required for a population to double in number if the current rate of growth continues (Chapter 1).

douche   washing of the vaginal area after intercourse to prevent conception (Chapter 5).

drought   a prolonged period of less-than-average rainfall (Chapter 10).

dual-system estimation (DSE)   a method of evaluating a census by comparing respondents in the census with respondents in a carefully selected postenumeration survey or through a matching with other records (Chapter 2).

Easterlin relative cohort size hypothesis   the perspective that fertility is influenced less by absolute levels of income than by relative levels of well-being produced by generational changes in cohort size (Chapter 3).

ecological footprint   the total area of productive land and water required to produce the resources for and assimilate the waste from a given population (Chapter 10).

economic development   a rise in the average standard of living associated with economic growth; a rise in per capita income (Chapter 10).

economic growth   an increase in the total amount of income produced by a nation or region without regard to the total number of people (Chapter 10).

ecosystem   a community of species interacting with one another and with the inanimate world (Chapter 10).

edge cities   cities that have been created in suburban, often unincorporated, areas and that replicate most of the functions of the older central city (Chapter 7).

emergency contraception   a means of averting pregnancy within a few days after intercourse, usually by taking a large dosage of the same hormones contained in the contraceptive pill ("Plan B"), or using the Copper-T Intrauterine Device (IUD) (see also *intrauterine device*) (Chapter 5).

emerging infectious disease   communicable (infectious) diseases that were previously unknown, but have come upon the scene recently and must be dealt with before they become an epidemic (Chapter 4).

emigrant   a person who leaves one country to settle permanently in another; an international out-migrant (Chapter 6).

enclave   a place within a larger community within which members of a particular subgroup tend to concentrate (Chapter 6).

endogenous factors   things that are within the scope of (internal to) one's own control (Chapter 5).

epidemiologic transition   the pattern of long-term shifts in health and disease patterns as mortality moves from high levels (dominated by death at young ages from communicable diseases) to low levels (dominated by death at older ages from degenerative diseases)—part of the health and mortality transition (Chapter 4).

ethnic group   a group of people of the same race or nationality who share a common and distinctive culture while living within a larger society (Chapter 9).

ethnicity   the ancestral origins of a particular group, typically manifested in certain kinds of attitudes and behaviors (Chapter 9).

ethnocentric   characterized by a belief in the inherent superiority of one's own group and culture accompanied by a feeling of contempt for other groups and cultures (Chapter 3).

exclusion   dealing with immigrants to an area by keeping them separate from most members of the host society, forcing them into separate enclaves or ghettos (Chapter 6).

exogenous factors   those things that are beyond the control of (external to) the average person (Chapter 5).

expectation of life at birth   see *life expectancy* (Chapter 4).

extended family   family members beyond the nuclear family (Chapter 9).

extensification of agriculture   increasing agricultural output by putting more land into production (Chapter 10).

exurbs   nonrural area beyond the suburbs (Chapter 7).

family   a group of people who are related to each other by birth, marriage, or adoption (Chapter 9).

family control   ways of limiting family size after the birth of children (Chapter 5).

family demography   the study and analysis of family households: their formation, their change over time, and their dissolution (Chapter 9).

family household   a household in which the householder is living with one or more persons related to her or him by birth, marriage, or adoption (Chapter 9).

family and household transition   the shift in family and household structure occasioned in societies by people living longer, with fewer children born, increasingly in urban settings, and subject to higher standards of living, all as part of the demographic transition (Chapters 3 and 10).

famine   food shortage accompanied by a significant increase in deaths (Chapter 10).

fecundity   the physical capacity to reproduce (Chapter 5).

female genital mutilation (FGM)   sometimes known as female circumcision, which typically involves removing a woman's clitoris, thus lessening her enjoyment of sexual intercourse (Chapter 5).

fertility   reproductive performance rather than the mere capacity to reproduce; one of the three basic demographic processes (Chapter 5).

fertility differential   a variable in which people show clear differences in fertility according to their categorization by that variable (Chapter 5).

fertility rate   see *general fertility rate* (Chapter 5).

fertility transition   the shift from "natural" fertility (high levels of fertility) to fertility limitation (low levels of fertility) (Chapter 5).

food security   a term meaning that people have physical and economic access to the basic food they need in order to work and function normally (Chapter 10).

force of mortality   the factors that prevent people from living to their biological maximum age (Chapter 4).

forced migrant   someone who has been forced to leave his or her home because of a real or perceived threat to life and well-being (Chapter 6).

forward survival (or residual) method of migration estimation   a method of estimating migration between two censuses by combining census data with life table probabilities of survival between the two censuses (Chapter 6).

fosterage   the practice of placing an "excess" child in someone else's home (Chapter 5).

gender role   a social role considered appropriate for males or females (Chapter 9).

general fertility rate   the total number of births in a year divided by the total midyear number of women of child-bearing age (Chapter 5).

generational replacement   a net reproduction rate of one, which indicates that each generation of females has the potential to just replace itself (Chapter 5).

gentrification   restoration and habitation of older homes in central city areas by urban or suburban elites (Chapter 7).

geodemographics   analysis of demographic data that have been georeferenced to specific locations (Chapter 2).

geographic information system (GIS)   a computer-based system that allows the user to combine maps with data that refer to particular places on those maps and then to analyze those data and display the results as thematic maps or some other graphic format (Chapter 2).

georeferenced   a piece of information that includes some form of geographic identification such as precise latitude-longitude coordinates, a street address, ZIP code, census tract, county, state, or country (Chapter 2).

global warming   an increase in the global temperature caused by a buildup of greenhouse gases (Chapter 10).

Great Migration   a term that describes the phenomenon of white and black migrants moving from southern states to northeastern and north central states between World War I and the 1960s (Chapter 6).

Green Revolution   an improvement in agricultural production begun in the 1940s based on high-yield variety strains of grain and increased use of fertilizers, pesticides, and irrigation (Chapter 10).

greenhouse gases   those atmospheric gases (especially carbon dioxide and water) that trap radiated heat from the sun and warm the surface of the earth (Chapter 10).

gross domestic product (GDP)   the total value of goods and services produced within the geographic boundaries of a nation in a given year, without reference to international trade (Chapter 10).

gross national income (GNI)   the most commonly used index of a nation's income, defined by the World Bank as the sum of value added by all resident producers plus any product taxes (less subsidies) not included in the valuation of output plus net receipts of primary income (compensation of employees and property income) from abroad Chapter 11).

gross national income in purchasing power parity (GNI PPP)   gross national income expressed in terms of purchasing power parity (rather than the official exchange rates) (Chapter 10).

gross national product (GNP)   the total output of goods and services produced by a country, including income earned from abroad (Chapter 10).

gross (or crude) rate of in-migration   the total number of in-migrants divided by the total midyear population in the area of destination (Chapter 6).

gross (or crude) rate of out-migration   the total number of out-migrants divided by the total midyear population in the area of origin (Chapter 6).

gross reproduction rate (GRR)   the total fertility rate multiplied by the proportion of all births that are girls. It is generally interpreted as the number of female children that a female just born may expect to have in her lifetime, assuming that birth rates stay the same and ignoring her chances of survival through her reproductive years (Chapter 5).

health and mortality transition   the shift from deaths at younger ages due to communicable diseases to deaths at older ages due to degenerative diseases (Chapter 4).

healthspan   the maximum number of years lived in good health (Chapter 4).

healthy life expectancy   the calculation of the average expected number of years of life lived in good health in a particular population (Chapter 4).

high growth potential   the first stage in the demographic transition, in which a population has a pattern of high birth and death rates (Chapter 3).

high-yield varieties (HYV)   dwarf types of grains that have shorter stems and produce more stalks than most traditional varieties (Chapter 10).

historical data   data derived from sources such as early censuses, genealogies, family reconstitution, grave sites, and archaeological findings (Chapter 2).

homeostasis   population stability, meaning that the birth and death rates are equal and the age structure is unchanging (Chapter 3).

host area   the destination area of migrants; the area into which they migrate (Chapter 6).

household   all of the people who occupy a housing unit (Chapter 9).

householder   the person in whose name the house is owned or rented (sometimes called the head of household) (Chapter 9).

housing unit   a house, apartment, mobile home or trailer, group of rooms (or even a single room if occupied as a separate living quarters) intended for occupancy as a separate living quarters (Chapter 9).

human capital   investments in individuals that can improve their economic productivity and thus their overall standard of living; including things such as education and job-training, and often enhanced by migration (Chapters 7 and 10).

human resources   a complement to natural resources and defined as   the application of human ingenuity to convert natural resources to uses not originally intended by nature (Chapter 10).

hydrologic cycle   the water cycle by which ocean and land water evaporates into the air, is condensed, and then returns to the ground as precipitation (Chapter 10).

illegal (undocumented) immigrants   immigrants who lack government permission to reside in the country to which they have moved (Chapter 6).

immigrant   a person who moves into a country of which he or she is not a native for the purpose of taking up permanent residence—an international in-migrant (Chapter 6).

impact (IPAT) equation   a formula developed by Paul Ehrlich and associates to express the relationship between population growth, affluence, and technology and their impact on the environment: Impact (I) = Population (P) $\times$ Affluence (A) $\times$ Technology (T) (Chapter 10).

impaired fecundity   a reduced ability to reproduce, defined as a woman who believes that it is impossible for her to have a baby; or a physician has told her not to become pregnant because the pregnancy would pose a health risk for her or her baby; or she has been continuously married for at least 36 months, has not used contraception, and yet has not gotten pregnant (Chapter 5).

implementing strategy   a possible means (such as migration) whereby a goal (such as an improvement in income) might be attained (Chapter 6).

incipient decline   the third stage in the demographic transition when a country has moved from having a very high rate of natural increase to having a very low (possibly negative) rate of increase (Chapter 3).

infant mortality   death during the first year of life (Chapter 4).

infant mortality rate   the number of deaths to infants under one year of age divided by the number of live births in that year (and usually multiplied by 1,000) (Chapter 4).

infanticide   the deliberate killing or abandonment of an infant; a method of "family control" in many premodern and some modern societies (Chapter 5).

infecundity   the inability to produce offspring, synonymous with sterility (Chapter 5).

in-migrant   a person who migrates permanently into an area from somewhere else. This term usually refers to an internal migrant; an international in-migrant is an *immigrant* (Chapter 6).

integration   incorporating immigrants into the receiving society through the mechanism of mutual accommodation (Chapter 6).

intensification of agriculture   the process of increasing crop yield by any means—mechanical, chemical, or otherwise (Chapter 10).

intercensal   the period between the taking of censuses (Chapter 2).

intermediate variables   means for regulating fertility; the variables through which any social factors influencing the level of fertility must operate (Chapter 5).

internal migration   permanent change in residence within national boundaries (Chapter 6).

internally displaced person (IDP)   a person who is forced to flee from home but seeks refuge elsewhere in the country of origin (Chapter 6).

international migration   permanent change of residence involving movement from one country to another (Chapter 6).

intervening obstacles   factors that may inhibit migration even if a person is motivated to migrate (Chapter 6).

intrauterine device (IUD)   any small, mechanical device for semi-permanent insertion in the uterus as a contraceptive (Chapter 5).

legal immigrants   immigrants who have legal permission to be permanent residents of the country to which they have moved (Chapter 6).

life chances   the probability of having a particular set of demographic characteristics, such as having a high-prestige job, lots of money, a stable marriage or not marrying at all, a small family or no family at all (Chapter 9).

life course perspective   the idea that people's live are embedded in specific times and places and that people are influenced throughout their life by events shared by other members of their age cohort (Chapter 9).

life expectancy   the average duration of life beyond a specific age, of people who have attained that age, calculated from a life table (Chapter 4).

life span   the oldest age to which an organism or species may live (Chapter 4).

life table   an actuarial table showing the number of people who die at any given age, from which life expectancy is calculated (Chapter 4).

long-acting reversible contraceptives   (LARC) devices in which ovulation-suppressing hormones are administered by means of a small stick implanted under the skin, or through an intrauterine device (IUD) which is inserted into the uterus (Chapter 5).

long-term immigrant   an international migrant whose stay in the place of destination is more than one year (Chapter 6).

longevity   the ability to resist death, measured as the average age at death (Chapter 4).

male condom   a thin sheath, usually of rubber, worn over the penis during sexual intercourse to prevent conception or venereal disease (Chapter 5).

Malthusian   a term pertaining to the theories of Malthus, which state that population tends to increase at a geometric rate, while the means of subsistence increase at an arithmetic rate, resulting in an inadequate supply of the goods supporting life, unless a catastrophe occurs to reduce (check) the population or the increase of population is checked by sexual restraint (Chapter 3).

marital status   the state of being single, married, separated, divorced, widowed, or living in a consensual union (cohabiting) (Chapter 9).

marriage squeeze   an imbalance between the numbers of males and females in the prime marriage ages (Chapter 9).

Marxian   a term pertaining to the theories of Karl Marx, which reject Malthusian theory and argue instead that each society at each point in history has its own law of population that determines the consequences of population growth (Chapter 3).

maternal mortality   the death of a woman as a result of pregnancy or childbearing (Chapter 4).

maternal mortality ratio (MMR)   the number of deaths to women due to pregnancy and childbirth divided by the number of live births in a given year (and usually multiplied by 100,000) (Chapter 4).

maximum level of reproduction   a set of calculations suggesting that 16 children born per woman is the maximum possible for any human population (Chapter 5).

mean length of generation   the average age at childbearing (Chapter 5).

means of subsistence   the amount of resources (especially food) available to a population (Chapter 3).

mega-city   a term used by the United Nations to denote any urban agglomeration with more than 10 million people (Chapter 7).

megalopolis   see *urban agglomeration* (Chapter 7).

menarche   the onset of menstruation, usually occurring when a woman is in her teens (Chapter 5).

menopause   the time when menstruation ceases permanently, usually between the ages of 45 and 50 (Chapter 5).

mercantilism   the view that a nation's wealth depended on its store of precious metals and that generating this kind of wealth was facilitated by population growth (Chapter 3).

metropolitan area   an urban place extending beyond a core city; in the United States, this refers to a core-based statistical area with at least 50,000 people (Chapter 7).

micropolitan area   in the United States, this is a core-based statistical area with at least 10,000 people, but less than 50,000 (Chapter 7).

migrant   a person who makes a permanent change of residence substantial enough in distance to involve a shift in that individual's round of social activities (Chapter 6).

migrant stock   the number of people in a region who have migrated there from somewhere else (Chapter 6).

migration   the process of permanently changing residence from one geographic location to another; one of the three basic demographic processes (Chapter 6).

migration effectiveness   the crude net migration rate divided by the total migration rate (Chapter 6).

migration evolution   the current state of migration, with the population largely urban-based and people moving between and within urban places (Chapter 6).

migration flow   the movement of people between regions (Chapter 6).

migration ratio   the ratio of the net number of migrants (in-migrants minus out-migrants) to the difference between the number of births and deaths—measuring the contribution that migration makes to overall population growth (Chapter 6).

migration transition   the shift of people from rural to urban places (see urban transition), and the shift to higher levels of international migration (Chapter 6).

migration turnover rate   the total migration rate divided by the crude net migration rate (Chapter 6).

mobility   geographic movement that is either not permanent, or is of sufficiently short distance that it is not considered to be migration (Chapter 6).

modernization   the process of societal development involving urbanization, industrialization, rising standards of living, better education, and improved health that is typically associated with a "Western" lifestyle and worldview and was the basis for early explanations of the demographic transition (Chapter 3).

momentum of population growth   the potential for a future increase in population size that is inherent in any present age and sex structure even if fertility levels were to drop to replacement level (Chapter 8).

moral restraint   according to Malthus, the avoidance of sexual intercourse prior to marriage and the delay of marriage until a man can afford all the children his wife might bear; a desirable preventive check on population growth (Chapter 3).

morbidity   the prevalence of disease in a population (Chapter 4).

mortality   deaths in a population; one of the three basic demographic processes (Chapter 4).

mortality transition   the shift from deaths at younger ages due to communicable diseases to deaths at older ages due to degenerative diseases (Chapter 4).

mover   a person who moves within the same county and thus, according to the U.S. Census Bureau definitions, has not moved far enough to become a migrant (Chapter 6).

multiculturalism   incorporating immigrants into a host society in a manner that allows the immigrants to retain their ethnic communities but share the same legal rights as other members of the host society (Chapter 6).

natural fertility   fertility levels that exist in the absence of deliberate, or at least modern, fertility control (Chapter 5).

natural increase   the excess of births over deaths; the difference between the crude birth rate and the crude death rate is the rate of natural increase (Chapter 1).

natural resources   those resources available to us on the planet (Chapter 10).

Neolithic Agrarian Revolution   see *Agricultural Revolution* (Chapter 1).

Neolithic Demographic Transition   the increase in fertility, not quite matched by an increase in mortality, that occurred as societies settled into agriculture and which led to an increase in population growth as a result of the Agricultural Revolution (Chapter 1).

neo-Malthusian   a person who accepts the basic Malthusian premise that population growth tends to outstrip resources, but (unlike Malthus) believes that birth control measures are appropriate checks to population growth (Chapter 3).

neo-Marxist   a person who accepts the basic principle of Marx that societal problems are created by an unjust and inequitable distribution of resources of any and all kinds, without necessarily believing that communism is the answer to those problems (Chapter 10).

net census undercount   the difference between the undercount and the overcount (Chapter 2).

net migration   the difference between those who move in and those who move out of a particular region in a given period of time (Chapter 6).

net reproduction rate (NRR)   a measure of generational replacement; specifically, the average number of female children that will be born to the female babies who were themselves born in a given year, assuming no change in the age-specific fertility and mortality rates and ignoring the effect of migration (Chapter 5).

noncommunicable disease   disease that continues for a long time or recurs frequently (as opposed to acute)—often associated with degeneration (Chapter 4).

nonfamily household   one that includes people who live alone, or with nonfamily coresidents (friends living together, a single householder who rents out rooms, etc.) (Chapter 9).

non-governmental organizations (NGOs)   private social service agencies that work to implement specific social policies (Chapter 10).

nonsampling error   an error that occurs in the enumeration process as a result of missing people who should be counted, counting people more than once, respondents providing inaccurate information, or recording or processing information inaccurately (Chapter 2).

nuclear family   at least one parent and his/her/their children (Chapter 9).

nutrition transition   a predictable shift in diet that accompanies the stages of the health and mortality transition (Chapter 4).

opportunity costs   with respect to fertility, the things foregone in order to have children (Chapter 5).

optimum population   the number of people that would provide the best balance of people and resources for a desired standard of living (Chapter 10).

oral contraceptive   popularly known as "the pill," a compound of synthetic hormones that suppress ovulation by keeping the estrogen level high in a female (Chapter 5).

oral rehydration therapy   an inexpensive glucose and electrolyte solution that is very effective in controlling diarrhea, especially among young children (Chapter 4).

orphanage   the practice of abandoning children in such a way that they are likely to be cared for by strangers (Chapter 5).

out-migrant   a person who permanently leaves an area and migrates someplace else. This term usually refers to internal migration, whereas *emigrant* refers to an international migrant (Chapter 6).

overpopulation   a situation in which the population has overshot a region's carrying capacity (Chapter 10).

overshoot   exceeding a region's carrying capacity (Chapter 10).

parity progression ratio   the proportion of women with a given number of children (parity refers to how many children have already been born) who "progress" to having another child (Chapter 5).

per-capita (per-person) income   a common measure of average income, calculated by dividing the total value of goods and services produced (gross national product or gross domestic product or purchasing power parity) by the total population size (Chapter 10).

period data   population data that refer to a particular year and represent a cross section of population at one specific time (Chapter 5).

periodic abstinence   a method of birth control that involves restricting intercourse to the period during the menstrual cycle in which a woman believes that she is not ovulating (Chapter 5).

period rates   rates referring to a specific, limited period of time, usually one year (Chapter 5).

peri-urban region   the periphery of the urban zone that looks rural to the naked eye but houses people who are essentially urban (Chapter 7).

physiocratic   the philosophy that the real wealth of a nation is in the land, not in the number of people (Chapter 3).

planned obsolescence   theories of aging based on the idea that each person has a built-in programmed biological time clock; barring death from accidents or disease, cells still die because each is programmed to reproduce itself only a fixed number of times (Chapter 8).

population (or demographic) characteristics   those demographic traits or qualities that differentiate one individual or group from another, including age, sex, race, ethnicity, marital status, occupation, education, income, wealth, and urban-rural residence (Chapters 1 through 9).

population distribution   where people are located and why (Chapters 1, 2, and 7).

population explosion   a popular term referring to a rapid increase in the size of the world's population, especially the increase since World War II (Chapters 1, 3, and 10).

population forecast   a statement about what you expect the future population to be; distinguished from a projection, which is a statement about what the future population could be under a given set of assumptions (Chapter 8).

population growth or decline   how the number of people in a particular place is changing over time (Chapter 1).

population implosion   a popular term referring (somewhat misleadingly) to the end of the population explosion, but more generally meaning a decline in population size (Chapter 1).

population momentum   see *momentum of population growth* (Chapter 8).

population policy   a formalized set of procedures designed to achieve a particular pattern of population change (Chapter 10).

population processes   fertility, mortality, and migration; the dynamic elements of demographic analysis (Chapter 1).

population projection   the calculation of the number of people we can expect to be alive at a future date, given the number now alive and given reasonable assumptions about age-specific mortality and fertility rates and migration (Chapter 8).

population pyramid   see *age pyramid* (Chapter 8).

population register   a list of all people in a country on which are recorded all vital events for each individual, typically birth, death, marriage, divorce, and change of residence (Chapter 2).

population size   how many people are in a given place (Chapter 1).

population structure   how many males and females there are of each age (Chapter 1).

positive checks   a term used by Malthus to refer to factors (essentially mortality) that limit the size of human populations by "weakening" or "destroying the human frame" (Chapter 3).

postpartum   following childbirth (Chapter 5).

posttransitional   a term describing an era in a country after a transition when things stabilize demographically (Chapter 3).

poverty index   a measure of need that in the United States is based on the premise that one-third of a poor family's income is spent on food; then calculated as the cost of an economy food plan multiplied by three. Since 1964, it has increased at the same rate as the consumer price index (Chapter 9).

preconditions for a substantial fertility decline   Ansley Coale's theory as to how an individual would have to perceive the world on a daily basis if fertility were to be consciously limited (Chapter 5).

preventive checks   in Malthus's writings, any limits to birth, among which Malthus himself preferred moral restraint (Chapter 3).

primary metropolitan statistical area (PMSA)   a metropolitan statistical area within a consolidated metropolitan statistical area (Chapter 7).

primate city   a disproportionately large leading city (Chapter 7).

principle of population   the Malthusian theory that human population increases geometrically whereas the available food supply increases only arithmetically, leading constantly to "misery" (Chapter 3).

pronatalist   an attitude, doctrine, or policy that favors a high birth rate (Chapter 3).

proximate determinants of fertility   a renaming of the intermediate variables (defined previously) with an emphasis on age at entry into marriage and proportions married, use of contraception, use of abortion, and prevalence of breastfeeding (Chapter 5).

prudential restraint   a Malthusian concept referring to delaying marriage without necessarily avoiding premarital intercourse (Chapter 3).

Public Use Microdata Sample (PUMS) data   a random sample of individual census records that have been stripped of personally identifying information (Chapter 2).

purchasing power parity (PPP)   a refinement of gross domestic product that is defined as the number of units of a country's currency required to buy the same amounts of goods and services in the domestic market as one dollar would buy in the United States (Chapter 10).

push–pull theory   a theory of migration that says some people move because they are pushed out of their former location, whereas others move because they have been pulled, or attracted, to another location (Chapter 6).

race   a group of people characterized by a more or less distinctive combination of inheritable physical traits (Chapter 9).

racial stratification   a socially constructed system that characterizes one or more groups as being distinctly different (Chapter 9).

radix   the initial hypothetical group of 100,000 babies that is used as a starting point for life table calculations (Chapter 4).

rank–size rule   a hypothesis derived from studies of city–systems that says that the population size of a given city in a country will be approximately equal to the population of the largest city divided by the city's rank in the city-system (Chapter 7).

rational choice theory   any theory based on the idea that human behavior is the result of individuals making calculated cost–benefit analyses about how to act (Chapter 3).

rectangularization a term referring to the process whereby the continuing decline in death rates at older ages means that the proportion of people surviving to any given age begins to square off at the oldest ages, rather than dropping off smoothly over all ages (Chapter 4).

redistricting spatially redefining U.S. congressional districts (geographic areas) represented by each seat in Congress (Chapter 2).

refugee a person who has been forced out of his or her country of nationality (Chapter 6).

religious pluralism the existence of two or more religious groups side by side in society without one group dominating the other (Chapter 9).

religiosity the strength with which one adheres to religious beliefs (Chapter 9).

remittances money sent by migrants back to family members in their country of origin (Chapter 6).

residential mobility the process of changing residence over a short or a long distance (Chapter 6).

rural of, or pertaining to, the countryside. Rural populations are generally defined as those that are nonurban in character (Chapter 7).

sample survey a method of collecting data by obtaining information from a sample of the total population, rather than by a complete census (Chapter 2).

sampling error an error that occurs in sampling due to the fact that a sample is rarely identical in every way to the population from which it was drawn (Chapter 2).

secularization a spirit of autonomy from other worldly powers; a sense of responsibility for one's own well-being (Chapter 3).

segmented assimilation a situation in which the children of immigrants either adopt the host language and behavior, but are prevented from fully participating in society by their identification with a racial/ethnic minority group, or assimilate economically in the new society, but retain strong attachments to their own ethnic/racial group (Chapter 6).

senescence a decline in physical viability accompanied by a rise in vulnerability to disease (Chapter 4).

sex ratio the number of males per the number of females in a population (usually multiplied by 100 to get rid of the decimal point) (Chapter 8).

sex structure see *age and sex structure* (Chapter 8).

social capillarity Arsène Dumont's term for the desire of a person to rise on the social scale to increase one's individuality as well as one's personal wealth (Chapter 3).

social capital the network of family, friends, and acquaintances that increases a person's chances of success in life (Chapters 7 and 10).

social institutions sets of procedures (norms, laws, etc.) that organize behavior in society in fairly predictable and ongoing ways (Chapter 3).

social roles the set of obligations and expectations that characterize a particular position within society (Chapter 8).

social status relative position or standing in society (Chapter 8).

socialism an economic system whereby the community as a whole (i.e., the government) owns the means of production; a social system that minimizes social stratification (Chapter 3).

socialization the process of learning the behavior appropriate to particular social roles (Chapter 8).

sojourner an international mover seeking paid employment in another country but never really setting up a permanent residence in the new location (Chapter 6).

spatial autocorrelation the concept that everything is related to everything else, but near things are more related than distant things (Chapter 2).

spatial demography any analysis of population data that takes location into account by using georeferenced information (Chapter 2).

stable population a population in which the percentage of people at each age and sex eventually stabilizes (no longer changes) because age-specific rates of fertility, mortality, and migration remain constant over a long period of time (Chapter 8).

standard metropolitan statistical area (SMSA) a term used by the U.S. Census Bureau to define a county or group of contiguous counties that contain at least one city of 50,000 inhabitants or more and any contiguous counties that are socially and economically integrated with the central city or cities (Chapter 7).

standardization a method to calculate age-specific death rates for two different populations and then apply those rates to a standard population (Chapter 4).

stationary population a type of stable population in which the birth rate equals the death rate, so that the number of people remains the same, as does the age/sex distribution (Chapter 8).

step migration the process whereby a migrant moves in stages progressively farther away from his or her place of origin (Chapter 6).

sterilization the process (either voluntarily—surgically—or involuntarily) of rendering a person permanently incapable of reproducing (Chapter 5).

structural mobility the situation in which most, if not all, people in an entire society experience an improvement in living levels, even though some people may be improving faster than others (Chapter 9).

subfecundity see *impaired fecundity* (Chapter 5).

suburban pertaining to populations in low-density areas close to and integrated with central cities (Chapter 7).

suburbanize to become suburban—a city suburbanizes by growing in its outer rings (Chapter 7).

supply-demand framework a version of neoclassical economics in which it is assumed that couples attempt to maintain a balance between the potential supply of and demand for children, taking into account the costs of fertility regulation (Chapter 5).

surgical contraception   permanent methods of contraception, including tubal ligation for women and vasectomy for men (Chapter 5).

sustainable development   defined by the Brundtland Commission as "development that meets the needs of the present without compromising the ability of future generations to meet their own needs" (Chapter 10).

synthetic cohort   a measurement obtained by treating period data as though they represented a cohort (Chapter 5).

theory   a system of assumptions, accepted principles, and rules of procedure devised to analyze, predict, or otherwise explain a set of phenomena (Chapter 3).

total fertility rate (TFR)   a synthetic cohort estimate of the average number of children who would be born to each woman if the current age-specific birth rates remained constant (Chapter 5).

total or gross migration rate   the sum of in-migrants plus out-migrants, divided by the total midyear population (Chapter 6).

transitional growth   the second (middle) stage of the demographic transition when death rates have dropped but birth rates are still high. During this time, population size increases steadily—this is the essence of the "population explosion" (Chapter 3).

transnational migrant   an international migrant who maintains close ties in both his or her country of origin and his or her country of destination (Chapter 6).

tubal ligation   method of female sterilization (surgical contraception) in which the fallopian tubes are "tied" off with rings or by some other method (Chapter 5).

unmet need   as applied to family planning, the number of sexually active women who would prefer not to get pregnant but are nevertheless not using any method of contraception (Chapter 10).

urban   describes a spatial concentration of people whose lives are organized around nonagricultural activities (Chapter 7).

urban agglomeration   according to the United Nations, the population contained within the contours of contiguous territory inhabited at urban levels of residential density without regard to administrative boundaries (Chapter 7).

urban area (UA)   see *urban cluster (UC)*.

urban cluster (UC)   part of the U.S. Census Bureau's definition of a place considered to be "urban"; an urban cluster has 2,500–50,000 people (Chapter 7).

urban sprawl   the straggling expansion of an urban area into the adjoining countryside (Chapter 7).

urban transition   the shift over time from a largely rural population to a largely urban population (see *urbanization*) (Chapter 7).

urbanism   the changes that occur in lifestyle and social interaction as a result of living in urban places (Chapter 7).

urbanization   the process whereby the proportion of people in a population who live in urban places increases (Chapter 7).

use-effectiveness   the actual pregnancy prevention performance associated with using a particular fertility control measure (Chapter 5).

usual residence   the concept of including people in the census on the basis of where they usually reside (Chapter 2).

vasectomy   a technique of male sterilization (surgical contraception) in which each vas deferens is cut and tied, thus preventing sperm from being ejaculated during intercourse (Chapter 5).

vital statistics   data referring to the so-called vital events of life, especially birth and death, but usually also including marriage, divorce, and sometimes abortion (Chapter 2).

wealth flow   a term referring to the intergenerational transfer of income (Chapter 3).

wealth of a nation   the sum of known natural resources and our human capacity to transform those resources into something useful (Chapter 10).

wear-and-tear theory   the theory of aging that argues that humans are like machines that eventually wear out due to the stresses and strains of constant use (Chapter 8).

withdrawal   a form of fertility control that requires the male to withdraw his penis from his partner's vagina prior to ejaculation; also called *coitus interruptus* (Chapter 5).

world–systems theory   the theory that since the sixteenth century the world market has developed into a set of core nations and a set of peripheral countries dependent on the core (Chapters 6 and 7).

xenophobia   fear of strangers, which often leads to discrimination against migrants (Chapter 6).

zero population growth (ZPG)   a situation in which a population is not changing in size from year to year, as a result of the combination of births, deaths, and migration (Chapter 8).

BIBLIOGRAPHY

Adioetomo, Sri Moertinigsih, Gervais Beningisse, Socorro Guitiano, Yan Hao, Kourtoum Nacro and Ian Pool. 2005. *Policy Implications of Age-Structural Changes.* Paris: CICRED.

Adlahka, Arjun and Judith Banister. 1995. "Demographic Perspectives on China and India." *Journal of Biosocial Science* 27:163–78.

Agnew, John A. 2010 "Slums, Ghettos, and Urban Marginality." *Urban Geography* 31(2):144–47.

Agunias, Dovelyn Rannveig. 2009, "Guiding the Invisible Hand: Making Migration Intermediaries Work for Development (Human Development Research Paper 2009/22)", New York: United Nations Development Programme. (http://www.migrationpolicy.org/pubs/agunias_HDRP_2009.pdf).

Alba, Richard and Victor Nee. 1997. "Rethinking Assimilation Theory for a New Era of Immigration." *International Migration Review* 31(4):826–74.

Alchon, Suzanne Austin. 1997. "The Great Killers in Precolumbian America: A Hemispheric Perspective." *Latin American Population History Bulletin* (27):2–11.

Alonso, William and Paul Starr. 1982. "The Political Economy of National Statistics." *Social Science Research Council Items* 36(3):29–35.

Alter, George and Michael Oris. 2005. "Childhood Conditions, Migration, and Mortality: Migrants and Natives in 19th-Century Cities." *Social Biology* 52(3–4):178–91.

Alvaredo, Facundo, Lucas Chancel, Thomas Piketty, Emmanuel Saez and Gabriel Zucman. 2018, "World Inequality Report 2018 Executive Summary (English Version)". (https://wir2018.wid.world/files/download/wir2018-summary-english.pdf).

Anderson, Margo J. and Stephen E. Fienberg. 1999. *Who Counts? The Politics of Census-Taking in Contemporary America.* New York: Russell Sage Foundation.

Andersson, Eva K., Bo Malmberg, Rafael Costa, Bart Sleutjes, Marcin Jan Stonawski and Helga A. G. de Valk. 2018. "A Comparative Study of Segregation Patterns in Belgium, Denmark, the Netherlands, and Sweden: Neighbourhood Concentration and Representation of Non-European Migrants." *European Journal of Population* 34:251–75.

Angel, Jacqueline L. 2007. *Inheritance in Contemporary America: The Social Dimensions of Giving across Generations.* Baltimore: Johns Hopkins University Press.

Arias, Elizabeth, Brian L. Rostron and Betzaida Tejada-Vera. 2010. "United States Life Tables, 2005." *National Vital Statistics Reports* 58(10).

Arias, Elizabeth, Melonie Heron and Jiaquan Xu. 2017. "United States Life Tables, 2014." *National Vital Statistics Reports* 66(4).

Arias, Elizabeth, L.A. Kennedy, C. Fu and J. Cisewski. 2018. "U.S. Small-Area Life Expectancy Estimates Project: Methodology and Results Summary." *National Center for Health Statistics, Vital Health Statistics* 2(181).

Arias, Elizabeth and Jiaquan Xu. 2018. "United States Life Tables, 2015." *National Vital Statistics Reports* 67(7).

Aries, P. 1962. *Centuries of Childhood.* New York: Vintage Books.

Arnold, Fred, Minja Kim Choe and T.K. Roy. 1998. "Son Preference, the Family-Building Process and Child Mortality in India." *Population Studies* 52:301–15.

Arnott, Robert D. and Denis B. Chaves. 2012. "Demographic Changes, Financial Markets, and the Economy." *Financial Analysts Journal* 68(1):23–46.

Arriaga, Eduardo. 1970. *Mortality Decline and Its Demographic Effects in Latin America.* Berkeley: University of California Institute of International Studies.

Associated Press. 1980. "Study on Old Age Released in China." *San Diego Union-Tribune.*

Associated Press. 2009. "Census Won't Count Missionaries Abroad." *San Diego Union-Tribune.*

Attané, Isabell. 2001. "Chinese Fertility on the Eve of the 21st Century: Fact and Uncertainty." *Population: An English Selection* 13(2):71–100.

Auerbach, Frank. 1961. *Immigration Laws of the United States, Second Edition.* Indianapolis: Bobbs-Merrill.

Bachu, Amara. 1993. "Fertility of American Women: June 1992." *Current Population Reports* Series P20(No. 470).

Bachu, Amara. 1999. "Trends in Premarital Childbearing: 1930 to 1994." *Current Population Reports* (P23–197).

Baird, Donna D., Clarice R. Weinberg, Lynda F. Voigt and Janet R. Daling. 1996. "Vaginal Douching and Reduced Fertility." *American Journal of Public Health* 86(6):844–50.

Baker, Bryan. 2017, "Immigration Enforcement Actions: 2016; Annual Report", Washington, DC: Department of Homeland Security. (https://www.dhs.gov/sites/default/files/publications/Enforcement_Actions_2016.pdf).

Banister, Judith. 2004. "Shortage of Girls in China Today." *Journal of Population Research* 21(1):20–45.

Banks, J.A. and O. Banks. 1964. *Feminism and Family Planning in Victorian England*. Liverpool, UK: Liverpool University Press.

Banks, J.A. 1954. *Prosperity and Parenthood: A Study of Family Planning among the Victorian Middle Classes*. London: Routledge & Kegan Paul.

Barr, Donald A. 2008. *Health Disparities in the United States: Social Class, Race, Ethnicity, and Health*. Baltimore: Johns Hopkins University Press.

Bashford, Alison and Joyce E. Chaplin. 2016. *The New Worlds of Thomas Robert Malthus: Rereading the Principle of Population*. Princeton: Princeton University Press.

Basten, Stuart, Wolfgang Lutz and Sergei Scherbov. 2013. "Very Long Range Global Population Scenarios to 2300 and the Implications of Sustained Low Fertility." *Demographic Research* 28(39):1145–66.

Bastin, Jean-Francois, Yelena Finegold, Claude Garcia, Danilo Mollicone, Marcelo Rezende and Devin Routh. 2019. "The Global Tree Restoration Potential." *Science* 365(6448):76–79.

Batty, Michael. 2008. "The Size, Scale, and Shape of Cities." *Science* 319(5864):769–71.

Baum-Snow, Nathaniel and Ronni Pavan. 2013. "Inequality and City Size." *Review of Economics and Statistics* 95(5):1535–48.

Beaujot, Roderic. 1978. "Canada's Population: Growth and Dualism." *Population Bulletin* 33.

Becker, Gary. 1960. "An Economic Analysis of Fertility." in *Demographic Change and Economic Change in Developed Countries*, edited by National Bureau of Economic Research. Princeton: Princeton University Press.

Becker, Jasper. 1997. *Hungry Ghosts: Mao's Secret Famine*. New York: Free Press.

Beckett, Megan K. and Peter A. Morrison. 2010. "Assessing the Need for a New Medical School: A Case Study in Applied Demography." *Population Research and Policy Review* 29:19–32.

Bell, Robert and Michael L. Cohen, eds. 2008. *Coverage Measurement in the 2010 Census*. Washington, DC: The National Academies Press.

Benza, Magdalena, John R. Weeks, Douglas Stow, David Lopez-Carr and Keith C. Clarke. 2017. "Fertility and Urban Context: A Case Study from Ghana, West Africa, Using Remotely Sensed Imagery and GIS." *Population, Space and Place* 23(8).

Bernardi, Laura and Andreas Klärner. 2014. "Social Networks and Fertility." *Demographic Research* 30(22):641–70.

Berry, Brian, C. Goodwin, R. Lake and K. Smith. 1976. "Attitudes toward Integration: The Role of Status." in *The Changing Face of the Suburbs*, edited by B. Schwartz. Chicago: University of Chicago Press.

Berube, Alan and Tiffany Thacher. 2004. *The Shape of the Curve: Household Income Distributions in U.S. Cities, 1979–1999*. Washington, DC: The Brookings Institution Living Cities Census Series.

Berube, Alan, Audrey Singer, Jill H. Wilson and William H. Frey. 2006. *Finding Exurbia: America's Fast-Growing Communities at the Metropolitan Fringe*. Washington, DC: The Brookings Institution.

Bin Yu. 2008. *Chain Migration Explained: The Power of the Immigration Multiplier*. New York: LFB Scholarly Publishing.

Blake, Judith. 1967. "Family Size in the 1960s—A Baffling Fad." *Eugenics Quarterly* 14:60–74.

Blake, Judith. 1974. "Can We Believe Recent Data in the United States." *Demography* 11(1):25–44.

Blake, Judith. 1979. Personal Communication.

Bledsoe, Caroline and Allan G. Hill. 1998. "Social Norms, Natural Fertility, and the Resumption of Post-Partum 'Contact' in the Gambia." Ch 12 in *The Methods and Uses of Anthropological Demography*, edited by A. M. Basu and P. Aaby. Oxford, UK: Clarendon Press.

Bloom, David E., David Canning and Jaypee Sevilla. 2003. *The Demographic Dividend: A New Perspective on the Economic Consequences of Population Change*. Santa Monica: RAND.

Bloom, David E., Michael Kuhn and Klaus Prettner. 2017. "Africa's Prospects for Enjoying a Demographic Dividend." *Journal of Demographic Economics* 83(1): 63–76.

Blossfeld, H. and A. de Rose. 1992. "Educational Expansion and Changes in Entry into Marriage and Motherhood, the Experience of Italian Women." *Genus* XLVIII(3–4):73–91.

Bocquet-Appel, Jean-Pierre. 2008. "Explaining the Neolithic Demographic Transition." in *The Neolithic Demographic Transition and Its Consequences*, edited by J.-P. Bocquet-Appel and O. Bar-Yosef. New York: Springer.

Bolton, C. and J. William Leasure. 1979. "Evolution Politique Et Baisse De La Fecondite En Occident." *Population* 34:825–44.

Bongaarts, J., W.P. Mauldin and J. Phillips. 1990. "The Demographic Impact of Family Planning Programs." *Studies in Family Planning* 21:299–310.

Bongaarts, John. 1978. "A Framework for Analyzing the Proximate Determinants of Fertility." *Population and Development Review* 4(1):105–32.

Bongaarts, John. 1982. "The Fertility-Inhibiting Effects of the Intermediate Fertility Variables." *Studies in Family Planning* 13:179–89.

Bongaarts, John. 1993. "The Supply-Demand Framework for the Determinants of Fertility: An Alternative Implementation." *Population Studies* 47:437–56.

Bongaarts, John and Griffith Feeney. 1998. "On the Quantum and Tempo of Fertility." *Population and Development Review* 24(2):271–92.

Bongaarts, John and Rodolfo A. Bulatao, eds. 2000. *Beyond Six Billion: Forecasting the World's Population.* Washington, DC: National Academies Press.

Bongaarts, John and Charles F. Westoff. 2000. "The Potential Role of Contraception in Reducing Abortion." *Studies in Family Planning* 31(3):193–202.

Bongaarts, John and Griffith Feeney. 2003. "Estimating Mean Lifetime, Population Council Working Paper No. 179." Vol. New York: Population Council.

Bongaarts, John and Tomáš Sobotka. 2012. "A Demographic Explanation for the Recent Rise in European Fertility." *Population and Development Review* 38(1):83–120.

Bongaarts, John. 2014. "The Impact of Family Planning Programs on Unmet Need and Demand for Contraception." *Studies in Family Planning* 45(2):247–62.

Borlaug, Norman. 2002. "We Can Feed the World. Here's How." Pp. A16 in *Wall Street Journal.*

Boserup, Ester. 1965. *The Conditions of Agricultural Growth.* Chicago: Aldine.

Boserup, Ester. 1970. *Woman's Role in Economic Development.* New York: St. Martin's Press.

Boserup, Ester. 1981. *Population and Technological Change: A Study of Long-Term Trends.* Chicago: University of Chicago Press.

Boyd, Monica. 1976. "Immigration Policies and Trends: A Comparison of Canada and the United States." *Demography* 13:83–104.

Boyd, Monica, Gustave Goldmann and Pamela White. 2000. "Race in the Canadian Census." in *Race and Racism: Canada's Challenge*, edited by L. Driedger and S. S. Halli. Montreal: McGill/Queen's University Press.

Brackett, James. 1968. "The Evolution of Marxist Theories of Population: Marxism Recognizes the Population Problem." *Demography* 5(1):158–73.

Bradshaw, York and E. Fraser. 1989. "City Size, Economic Development, and Quality of Life in China: New Empirical Evidence." *American Sociological Review* 54:986–1003.

Brandes, Stanley. 1990. "Ritual Eating and Drinking in Tzintzuntzan: A Contribution to the Study of Mexican Foodways." *Western Folklore* 49:163–75.

Brandon, Emily. 2019. "The Ideal Retirement Age, and Why You Won't Retire by Then." *U.S. News & World Report.*

Brant, Robin. 2016, "Enforcing Family Care by Law in Shanghai." *BBC News*, London. (https://www.bbc.com/news/world-asia-china-36394941).

Brentano, Ludwig. 1910. "The Doctrine of Malthus and the Increase of Population During the Last Decade." *Economic Journal* 20:371–93.

Brodie, Janet Farrell. 1994. *Contraception and Abortion in Nineteenth-Century America.* Ithaca: Cornell University Press.

Brokaw, Tom. 1998. *The Greatest Generation.* New York: Random House.

Brown, Dustin C., Mark D. Hayward, Jennifer Karas Montez, Robert A. Hummer, Chi-Tsun Chiu and Mira M. Hidajat. 2012. "The Signficance of Education for Mortality Compression in the United States." *Demography* 49:819–40).

Brown, Lawrence A. 1981. *Innovation Diffusion: A New Perspective.* London and New York: Methuen.

Brown, Lesley, ed. 1993. *The New Shorter Oxford English Dictionary on Historical Principles.* Oxford, UK: Clarendon Press.

Brown, Lester. 2012. *Full Planet, Empty Plates: The New Geopolitics of Food Scarcity.* New York: W.W. Norton & Company.

Bryan, Thomas. 2004. "Basic Sources of Statistics." in *The Methods and Materials of Demography, Second Edition*, edited by J. S. Siegel and D. A. Swanson. San Diego: Elsevier Academic Press.

Bulatao, R. and R. Lee. 1983. *Determinants of Fertility in Developing Countries, Volume 1, Supply and Demand for Children.* New York: Academic Press.

Bulpett, Carol. 2002. "Regimes of Exclusion." *European Urban and Regional Studies* 9(2):137–49.

Caldwell, John. 1976. "Toward a Restatement of Demographic Transition Theory." *Population and Development Review* 2(3–4):321–66.

Caldwell, John. 1986. "Routes to Low Mortality in Poor Countries." *Population and Development Review* 12(2):171–220.

Caldwell, John C. and Bruce K. Caldwell. 2003. "Pretransitional Population Control and Equilibrium." *Population Studies* 57(2):199–215.

Calhoun, John. 1962. "Population Density and Social Pathology." *Scientific American* (May):118–25.

California Department of Finance. 2018, "California County Population Estimates and Components of Change by Year, July 1, 2010–2018", Sacramento: Demographic Research Unit of the California Department of Finance. (http://www.dof.ca.gov/Forecasting/Demographics/Estimates/).

Camarota, Steven A., Karen Zeigler and Jason Richwine. 2018. "Births to Legal and Illegal Immigrants in the U.S." Washington, DC: Center for Immigration Studies.

Cann, Rebecca L. and Allan C. Wilson. 2003. "The Recent African Genesis of Humans." *Scientific American Special Edition* 13(2):54–61.

Cantillon, Richard. 1755 [1964]. *Essai Sur La Nature Du Commerce En General, Edited with an English Translation by Henry Higgs*. New York: A. M. Kelley.

Cantor, Norman F. 2001. *In the Wake of the Plague: The Black Death & the World It Made*. New York: Free Press.

Cardenas, Rosario and Carla Makhlour Obermeyer. 1997. "Son Preference and Differential in Morocco and Tunisia." *Studies in Family Planning* 28(3):235–44.

Carey, James R. and Debra S. Judge. 2001. "Principles of Biodemography with Special Reference to Longevity." *Population: An English Selection* 13(1):9–40.

Carlson, Elwood. 2008. *The Lucky Few: Between the Greatest Generation and the Baby Boom*. New York: Springer.

Carr-Saunders, A. M. 1936. *World Population: Past Growth and Present Trends*. Oxford, UK: Clarendon Press.

Case, Anne and Angus Deaton. 2015. "Rising Morbidity and Mortality in Midlife among White Non-Hispanic Americans in the 21st Century." *Proceedings of the National Academy of Sciences* 112(49):15078–83.

Case, Anne and Angus Deaton. 2017, "Mortality and Morbidity in the 21st Century", Washington, DC: Brookings Institution. (https://www.brookings.edu/bpea-articles/mortality-and-morbidity-in-the-21st-century/).

Caselli, Graziella and Jacques Vallin. 2001. "Demographic Trends: Beyond the Limits?". *Population: An English Selection* 13(1):41–72.

Casterline, John B. 2001. "Diffusion Processes and Fertility Transition: Introduction." in *Diffusion Processes and Fertility Transition: Selected Perspectives*, edited by J. B. Casterline. Washington, DC: National Research Council.

Castles, Stephen, Hein de Haas and Mark J. Miller. 2013. *The Age of Migration, Fifth Edition*. New York: The Guilford Press.

Castro-Martín, Teresa. 2010. "Single Motherhood and Low Birthweight in Spain: Narrowing Social Inequalities in Health?". *Demographic Research* 22:863–90.

Cerrutti, Marcela and Douglas S. Massey. 2001. "On the Auspices of Female Migration from Mexico to the United States." *Demography* 38(2):187–200.

Chambers, Nicky, Craig Simmons and Mathis Wackernagel. 2002. *Sharing Nature's Interest*. London: Earthscan Publications.

Chamie, Joseph. 1981. *Religion and Fertility: Arab Christian-Muslim Differentials*. Cambridge, UK: Cambridge University Press.

Chandler, R.F. 1971. "The Scientific Basis for the Increased Yield Potential of Rice and Wheat." in *Food, Population and Employments: The Impact of the Green Revolution*, edited by T. Poleman and D. Freebain. New York: Praeger.

Chandler, T. and G. Fox. 1974. *3000 Years of Urban Growth*. New York: Academic Press.

Chandra, Anjani, Casey E. Copen and Elizabeth H. Stephen. 2013. "Infertility and Impaired Fecundity in the United States, 1982–2010: Data from the National Survey of Family Growth." *National Health Statistics Reports* 67(August 14).

Chandrasekhar, S. 1979. *"A Dirty, Filthy Book"—the Writings of Charles Knowlton and Annie Besant on Reproductive Physiology and Birth Control and an Account of the Bradlaugh-Besant Trial*. Berkeley: University of California Press.

Chang, Leslie. 2000. "In China, a Headache of a Head Count." *Wall Street Journal*. November 2, page A21.

Charbit, Yves. 2002. "The Platonic City: History and Utopia." *Population-E* 57(2):207–36.

Charles, Enid. 1936. *The Twilight of Parenthood*. London: Watt's and Co.

Chase-Dunn, Christopher. 1998. *Global Formation: Structures of the World Economy, Updated Edition*. Lanham, MD: Rowman and Littlefield.

Chase-Dunn, Christopher. 2006. "Globalization: A World-Systems Perspective." in *Global Social Change: Historical and Comparative Perspectives*, edited by C. Chase-Dunn and S. Babones. Baltimore: Johns Hopkins University Press.

Cherlin, Andrew J. 2013. *Public and Private Families: An Introduction, Seventh Edition*. New York: McGraw-Hill Higher Education.

Chesnais, Jean-Claude. 1996. "Fertility, Family, and Social Policy in Contemporary Western Europe." *Population and Development Review* 22(4):729–40.

Choldin, Harvey. 1994. *Looking for the Last Percent: The Controversy over the Census Undercounts*. New Brunswick, NJ: Rutgers University Press.

Christakos, George, Ricardo A. Olea, Marc L. Serre, Hwa-Lung Yu and Lin-Lin Wang. 2005. *Interdisciplinary Public Health Reasoning and Epidemic Modelling: The Case of the Black Death*. New York: Springer.

Christaller, Walter. 1966. *Central Places in Southern Germany: Translated from from Die Zentralen Orte in Süddeutschland by Carlisle W. Baskin*. Englewood Cliffs, NJ: Prentice-Hall.

Cicourel, Aaron. 1974. *Theory and Method in a Study of Argentina*. New York: Wiley.

Cipolla, Carlo. 1965. *The Economic History of World Population*. London: Penguin.

Cipolla, Carlo. 1981. *Fighting the Plague in Seventeenth-Century Italy*. Madison: University of Wisconsin Press.

Clark, Colin. 1967. *Population Growth and Land Use*. New York: St. Martin's Press.

Clarke, John I. 2000. *The Human Dichotomy: The Changing Numbers of Males and Females*. Amsterdam: Pergamon.

Coale, Ansley and Melvin Zelnick. 1963. *Estimates of Fertility and Population in the United States*. Princeton: Princeton University Press.

Coale, Ansley. 1973. "The Demographic Transition." Pp. Vol 1, 53–72 in *Proceedings of International Population Conference*, Vol. I, edited by IUSSP. Liege, Belgium: IUSSP.

Coale, Ansley and James Trussell. 1974. "Model Fertility Schedules: Variations in the Age Structure of Child-Bearing in Human Populations." *Population Index* 40(2):185–256.

Coale, Ansley. 1986. "Preface." in *The Decline of Fertility in Europe*, edited by A. Coale and S. C. Watkins. Princeton: Princeton University Press.

Coale, Ansley and Judith Banister. 1994. "Five Decades of Missing Females in China." *Demography* 31(3):459–80.

Cohen, Barney and Mark R. Montgomery. 1998. "Introduction." in *From Birth to Death: Mortality Decline and Reproductive Change*, edited by M. R. Montgomery and B. Cohen. Washington, DC: National Academies Press.

Cohen, Joel. 1995. *How Many People Can the Earth Support*. New York: W.W. Norton.

Cohen, Mark Nathan. 1977. *The Food Crisis in Prehistory: Overpopulation and the Origins of Agriculture*. New Haven: Yale University Press.

Coleman, James and T. J. Fararo, eds. 1992. *Rational Choice Theory: Advocacy and Critique*. Newbury Park: Sage Publications.

Coleman, R. and Lee Rainwater. 1978. *Social Standing in America*. New York: Basic Books.

Condorcet, Marie Jean Antoine Nicolas de Caritat. 1795 [1955]. *Sketch for an Historical Picture of the Progress of the Human Mind, Translated from the French by June Baraclough*. London: Weidenfield and Nicholson.

Conners, Erin, Joseph Vinetz, John R. Weeks and Kimberly C. Brouwer. 2016. "A Global Systematic Review of Chagas Disease Prevalence among Migrants." *Acta tropica* 156:68–78.

Cornelius, Wayne, Scott Borger, Adam Sawyer, David Keyes, Clare Appleby, Kristen Parks, Gabriel Lozada and Jonathan Hicken. 2008. *Controlling Unauthorized Immigration from Mexico: The Failure of 'Prevention through Deterrence' and the Need for Comprehensive Reform*. San Diego: UCSD Center for Comparative Immigration Studies.

Cornelius, Wayne, David Fitzgerald and Pedro Lewin Fischer, eds. 2008. *Mayan Journeys: The New Migration from Yucatán to the United States*. Boulder: Lynne Rienner Publishers.

Corona Vásquez, Rodolfo. 1991. "Confiabilidad De Los Resultados Preliminares Del Xi Censo General De Población Y Vivienda De 1990." *Estudios Demográficos y Urbanos* 6(1):33–68.

Coupland, Douglas. 1991. *Generation X: Tales for an Accelerated Culture*. New York St. Martin's Press.

Courbage, Youssef and Emmanuel Todd. 2011. *A Convergence of Civilizations: The Transformation of Muslim Societies around the World*. New York: Columbia University Press.

Crenshaw, Edward M., Ansari Z. Ameen and M. Christenson. 1997. "Population Dynamics and Economic Development: Age-Specific Population Growth Rates and Economic Growth in Developing Countries, 1965 to 1990." *American Sociological Review* 62:974–84.

Critchfield, Richard. 1994. *The Villagers: Changed Values, Altered Lives: The Closing of the Urban-Rural Gap*. New York: Anchor Books.

Crosby, Alfred W. 1972. *The Columbian Exchange: Biological and Cultural Consequences of 1492*. Westport, CT: Greenwood Press.

Crowder, Kyle, Jeremy Pais and Scott J. South. 2012. "Neighborhood Diversity, Metropolitan Constraints, and Household Migration." *American Sociological Review* 77(3):325–53.

Curtis, Katherine J. and Annemarie Schneider. 2011. "Understanding the Demographic Implications of Climate Change: Estimates of Localized Population Predictions under Future Scenarios of Sea-Level Rise." *Population & Environment* 33:28–54.

Cutler, David and Grant Miller. 2005. "The Role of Public Health Improvements in Health Advances: The Twentieth-Century United States." *Demography* 42(1):1–22.

Cutright, Phillips and Robert M. Fernquist. 2000. "Effects of Societal Integration, Period, Region, and Culture of Suicide on Male Age-Specific Suicide Rates: 20 Developed Countries, 1955–1989." *Social Science Research* 29:148–72.

Cutter, S.L., J.T. Mitchell and M.S. Scott. 2000. "Revealing the Vulnerability of Places: A Case Study of Georgetown County, South Carolina." *Annals of the Association of American Geographers* 90(4):713–37.

Daly, H. 1971. "A Marxian-Malthusian View of Poverty and Development." *Population Studies* 25(1):25–37.

Daniels, Kimberly and Joyce C. Abma. 2018. "Current Contraceptive Status among Women Aged 15–49: United States, 2015–2017." *NCHS Data Brief* (327).

Dankovchick, Jenine, Megan J. Hoopes, Victoria Warren-Mears and Elizabeth Knaster. 2015. "Disparities in Life Expectancy of Pacific Northwest American Indians and Alaska Natives: Analysis of Linkage-Corrected Life Tables." *Public Health Reports* 130(1):71–80.

Danziger, Pamela N. 2018. "9 Demographic Trends Shaping Retail's Future." *Forbes.com*, September. New York City: Forbes.

Darwin, Charles. 1872 [1991]. *On the Origin of Species*. Norwalk, CT: The Easton Press.

Davidson, Karina, Elizabeth Mostofsky and William Whang. 2010. "Don't Worry, Be Happy: Positive Affect and Reduced 10-Year Incident Coronary Heart Disease: The Canadian Nova Scotia Health Survey." *European Heart Journal* 31(9):1065–1070.

Davis, Kingsley. 1945. "The World Demographic Transition." *The Annals of the American Academy of Political and Social Science* 237(January):1–11.

Davis, Kingsley. 1949. *Human Society*. New York: Macmillan.

Davis, Kingsley. 1955. "Malthus and the Theory of Population." in *The Language of Social Research*, edited by P. Lazarsfeld and M. Rosenberg. New York: Free Press.

Davis, Kingsley and Judith Blake. 1955. "Social Structure and Fertility: An Analytic Framework." *Economic Development and Cultural Change* 4:211–35.

Davis, Kingsley. 1963. "The Theory of Change and Response in Modern Demographic History." *Population Index* 29(4):345–66.

Davis, Kingsley. 1965. "The Urbanization of the Human Population." *Scientific American* 213(3):40–54.

Davis, Kingsley. 1967. "Population Policy: Will Current Programs Succeed?". *Science* 158:730–39.

Davis, Kingsley. 1972. "The American Family in Relation to Demographic Change." in *U.S. Commission on Population Growth and the American Future, Volume 1, Demographic and Social Aspects of Population Growth*, edited by C. Westoff and R. Parke. Washington, DC: Government Printing Office.

Davis, Kingsley. 1973. *Cities and Mortality*. Liège: IUSSP.

Davis, Kingsley. 1974. "The Migration of Human Populations." *Scientific American* 231:92–105.

Davis, Kingsley. 1984. "Wives and Work: The Sex Role Revolution and Its Consequences." *Population and Development Review* 10(3):397–418.

Davis, Mike. 2007. *Planet of Slums*. London: Verso.

de Beauvoir, Simone. 1953. *The Second Sex; Translated and Edited by H.M. Parshley*. New York: Knopf.

De Grey, Aubrey and Johnathan Rossiter, eds. 2017. *The Next Step: Exponential Life*. Bilbao, Spain: BBVA Open Mind.

de Groot, Natasja G. , Nel Otting, Gaby G. M. Doxiadis, Sunita S. Balla-Jhagjhoorsingh, Jonathan L. Heeney, Jon J. van Rood, Pascal Gagneux and Ronald E. Bontrop. 2002. "Evidence for an Ancient Selective Sweep in the MHC Class I Gene Repertoire of Chimpanzees." *Proceedings of the National Academy of Sciences* 99(18):11742–47.

De Jong, G. and J. Fawcett. 1981. "Motivations for Migration: An Assessment on a Value-Expectancy Model." in *Migration Decision Making*, edited by G. De Jong and R. Gardner. New York: Pergamon Press.

De Jong, Gordon. 2000. "Expectations, Gender, and Norms in Migration Decision-Making." *Population Studies* 54:307–19.

DeCarlo, Scott. 2010, "What the Boss Makes." *Forbes.com*. (http://www.forbes.com/2010/04/27/compensation-chief-executive-salary-leadership-boss-10-ceo-compensation-intro.html).

DellaPergola, Sergio. 1980. "Patterns of American Jewish Fertility." *Demography* 17(3):261–73.

DellaPergola, Sergio, John F. May and Allyson C. Lynch. 2014. *Israel's Demography Has a Unique History*. Washington, DC: Population Reference Bureau.

Delmelle, Elizabeth. 2019. "The Increasing Sociospatial Fragmentation of Urban America." *Urban Science* 3(9).

Demeny, Paul. 1968. "Early Fertility Decline in Austria-Hungary: A Lesson in Demographic Transition." *Daedalus* 97(2):502–22.

Demos, J. 1965. "Notes on Life in Plymouth Colony." *William and Mary Quarterly* 22(264–86).

DeNavas-Walt, Carmen, Robert W. Cleveland and Bruce H. Webster. 2003, "Income in the United States: 2002; Current Population Reports P60–221", Washington, DC: U.S. Census Bureau. (http://www.census.gov/prod/2003pubs/p60-221.pdf).

DHS Program. 2019, "Demographic and Health Surveys Statcompiler". (http://www.statcompiler.com/en/).

Diamond, Jared. 1997. *Guns, Germs, and Steel*. New York: W.W. Norton.

Dicker, Daniel, Christopher J. L. Murray and Emmanuela Gakidou. 2018. "Global, Regional, and National Age-Sex-Specific Mortality and Life Expectancy, 1950–2017: A Systematic Analysis for the Global Burden of Disease Study 2017." *The Lancet* 392:1684–735.

Divine, R. 1957. *American Immigration Policy, 1924–1952*. New Haven, CT: Yale Univeristy Press.

Dogan, M. and John Kasarda. 1988. "Introduction: How Giant Cities Will Multiply and Grow." in *The Metropolis Era, Volume 1, a World of Giant Cities*, edited by M. Dogan and J. Kasarda. Newbury Park, CA: Sage Publications.

Domingo, Andreu. 2008. "'Demodystopias': Prospects of Demographic Hell." *Population and Development Review* 34(4):725–45.

Domschke, E. and D. Goyer. 1986. *The Handbook of National Population Censuses: Africa and Asia*. Westport, CT: Greenwood Press.

Donaldson, Peter J. 1990. *Nature against Us: The United States and the World Population Crisis, 1965–1980*. Chapel Hill: University of North Carolina Press.

Douglas, Emily Taft. 1970. *Margaret Sanger: Pioneer of the Future*. New York: Holt, Rinehart and Winston.

Dublin, Louis, Alfred Lotka and Mortimer Spiegleman. 1949. *Length of Life: A Study of the Life Table*. New York: Ronald Press.

Dumond, D. 1975. "The Limitation of Human Population: A Natural History." *Science* 232:713–20.

Dumont, Arsène. 1890. *Depopulation Et Civilisation: Etude Demographique*. Paris: Lecrosnier & Babe.

Duncan, Greg J., Katherine Magnuson and Elizabeth Votruba-Drzal. 2017. "Moving Beyond Correlations in Assessing the Consequences of Poverty." *Annual Review of Psychology* 68:413–34.

Dunlop, John E. and Victoria A. Velkoff. 1999. "Women and the Economy in India, Report WID/98-2." Washington, DC: U.S. Census Bureau.

Durand, John D. 1967. "The Modern Expansion of World Population." *Proceedings of the American Philosophical Society* 3(June):137–40.

Durkheim, Emile. 1893 [1933]. *The Division of Labor in Society, Translated by George Simpson.* Glencoe, IL: Free Press.

Easterlin, Richard and Eileen Crimmins. 1985. *The Fertility Revolution: A Supply-Demand Analysis.* Chicago: University of Chicago Press.

Easterlin, Richard. 2008. "Introduction." In *The Lucky Few,* edited by E. Carlson. New York: Springer.

Easterlin, Richard A. 1968. *Population, Labor Force, and Long Swings in Economic Growth.* New York: National Bureau of Economic Research.

Easterlin, Richard A. 1978. "The Economics and Sociology of Fertility: A Synthesis." in *Historical Studies of Changing Fertility,* edited by C. Tilly. Princeton: Princeton University Press.

Eaton, J. and A. Mayer. 1954. *Man's Capacity to Reproduce.* Glencoe: Free Press.

Ehrlich, Paul. 1968. *The Population Bomb.* New York: Ballantine Books.

Ehrlich, Paul. 1971. *The Population Bomb, Second Edition.* New York: Sierra Club/Ballantine Books.

Ehrlich, Paul and Anne Ehrlich. 1990. *The Population Explosion.* New York: Simon & Schuster.

Eichenlaub, Suzanne C., Stewart E. Tolnay and J. Trent Alexander. 2010. "Moving Out but Not Up: Economic Outcomes in the Great Migration." *American Sociological Review* 75(1):101–25.

Elliott, Diana B., Kristy Krivickas, Matthew W. Brault and Rose M. Kreider. 2012, "Historical Marriage Trends from 1890–2010: A Focus on Race Differences", *Paper presented at 2012 PAA Annual Meetings,* Washington, DC: U.S. Census Bureau. (http://www.census.gov/hhes/socdemo /marriage/data/acs/ElliottetalPAA2012presentation.pdf).

Elliott, James R. 1999. "Putting 'Global Cities' in Their Place: Urban Hierarchy and Low-Income Employment During the Post-War Era." *Urban Geography* 20(2):95–115.

Emch, Michael, Elisabeth Dowling Root and Margaret Carrel. 2017. *Health and Medical Geography, Fourth Edition.* New York: Guilford Press.

Engels, Frederich. 1844 [1953]. *Outlines of a Critique of Political Economy, Reprinted in R. L. Meek, 1953, Marx and Engels on Malthus.* London: Lawrence and Wishart.

Espenshade, Thomas J., Analia S. Olgiati and Simon A. Levin. 2011. "On Nonstable and Stable Population Momentum." *Demography* 48:1581–99.

Esping-Anderson, G. and Francesco C. Billari. 2015. "Re-Theorizing Family Demographics." *Population and Development Review* 38:707–27.

Evans, Simon M. and Peter Peller. 2015. "A Brief History of Hutterite Demography." *Great Plains Quarterly* 35(1).

Eversley, D. 1959. *Social Theories of Malthus and the Malthusian Debate.* Oxford, UK: Clarendon Press.

Fagan, Brian. 2000. *The Little Ice Age: How Climate Made History 1300–1850.* New York: Basic Books.

Fan, C. Cindy. 1999. "The Vertical and Horizontal Expansions of China's City System." *Urban Geography* 20(6):493–515.

Fan, C. Cindy. 2008. *China on the Move: Migration, the State, and the Household.* London and New York: Routledge.

Fargues, Philippe. 1995. "Changing Hierarchies of Gender and Generation in the Arab World." in *Family, Gender, and Population in the Middle East,* edited by C. M. Obermeyer. Cairo: American University in Cairo.

Farley, Reynolds. 1970. *Growth of the Black Population.* Chicago: Markham.

Farley, Reynolds. 1976. "Components of Suburban Population Growth." in *The Changing Face of the Suburbs,* edited by B. Schwartz. Chicago: University of Chicago Press.

Feehan, Dennis M. 2018. "Separating the Signal from the Noise: Evidence for Deceleration in Old-Age Death Rates." *Demography.* (https://doi.org/10.1007/s1352).

Feliciano, Cynthia and Rubén Rumbaut. 2018. "Varieties of Ethnic Self-Identities: Children of Immigrants in Middle Adulthood." *The Russell Sage Foundation Journal of the Social Sciences* 4(5):26–46.

Feng, Nailin. 2012, "Analysis on Quality of China's Population Census Data: Thoughts for 2010", *Tokyo: 13th East Asian Statistical Conference of the Statistics Bureau of Japan.* (http://www.stat.go.jp/english/info/meetings /eastasia/pdf/t1chpp.pdf).

Feshbach, Murray and Alfred Friendly. 1992. *Ecocide in the USSR: Health and Nature under Siege.* New York: Basic Books.

Fields, Jason and Lynne Casper. 2001. "America's Families and Living Arrangements: 2000." *Current Population Reports* P20–537.

Findlay, Allan M. 1995. "Skilled Transients: The Invisible Phenomenon." In *The Cambridge Survey of World Migration,* edited by R. Cohen. Cambridge, UK: Cambridge University Press.

Firebaugh, Glenn. 2003. *The New Geography of Global Income Inequality.* Cambridge, MA: Harvard University Press.

Fischer, Claude. 1976. *The Urban Experience.* New York: Harcourt Brace Jovanovich.

Fischer, Claude. 1981. "The Public and Private Worlds of City Life." *American Sociological Review* 46:306–16.

Fischer, Claude S. 2011. *Still Connected: Family and Friends in America since 1970.* New York: Russell Sage Foundation.

Fitzgerald, David and Rawan Arar. 2018. "The Sociology of Refugee Migration." *Annual Review of Sociology* 44:387–406.

Fitzsimmons, James D. and Michael R. Ratcliffe. 2004. "Reflections on the Review of Metropolitan Area Standards in the United States, 1990–2000." in *New Forms of Urbanization: Beyond the Urban-Rural Dichotomy*, edited by A. G. Champion and G. Hugo. London: Ashgate Publishing Company.

Florida, Richard, Charlotta Mellander and Tim Gulden. 2012. "Global Metropolis: Assessing Economic Activity in Urban Centers Based on Nighttime Satellite Images." *The Professional Geographer* 64(2):178–87.

Floud, Roderick, Robert W. Fogel, Bernard Harris and Sok Chui Hong. 2011. *The Changing Body: Health, Nutrition, and Human Development in the Western World since 1700*. Cambridge, UK: Cambridge University Press.

Fogel, Robert W. and Lorens A. Helmchen. 2002. "Economic and Technological Development and Their Relationships to Body Size and Productivity." In *The Nutrition Transition: Diet and Disease in the Developing World*, edited by B. Caballero and B. M. Popkin. San Diego: Academic Press.

Fogel, Robert W. 2004. *The Escape from Hunger and Premature Death, 1700–2100: Europe, America, and the Third World*. New York: Cambridge University Press.

Foner, Anne. 1975. "Age in Society: Structure and Change." *American Behavioral Scientist* 19(2):144–65.

Fontenot, Kayla, Jessica Semega and Melissa Kollar. 2018. "Income and Poverty in the United States." *Report Number P60–263*. Washington, DC: U.S. Census Bureau.

Food and Agriculture Organization. 2013. *The International Year of Quinoa*. Rome: Food and Agriculture Organization. (http://www.fao.org/quinoa-2013/en/).

Food and Agriculture Organization. 2019a. *The State of Food Security and Nutrition in the World 2018*. Rome: FAO.

Food and Agriculture Organization. 2019b. *Faostat*. Rome: Food and Agriculture Organization. (http://www.fao.org/faostat/en/#data/FS).

Forbes. 2018. *Forbes 400: The Definitive Ranking of the Wealthiest Americans*. New York: Forbes. (https://www.forbes.com/forbes-400/#5f06d7c97e2f).

Ford, Larry R. 2003. *America's New Downtowns: Reinvention or Revitalization*. Baltimore, MD: Johns Hopkins University Press.

Ford, Tania. 1999. "Understanding Population Growth in the Peri-Urban Region." *International Journal of Population Geography* 5:297–311.

Foster, George. 1967. *Tzintzuntzan: Mexican Peasants in a Changing World*. Boston: Little, Brown.

Fowler, Christopher S., Barrett A. Lee and Stephen A. Matthews. 2016. "The Contributions of Places to Metropolitan Ethnoracial Diversity and Segregation: Decomposing Change across Space and Time." *Demography* 53:1955–77.

Francese, Peter and Rebecca Piirto. 1990. *Capturing Customers: How to Target the Hottest Markets of the '90s*. Ithaca, NY: American Demographics Press.

Freedman, Ronald, Ming-Cheng Chang and Te-Hsiung Sun. 1994. "Taiwan's Transition from High Fertility to Below-Replacement Levels." *Studies in Family Planning* 25(6):317–31.

Freeman, O.L. 1992. "Perspectives and Prospects." *Agricultural History* 66(2):3–11.

Frey, William H. 2004a. "The Fading of City-Suburb and Metro-Nonmetro Distinctions in the United States." in *New Forms of Urbanization: Beyond the Urban-Rural Dichotomy*, edited by A. G. Champion and G. Hugo. London: Ashgate Publishing Company.

Frey, William H. 2004b. *The New Great Migration: Black Americans' Return to the South, 1965–2000*. Washington, DC: The Brookings Institution.

Frey, William H. 2006. *Diversity Spreads Out: Metropolitan Shifts in Hispanic, Asian, and Black Populations since 2000*. Washington, DC: The Brookings Institution.

Frey, William H. 2009. *A Rollercoaster Decade for Migation*. Washington, DC: Brookings Institution. (http://www.brookings.edu/opinions/2009/1229_migration_frey.aspx).

Frey, William H. 2018. *Diversity Explosion: How New Racial Demographics Are Remaking America*. Washington, DC: Brookings Institution Press.

Friedlander, Dov. 1983. "Demographic Responses and Socioeconomic Structure: Population Processes in England and Wales in the Nineteenth Century." *Demography* 20(3):249–72.

Friedman, Thomas L. 2012. "The Other Arab Spring." *New York Times*. http://www.nytimes.com/2012/04/08/opinion/sunday/friedman-the-other-arab-spring.html?

Friedman, Thomas L. 2013, "Without Water, Revolution". *New York Times*. (http://www.nytimes.com/2013/05/19/opinion/sunday/friedman-without-water-revolution.html?).

Friedman, Thomas L. 2019, "Mother Nature Will Be on the Ballot in 2020." *Morning Joe, MSNBC*. (http://www.msnbc.com/morning-joe).

Friedmann, John. 1966. *Regional Development Policy: A Case Study of Venezuela*. Cambridge, MA: The M.I.T. Press.

Friedmann, John. 2005. *China's Urban Transition*. Minneapolis, MN: University of Minnesota Press.

Frier, Bruce. 1983. "Roman Life Expectancy: The Pannonian Evidence." *Phoenix* 37(4):328–44.

Frier, Bruce W. 1999. "Roman Demography." in *Life, Death, and Entertainment in the Roman Empire*, edited by D. S. Potter and D. J. Mattingly. Ann Arbor: University of Michigan Press.

Frisch, Rose. 1978. "Population, Food Intake, and Fertility." *Science* 199:22–30.

Frisch, Rose. 2002. *Female Fertility and the Body Fat Connection.* Chicago: University of Chicago Press.

Fuguitt, Glenn and James Zuiches. 1975. "Residential Preferences and Population Distribution." *Demography* 12:491–504.

Fuguitt, Glenn and D. Brown. 1990. "Residential Preferences and Population Redistribution in 1972–88." *Demography* 27:589–600.

Galle, Omer, Walter Gove and J. McPherson. 1972. "Population Density and Pathology: What Are the Relations for Man." *Science* 176:23–30.

Galloway, P. 1984. *Long Term Fluctuations in Climate and Population in the Pre-Industrial Era.* Berkeley: University of California.

Gao, F., E. Bailes, D.L. Robertson, Y. Chen, C.M. Rodenburg, S.F. Michael, L.B. Cummins, L.O. Arthur, M. Peeters, G.M. Shaw, P.M. Sharp and B.H. Hahn. 1999. "Origin of HIV-1 in the Chimpanzee Pan Troglodytes Troglodytes." *Nature* 397(6718):436–41.

Garcia y Griego, Manuel, John R. Weeks and Roberto Ham-Chande. 1990. "Mexico." in *Handbook on International Migration,* edited by W.J. Serow, C.B. Nam, D.F. Sly and R.H. Weller. New York: Greenwood Press.

Garreau, Joel. 1991. *Edge City: Life on the New Frontier.* New York: Doubleday.

Gartner, R. 1990. "The Victims of Homicide: A Temporal and Cross-National Comparison." *American Sociological Review* 55:92–106.

Gendell, Murray. 2001. "Retirement Age Declines Again in 1990s." *Monthly Labor Review* (October):12–21.

Gillis, J.R., L.A. Tilly and D. Levine, eds. 1992. *The European Experience of Declining Fertility: A Quiet Revolution 1850–1970.* Oxford, UK: Basil Blackwell.

Glass, D.V. 1953. *Introduction to Malthus.* New York: Wiley.

Glenn, Evelyn Nakano, ed. 2009. *Shades of Difference: Why Skin Color Matters.* Stanford, CA: Stanford University Press.

Global Aging Report. 1997. "Guaranteeing the Rights of Older People: China Takes a Great Leap Forward." *Global Aging Report* 2(5):3.

Godwin, William. 1793 [1946]. *Enquiry Concerning Political Justice and Its Influences on Morals and Happiness.* Toronto: University of Toronto Press.

Goldberg, Michelle. 2017, "Trump Didn't Just Reinstate the Global Gag Rule. He Massively Expanded It", Slate: January 24. (https://slate.com/news-and-politics/2017/01/trumps-global-gag-rule-is-even-worse-than-it-seemed.html).

Goldman, Noreen. 1984. "Changes in Widowhood and Divorce and Expected Durations of Marriage." *Demography* 21(3):297–308.

Goldscheider, Calvin. 1971. *Population, Modernization, and Social Structure.* Boston: Little, Brown.

Goldscheider, Calvin. 2006. "Religion, Family, and Fertility: What Do We Know Historically and Comparatively?" in *Religion and the Decline of Fertility in the Western World,* edited by R. Derosas and F. van Poppel. Dordrecht: Springer.

Goldscheider, F., E. Bernhardt and Trude Lappegård. 2015. "The Gender Revolution: A Framework for Understanding Changing Family and Demographic Behavior." *Population and Development Review* 41(2):207–39.

Goldstein, Alice and Wang Feng, eds. 1996. *China: The Many Facets of Demographic Change.* Boulder, CO: Westview Press.

Goldstein, Sidney. 1988. "Levels of Urbanization in China." in *The Metropolis Era: A World of Giant Cities,* edited by M. Dogan and J.D. Kasarda. Newbury Park, CA: Sage Publications.

Gonzalez-Barrera, Ana and Jens Manuel Krogstad. 2018, *What We Know About Illegal Immigration from Mexico.* Washington, DC: Pew Research Center. (http://www.pewresearch.org/fact-tank/2018/12/03/what-we-know-about-illegal-immigration-from-mexico/).

Goode, William J. 1993. *World Changes in Divorce Patterns.* New Haven: Yale University Press.

Goodkind, D.M. 1995. "Vietnam's One-or-Two Child Policy in Action." *Population and Development Review* 21(1):85–112.

Goodkind, Daniel M. 2011. "Child Underreporting, Fertility, and Sex Ratio Imbalance in China." *Demography* 48(1):291–316.

Gordon, Charles and Charles F. Longino, Jr. 2000. "Age Structure and Social Structure." *Contemporary Sociology* 29(5):699–703.

Grabill, W., Clyde Kiser and Pascal Whelpton. 1958. *The Fertility of American Women.* New York: Wiley.

Graebner, W. 1980. *A History of Retirement.* New Haven: Yale University Press.

Grant, Monica J. and Jere R. Behrman. 2010. "Gender Gaps in Educational Attainment in Less Developed Countries." *Population and Development Review* 36(1):71–89.

Graunt, John. 1662 [1939]. *Natural and Political Observations Made Upon the Bills of Mortality, Edited with an Introduction by Walter F. Willcox.* Baltimore: Johns Hopkins University Press.

Greenhalgh, Susan. 1986. "Shifts in China's Population Policy 1984–86: Views from the Central, Provincial, and Local Levels." *Population and Development Review* 12(3):491–516.

Greville, Thomas. 1947. *United States Life Tables and Actuarial Tables 1939–1941.* Washington, DC: US Government Printing Office.

Grossbard, Shoshana and Elena Stancenelli. 2010. "Whose Time? Who Saves? Introduction to a Special Issue on Couples' Savings, Time Use and Children." *Review of Economics of the Household* 8(3):289–96.

Gu Baochang, Wang Feng, Guo Zhigang and Zhang Erli. 2007. "China's Local and National Fertility Policies at the End of the Twentieth Century." *Population and Development Review* 33(1):129–47.

Guengant, Jean-Pierre and John F. May. 2013. "African Demography." *Global Journal of Emerging Market Economies* 5(3):269–328.

Guillard, Achille. 1855. *Éléments De Statistique Humaine Ou Démographie Comparée.* Paris: Guillaumin et Cie Libraires.

Guinness World Records. 2018. *Most Prolific Mother Ever.* (http://www.guinnessworldrecords.com/world -records/most-prolific-mother-ever).

Gupta, Geeta Rao. 1998. "Claiming the Future." in *The Progress of Nations: 1998*, edited by UNICEF. New York: United Nations Childrens Fund.

Gutmann, Myron P. and Vincenzo Field. 2010. "Katrina in Historical Context: Environment and Migration in the U.S." *Population and Environment* 31:3–19.

Guttmacher Institute. 2014. *Fact Sheet: Induced Abortion in the United States.* New York: Guttmacher Institute. (http:// www.guttmacher.org/pubs/fb_induced_abortion.html).

Hacker, J. David. 2003. "Rethinking the 'Early' Decline of Marital Fertility in the United States." *Demography* 40(4):605–20.

Hackett, Conrad and David McClenton. 2017. *Christians Remain World's Largest Religious Group, but They Are Declining in Europe.* Washington, DC: Pew Research Center. (https://www.pewresearch.org /fact-tank/2017/04/05/christians-remain-worlds-largest -religious-group-but-they-are-declining-in-europe/).

Hager, Thomas. 2006. *The Demon under the Microscope: From Battlefield Hospitals to Nazi Labs, on Doctor's Heroic Search for the World's First Miracle Drug.* New York: Random House.

Hailu, Ashagre. 2019. *Ethiopia to Delay Census Because of Instability.* BBC News. (https://www.bbc.com/news /live/world-africa).

Hales, Craig M., Margaret D. Carrol, Cheryl D. Fryar and Cynthia L. Ogden. 2017. "Prevalence of Obesity among Adults and Youth: United States, 2015–2016." *NCHS Data Brief No. 288.* Washington, DC: National Center for Health Statistics, U.S. Centers for Disease Control and Prevention.

Hamilton, Brady E., Joyce A. Martin, Michelle J.K. Osterman and Lauren M. Rossen. 2019. "Births: Provisional Data for 2018." *NVSS Vital Statistics Rapid Release.* Washington, DC: National Center for Health Statistics, U.S. Centers for Disease Control and Prevention.

Hampshire, S. 1955. "Introduction." in *Sketch for an Historical Picture of the Progress of the Human Mind*, edited by Marie Jean Antoine Nicolas de Caritat Condorcet. London: Weidenfield and Nicholson.

Han, Sun Sheng and Shue Tuck Wong. 1994. "The Influence of Chinese Reform and Pre-Reform Policies on Urban Growth in the 1980s." *Urban Geography* 15(6):537–64.

Harari, Yuval Noah. 2015. *Sapiens: A Brief History of Humankind.* New York: HarperCollins.

Harbison, Sarah F. and Warren C. Robinson. 2002. "Policy Implications of the Next World Demographic Transition." *Studies in Family Planning* 33:37–48.

Hardin, Garrett. 1968. "The Tragedy of the Commons." *Science* 162:1243–48.

Harkavy, Oscar. 1995. *Curbing Population Growth: An Insider's Perspective on the Population Movement.* New York: Plenum Press.

Harris, David R. and Jeremiah Joseph Sim. 2002. "Who Is Multiracial? Assessing the Complexity of Lived Race." *American Sociological Review* 67:614–27.

Harris, Marvin and Eric B. Ross. 1987. *Death, Sex, and Fertility: Population Regulation in Preindustrial and Developing Societies.* New York: Columbia University Press.

Harris, Richard, Peter Sleight and Richard Webber. 2005. *Geodemographics, GIS and Neighborhood Targeting.* Chichester, UK: John Wiley & Sons, Ltd.

Harrison, Harry. 1967. *Make Room! Make Room!* New York: Berkley Publishing.

Harrison, J. Richard and Glenn R. Carroll. 2005. *Culture and Demography in Organizations.* Princeton: Princeton University Press.

Harrison, Paul. 1993. *The Third Revolution: Population, Environment and a Sustainable World.* London: Penguin Books.

Harvey, W. 1986. "Homicide among Young Black Adults: Life in the Subculture of Exasperation." in *Homicide among Black Americans*, edited by D. Hawkins. New York: University Press of America.

Hattersly, Lin. 2005. "Trends in Life Expectancy by Social Class—an Update." *Health Statistics Quarterly* 2:533–39.

Hatton, T.J. and J.G. Williamson. 1994. "What Drove the Mass Migrations from Europe in the Late Nineteenth Century?". *Population and Development Review* 20(3):533–59.

Haub, Carl. 2011. *How Many People Have Ever Lived on Earth?* Washington, DC: Population Reference Bureau. (http://www.prb.org/Publications/Articles/2002 /HowManyPeopleHaveEverLivedonEarth.aspx).

Haug, Werner. 2000. "National and Immigrant Minorities: Problems of Measurement and Definition." *Genus* LVI(1–2):133–47.

Hawass, Zahi, Yehia Gad, Somaia Ismail, Rabab Khairat, Dina Fathalla, Naglaa Hasan, Amal Ahmed, Hisham Elleithy, Markus Ball, Fawzi Gaballah, Sally Wasef, Mohamed Fateen, Hany Amer, Paul Gostner, Ashraf Selim, Albert Zink and Carsten Pusch. 2010. "Ancestry and Pathology in King Tutankhamun's Family." *Journal of the American Medical Association* 303(7):638–47.

Hawley, Amos. 1972. "Population Density and the City." *Demography* 91:521–30.

Hayford, Sarah R. 2013. "Marriage (Still) Matters: The Contribution of Demographic Change to Trends in Childlessness in the United States." *Demography* 50(5):1641–61.

Headey, Derek D. and Andrew Hodge. 2009. "The Effect of Population Growth on Economic Growth: A Meta-Regression Analysis of the Macroeconomic Literature." *Population and Development Review* 35(2):221–48.

Hecht, Jacqueline. 1987. "Johann Peter Süssmilch: A German Prophet in Foreign Countries." *Population Studies* 41:31–58.

Heer, David. 1965. "Abortion, Contraception, and Population Policy in the Soviet Union." *Demography* 2:531–39.

Henry, Louis. 1961. "Some Data on Natural Fertility." *Eugenics Quarterly* 8:81–91.

Henry, Louis. 1967. *Manuel De Demographique Historique*. Paris: Droz.

Herlihy, David and Christiane Klapisch-Zuber. 1985. *Tuscans and Their Families: A Study of the Florentine Catasto of 1427*. New Haven: Yale University Press.

Heuser, Robert. 1976. *Fertility Tables for Birth Cohorts by Color: United States, 1917–73*. Rockville, MD: National Center for Health Statistics.

Himes, Norman E. 1976. *Medical History of Contraception*. New York: Schocken Books.

Himmelfarb, Gertrude. 1984. *The Idea of Poverty: England in the Early Industrial Age*. New York: Alfred A. Knopf.

Hinde, Thomas. 1995. *The Domesday Book: England's Heritage, Then & Now*. London: Tiger Books International.

Hirschman, Albert. 1958. *The Strategy of Economic Development*. New Haven: Yale University Press.

Ho, J.Y. and I.T. Elo. 2013. "The Contribution of Smoking to Black-White Differences in U.S. Mortality." *Demography* 50(545–568).

Hobbs, Frank and Nicole Stoops. 2002. *Demographic Trends in the 20th Century*. Washington, DC: U.S. Census Bureau.

Hockings, Paul. 1999. *Kindreds of the Earth: Badaga Household Structure and Demography*. Walnut Creek, CA: Alta Mira Press.

Hodell, David, Jason Curtis and Mark Brenner. 1995. "Possible Role of Climate in the Collapse of Classic Mayan Civilization." *Nature* 375:391–94.

Hodgson, Dennis. 2009. "Malthus' Essay on Population and the American Debate over Slavery." *Comparative Studies in Society and History* 51(4):1–29.

Hoefer, Michael, Nancy Rytina and Bryan C. Baker. 2012. *Estimates of the Unauthorized Immigrant Population Residing in the United States: January 2011*. Washington DC: US Department of Homeland Security. (http:// www.dhs.gov/xlibrary/assets/statistics/publications/ois _ill_pe_2011.pdf).

Holdren, John. 1990. "Energy in Transition." *Scientific American* 263(3):156–63.

Holloway, Steven R., Richard Wright and Mark Ellis. 2012. "The Racially Fragmented City? Neighborhood Racial Segregation and Diversity Jointly Considered." *The Professional Geographer* 64(1):63–82.

Hoque, Nazrul, Mary A. McGehee and Benjamin S. Bradshaw, eds. 2013. *Applied Demography and Public Health*. Dordrecht: Springer.

Horiuchi, Shiro and John R. Wilmoth. 1998. "Deceleration in the Age Pattern of Mortality at Older Ages." *Demography* 35:391–412.

Howe, Neil and William Strauss. 1991. *Generations: The History of America's Future, 1584 to 2069*. New York: William Morrow and Company, Inc.

Howe, Neil and William Strauss. 2000. *Millennials Rising*. New York: Random House.

Howell, Nancy. 1979. *Demography of the Dobe Kung*. New York: Academic Press.

Hsu, Mei-Ling. 1994. "The Expansion of the Chinese Urban System, 1953–1990." *Urban Geography* 15(6):514–36.

Hu, Y. and N. Goldman. 1990. "Mortality Differentials by Marital Status: An International Comparison." *Demography* 27:233–50.

Hulchanski, David, Robert Murdie, Alan Walks and Larry Bourne. 2013. "Canada's Voluntary Census Is Worthless. Here's Why." *The Globe and Mail*. (http://www .theglobeandmail.com/globe-debate/canadas-voluntary -census-is-worthless-heres-why/article14674558/).

Hume, David. 1752 [1963]. "Of the Populousness of Ancient Nations." in *Essays: Moral, Political and Literary, Part II, Essay XI*, edited by D. Hume. London: Oxford University Press.

Hunter, Lori M., Jessie K. Luna and Rachel M. Norton. 2015. "Environmental Dimensions of Migration." *Annual Review of Sociology* 41:377–97.

Hutchinson, E. P. 1967. *The Population Debate: The Development of Conflicting Theories up to 1900*. Boston: Houghton Mifflin.

Huzel, J. 1969. "Malthus, the Poor Law, and Population in Early Nineteenth-Century England." *Economic History Review* 22:430–52.

Huzel, J. 1980. "The Demographic Impact of the Old Poor Law: More Reflexions on Malthus." *Economic History Review* 33:367–81.

Huzel, J. 1984. "Parson Malthus and the Pelican Inn Protocol: A Reply to Proessor Levine." *Historical Method* 17:25–27.

Huzel, James. 2006. *The Popularization of Malthus in Early Nineteenth-Century England: Martineau, Cobbett and the Pauper Press*. Aldershot, UK: Ashgate Publishing Company.

Iceland, John and Kyle Anne Nelson. 2008. "Hispanic Segregation in Metropolitan America: Exploring the Multiple Forms of Spatial Assimilation." *American Sociological Review* 73:741–65.

Iceland, John. 2019. "Racial and Ethnic Inequality in Poverty and Affluence, 1959–2015." *Population Research and Policy Review.* (https://doi.org/10.1007/s11113-019-09512-7).

Idler, Jose Enrique. 2007. *Officially Hispanic: Classification Policy and Identity.* Lanham, MD: Rowman and Littlefield.

INEGI. 2010. *Cuéntame...Poblacion.* Mexico City: INEGI. (http://cuentame.inegi.org.mx/poblacion/rur_urb.aspx?tema=P).

INEGI. 2013. *Tasa Global De Fecundidad Pro Entidad Federativa, 2000 a 2013.* Mexico City: INEGI (http://www3.inegi.org.mx/sistemas/temas/default.aspx?s=est&c=17484).

INEGI. 2018. *Intercensal Survey 2015.* Mexico City: INEGI. (http://en.www.inegi.org.mx/proyectos/enchogares/especiales/intercensal/).

Inglehart, R. and P. Norris. 2003. *Rising Tide: Gender Equality and Cultural Change around the World.* New York: Cambridge University Press.

Inglehart, Ronald and Wayne E. Baker. 2000. "Modernization, Cultural Change, and the Persistence of Traditional Values." *American Sociological Review* 65:19–51.

International Labour Organization. 2013a. *Child Labour and Armed Conflict.* (http://www.ilo.org/ipec/areas/Armedconflict/lang--en/index.htm).

International Labour Organization. 2013b. *Decent Work and Gender Equality: Policies to Improve Employment Access and Quality for Women in Latin America and the Caribbean.* Santiago, Chile: ILO. (http://www.ilo.org/wcmsp5/groups/public/---americas/---ro-lima/---sro-santiago/documents/publication/wcms_229430.pdf).

IPBES. 2019. *Intergovernmental Science-Policy Platform on Biodiversity and Ecosystem Services Global Assessment.* New York: United Nations. (https://www.un.org/sustainabledevelopment/blog/2019/05/nature-decline-unprecedented-report/).

IPC Global Partners. 2008. *Integrated Food Security Phase Classification Technical Manual. Version 1.1.* Rome: FAO. (http://www.fao.org/docrep/010/i0275e/i0275e.pdf).

IPCC. 2014. *Climate Change 2014: Impacts, Adaptation, and Vulnerability: Summary for Policymakers.* New York: United Nations Intergovernmental Panel on Climate Change, Working Group II. (http://ipcc-wg2.gov/AR5/images/uploads/IPCC_WG2AR5_SPM_Approved.pdf).

Isik, Oguz and M. Melih Pinarcioglu. 2006. "Geographies of a Silent Transition: A Geographically Weighted Regression Approach to Regional Fertility Differences in Turkey." *European Journal of Population* 22:399–421.

Issawi, C. 1987. *An Arab Philosophy of History: Selections from the Prolegomena of Ibn Khaldun of Tunis (1332–1406).* Princeton: Princeton University Press.

Itkowitz, Colby. 2019. "Sen. Mike Lee Syas We Can Solve Climate Change with More Babies. Science Says Otherwise." *Washington Post,* March 26.

Iversen, Roberta Rehner, Frank F. Furstenberg, Jr. and Alisa A. Belzer. 1999. "How Much Do We Count? Interpretation and Error-Making in the Decennial Census." *Demography* 36(1):121–34.

James, Patricia. 1979. *Population Malthus: His Life and Times.* London: Routledge & Kegan Paul.

Jankowska, Marta, Magdalena Benza and John R. Weeks. 2013. "Estimating Spatial Inequalities of Urban Child Mortality." *Demographic Research* 28(2):33–62.

Jing, Yijia. 2013. "The One-Child Policy Needs an Overhaul." *Journal of Policy Analysis and Management* 32(2):392–99.

Jones, Colin. 2002. *The Great Nation: France from Louis Xv to Napolean 1715–99.* New York: Columbia University Press.

Kahneman, Daniel. 2011. *Thinking, Fast and Slow.* New York: Macmillan.

Kalleberg, Arne L. 2018. *Precarious Lives: Job Insecurity and Well-Being in Rich Democracies.* Cambridge, UK: Polity Press.

Kaneda, Toshiko and Carl Haub. 2018. *How Many People Have Ever Lived on Earth?* Washington, DC: Population Reference Bureau. (https://www.prb.org/howmanypeoplehaveeverlivedonearth/).

Kannisto, Väinö. 2007. "Central and Dispersion Indicators of Individual Life Duration: New Methods." in *Human Longevity, Individual Life Duration, and the Growth of the Oldest-Old Population,* edited by J.-M. Robine, E. M. Crimmins, S. Horiuchi and Z. Yi. Dordrecht: Springer.

Kaplan, C. and T. Van Valey. 1980. *Census 80: Continuing the Factfinder Tradition.* Washington, DC: U.S. Bureau of the Census.

Kaplan, David. 1994. "Population and Politics in a Plural Society: The Changing Geography of Canada's Linguistic Groups." *Annals of the Association of American Geographers* 84(1):46–67.

Kaplan, Robert and Richard Kronick. 2006. "Marital Status and Longevity in the United States." *Journal of Epidemiology and Community Health* 60:760–65.

Kara, Siddharth. 2017. *Modern Slavery: A Global Perspective.* New York: Columbia University Press.

Kasinitz, Philip, John H. Millenkopf, Mary C. Waters and Jennifer Holdaway. 2008. *Inheriting the City: The Children of Immigrants Come of Age.* New York: Russell Sage Foundation.

Keely, Charles. 1971. "Effects of the Immigration Act of 1965 on Selected Population Characteristics of Immigrants to the United States." *Demography* 8:157–70.

Kemper, Robert Van and George Foster. 1975. "Urbanization in Mexico: The View from Tzintzuntzan." *Latin American Urban Research* 5:53–75.

Kemper, Robert Van. 1977. *Migration and Adaptation.* Beverly Hills, CA: Sage Publications.

Kemper, Robert Van. 1996. "Migration and Adaptation: Tzintzuntzenos in Mexico City and Beyond." in *rban Life: Readings in Urban Anthropology, Third Edition,* edited by G. Gmelch and W. P. Zenner. Prospect Heights, IL: Waveland Press.

Kemper, Robert Van and Julie Adkins. 2006. *From the "Modern Tarascan Area" to the "Patria Purepecha": Changing Concepts of Ethnic and Regional Identity.* Dallas: Southern Methodist University.

Kennedy, Sheela and Larry Bumpass. 2008. "Cohabitation and Children's Living Arrangements: New Estimates from the United States." *Demographic Research* 19:1663–92.

Kephart, W. 1982. *Extraordinary Groups: The Sociology of Unconventional Life-Styles, Second Edition.* New York: St. Martins Press.

Kertzer, D.I. 1995. "Toward a Historical Demography of Aging." in *Aging in the Past: Demography, Society, and Old Age,* edited by D. I. Kertzer and P. Laslett. Berkeley: University of California Press.

Kertzer, David I., Michael J. White, Laura Bernardi and Giuseppe Gabrielli. 2009. "Italy's Path to Very Low Fertility: The Adequacy of Economic and Second Demographic Transition Theories." *European Journal of Population* 25:89–115.

Kesztenbaum, Lionel and Jean-Laurent Rosenthal. 2017. "Sewers' Diffusion and the Decline of Mortality: The Case of Paris, 1880–1914." *Journal of Urban Economics* 98(C):174–86.

Keyfitz, Nathan. 1966. "How Many People Have Ever Lived on the Earth?". *Demography* 3(2):581–82.

Keyfitz, Nathan. 1968. *Introduction to the Mathematics of Population.* Reading, MA: Addison-Wesley.

Keyfitz, Nathan. 1972. "Population Theory and Doctrine: A Historical Survey." in *Readings in Population,* edited by W. Petersen. New York: MacMillan.

Keyfitz, Nathan. 1973. "Population Theory." Chapter III in *The Determinants and Consequences of Population Trends, Volume I,* edited by United Nations. New York: United Nations.

Keyfitz, Nathan. 1982. "Can Knowledge Improve Forecasts?". *Population and Development Review* 8(4):729–51.

Keyfitz, Nathan and Hal Caswell. 2005. *Applied Mathematical Demography, Third Edition.* New York: John Wiley & Sons, Inc.

Keyser, Hannah. 2018, "How Do Generations Get Their Names?" *MentalFloss.* (http://mentalfloss.com/article /59963/how-do-generations-get-their-names).

Kim, Y.J. and Robert Schoen. 1997. "Population Momentum Expresses Population Aging." *Demography* 34(3):421–28.

Kitagawa, E. and P. Hauser. 1973. *Differential Mortality in the United States: A Study in Socioeconomic Epidemiology.* Cambridge: Harvard University Press.

Knodel, John. 1970. "Two and a Half Centuries of Demographic History in a Bavarian Village." *Population Studies* 24:353–69.

Knodel, John and Etienne van de Walle. 1979. "Lessons from the Past: Policy Implications of Historical Fertility Studies." *Population and Development Review* 5:217–45.

Kohler, Iliana, Samuel H. Preston and Laurie Bingaman Lackey. 2006. "Comparative Mortality Levels among Selected Species of Captive Animals." *Demographic Research* 15(14):413–34.

Komlos, J. 1989. "The Age at Menarche in Vienna: The Relationship between Nutrition and Fertility." *Historical Methods* 22:158–63.

Krach, Constance A. and Victoria A. Velkoff. 1999. "Centenarians in the United States: 1990." *Current Population Reports* (P23–199RV).

Kraly, Ellen Percy and Robert Warren. 1992. "Estimates of Long-Term Immigrationto the United States: Moving Us Statistics toward United Nations Concepts." *Demography* 29(4):613–26.

Kreager, Philip. 1986. "Demographic Regimes as Cultural Systems." in *The State of Population Theory: Forward from Malthus,* edited by D. Coleman and R. Schofield. Oxford: Basil Blackwell.

Kreager, Philip. 1988. "New Light on Graunt." *Population Studies* 42(1):129–40.

Kreager, Philip. 1993. "Histories of Demography: A Review Article." *Population Studies* 47(3):519–39.

Kreager, Philip. 2017. "Adam Smith, the Division of Labor, and the Renewal of Population Heterogeneity." *Population and Development Review* 43(3):513–39.

Kreider, Rose M. and Jason M. Fields. 2002. "Number, Timing, and Duration of Marriages and Divorces: 1996." *Current Population Reports* P70–80.

Krogstad, Jens Manuel, Jeffrey S. Passel and D'Vera Cohn. 2018. *5 Facts About Illegal Immigration in the U.S.* Washington, DC: Pew Research Center. (http://www .pewresearch.org/fact-tank/2018/11/28/5-facts-about -illegal-immigration-in-the-u-s/).

Kulu, Hill. 2005. "Migration and Fertility: Competing Hypotheses Re-Examined." *European Journal of Population* 21(1):51–87.

Kunstler, J.H. 1993. *The Geography of Nowhere: The Rise and Decline of America's Man-Made Landscape.* New York: Simon & Schuster.

Lacy, Karyn. 2016. "The New Sociology of Suburbs: A Research Agenda for Analysis of Emerging Trends." *Annual Review of Sociology* 42(369–84).

Lalasz, Robert. 2006. *In the News: The Nigerian Census.* Washington, DC: Population Reference Bureau. (www .prb.org).

Landers, John. 1993. *Death and the Metropolis: Studies in the Demographic History of London 1670–1830.* Cambridge: Cambridge University Press.

Lanzieri, Giampaolo. 2013, "Fertility Statistics in Relation to Economy, Parity, Education and Migration." *Statistics in Focus.* Brussels:European Commission. (http://epp.eurostat.ec.europa.eu/statistics_explained /index.php/Fertility_statistics_in_relation_to_economy, _parity,_education_and_migration).

Lariscy, Joseph T., Robert A. Hummer and Richard G. Rogers. 2018. "Cigarette Smoking and All-Cause and Cause-Specific Adult Mortality in the United States." *Demography* 55(5):1855–85.

Laslett, Peter. 1971. *The World We Have Lost.* London: Routledge & Kegan Paul.

Laslett, Peter. 1991. *A Fresh Map of Life: The Emergence of the Third Age.* Cambridge, MA: Harvard University Press.

Laxton, Paul. 1987. *London Bills of Mortality.* Cambridge, UK: Chadwyk-Healey Ltd.

Leasure, J. William. 1962. "Factors Involved in the Decline of Fertility in Spain: 1900–1950." Doctoral Dissertation, Economics, Princeton University.

Leasure, J. William. 1982. "L' Baisse De La Fecondité Aux États-Unis De 1800 a 1860." *Population* 3:607–22.

Leasure, J. William. 1989. "A Hypothesis About the Decline of Fertility: Evidence from the United States." *European Journal of Population* 5:105–17.

Lee, Everett. 1966. "A Theory of Migration." *Demography* 3:47–57.

Lee, James Z. and Wang Feng. 1999. *One Quarter of Humanity: Malthusian Mythology and Chinese Realities.* Cambridge, MA: Harvard University Press.

Lee, Richard B. 1972. "Population Growth and the Beginnings of Sedentary Life among the Kung Bushmen." in *Population Growth: Anthropological Implications,* edited by B. Spooner. Cambridge, MA: MIT Press.

Lee, Ronald. 1987. "Population Dynamics in Humans and Other Animals." *Demography* 24:443–65.

Lee, Ronald and Andrew Mason. 2010. "Fertility, Human Capital, and Economic Growth over the Demographic Transition." *European Journal of Population* 26(2):159–82.

Lee, Ronald and Yi Zhou. 2017. "Does Fertility or Mortality Drive Contemporary Population Aging? The Revisionist View Revisited." *Population and Development Review* 43(2):285–301.

Leibenstein, Harvey. 1957. *Economic Backwardness and Economic Growth.* New York: John Wiley & Sons.

Lengyel-Cook, M. and R. Repetto. 1982. "The Relevance of the Developing Countries to Demographic Transition Theory: Further Lessons from the Hungarian Experience." *Population Studies* 36(1):105–28.

Leonhardt, David and Kevin Quealy. 2014. "The American Middle Class Is No Longer the World's Richest." *New York Times* (April 22).

Leroux, C. 1984. "Ellis Island." *San Diego Union* (26 May).

Lesthaeghe, Ron J. 1977. *The Decline of Belgian Fertility, 1800–1970.* Princeton: Princeton University Press.

Lesthaeghe, Ron J. and Chris Wilson. 1986. "Modes of Production, Secularization, and the Pace of the Fertility Decline in Western Europe, 1870–1930." in *The Decline of Fertility in Europe,* edited by A. Coale and S.C. Watkins. Princeton: Princeton University Press.

Lesthaeghe, Ron J. and J. Surkyn. 1988. "Cultural Dynamics and Economic Theories of Fertility Change." *Population and Development Review* 14:1–45.

Lesthaeghe, Ron J. 1995. "The Second Demographic Transition in Western Countries: An Interpretation." in *Gender and Family Change in Industrialized Countries,* edited by K.O. Mason and A.M. Jensen. Oxford, UK: Clarendon Press.

Lesthaeghe, Ron J. 2010. "The Unfolding Story of the Second Demographic Transition." *Population and Development Review* 36(2):211–51.

Levine, Morgan E. and Eileen M. Crimmins. 2018. "Is 60 the New 50? Examining Changes in Biological Age over the Past Two Decades." *Demography* 55:387–402.

Levitt, Peggy, Josh DeWind and Steven Vertovec. 2003. "International Perspectives on Transnational Migration: An Introduction." *International Migration Review* 37(3):565–75.

Lewis, Bernard. 1995. *The Middle East: A Brief History of the Last 2,000 Years.* New York: Scribner.

Lexis, W. 1875. *Einleitung Ein Die Theorie Der Bevölkerungs-Statistik.* Strasbourg: Trubner.

Li, Nan and Shripad Tuljapurkar. 1999. "Population Momentum for Gradual Demographic Transitions." *Population Studies* 53:255–62.

Lieberman, Daniel E. 2013. *The Story of the Human Body: Evolution, Health, and Disease.* New York: Pantheon Books.

Lingappa, J.R., L.C. McDonald, P. Simone and U.D. Parashar. 2004. "Wresting Sars from Uncertainty." *Emerging Infectious Diseases* 10(2).

Liu, L., S. Oza, D. Hogan, J. Perin, I. Rudan, J.E. Lawn, S. Cousens, C. Mathers and R.E. Black. 2015. "Global, Regional, and National Causes of Child Mortality in 2000–13, with Projections to Inform Post-2015 Priorities: An Updated Systematic Analysis." *Lancet* 385(9966):430–40.

Livi-Bacci, Massimo. 2017. *A Concise History of World Population, Sixth Edition.* Malden, MA: Wiley Blackwell.

Lloyd, Cynthia B. and Serguey Ivanov. 1988. "The Effects of Improved Child Survival on Family Planning Practice and Fertility." *Studies in Family Planning* 19(3):141–61.

Lofquist, Daphne, Terry Lugaila, Martin O'Connell and Sarah Feliz. 2012, "Households and Families: 2010" *2010 Census Briefs: C2010BR-14,* Washington, DC: U.S. Census Bureau.

Logan, J.R., Richard Alba and Wenquan Zhang. 2002. "Immigrant Enclaves and Ethnic Communities in New York and Los Angeles." *American Sociological Review* 67(2):299–322.

Logan, John R. 2018. "Relying on the Census in Urban Social Science." *City & Community* 17(3):540–49.

Lopez, Alan D., Colin D. Mathers, Majid Ezzati, Dean T. Jamison and Christopher J.L. Murray. 2006. "Measuring the Global Burden of Disease and Risk Factors, 1990–2001." in *Global Burden of Disease and Risk Factors*, edited by A.D. Lopez, C.D. Mathers, M. Ezzati, D.T. Jamison and C.J.L. Murray. New York: Oxford University Press.

López-Carr, David, Narcisa G. Pricope, Juliann E. Aukema, Marta M. Jankowska, Christopher Funk, Gregory Husak and Joel Michaelson. 2014. "A Spatial Analysis of Population Dynamics and Climate Change in Africa: Potential Vulnerability Hot Spots Emerge Where Precipitation Declines and Demographic Pressures Coincide." *Population & Environment* 35(323–39).

Lou, Sha, Wenrui Huang, Shuguang Liu and Guihui Zhong. 2019. "Scarcity of Drinking Water in Taihu Lake Basin, China: A Case Study of Yixing City." *Water* 11(2).

Lovejoy, Paul E. and Jan S. Hogendorn. 1993. *Slow Death for Slavery: The Course of Abolition in Northern Nigeria 1897–1936*. New York: Cambridge University Press.

Low, Nicholas, Brendan Gleeson, Ray Green and Darko Radovic. 2005. *The Green City: Sustainable Homes, Sustainable Suburbs*. Oxfordshire, UK: Routledge.

Lundberg, Shelly and Robert A. Pollak. 2013, "Cohabitation and the Uneven Retreat from Marriage in the U.S., 1950–2010", *NBER-Spencer Conference on "Human Capital and History: The American Record*, Cambridge, MA: NBER. (http://www.nber.org/chapters/c12896.pdf).

Lutz, Wolfgang, Warren C. Sanderson and Sergei Scherbov. 2008. *IIASA's 2207 Probabilistic World Population Projections, IIASA World Population Program Online Data Base of Results*. (http://www.iiasa.ac.at/Research/POP/proj07/index.html?sb=5).

Lutz, Wolfgang. 2009. "What Can Demographers Contribute to Understanding the Link between Population and Climate Change." *PopNet (Population Network Newsletter of IIASA)* 41(Winter):1–2.

Lutz, Wolfgang, Jesus Crespo Cuaresma and Mohammad Jalal Abbasi-Shavazi. 2010. "Demography, Education, and Democracy, Global Trends and the Case of Iran." *Population and Development Review* 36(2):253–81.

Mackie, Gerry. 1996. "Ending Footbinding and Infibulation: A Convention Account." *American Sociological Review* 61:999–1017.

Maloutas, Thomas. 2004. "Segregation and Residential Mobility: Spatially Entrapped Social Mobility and Its Impact on Segregation in Athens." *European Urban and Regional Studies* 11(3):195–211.

Malthus, Thomas Robert. 1798 [1965]. *An Essay on Population*. New York: Augustus M. Kelley.

Malthus, Thomas Robert. 1872 [1971]. *An Essay on the the Principle of Population, Seventh Edition (Reprint of the 1872 Edition)*. New York: Augustus M. Kelley.

Mann, Charles C. 2011. *1491: New Revelations of the Americas before Columbus, Second Edition*. New York: Vintage Books.

Manning, Patrick and William Griffith. 1988. "Divining the Unprovable: Simulating the Demography of the African Slave Trade." *Journal of Interdisciplinary History* 19(2):177–202.

Manson, Gary A. and Richard E. Groop. 2000. "U.S. Intercounty Migration in the 1990s: People and Income Move Down the Urban Hierarchy." *Professional Geographer* 52(3):493–504.

Mare, Robert D. 2016. "Educational Homogamy in Two Gilded Ages: Evidence from Inter-Generational Social Mobility Data." *The Annals of the American Academy of Political and Social Science* 663(1):117–39.

Marini, Margaret Mooney and Pi-Ling Fan. 1997. "The Gender Gap in Earnings at Career Entry." *American Sociological Review* 62:588–604.

Marquez, Patricio V. and Jill L. Farrington. 2013. *The Challenge of Non-Communicable Diseases and Road Traffic Injuries in Sub-Saharan Africa: An Overview*. Washington, DC: The World Bank.

Martin, Joyce A., Brady E. Hamilton, Paul D. Sutton, Stephanie J. Ventura, Fay Menacker and Martha L. Munson. 2003. "Births: Final Data for 2002." *National Vital Statistics Reports* 52(10).

Martin, Joyce A., Brady E. Hamilton, Michelle J.K. Osterman, Sally C. Curtin and T.J. Mathews. 2013. "Births: Final Data for 2012." *National Vital Statistics Reports* 62(9).

Martin, Joyce A., Brady E. Hamilton and Michelle J.K. Osterman. 2018. "Births in the United States, 2017." *NCHS Data Brief* (318).

Martin, Joyce A., Brady E. Hamilton, Michelle J.K. Osterman, Anne K. Driscoll and Patrick Drake. 2018. "Births: Final Data for 2017." *National Vital Statistics Reports* 67(8).

Martine, George. 1996. "Brazil's Fertility Decline, 1965–95: A Fresh Look at Key Factors." *Population and Development Review* 22(1):47–75.

Martinez, Gladys M. and Joyce C. Abma. 2015. "Sexual Activity, Contraceptive Use, and Childbearing of Teenagers Aged 15–19 in the United States." *NCHS Data Brief* (209).

Martinez, Gladys M., Kimberly Daniels and Isaedmarie Febo-Vazquez. 2018. "Fertility of Men and Women Aged 15–44 in the United States: National Survey of Family. Growth, 2011–2015." *National Health Statistics Reports* (113).

Marx, Karl. 1890 [1906]. *Capital: A Critique of Political Economy, Translated from the Third German Edition by Samuel Moore and Edward Aveling and Edited by Frederich Engels*. New York: The Modern Library.

Massey, Douglas, J. Arango, G. Hugo, A. Kouaouci, A. Pellegrino and J.E. Taylor. 1993. "Theories of International Migration: A Review and Appraisal." *Population and Development Review* 19(3):431–66.

Massey, Douglas and Nancy Denton. 1993. *American Aprtheid: Segregation and the Making of the Underclass*. Cambridge, MA: Harvard University Press.

Massey, Douglas, J. Arango, G. Hugo, A. Kouaouci, A. Pellegrino and J.E. Taylor. 1994. "An Evaluation of International Migration Theory: The North American Case." *Population and Development Review* 20(4):699–752.

Massey, Douglas. 1996a. "The False Legacy of the 1965 Immigration Act." *World on the Move: Newsletter of the Section on International Migration of the American Sociological Association* 2(2):2–3.

Massey, Douglas. 1996b. "The Age of Extremes: Concentrated Affluence and Poverty in the Twenty-First Century." *Demography* 33(4):395–412.

Massey, Douglas and Kristin Espinosa. 1997. "What's Driving Mexico-U.S. Migration? A Theoretical, Empirical, and Policy Analysis." *American Journal of Sociology* 102(4):939–99.

Massey, Douglas. 2008. "Assimilation in a New Geography." in *New Faces in New Places: The Changing Geography of American Immigration*, edited by D. Massey. New York: Russell Sage Foundation.

Massey, Douglas S. 2002. "A Brief History of Human Society: The Origin and Role of Emotion in Social Life." *American Sociological Review* 67:1–29.

Massey, Douglas S., Jorge Durand and Nolan J. Malone. 2002. *Beyond Smoke and Mirrors: Mexican Immigration in an Era of Economic Integration*. New York: Russell Sage Foundation.

Mathews, T.J. and Brady E. Hamilton. 2018. "Declines in Births to Females Aged 10–14 in the United States, 2000–2016." *NCHS Data Brief* (308).

Matthews, Stephen A. and Daniel M. Parker. 2013. "Progress in Spatial Demography." *Demographic Research* 28(10):271–312.

Mayhew, B. and R. Levinger. 1976. "Size and the Density of Interaction in Human Aggregates." *American Journal of Sociology* 82(1):86–109.

Mayhew, Robert J., ed. 2016. *New Perspectives on Malthus*. Cambridge, UK: Cambridge University Press.

McAuley, Mark T., Kathleen M. Mooney, Peter J. Angeli and Stephen J. Wilkinson. 2015. "Mathematical Modeling of Metabolic Regulation in Aging." *Metabolites* 5(2):232–51.

McCaa, Robert. 1994. "Child Marriage and Complex Families among the Nahuas of Ancient Mexico." *Latin American Population History* (26):2–11.

McCann, Carole R. 2017. *Figuring the Population Bomb: Gender and Demography in the Mid-Twentieth Century*. Seattle: University of Washington Press.

McDaniel, Antonio. 1995. *Swing Low, Sweet Chariot: The Mortality Cost of Colonizing Liberia in the Nineteenth Century*. Chicago: University of Chicago Press.

McDonald, P. 1993. "Fertility Transition Hypothesis." in *The Revolution in Asian Fertility: Dimensions, Causes, and Implications*, edited by R. Leete and I. Alam. Oxford: Clarendon Press.

McDonald, Peter. 2000. "Gender Equity in Theories of Fertility Transition." *Population and Development Review* 26(3):427–39.

McEvedy, Colin and Richard Jones. 1978. *Atlas of World Population History*. New York: Penguin Books.

McGinnis, J.M. and W.H. Foege. 1993. "Actual Causes of Death in the United States." *Journal of the American Medical Association* 270(18):2207–12.

McHenry, H.M. 2009. "Human Evolution." in *Evolution: The First Four Billion Years*, edited by M. Ruse and J. Travis. Cambridge, MA: Belknap Press of Harvard University Press.

Mckenzie, Brian and Melanie Rapino. 2011. "Commuting in the United States: 2009." *American Community Survey Reports, ACS-15*. Washington, DC: U.S. Census Bureau.

McKeown, T. and R. Record. 1962. "Reasons for the Decline of Mortality in England and Wales During the 19th Century." *Population Studies* 16(2):94–122.

McKeown, T. 1988. *The Origins of Human Disease*. Oxford, UK: Basil Blackwell.

McKeown, Thomas. 1976. *The Modern Rise of Population*. London: Edward Arnold.

McKinnish, Terra, Randall Walsh and T. Kirk White. 2010. "Who Gentrifies Low-Income Neighborhoods?". *Journal of Urban Economics* 67:180–93.

McLanahan, Sara and L. Casper. 1995. "Growing Diversity and Inequality in the American Family." in *State of the Union: America in the 1990s, Volume Two: Social Trends*, edited by R. Farley. New York: Russell Sage Foundation.

McMichael, Philip. 2012. "The Land Grab and Corporate Food Regime Restructuring." *The Journal of Peasant Studies* 39(3–4):681–701.

McNeill, William H. 1976. *Plagues and People*. New York: Doubleday.

McQuillan, Kevin. 2004. "When Does Religion Influence Fertility?". *Population and Development Review* 30(1):25–56.

Meek, R. 1971. *Marx and Engels on the Population Bomb*. Berkeley, CA: Ramparts Press.

Merchant, Emily. 2017. "A Digital History of Anglophone Demography and Global Population Control, 1915–1984." *Population and Development Review* 43(1):83–117.

Metchnikoff, E. 1908. *Prolongation of Life*. New York: Putnam.

Miech, Richard, Fred Pampel, Jinyoung Kim and Richard G. Rogers. 2011. "The Enduring Association between Education and Mortality: The Role of Widening and Narrowing Disparities." *American Sociological Review* 76(6):913–34.

Mier y Terán, Martha. 1991. "El Gran Cambio Demográfico." *Demos* 4:4–5.

Migration Policy Institute. 2013. *Major Us Immigration Laws, 1790–Present.* Washington, DC: Migration Policy Institute. (https://www.migrationpolicy.org/research/timeline-1790).

Mill, John Stuart. 1848 [1929]. *Principles of Political Economy.* London: Longmans & Green.

Mill, John Stuart. 1873 [1924]. *Autobiography.* London: Oxford University Press.

Miller, G. Tyler. 2004. *Living in the Environment: Principles, Connections and Solutions, Thirteenth Edition.* Belmont, CA: Brooks/Cole Thomson Learning.

Miller, G. Tyler and Scott E. Spoolman. 2012. *Living in the Environment: Principles, Connections, and Solutions, Seventeenth Edition.* Belmont, CA: Brooks/Cole Cengage Learning.

Mokdad, Ali H., James S. Marks, Donna F. Stroup and Julie L. Gerberding. 2004. "Actual Causes of Death in the United States, 2000." *Journal of the American Medical Association* 291:1238–45.

Monteverde, Malena, Kenya Noronha, Alberto Palloni and Beatriz Novak. 2010. "Obesity and Excess Mortality among the Elderly in the United States and Mexico." *Demography* 47(1):79–96.

Montgomery, Mark and Paul C. Hewett. 2005. "Urban Poverty and Health in Developing Countries: Household and Neighborhood Effects." *Demography* 42(3):397–425.

Montgomery, Mark 2009. "Urban Poverty and Health in Developing Countries." *Population Bulletin* 64(2).

Morelos, José B. 1994. "La Mortalidad En México: Hechos Y Consensos." in *La Población En El Desarrollo Contemporáneo De México,* edited by F. Alba and G. Cabrera. Mexico City: El Colegio de Mexico.

Morens, David M. and Anthony S. Fauci. 2013. "Emerging Infectious Diseases: Threats to Human Health and Global Stability." *PLOS Pathog* 9(7):e1003467. (doi:10.1371/journal.ppat.67).

Morgan, S. Philip. 2001. "Should Fertility Intentions Inform Fertility Forecasts?". in *The Direction of Fertility in the United States,* edited by U.S. Census Bureau. Washington, DC: Council of Professional Associations on Federal Statistics.

Morgan, S. Philip and Heather Rackin. 2010. "The Correspondence between Fertility Intentions and Behavior in the United States." *Population and Development Review* 36(1):91–118.

Mosher, Steven W. 1983. *Broken Earth: The Rural Chinese.* New York: Free Press.

Mouw, Ted. 2000. "Job Relocation and the Racial Gap in Unemployment in Detroit and Chicago, 1980 to 1990." *American Sociological Review* 65:730–53.

Muhua, C. 1979. "For the Realization of the Four Modernizations, There Must Be Planned Control of Population Growth." *Excerpted in Population and Development Review* 5:723–30.

Muhuri, P.K. and S.H. Preston. 1991. "Effects of Family Composition on Mortality Differentials by Sex among Children in Matlab, Bangladesh." *Population and Development Review* 17(3):415–34.

Mulder, Tammany J. 2001. "Accuracy of the U.S. Census Bureau National Population Projections and Their Respective Components of Change." in *The Direction of Fertility in the United States,* edited by U.S. Census Bureau. Washington, DC: Council of Professional Associations on Federal Statistics.

Mumford, Lewis. 1968. "The City: Focus and Function." in *International Encyclopedia of the Social Sciences,* edited by D. Sills. New York: Macmillan.

Murdock, Steven, Chris Kelley, Jeffrey Jordan, Beverly Pecotte and Alvin Luedke. 2006. *Demographics: A Guide to Methods and Data Sources for Media, Business, and Government.* Boulder, CO: Paradigm Publishers.

Murphy, Michelle. 2017. *The Economization of Life.* Durham, NC: Duke University Press.

Murphy, Sherry L., Jiaquan Xu, Kenneth Kochanek, Sally C. Curtin and Elizabeth Arias. 2017. "Deaths: Final Data for 2015." *National Vital Statistics Reports* 66(6).

Murray, Christopher J.L., S. Kulkarni and Majid Ezzati. 2006. "Eight Americas: New Perspectives on Us Health Disparities." *American Journal of Preventive Medicine* 29:4–10.

Murray, Christopher J.L. and Alan D. Lopez. 1996. *The Global Burden of Disease: A Comprehensive Assessment of Mortality and Disability from Diseases, Injuries, and Risk Factors in 1990 and Projected to 2020.* Cambridge: Harvard University Press.

Mustafi, Sambuddha Mitra. 2013. "India's Middle Class: Growth Engine or Loose Wheel." *New York Times* (May 13).

Myers, Dowell and Morris Levy. 2018. "Racial Population Projections and Reactions to Alternative News Accounts of Growing Diversity." *Annals of the American Academy of Political and Social Science* 677(1):215–28.

Myers, Steven Lee and Olivia Mitchell Ryan. 2018. "Burying 'One Child' Limits, China Pushes Women to Have More Babies." *New York Times* (August 11).

Myrdal, Gunnar. 1957. *Economic Theory and Underdeveloped Areas.* London: G. Duckworth.

Nag, Moni. 1962. *Factors Affecting Human Fertility in Non-Industrial Societies: A Cross-Cultural Study.* New Haven: Yale University Press.

NASA. 2018. *Nasa Earth Observatory Images.* Washington, DC: NASA. (https://earthobservatory.nasa.gov/images).

National Academy of Sciences. 2018. *Letter Report on the 2020 Census.* Washington, DC: National Academies Press.

National Academy of Sciences. 2019. *A Roadmap to Reducing Child Poverty.* Washington, DC: National Academies Press.

National Center for Health Statistics. 2017. *Health, United States, 2016: With Chartbook on Long-Term Trends in Health.* Hyattsville, MD: U.S. Government Printing Office.

National Climate Assessment Committee. 2014. *Climate Change Impacts in the United States.* Washington, DC: National Climate Assessment Committee. (http://nca2014.globalchange.gov).

National Population Commission [Nigeria] and ICF Macro. 2009. *Nigeria Demographic and Health Survey 2008.* Abuja, Nigeria: National Population Commission and ICF Macro.

Neyer, Gerda, Gunnar Anderrson, Hill Kulu, Laura Bernardi and Cristoph Bühler, eds. 2013. *The Demography of Europe.* Dordrecht: Springer.

Ng, Marie, Micheal K. Freeman, Thomas D. Fleming, Margaret Robinson, Laura Dwyer-Lindgren, Blake Thomson, Alexandra Wollum, Ella Sanman, Sarah Wulf, Alan D. Lopez, Christopher J. L. Murray and Emmanuela Gakidou. 2014. "Smoking Prevalence and Cigarette Consumption in 187 Countries, 1980–2012." *JAMA: The Journal of the American Medical Association* 311(2):183–92.

Nickerson, J. 1975. *Homage to Malthus.* Port Washington, NY: National University Publications.

Nielsen, J. 1978. *Sex in Society: Perspectives on Stratification.* Belmont, CA: Wadsworth Publishing Co.

Nonaka, K., T. Miura and K. Peter. 1994. "Recent Fertility Decline in Dariusleut Hutterites: An Extension of Eaton and Mayer's Hutterite Fertility." *Human Biology* 66:411–20.

Norris, P. and R. Inglehart. 2004. *Sacred and Secular: Religion and Politics Worldwide.* New York: Cambridge University Press.

Notestein, Frank W. 1945. "Population—the Long View." in *Food for the World*, edited by T.W. Schultz. Chicago: University of Chicago Press.

Nu'Man, Fareed. 1992. *The Muslim Population in the United States: A Brief Statement.* Washington, DC: American Muslim Council.

Nugent, Colleen N. and Jill Daugherty. 2018. "A Demographic, Attitudinal, and Behavioral Profile of Cohabiting Adults in the United States, 2011–2015." *National Health Statistics Reports* May 31(111).

Nunn, Nathan and Nancy Qian. 2011. "The Potato's Contribution to Population and Urbanization: Evidence from a Historical Experiment." *The Quarterly Journal of Economics* 126:593–650.

O'Donnell, James J. 2006. *Augustine: A New Biography.* New York: Harper Perennial.

O'Hare, William P., Yeris Mayol-Garcia, Elizabeth Wildsmith and Alicia Torres. 2016. *The Invisible Ones: How Latino Children Are Left out of Our Nation's Census Count.* Washington, DC: Child Trends, Inc.

OECD. 2018. *Meat Consumption.* Paris, France: OECD. (https://data.oecd.org/agroutput/meat-consumption.htm#indicator-chart).

Oeppen, J. 1993. "Back Projection and Inverse Projection: Members of a Wider Class of Constrained Projection Models." *Population Studies* 47(2):245–68.

Oeppen, Jim and James W. Vaupel. 2002. "Broken Limits to Life Expectancy." *Science* 296(10):1029–31.

Okolo, Abraham. 1999. "The Nigerian Census: Problems and Prospects." *The American Statistician* 53(4):321–25.

Olshansky, S. Jay and Bruce A. Carnes. 1997. "Ever since Gompertz." *Demography* 34(1):1–15.

Olshansky, S. Jay, Toni Antonucci, Linda F. Berkman, Robert H. Binstock, Axel Boersch-Supan, John T. Cacioppo, Bruce A. Carnes, Laura L. Carstensen, Linda P. Fried, Dana P. Goldman, James Jackson, Martin Kohli, John Rother, Yuhui Zheng and John Rowe. 2012. "Differences in Life Expectancy Due to Race and Educational Differences Are Widening, and Many May Not Catch Up." *Health Affairs* 31(8):1803–13.

Olshansky, S. Jay. 2018. "From Lifespan to Healthspan." *Journal of the American Medical Association* 320(13):1323–24.

Omran, Abdel. 1971. "The Epidemiological Transition: A Theory of the Epidemiology of Population Change." *Milbank Memorial Fund Quarterly* 49:509–38.

Omran, Abdel. 1977. "Epidemiologic Transition in the United States." *Population Bulletin* 32(2).

Omran, Abdel R. and Farzaneh Roudi. 1993. "The Middle East Population Puzzle." *Population Bulletin* 48(1).

Ontiveras, Maria Linda. 2018. "Exploitation Based on Migrant Status in the United States: Current Trends and Historical Roots." in *Migrant Labour and the Reshaping of Employment Law*, edited by B. Ryan. London: Hart Publishers.

Oppenheimer, Valerie K. 1967. "The Interaction of Demand and Supply and Its Effect on the Female Labour Force in the U.S.". *Population Studies* 21(3):239–59.

Oppenheimer, Valerie K. 1994. "Women's Rising Employment and the Future of the Family in Industrializing Societies." *Population and Development Review* 20(2):293–342.

Oren, Michael B. 2002. *Six Days of War: June 1967 and the Making of the Modern Middle East.* New York: Oxford University Press.

Orshansky, Mollie. 1969. "How Poverty Is Measured." *Monthly Labor Review* 92(2):37–41.

Ortiz de Montellano, Bernard R. 1975. "Empirical Aztec Medicine." *Science* 188:215–20.

Oster, Emily. 2009. "Proximate Sources of Population Sex Imbalance in India." *Demography* 46(2):325–39.

Over, Mead and Owen McCarthy. 2010. *Global Health Policy: Death Toll from Haiti's Earthquake in Perspective.* Washington, DC: Center for Global Development.

Oxfam International. 2014. *Working for the Few: Political Capture and Economic Inequality/178 Oxfam Briefing Paper.* Oxford, UK: Oxfam International.

Parton, Charles. 2018. "China's Acute Water Shortage Imperils Economic Future." *Financial Times,* London.

Passarino, Giuseppe, Francesco De Rango and Alberto Montesanto. 2016. "Human Longevity: Genetics or Lifestyle? It Takes Two to Tango." *Immunity & Ageing* 13(12).

Patterson, Orlando and Xiaolin Zhuo. 2018. "Modern Trafficking, Slavery, and Other Forms of Servitude." *Annual Review of Sociology* 44:407–39.

Payne, K.K., W.D. Manning and S.L. Brown. 2012. *Unmarried Births to Cohabiting and Single Mothers, 2005–2010 (Fp- 12–06).* Bowling Green State University: National Center for Family and Marriage Research.

Pearlman, Deborah N., Sally Zierler, Stephen Meersman, Hyun K. Kim, Samara Viner-Brown and Colleen Caron. 2006. "Race Disparities in Childhood Asthma: Does Where You Live Matter?". *Journal of the American Medical Association* 98(2):239–47.

Peng, Peiyun. 1996. "Population and Development in China." in *The Population Situation in China: The Insiders' View,* edited by China Population Association and the State Family Planning Commission of China. Liege, Belgium: International Union for the Scientific Study of Population.

Pennisi, Elizabeth. 2001. "Malaria's Beginnings: On the Heels of Hoes?". *Science* 293(5529):416–17.

Perelli-Harris, Brienna, Michaela Kreyenfeld, Wendy Sigle-Rushton, Renske Keizer, Trude Lappegård, Aiva Jasilioniene, Caroline Berghammer and Paola Di Giulio. 2012. "Changes in Union Status During the Transition to Parenthood in Eleven European Countries, 1970s to Early 2000s." *Population Studies* 66(2):167–82.

Perez, Anthony Daniel and Charles Hirschman. 2009. "The Changing Racial and Ethnic Composition of the Us Population: Emerging American Identities." *Population and Development Review* 35(1):1–51.

Perlmann, Joel. 2005. *Italians Then, Mexicans Now: Immigrant Origins and Second-Generation Progress, 1890–2000.* New York: Russell Sage Foundation.

Perry, Pamela. 2001. "White Means Never Having to Say You're Ethnic: White Youth and the Construction of 'Cultureless' Identities." *Journal of Contemporary Ethnography* 30(1):56–91.

Peter, K. 1987. *The Dynamics of Hutterite Society.* Canada: University of Alberta Press.

Petersen, William. 1975. *Population.* New York: MacMillan Publishing Co.

Petersen, William. 1979. *Malthus.* Cambridge, MA: Harvard University Press.

Petersen, William. 1999. *Malthus: Founder of Modern Demography, with a New Introduction by the Author.* New Brunswick, NJ: Transaction Publishers.

Pew Pesearch Center. 2017. *The Changing Global Religious Landscape.* Washington, DC: Pew Research Center.

Piketty, Thomas. 2014. *Capital in the Twenty-First Century.* Cambridge, MA: The Belknap Press of the Harvard University Press.

Pimentel, David, X. Huang, A. Cardova and Pimentel. M. 1997. "Impact of Population Growth on Food Supplies and Environment." *Population and Environment* 19(1):9–14.

Pinker, Steven. 2012. *The Better Angels of Our Nature: Why Violence Has Declined.* New York: Penguin.

Plane, David and Peter Rogerson. 1994. *The Geographical Analysis of Population: With Applications to Planning and Business.* New York: John Wiley & Sons.

Plato. 360BC [1960]. *The Laws.* New York: Dutton.

Pol, Louis G. and Richard K. Thomas. 2001. *The Demography of Health and Health Care, Second Edition.* New York: Kluwer Academic/Plenum Publishers.

Pollack, R.A. and Susan Cotts Watkins. 1993. "Cultural and Economic Approaches to Fertility: Proper Marriage or Mésalliance." *Population and Development Review* 19(3):467–96.

Popkin, Barry M. 1993. "Nutritional Patterns and Transitions." *Population and Development Review* 19:138–57.

Popkin, Barry M. 2002. "The Dynamics of the Dietary Transition in the Developing World." in *The Nutrition Transition: Diet and Disease in the Developing World,* edited by B. Caballero and B.M. Popkin. San Diego: Academic Press.

Popkin, Barry M., Linda S. Adair and Shu Wen Ng. 2012. "Global Nutrition Transition and the Pandemic of Obesity in Developing Countries." *Nutrition Reviews* 70(1):3–21.

Population Reference Bureau. 2018. *2018 World Population Data Sheet.* Washington, DC: Population Reference Bureau.

Portes, Alejandro and Rubén G. Rumbaut. 2014. *Immigrant America: A Portrait, Fourth Edition.* Berkeley: University of California Press.

Poston, Dudley L., Chiung-Fang Chang and Hong Dan. 2006. "Fertility Differences between the Majority and Minority Nationality Groups in China." *Population Research and Policy Review* 25:67–101.

Poston, Dudley L., Samsik Lee and Han Gon Kim, eds. 2018. *Low Fertility Regimes and Demographic and Social Change.* Dordrecht: Springer.

Potts, Malcolm and Roger Short. 1999. *Ever since Adam and Eve: The Evolution of Human Sexuality.* Cambridge, UK: Cambridge University Press.

Pray, Leslie. 2014. *Sustainable Diets: Food for Healthy People and a Healthy Planet, Workshop Summary.* Washington, DC: National Academies Press.

Preston, Samuel and M. R. Haines. 1991. *Fatal Years: Child Mortality in Late Nineteenth-Century America.* Princeton: Princeton University Press.

Preston, Samuel H. 1970. *Older Male Mortality and Cigarette Smoking*. Berkeley: Institute of International Studies, University of California.

Preston, Samuel H., Patrick Heuveline and Michel Guillot. 2001. *Demography: Measuring and Modeling Population Processes*. Oxford, UK: Blackwell Publishers.

Preston, Samuel H., Yana C. Vierboom and Andrew Stokes. 2018. "The Role of Obesity in Exceptionally Slow US Mortality Improvement." *Proceedings of the National Academy of Sciences* 115(5):957–61.

Prewitt, Kenneth. 2018. "The Census Race Classification: Is It Doing Its Job?". *The Annals of the American Academy of Political and Social Science* 677(1):8–24.

Price, Daniel O. 1947. "A Check on Underenumeration in the 1940 Census." *American Sociological Review* 12(1):44–49.

Princeton University Office of Population Research. 2013, "The Emergency Contraception Website". (http://ec.princeton.edu/info/eciud.html).

Pumain, Denise. 2004. "An Evolutionary Approach to Settlement Systems." in *New Forms of Urbanization: Beyond the Urban-Rural Dichotomy*, edited by A.G. Champion and G. Hugo. London: Ashgate Publishing Company.

Pumphrey, G. 1940. *The Story of Liverpool's Public Service*. London: Hodden & Stoughton.

Quesnel-Vallée, Amélie and S. Philip Morgan. 2003. "Missing the Target? Correspondence of Fertility Intentions and Behavior in the U.S.". *Population Research and Policy Review* 22:497–525.

Raftery, Adrian, Jennifer Chunn, Patrick Gerland and Hana Sevcíková. 2013. "Bayesian Probabilistic Projections of Life Expectancy for All Countries." *Demography* 50(3):777–801.

Raley, R. Kelly and Larry Bumpass. 2003, "The Topography of the Divorce Plateau." *Demographic Research* 8–8.

Rashad, Hoda and Eltigani E. Eltigani. 2005. "Explaining Fertility Decline in Egypt." In *Islam, the State and Population* edited by G.W. Jones and M.S. Karim. London: Hurst & Company.

Rashed, Tarek and John R. Weeks. 2003. "Assessing Vulnerability to Earthquake Hazards through Spatial Multicriteria Analysis of Urban Areas." *International Journal of Geographical Information Science* 17(6):549–78.

Rashed, Tarek, John R. Weeks, Helen Couclelis and Martin Herold. 2007. "An Integrative GIS and Remote Sensing Model for Place-Based Urban Vulnerability Analysis." in *The Integration of RS and GIS*, edited by V. Mesev. New York: John Wiley & Sons.

Ravenstein, Ernst Georg. 1889. "The Laws of Migration." *Journal of the Royal Statistical Society* 52:241–301.

Raymer, James, Frans Willekens and Andrei Rogers. 2018. "Spatial Demography: A Unifying Core and Agenda for Further Research." *Population Space and Place*. (https://doi.org/10.1002/psp.2179).

Reed, Holly, John Haaga and Charles Keely, eds. 1998. *The Demography of Forced Migration: Summary of a Workshop*. Washington, DC: National Academies Press.

Rees, Philip. 2019. "Education and Demography: A Review of World Population and Human Capital in the 21st Century." *Vienna Yearbook of Population Research 2019* 16:1–17.

Rees, William E. 1996. "Revisiting Carrying Capacity: Area-Based Indicators of Sustainability." *Population and Environment* 17(3):195–215.

Reher, D. and R. Schofield. 1993. *Old and New Methods in Historical Demography*. Oxford, UK: Clarendon Press.

Reissman, L. 1964. *The Urban Process: Cities in Industrial Societies*. New York: The Free Press.

Ren, Xuefei. 2018. "From Chicago to China and India: Studying the City in the Twenty-First Century." *Annual Review of Sociology* 44:497–513.

Rérat, Patrick, Ola Söderström and Etienne Piguet. 2009. "Guest Editorial: New Forms of Gentrification Issues and Debates." *Population, Space and Place*. (https://doi.org/10.1002/psp.585).

Retherford, Robert D. 1975. *The Changing Sex Differentials in Mortality*. Westport: Greenwood Press.

Riddle, J.M. 1992. *Contraception and Abortion from the Ancient World to the Renaissance*. Cambridge: Harvard University Press.

Riley, James C. 2005. "Estimates of Regional and Global Life Expectancy, 1800–2001." *Population and Development Review* 31(3):537–43.

Riley, Matilda White. 1976. "Social Gerontology and the Age Stratification of Society." In *Aging in America*, edited by C. S. Kart and B. Manard. Port Washington, NY: Alfred Publishing Co.

Riley, Nancy. 1997. "Similarities and Differences: Anthropological and Demographic Perspectives on Gender." Pp. 115–38 in *Anthropological Demography: Toward a New Synthesis*, edited by D. Kertzer and T. Fricke. Chicago: University of Chicago Press.

Riley, Nancy. 2004. "China's Population: New Trends and Challenges." *Population Bulletin* 59.

Riley, Nancy. 2017. *Population in China*. Cambridge, UK: Polity Press.

Rindfuss, R.R. and M.K. Choe. 2015. *Low and Lower Fertility: Variations across Developed Countries*. Cham, Switzerland: Springer International.

Ritchie, Hannah. 2019. "Which Countries Eat the Most Meat?" *BBC News*. (https://www.bbc.com/news/health-47057341).

Robards, James, Maria Evandrou, Jane Falkingham and Athina Vlachantoni. 2012. "Marital Status, Health and Mortality." *Maturitas* 73(4):295–99.

Robey, B. 1983. "Achtung! Here Comes the Census." *American Demographics* 5(10):2–4.

Robinson, J. Gregory, Kirsten K. West and Arjun Adlakha. 2002. "Coverage of the Population in Census 2000:

Results from Demographic Analysis." *Population Research and Policy Review* 21:19–38.

Robinson, Warren C. 1986. "Another Look at the Hutterites and Natural Fertility." *Social Biology* 33:65–76.

Robinson, Warren C. 1997. "The Economic Theory of Fertility over Three Decades." *Population Studies* 51:63–74.

Rodenbeck, Max. 1999. *Cairo: The City Victorious*. New York: Alfred A. Knopf.

Rodriguez, Germán. 2006. "Demographic Translation and Tempo Effects: An Accelerated Failure Time Perspective." *Demographic Research* 14(6):85–110.

Rogers, Everett M. 1995. *Diffusion of Innovations, Fourth Edition*. New York: The Free Press.

Rogers, Richard G. and Eve Powell-Griner. 1991. "Life Expectancies of Cigarette Smokers and Nonsmokers in the United States." *Social Science and Medicine* 32:1151–59.

Rogers, Richard G., Robert A. Hummer and Charles B. Nam. 2000. *Living and Dying in the USA: Behavioral, Health, and Social Differentials of Adult Mortality*. San Diego: Academic Press.

Romeis, Jorg, Steven E. Naranjo, Michael Meissle and Anthony M. Shelton. 2019. "Genetically Engineered Crops Help Support Conservation Biological Control." *Biological Control* 130(March):136–54.

Rosental, Paul-Andre. 2003. "The Novelty of an Old Genre: Louis Henry and the Founding of Historical Demography." *Population-E* 58(3):97–130.

Roser, Max and Hannah Ritchie. 2019a. *Food Per Person*. Oxford, UK: University of Oxford. (https://ourworldindata.org/food-per-person).

Roser, Max and Hannah Ritchie. 2019b. *Hunger and Undernourishment: Empirical View*. Oxford, UK: University of Oxford. (https://ourworldindata.org/hunger-and-undernourishment).

Ross, Catherine E. and Chia-ling Wu. 1995. "The Links between Education and Health." *American Sociological Review* 60:719–45.

Ross, Will. 2018. "Lake Chad: Can the Vanishing Lake Be Saved?" *BBC News*. (https://www.bbc.com/news/world-africa-43500314).

Ruggles, Steven. 1994. "The Transformation of American Family Structure." *American Historical Review* 99(1):103–28.

Ruggles, Steven. 1997. "The Rise of Divorce and Separation in the United States, 1880–1990." *Demography* 34(4):455–66.

Ruggles, Steven and Misty Heggeness. 2008. "Intergenerational Coresidence in Developing Countries." *Population and Development Review* 34(2):253–81.

Ruggles, Steven, Sarah Flood, Ronald Goeken, Josiah Grover, Erin Meyer, Jose Pacas and Matthew Sobek. 2018. *IPUMS USA: Version 8.0 [Dataset]*. Minneapolis: IPUMS, 2018. (https://doi.org/10.18128/D010.V8.0).

Rumbaut, Rubén, Douglas S. Massey and Frank D. Bean. 2006. "Linguistic Life Expectancies: Immigrant Language Retention in Southern California." *Population and Development Review* 32(3):447–60.

Rumbaut, Rubén G. 1994. "Origins and Destinies: Immigration to the United States since World War Ii." *Sociological Forum* 9(4):583–621.

Rumbaut, Rubén G. 1997. "Assimilation and Its Discontents: Between Rhetoric and Reality." *International Migration Review* 31(4):923–60.

Russell, Bertrand. 1951. *New Hopes for a Changing World*. New York: Simon & Schuster.

Russell, Cheryl. 1999. "Been There, Done That!". *American Demographics* 21(1):54–58.

Ryder, Norman. 1965. "The Cohort as a Concept in the Study of Social Change." *American Sociological Review* 30(6):843–61.

Ryder, Norman. 1990. "What Is Going to Happen to American Fertility?". *Population and Development Review* 16(3):433–54.

Sabin, Paul. 2013. *The Bet: Paul Ehrlich, Julian Simon, and Our Gamble over Earth's Future*. New Haven: Yale University Press.

Saez, Emmanuel. 2013. *Striking It Richer: The Evolution of Top Incomes in the United States (Updated with 2012 Preliminary Estimates)*. University of California, Berkeley: Department of Economics. (http://eml.berkeley.edu/~saez/saez-UStopincomes-2012.pdf).

Sagan, Carl. 1989. "The Secret of the Persian Chessboard." *Parade Magazine* 5 February:14.

Salomon, Joshua A., Haidong Wang, Micheal K. Freeman, Theo Vos, Abraham D. Flaxman, Alan D. Lopez and Christopher J. L. Murray. 2012. "Healthy Life Expectancy for 187 Countries, 1990–2010: A Systematic Analysis for the Global Burden Disease Study 2010." *The Lancet* 380(December):2144–62.

Samir, K.C., Bilal Barakat, Anne Goujon, Vegard Skirbekk, Warren C. Sanderson and Wolfgang Lutz. 2010. "Projection of Populations by Level of Educational Attainment, Age, and Sex for 120 Countries for 2005–2050." *Demographic Research* 22(15):383–472.

Samuel, T. John. 1994. *Quebec Separatism Is Dead: Demography Is Destiny*. Toronto: John Samuel and Associates.

Sanchez-Albornoz, N. 1974. *The Population of Latin America: A History*. Berkeley: University of California Press.

Sanchez-Albornoz, N. 1988. *Españoles Hacia America: La Emigración En Masa, 1880–1930*. Madrid: Alianza Editorial.

Sanderson, Stephen K. 1995. *Social Transformations: A General Theory of Historical Development*. Cambridge, MA: Blackwell.

Sanderson, Warren C., Sergei Scherbov and Patrick Gerland. 2018. "The End of Population Aging in High-Income Countries." *Vienna Yearbook of Population Research 2018* 16:1–13.

Sanger, Margaret. 1938. *Margaret Sanger: An Autobiography*. New York: W.W. Norton & Company.

Sassen, Saskia. 2001. *The Global City: New York, London, Tokyo, Second Edition*. Princeton: Princeton University Press.

Sassen, Saskia. 2012. *Cities in a World Economy, Fourth Edition*. Thousand Oaks, CA: Pine Forge Press.

Sauter, Michael B. and Samuel Stebbins. 2018. "Fortune 500 Companies List: 1 out of 3 Are Located in Just Six Major Cities." *USA Today* (November 1).

Sauvy, Alfred. 1969. *General Theory of Population*. New York: Basic Books.

Sawhill, Isabel V. 2014. *Generation Unbound*. Washington, DC: Brookings Institution Press.

Sawyer, Anne-Maree and Sara James. 2018. "Are Baby Boomer Women Redefining Retirement?". *Sociology Compass*. (https://doi.org/10.1111/soc4.12625).

Scammon, Richard and Ben J. Wattenberg. 1970. *The Real Majority*. New York: Coward-McCann.

Schapera, Isaac. 1941. *Married Life in an African Tribe*. New York: Sheridan House.

Schermer, Michael. 2012. *The Believing Brain: From Ghosts and Gods to Politics and Conspiracies—How We Construct Beliefs and Reinforce Them as Truths*. New York: St. Martin's Griffin.

Schmertmann, Carl P., Joseph E. Potter and Suzana M. Cavenaghi. 2008. "Exploratory Analysis of Spatial Patterns in Brazil's Fertility Transition." *Population Research and Policy Review* 27:1–15.

Schnore, Leo, C. Andre and H. Sharp. 1976. "Black Suburbanization 1930–1970." in *The Changing Face of the Suburbs*, edited by B. Schwartz. Chicago: University of Chicago Press.

Schoen, Robert and Young J. Kim. 1998. "Momentum under a Gradual Approach to Zero Growth." *Population Studies* 52:295–99.

Schoen, Robert and Nicola Standish. 2001. "The Retrenchment of Marriage: Results from Marital Status Life Tables." *Population and Development Review* 27(3):553–63.

Schoen, Robert and Vladimir Canudas-Romo. 2005. "Changing Mortality and Average Cohort Life Expectancy." *Demographic Research* 13(5):117–42.

Schoen, Robert and Vladimir Canudas-Romo. 2006. "Timing Effects on Divorce: 20th Century Experience in the United States." *Journal of Marriage and Family* 68(749–758).

Schofield, R. and D. Coleman. 1986. "Introduction: The State of Population Theory." in *The State of Population Theory: Forward from Malthus*, edited by D. Coleman and R. Schofield. Oxford, UK: Basil Blackwell.

Schofield, Roger and David Reher. 1991. "The Decline of Mortality in Europe." in *The Decline of Mortality in Europe*, edited by R. Schofield, D. Reher and A. Bideau. Oxford, UK: Clarendon Press.

Schwartz, Christine R. and Robert D. Mare. 2005. "Trends in Educational Assortative Marriage from 1940 to 2003." *Demography* 42(4):621–46.

Schweber, Libby. 2006. *Disciplining Statistics: Demography and Vital Statistics in France and England, 1830–1885*. Durham, NC: Duke University Press.

Seghetti, Lisa M., Stephen R. Viña and Karma Ester. 2005. *Enforcing Immigration Law: The Role of State and Local Law Enforcement*. Washington, DC: Congressional Research Service.

Shabecoff, Alice. 2014, "Are Men the Weaker Sex?" *Scientific American* (February 18).

Shaefer, H. Luke, Pinghui Wu and Kathryn Edin. 2017. "Can Poverty in America Be Compared to Conditions in the World's Poorest Countries?". *American Journal of Medical Research* 4(1):84.

Shakya, Holly B., John R. Weeks and Nicholas A. Christakis. 2019. "Do Village-Level Normative and Network Factors Help Explain Spatial Variability in Adolescent Childbearing in Rural Honduras." *SSM-Population Health*.

Sharma, Samidha. 2013. "Taco Bell Will Beat KFC in India." *The Times of India* (October 23).

Shkolnikov, Vladimir, France Meslé and Jacques Vallin. 1996. "Health Crisis in Russia: Part I, Recent Trends in Life Expectancy and Causes of Death from 1970 to 1993." *Population: An English Selection* 8:123–54.

Short, John Rennie. 2004. "Black Holes and Loose Connections in a Global Urban Network." *Professional Geographer* 56(2):295–302.

Siegel, J. 1993. *A Generation of Change: A Profile of America's Older Population*. New York: Russell Sage Foundation.

Silver, Nate. 2012. "As Swing Districts Dwindle, Can a Divided House Stand." *New York Times* (December 27).

Simcox, David. 2013. *Senate Comprehensive Immigration Reform Bill (NPG Footnote)*. Washington, DC: Negative Population Growth.

Simmel, Georg. 1905. "The Metropolis and Mental Life." in *Classic Essays on the Culture of Cities*, edited by R. Sennet. New York: Appleton-Century-Crofts.

Simmons, I.G. 1993. *Environmental History: A Concise Introduction*. Oxford, UK: Basil Blackwell Publishers.

Simmons, L. 1960. "Aging in Preindustrial Societies." In *Handbook of Gerontology*, edited by C. Tibbetts. Chicago: University of Chicago Press.

Simon, Julian L. 1981. *The Ultimate Resource*. Princeton: Princeton University Press.

Simon, Julian L. 1992. *Population and Development in Poor Countries: Selected Essays*. Princeton: Princeton University Press.

Simons, Marlise. 2000. "Between Migrants and Spain: The Sea That Kills." *New York Times* (March 30).

Singh, Susheela, Lisa Remez, Gilda Sedgh, Lorraine Kwok and Tsuyoshi Onda. 2018. *Abortion World 2017: Uneven Progress and Unequal Access*. New York: Guttmacher Institute. (https://www.guttmacher.org/report/abortion-worldwide-2017).

Siri, Michael J. and Daniel L. Cork, eds. 2009. *Vital Statistics: Summary of a Workshop*. Washington, DC: National Academies Press.

Smith, Adam. 1776. *An Inquiry into the Nature and Causes of the Wealth of Nations*. (http://www.socsci.mcmaster.ca/~econ/ugcm/3ll3/smith/wealth/wealbk01).

Smith, C.A. and M. Pratt. 1993. "Cardiovascular Disease." in *Chronic Disease Epidemiology and Control*, edited by R.C. Brownson, P.L. Remington and J.R. Davis. Washington, DC: American Public Health Association.

Smith, D.S. 1978. "Mortality and Family in the Colonial Chesapeake." *Journal of Interdisciplinary History* 8(3):403–27.

Smith, David P. 1992. *Formal Demography*. New York: Plenum.

Smith, G., M. Shipley and G. Rose. 1990. "Magnitude and Causes of Socioeconomic Differentials in Mortality: Further Evidence from the Whitehall Study." *British Medical Journal* 301:429–32.

Smith, P., Z. Cai D. Martino, D. Gwary, H. Janzen, P. Kumar, B. McCarl, S. Ogle, F. O'Mara, C. Rice, B. Scholes and O. Sirotenko. 2007. "Agriculture." in *Climate Change 2007: Mitigation. Contribution of Working Group III to the Fourth Assessment Report of the Intergovernmental Panel on Climate Change*, edited by B. Metz, O.R. Davidson, P.R. Bosch, R. Dave and L.A. Meyer. Cambridge, UK: Cambridge University Press.

Smith, Rhonda, Lori Ashford, Jay Gribble and Donna Clifton. 2009. *Family Planning Saves Lives*. Washington, DC: Population Reference Bureau.

Snipp, C.M. 1989. *American Indian: The First of This Land*. New York: Russell Sage Foundation.

Snow, John. 1936. *Snow on Cholera*. London: Oxford University Press.

Social Security Administration. 2019. *Historical Background and Development of Social Security*. Washington, DC: U.S. Government. (https://www.ssa.gov/history/briefhistory3.html).

Sörenson, A. and H. Trappe. 1995. "The Persistence of Gender Equality in Earnings in the German Democratic Republic." *American Sociological Review* 60:398–406.

Spengler, Joseph J. 1979. *France Faces Depopulation: Postlude Edition, 1936–1976*. Durham, NC: Duke University Press.

Spooner, Brian, ed. 1972. *Population Growth: Anthropological Implications*. Cambridge, MA: MIT Press.

Spring, Jake. 2018. "Special Report: Appetite for Destruction—Soy Boom Devours Brazil's Tropical Savanna." *Reuters* (August 28).

Stangeland, Charles E. 1904. *Pre-Malthusian Doctrines of Population*. New York: Columbia University Press.

Starr, Paul. 1987. "The Sociology of Official Statistics." in *The Politics of Numbers*, edited by W. Alonso and P. Starr. New York: Russell Sage Foundation.

Statistics Canada. 2011. *From Urban Areas to Population Centres*. Ottawa: Statistics Canada.

Statistics Canada. 2013. *Final Estimates of 2011 Census Coverage*. Ottawa: Statistics Canada.

Statistics Canada. 2016. *Statistical Area Classification—Variant of SGC 2016*. Ottawa: Statistics Canada.

Statistics Canada. 2018a. *Immigration and Ethnocultural Diversity Highlight Tables, Canada, 2016 Census—25% Sample Data*. Ottawa: Statistics Canada.

Statistics Canada. 2018b. *Guide to the Census of Population, 2016: Chapter 10—Data Quality Assessment*. Ottawa: Statistics Canada.

Statistics Canada. 2019. *Methodological Changes to the Market Basket Measure in 2019*. Ottawa: Statistics Canada.

Statistika Centralbyran [Sweden]. 1983. *Pehr Wargentin: Den Svenska Statistikens Fader*. Stockholm: Statistika Centralbyran.

Stoler, Justin, Günther Fink, John R. Weeks, Richard Appiah Otoo, Joseph A. Ampofo and Allan G. Hill. 2011. "When Urban Taps Run Dry: Sachet Water Consumption and Health Effects in Low Income Neighborhoods of Accra, Ghana." *Health & Place* 18(2):250–62.

Stolnitz, George J. 1964. "The Demographic Transition: From High to Low Birth Rates and Death Rates." Chapter 2 in *Population: The Vital Revolution*, edited by R. Freedman. Garden City: Anchor Books.

Sun, Mingjie and C. Cindy Fan. 2011. "China's Permanent and Temporary Migrants: Differentials and Changes, 1990–2000." *The Professional Geographer* 63(1):92–112.

Sutherland, I. 1963. "John Graunt: A Tercentenary Tribute." *Royal Statistical Society Journal, Series A* 126:536–37, reprinted in K. Kammeyer 1975 (ed.), Population: Selected Essays and Research (Chicago: Rand McNally).

Sutton, Paul, Dar Roberts, Chris Elvidge and K. Baugh. 2001. "Census from Heaven: An Estimate of the Global Human Population Using Night-Time Satellite Imagery." *International Journal of Remote Sensing* 22(16):3061–76.

Sway, RoxAnna. 2018, "Demos Are Destiny." *The Robin Report*. (https://www.therobinreport.com/demos-are-destiny/).

Szreter, Simon and Eilidh Garrett. 2000. "Reproduction, Compositional Demography, and Economic Growth: Family Planning in England Long before the Fertility Decline." *Population and Development Review* 26(1):45–80.

Szreter, Simon. 2005. *Health and Wealth: Studies in History and Policy*. Rochester, NY: University of Rochester Press.

Ta-k'un, W. 1960. "A Critique of Neo-Malthusian Theory". *Excerpted in Population and Development Review (1979)* 5(4):699–707.

Tavernise, Sabrina. 2018. "U.S. Has Highest Share of For-eign-Born Since1910, with More Coming from Asia." *New York Times* (September 13).

Taylor, Paul. 2017, "Here's Looking at You, 2050" *Foreign Policy* (January 16).

Taylor, Robert M. and John Maurice. 2018. *Global Health Transitions and Sustainable Solutions: The Role of Partnerships*. Washington, DC: National Academies Press.

Tchkonia, Tamara and James L. Kirkland. 2018. "Aging, Cell Senescence, and Chronic Disease: Emerging Therapeutic Strategies." *Journal of the American Medical Association* 320(13):1319–20.

Teitelbaum, M. and J. Winter. 1988. "Introduction." In *Population and Resources in the Western Intellectual Tradition*, edited by M. Teitelbaum and J. Winter. New York: Population Council.

Teitelbaum, Michael. 1975. "Relevance of Demographic Transition for Developing Countries." *Science* 188:420–25.

Telles, Edward E. and Vilma Ortiz. 2008. *Generations of Exclusion: Mexican Americans, Assimilation, and Race*. New York: Russell Sage Foundation.

Testa, Maria Rita. 2013. *Women's Fertility Intentions and Level of Education: Why Are They Positively Correlated in Europe?* Vienna, Austria: Vienna Institute of Demography.

Thatcher, Roger. 2001. "The Demography of Centenarians in England and Wales." *Population: An English Selection* 13(1):139–56.

The Economist. 1998. "China: The X-Files." (14 February).

The Economist. 2009. "A Special Report on the Arab World." (July 25).

The Economist. 2013a. "Meet Sir William Petty, the Man Who Invented Economics." (21 December).

The Economist. 2013b. "The Census: Some Other Race; How Should America Count Its Hispanics?" (February 9).

The Economist. 2014. "Urbanisation: Moving on Up." (March 22).

The Economist. 2018a. "Defeating Dispair: Suicide Is Declining Almost Everywhere." (November 24).

The Economist. 2018b. "China, the Birthplace of Fake Meat: As Meat Substitutes Take Off in the West, Fuchsia Dunlop Lifts the Lid on the Ancient Art of Imitation." *1843 Magazine*. (https://www.1843magazine.com /food-drink/china-the-birthplace-of-fake-meat).

The Economist. 2019. "The Big Mac Index." (January 10).

Thomas, Hugh. 1997. *The Slave Trade: The Story of the Atlantic Slave Trade: 1440–1870*. New York: Simon & Schuster.

Thomas, Richard K. 2018. *Concepts, Methods and Practicalapplications in Applied Demography*. Dordrecht: Springer International.

Thompson, Warren. 1929. "Population." *American Journal of Sociology* 34(6):959–75.

Tietze, Christopher and S. Lewit. 1977. "Legal Abortion." *Scientific American* 236(1):21–27.

Tobias, A. 1979. "The Only Article on Inflation You Need to Read: We're Getting Poorer, but We Can Do Something About It." *Esquire* 92(5):49–55.

Tobler, Waldo. 1970. "A Computer Movie Simulating Urban Growth in the Detroit Region." *Economic Geography* 26:234–40.

Tobler, Waldo. 2004. "On the First Law of Geography: A Reply." *Annals of the Association of American Geographers* 94(2):304–10.

Tolnay, Stewart E., Katherine Curtis White, Kyle D. Crowder and Robert M. Adelman. 2005. "Distances Traveled During the 'Great Migration': An Analysis of Racial Differences among Male Migrants." *Social Science History* 29:523–48.

Torrieri, Nancy K. 2007. "America Is Changing, and So Is the Census: The American Community Survey." *The American Statistician* 61(1):16–21.

Toulemon, Laurent. 1997. "Cohabitation Is Here to Stay." *Population: An English Selection* 9:11–46.

Treas, Judith and Tsui-o Tai. 2012. "Apron Strings of Working Mothers: Maternal Employment and Housework in Cross-National Perspective." *Social Science Research* 41(4):833–42.

Tremlett, Giles and Peter Walker. 2009. "Spanish Woman Who Gave Birth through I V F at 66 Dies." in *The Guardian, 15 July*, Vol. 15 July.

Twenge, Jean M. 2017. *iGen: Why Today's Super-Connected Kids Are Growing up Less Rebellious, More Tolerant, Less Happy—and Completely Unprepared for Adulthood—and What That Means for the Rest of Us*. New York: Simon and Schuster.

U.K. National Archives. 2014. *Domesday Book*. (http:// www.nationalarchives.gov.uk/records/research-guides /domesday.htm).

U.K. Office for National Statistics. 2018. *Estimates of the Very Old, Including Centenarians, UK: 2002 to 2017*. London: Office for National Statistics. (https:// www.ons.gov.uk/peoplepopulationandcommunity /birthsdeathsandmarriages/ageing/bulletins/estimatesoft heveryoldincludingcentenarians/2002to2017).

U.S. Bureau of Labor Statistics. 2018. *Labor Force Statistics from the Current Population Survey*. Washington, DC: U.S. Bureau of Labor Statistics. (http://www.bls .gov/cps/tables.htm).

U.S. Census Bureau. 1975. *Historical Statistics of the United States*. Washington, DC: Government Printing Office.

U.S. Census Bureau. 1978. *History and Organization*. CFF No. 4 (rev). Washington, DC: U.S. Census Bureau.

U.S. Census Bureau. 1991. "Money Income of Households, Families, and Persons in the United States: 1991." *Current Population Reports P60–180*. Washington, DC: U.S. Census Bureau.

U.S. Census Bureau. 2010a. *Population Estimates: Metropolitan and Micropolitan Statistical Area Estimates,*

Components of Population Change. Washington, DC: U.S. Census Bureau.

U.S. Census Bureau. 2010b. *A Half-Century of Learning: Historical Census Statistics on Educational Attainment in the United States, 1940 to 2000: Detailed Tables.* Washington, DC: U.S. Census Bureau.

U.S. Census Bureau. 2012a. *Labor Force, Employment, & Earnings: Labor Force Status.* Washington, DC: U.S. Census Bureau.

U.S. Census Bureau. 2012b. *Census Bureau Releases Estimates of Undercount and Overcount in the 2010 Census.* (http://www.census.gov/newsroom/releases/archives/2010_census/cb12-95.html).

U.S. Census Bureau. 2012c. *Geographical Mobility /Migration: Calculating Migration Expectancy Using ACS Data.* Washington, DC: U.S. Census Bureau.

U.S. Census Bureau. 2012d. *Census Bureau Releases Results from the 2010 Census Race and Hispanic Origin Alternative Questionnaire Research.* (http://www.census.gov/newsroom/releases/archives/2010_census/cb12-146.html).

U.S. Census Bureau. 2013a. *America's Families and Living Arrangements: 2012: Adults (Table A2).* Washington, DC: U.S. Census Bureau.

U.S. Census Bureau. 2013b. *America's Families and Living Arrangements: 2012: Unmarried Couples (UC Table Series).* Washington, DC: U.S. Census Bureau.

U.S. Census Bureau. 2017. *Historical Time Series Tables: 2016.* Washington, DC: U.S. Census Bureau.

U.S. Census Bureau. 2018a. *Annual Estimates of the Resident Population for Selected Age Groups by Sex for the United States, States, Counties, and Puerto Rico Commonwealth and Municipios: April 1, 2010 to July 1, 2017; 2017 Population Estimates.* Washington, DC: U.S. Census Bureau.

U.S. Census Bureau. 2018b. *Survey of Income and Program Participation, 2014 Panel, Wave 2.* (https://www.census.gov/data/tables/2014/demo/wealth/wealth-asset-ownership.html).

U.S. Census Bureau. 2018c. *Questions Planned for the 2020 Census and American Community Survey.* Washington, DC: U.S. Census Bureau.

U.S. Census Bureau. 2018d. *American Community Survey (ACS): Respond to the Survey or Get Help.* Washington, DC: U.S. Census Bureau.

U.S. Census Bureau. 2018e. *Projected Age Groups and Sex Composition of the Population: Main Projections Series for the United States, 2017–2060.* Washington, DC: U.S. Census Bureau.

U.S. Census Bureau. 2018f. *Annual Estimates of the Resident Population for the United States, Regions, States, and Puerto Rico: April 1, 2010 to July 1, 2018 (NST-Est2018–01).* Washington, DC: U.S. Census Bureau.

U.S. Census Bureau. 2018g. *Current Population Survey Annual Social and Economic Supplement: Person Income in 2017.* Washington, DC: U.S. Census Bureau.

U.S. Census Bureau. 2018h. *Estimates of the Components of Resident Population Change for the United States, Regions, States, and Puerto Rico: July 1, 2017 to July 1, 2018: Table 5.* (https://www.census.gov/data/tables/time-series/demo/popest/2010s-national-total.html).

U.S. Census Bureau. 2018i. *People Are Waiting to Get Married: Median Age at First Marriage: 1890 to Present.* Washington, DC: U.S. Census Bureau.

U.S. Census Bureau. 2018j. *Historical Income Tables: Families.* (https://www.census.gov/data/tables/time-series/demo/income-poverty/historical-income-families.html).

U.S. Census Bureau. 2018k. *2017 American Community Survey 1-Year Estimates.* Washington, DC: U.S. Census Bureau.

U.S. Census Bureau. 2018. *Metropolitan and Micropolitan.* Washington, DC: U.S. Census Bureau.

U.S. Centers for Disease Control and Prevention. 2014. *Effectiveness of Family Planning Methods.* (http://www.cdc.gov/reproductivehealth/UnintendedPregnancy/PDF/Contraceptive_methods_508.pdf).

U.S. Centers for Disease Control and Prevention. 2018a. *Pregnancy Mortality Surveillance System.* Atlanta, GA: CDC. (https://www.cdc.gov/reproductivehealth/maternalinfanthealth/pregnancy-mortality-surveillance-system.htm).

U.S. Centers for Disease Control and Prevention. 2018b. *Ebola Virus Disease.* Atlanta: CDC. (https://www.cdc.gov/vhf/ebola/).

U.S. Centers for Disease Control and Prevention. 2018c. *1918 Flu Pandemic.* (https://www.cdc.gove/features/1918-flu-pandemic/index.html).

U.S. Department of Agriculture. 2019. *Census of Agriculture 2017.* Washington, DC: National Agricultural Statistics Service.

U.S. Department of Homeland Security. 2014. *Yearbook of Immigration Statistics: 2012.* Washington, DC: U.S. Department of Homeland Security Office of Immigration Statistics.

U.S. Department of Homeland Security. 2018. *2017 Yearbook of Immigration Statistics.* Washington, DC: Department of Homeland Security.

U.S. Department of Homeland Security. 2019. *Table 2. Persons Obtaining Lawful Permanent Resident Status by Region and Selected Country of Last Residence: Fiscal Years 2015 to 2017.* (https://www.dhs.gov/immigration-statistics/yearbook/2017/table2).

U.S. Energy Information Administration. 2013. *International Energy Outlook 2013.* Washington, DC: U.S. Energy Information Administration. (http://www.eia.doe.gov/oiaf/ieo/world.html).

U.S. Environmental Protection Agency. 2019. *About Smart Growth.* Washington, DC: US EPA. (https://www.epa.gov/smartgrowth/about-smart-growth).

U.S. Immigration and Naturalization Service. 1991. *An Immigrant Nation: United States Regulation of Immigration, 1798–1991.* Washington, DC: Government Printing Office.

U.S. National Center for Health Statistics. 2019. *Natality Trends in the United States, 1909–2015*. Washington, DC: National Center for Health Statistics, U.S. Centers for Disease Control and Prevention.

U.S. Office of Management and Budget. 2010. "2010 Standards for Defining Metropolitan and Micropolitan Statistical Areas." *Federal Register* 75(123):37246–52.

U.S. Social Security Administration. 2019. *Payments to Beneficiaries Outside the U.S., December 2018*. Washington, DC: Social Security Administration.

Udry, J. Richard. 1994. "The Nature of Gender." *Demography* 31(4):561–74.

Udry, J. Richard. 2000. "Biological Limits of Gender Construction." *American Sociological Review* 65:443–57.

UN-Habitat. 2014a. *The State of African Cities 2014: Reimagining Sustainable Urban Transitions*. Nairobi, Kenya: UN-Habitat.

UN-Habitat. 2014b. *Housing & Slum Upgrading*. Nairobi, Kenya: UN-Habitat.

UN-Habitat. 2016. *Slum Almanac 2015/2016: Tracking Improvement in the Lives of Slum Dwellers*. Nairobi: United Nations.

UN-Water. 2018. *Sustainable Development Goal 6: Synthesis Report on Water and Sanitation 2018*. New York: United Nations.

UNHCR. 2010. *Who Is a Refugee?* New York: United Nations. (http://www.unhcr.org.au/basicdef.shtml).

UNHCR. 2014. *Syrians Desperate for a New Life Drown Trying to Reach Greece*. New York: UN High Commissioner for Refugees.

United Nations. 1973. *The Determinants and Consequences of Population Trends: New Summary of Findings on Interaction of Demographic, Economic and Social Factors, Volume I*. New York: United Nations.

United Nations. 2019a. *Sustainable Development Knowledge Platform*. New York: United Nations. (https://sustainabledevelopment.un.org/sdgs).

United Nations. 2019b. *About the Sustainable Development Goals*. New York: United Nations. (https://www.un.org/sustainabledevelopment/sustainable-development-goals/).

United Nations Environment Programme. 2019. *Geo 6: Global Environment Outlook, Healthy Planet, Healthy People*. Cambridge, UK: Cambridge University PRess.

United Nations High Commissioner for Refugees. 2019. *Statistical Yearbooks: Figures at a Glance*. New York: United Nations.

United Nations Office on Drugs and Crime. 2014. *UNODC Homicide Statistics*. (https://www.unodc.org/unodc/en/data-and-analysis/homicide.html).

United Nations Population Division. 1999. *The World at Six Billion*. (http://www.un.org/esa/population/publications/sixbillion/sixbillion.htm).

United Nations Population Division. 2005. *Living Arrangements of Older Persons around the World*. New York: United Nations.

United Nations Population Division. 2013a. *Trends in International Migrant Stock: The 2013 Revision*. (http://esa.un.org/unmigration/wallchart2013.htm).

United Nations Population Division. 2013b. *World Marriage Data 2012*. New York: United Nations. (http://www.un.org/en/development/desa/population/publications/dataset/marriage/wmd2012/MainFrame.html).

United Nations Population Division. 2017a. *International Migration Report 2017 (St/Esa/Ser.A/403)*. New York: United Nations.

United Nations Population Division. 2017b. *World Marriage Data 2017*. New York: United Nations.

United Nations Population Division. 2017c. *World Population Prospects: The 2017 Revision; Total Fertility by Region, Subregion, and Country, 1950–2100*. (Pop/Db/Wpp/Rev.2017/Fert/F04). New York: United Nations.

United Nations Population Division. 2018a. *World Population Prospects: The 2017 Revision*. New York: United Nations. (http://www.un.org/en/development/desa/population/).

United Nations Population Division. 2018b, "World Population Prospects 2018", New York: United Nations. (https://population.un.org/wup/DataQuery/).

United Nations Population Division. 2018c. *Profiles of Ageing 2017*. New York: United Nations. (https://population.un.org/ProfilesOfAgeing2017/index.html).

United Nations Population Division. 2018d. *World Urbanization Prospects, the 2018 Revision, Methodology*. New York: United Nations. (https://population.un.org/wup/Publications/Files/WUP2018-Methodology.pdf).

United Nations Population Division. 2018e. *World Urbanization Prospects: The 2018 Revision*. New York: United Nations. (https://population.un.org/wup/).

United Nations Population Division. 2018f. *World Contraceptive Use 2018 (Pop/Db/Cp/Rev2018)*. New York: United Nations.

United Nations Population Division. 2019. *World Population Prospects 2019, Online Edition*. New York: United Nations. (https://population.un.org/wpp/).

United Nations Population Fund. 1987. *1986 Report by the Executive Director*. New York: United Nations.

United Nations Statistics Division. 2008. *Principles and Recommendations for Population and Housing Censuses, Revision 2*. New York: United Nations.

Vallin, Jacques and France Meslé. 2009. "The Segmented Trend Line of Highest Life Expectancies." *Population and Development Review* 35(1):159–87.

Van Cleave, Jeanne, Steven L. Gortmaker and James M. Perrin. 2010. "Dynamics of Obesity and Chronic Health Conditions among Children and Youth." *Journal of the American Medical Association* 3030(7):623–30.

Van Dam, Andrew. 2018. "Toys R Us's Baby Problem Is Everybody's Baby Problem." *Washington* (March 15).

van de Kaa, Dirk J. 1987. "Europe's Second Demographic Transition." *Population Bulletin* 42(1).

van de Walle, Etienne and John Knodel. 1980. "Europe's Fertility Transition: New Evidence and Lessions for Today's Developing World." *Population Bulletin* 34(6).

van de Walle, Etienne. 1992. "Fertility Transition, Conscious Choice and Numeracy." *Demography* 29:487–502.

van de Walle, Etienne. 2000. "'Marvellous Secrets': Birth Control in European Short Fiction, 1150–1650." *Population Studies* 54:321–30.

Vandeschrick, Christopher. 2001. "The Lexis Diagram, a Misnomer." *Demographic Research* 4(3).

VanLandingham, Mark J. 2017. *Weathering Katrina: Culture and Recovery among Vietnamese*. New York: Russell Sage Foundation.

Veyne, P. 1987. "The Roman Empire." in *A History of Private Life, Volume 1: From Pagan Rome to Byzantium*, edited by P. Veyne. Cambridge, MA: Harvard University Press.

Viscusi, W.K. 1979. *Welfare of the Elderly: An Economic Analysis and Policy Prescription*. New York: John Wiley & Sons.

Vogt, Gabriele. 2018. *Population Aging and International Health-Caregiver Migration to Japan*. Dordrecht: Springer.

Voss, Paul. 2007. "Demography as a Spatial Social Science." *Population Research and Policy Review* 26:457–76.

Wagmiller, Robert L., Jr. 2007. "Race and the Spatial Segregation of Jobless Men in Urban America." *Demography* 44(3):539–62.

Waite, Linda J. 2000. "The Family as a Social Organization: Key Ideas for the Twenty-First Century." *Contemporary Sociology* 20(3):463–69.

Walk Free Foundation. 2013. *The Global Slavery Index 2013*. Perth, Australia: Walk Free Foundation. (http://www.globalslaveryindex.org/).

Walk Free Foundation. 2018. *The Global Slavery Index: Unravelling the Numbers*. Perth, Australia: Walk Free Foundation. (https://www.globalslaveryindex.org/2018/findings/highlights/).

Wall, Richard, Jean Robin and Peter Laslett, eds. 1983. *Family Forms in Historic Europe*. New York: Cambridge University Press.

Wallace, Paul. 2001. *Agequake: Riding the Demographic Rollercoaster Shaking Business, Finance and Our World*. London: Nicholas Brealey Publishing.

Wallace, Robert. 1761 [1969]. *A Dissertation on the Numbers of Mankind, in Ancient and Modern Times, 1st and 2nd Editions, Revised and Corrected*. New York: Kelley.

Wallerstein, Immanuel. 1974. *The Modern World System*. New York: Academic Press.

Wallerstein, Immanuel. 1976. "Modernization: Requiescat in Pace." in *The Uses of Controversy in Sociology*, edited by L.A. Coser and O.N. Larsen. New York: Free Press.

Wallis, C. 1995. "How to Live to Be 120." *Time*. (March 6).

Walmart Stores. 2018. *China*. (https://corporate.walmart.com/our-story/our-locations#/china).

Ware, Helen. 1975. "The Limits of Acceptable Family Size in Western Nigeria." *Journal of Biosocial Science* 7:273–96.

Warren, Carol A.B. 1998. "Aging and Identity in Premodern Times." *Research on Aging* 20(1):11–35.

Warren, Robert. 2019. *US Undocumented Population Continued to Fall from 2016 to 2017, and Visa Overstays Significantly Exceeded Illegal Crossings for the Seventh Consecutive Year*. New York: Center for Migration Studies. (http://cmsny.org/publications/essay-2017-undocumented-and-overstays/).

Watkins, Susan Cotts. 1986. "Conclusion." in *The Decline of Fertility in Europe*, edited by A. Coale and S.C. Watkins. Princeton: Princeton University Press.

Watkins, Susan Cotts. 1991. *From Provinces into Nations: Demographic Integration in Western Europe, 1870–1960*. Princeton: Princeton University Press.

Weber, Adna. 1899. *The Growth of Cities in the Nineteenth Century*. New York: Columbia University Press.

Weeks, Gregory B. and John R. Weeks. 2010. *Irresistible Forces: Explaining Latin American Migration to the United States and Its Effects on the South*. Albuquerque: University of New Mexico Press.

Weeks, John R. 2004a. "Using Remote Sensing and Geographic Information Systems to Identify the Underlying Properties of Urban Environments." Pp. 325–46 in *New Forms of Urbanization: Conceptualizing and Measuring Human Settlement in the Twenty-First Century*, edited by A.G. Champion and G. Hugo. London: Ashgate Publishing Limited.

Weeks, John R. 2004b. "The Role of Spatial Analysis in Demographic Research." in *Spatially Integrated Social Science: Examples in Best Practice*, edited by M.F. Goodchild and D.G. Janelle. New York: Oxford University Press.

Weeks, John R., Arthur Getis, Allan G. Hill, M. Saad Gadalla and Tarek Rashed. 2004. "The Fertility Transition in Egypt: Intra-Urban Patterns in Cairo." *Annals of the Association of American Geographers* 94(1):74–93.

Weeks, John R., Dennis Larson and Debbie Fugate. 2005. "Patterns of Urban Land Use as Assessed by Satellite Imagery: An Application to Cairo, Egypt." Pp. 265–86 in *Population, Land Use, and Environment: Research Directions*, edited by B. Entwisle and P.C. Stern. Washington, DC: National Academies Press.

Weeks, John R. 2010a. "Unpublished Data from the 2000 Ghana Census of Population and Housing." San Diego: San Diego State University.

Weeks, John R. 2010b. "Defining Urban Areas." in *Remote Sensing of Urban and Suburban Areas*, edited by T. Rashed and C. Juergens. New York: Kluwer Press.

Weeks, John R. and Charles F. Westoff. 2010. "Religiousness and Reproduction in Muslim Countries." Paper presented at the Annual Meeting of the Population Association of America, Dallas, TX.

Weeks, John R., Piotr Jankowski and Justin Stoler. 2011. "Who's Knocking at the Door? New Data on Undocumented Immigrants to the United States." *Population, Space and Place* 17(1):1–26.

Weeks, John R. and Debbie Fugate, eds. 2012. *The Youth Bulge: Challenge or Opportunity*. New York: IDE-BATE Press.

Weeks, John R., Allan G. Hill and Justin Stoler, eds. 2013. *Spatial Inequalities: Health Poverty and Place in Accra, Ghana*. Dordrecht: Springer.

Weeks, John R. 2016. "Demography Is an Inherently Spatial Science." in *Recapturing Space: New Middle-Range Theory in Spatial Demography*, edited by F. Howell, J. Porter and S.A. Matthews. Dordrecht: Springer.

Weis, Tony. 2013. *The Ecological Hoofprint: The Global Burden of Industrial Livestock*. London and New York: Zed Books Ltd.

Weiss, K.H. 1973. "Demographic Models for Anthropology." *American Antiquity* 38(2: Part II).

Weiss, Michael J. 1988. *The Clustering of America*. New York: Harper & Row.

Weiss, Michael J. 2000. *The Clustered World: How We Live, What We Buy, and What It All Means About Who We Are*. Boston: Little, Brown and Company.

Weller, Robert, John Macisco and G. Martine. 1971. "Relative Importance of the Components of Urban Growth in Latin America." *Demography* 8(2):225–32.

Wells, R. 1971. "Family Size and Fertility Control in Eighteenth-Century America: A Study of Quaker Families." *Population Studies* 25(1):73–82.

Wells, R.V. 1982. *Revolutions in Americans' Lives: A Demographic Perspective on the History of Americans, Their Families, and Their Society*. Westport, CT: Greenwood Press.

Westoff, Charles and Ronald Rindfuss. 1974. "Sex Preselection in the United States: Some Implications." *Science* 184:633–36.

Westoff, Charles. 1990. "Reproductive Intentions and Fertility Rates." *International Family Planning Perspectives* 16:84–89.

Westoff, Charles F. and Ronald R. Rindfuss. 1973. "The Revolution in Birth Control Practices of U.S. Roman Catholics." *Science* 179:41–44.

Westoff, Charles F. and Elise F. Jones. 1979. "The End of 'Catholic' Fertility." *Demography* 16(209–217).

Westoff, Charles F. and Tomas Frejka. 2007. "Religiousness and Fertility among European Muslims." *Population and Development Review* 33(4):785–809.

Westoff, Leslie A. and Charles F. Westoff. 1971. *From Now to Zero: Fertility, Contraception and Abortion in America*. Boston: Little, Brown & Co.

White, Katherine J. Curtis. 2002. "Declining Fertility among North American Hutterites: The Use of Birth Control within a Darisusleut Colony." *Social Biology* 49(1–2):58–73.

Whitmore, Thomas M. 1992. *Disease and Death in Early Colonial Mexico*. Boulder: Westview Press.

Willcox, Walter F. 1936. *Natural and Political Observations Made Upon the Bills of Mortality by John Graunt*. Baltimore: The Johns Hopkins Press.

Williams, David R., H.W. Neighbors and J.S. Jackson. 2003. "Racial/Ethnic Discrimination and Health: Findings from Community Studies." *American Journal of Public Health* 93:200–08.

Williams, Naomi and Chris Galley. 1995. "Urban-Rural Differentials in Infant Mortality in Victorian England." *Population Studies* 49:401–20.

Wilmoth, John R. and Shiro Horiuchi. 1999. "Rectangularization Revisited: Variability of Age at Death within Human Populations." *Demography* 36(4):475–95.

Wilson, Allan C. and Rebecca L. Cann. 1992. "The Recent African Genesis of Humans." *Scientific American* 266(4):68–74.

Wilson, Thomas. 1991. "Urbanism, Migration, and Tolerance: A Reassessment." *American Sociological Review* 56:117–23.

Wirth, Louis. 1938. "Urbanism as a Way of Life." *American Journal of Sociology* 44(3–24).

World Bank. 2000. *World Development Report 2000/2001: Attacking Poverty*. New York: Oxford University Press.

World Bank. 2008. *Dealing with Water Scarcity in MENA*. Washington, DC: World Bank.

World Bank. 2019a. *World Development Indicators: Table 2.10: Education Completion and Outcomes*. Washington, DC: The World Bank. (http://wdi.worldbank.org/table/2.10#).

World Bank. 2019b. *GNI Per Capita, PPP (Constant 2011 International $)*. Washington, DC: World Bank Group. (https://data.worldbank.org/indicator/NY.GNP.PCAP.PP.KD?view=chart).

World Bank. 2019c. *World Bank Data*. Washington, DC: World Bank Group. (https://data.worldbank.org/indicator/).

World Bank. 2019d. *Poverty Headcount Ratios (% of Population)*. World Bank. (https://data.worldbank.org/indicator/).

World Bank. 2019e. *GNI, PPP (Constant 2011 International $)*. Washington, DC: World Bank.

World Commission on Environment and Development. 1987. *Our Common Future*. New York: Oxford University Press.

World Health Organization. 2018a. *Global Health Estimates 2016 Summary Tables: Deaths by Cause, Age and Sex, by World Bank Income Group, 2000–2015*. Geneva: WHO. 2018 (http://www.who.int/healthinfo/global_burden_disease/en/).

World Health Organization. 2018b. *Maternal Mortality*. Geneva: WHO. (http://www.who.int/en/news-room/fact-sheets/detail/maternal-mortality).

World Health Organization. 2018c. *Female Genital Mutilation*. Geneva: WHO. (https://www.who.int/news -room/fact-sheets/detail/female-genital-mutilation).

World Wide Fund for Nature. 2019. Ecological Footprint. Geneva: WWF. (https://wwf.panda.org/knowledge _hub/teacher_resources/webfieldtrips/ecological_balance /eco_footprint/).

Wrigley, E.A. 1974. *Population and History*. New York: McGraw-Hill.

Wrigley, E.A. and R.S. Schofield. 1981. *The Population History of England, 1541–1871: A Reconstruction*. Cambridge: Harvard University Press.

Wrigley, E.A. 1988. "The Limits to Growth." in *Population and Resources in Western Intellectual Tradition*, edited by M. Teitelbaum and J. Winter. New York: Population Council.

Wrigley, E.A. 1987. *People, Cities and Wealth*. Oxford: Blackwell Publishers.

Xu, Jiaquan, Sherry L. Murphy, Kenneth Kochanek, Brigham Bastian and Elizabeth Arias. 2018. "Deaths: Final Data Fro 2016." *National Vital Statistics Reports* 67(5).

Yoo, Sam Hyun, Sarah R. Hayford and Victor Agadjanian. 2017. "Old Habits Die Hard? Lingering Son Preference in an Era of Normalizing Sex Ratios at Birth in South Korea." *Population Research and Policy Review* 36(1):25–54.

Yount, Kathryn M. 2003. "Gender Bias in the Allocation of Curative Heatlh Care in Minia, Egypt." *Population Research and Policy Review* 22(3):267–99.

Zaidi, Batool and S. Philip Morgan. 2017. "The Second Demographic Transition Theory: A Review and Appraisal." *Annual Review of Sociology* 43:473–92.

Zengwang Xu and Robert Harriss. 2010. "A Spatial and Temporal Autocorrelated Growth Model for City Rank Size Distribution." *Urban Studies* 47(2):321–35.

Zhao, Z. 1994. "Demographic Conditions and Multigeneration Households in Chinese History: Results from Genealogical Research and Microsimulation." *Population Studies* 48(3):413–26.

Zhao, Zhongwei. 2001. "Chinese Genealogies as a Source for Demographic Research: A Further Assessment of Their Reliability and Biases." *Population Studies* 55:181–93.

Zimmer, Zachary, Linda G Martin, Mary Beth Ofstedal and Yi-Li Chuang. 2007. "Education of Adult Children and Mortality of Their Elderly Parents in Taiwan." *Demography* 44(2):289–305.

Zinsser, Hans. 1935. *Rats, Lice and History*. Boston: Little, Brown.

Zipf, George K. 1949. *Human Behavior and the Principle of Least Effort*. Reading, MA: Addison-Wesley.

Zuberi, Tukufu. 2001. *Thicker Than Blood: How Racial Statistics Lie*. Minneapolis: University of Minnesota Press.

GEOGRAPHIC INDEX

Note: page numbers followed by an "f" indicate figures; by a "t" indicate tables.

A

Afghanistan, 9, 158
  birth rates lower in urban than in rural areas, 300t
  death rates lower in urban than in rural areas, 298t
  ecological footprint of, 437t, 438
  "hot spot" where literacy rate among women is at least 10% lower than for men, 386t
  infant death rate decline since World War II, 154, 154f
  maternal mortality, 9
  migrants from, 265, 266t
  not yet an urban-majority nation, 293
  polio victims, 148
  refugees and internally displaced people, 279–280
Africa, 278. *See also* North Africa; South Africa; Sub-Saharan Africa
  changes in life expectancy since World War II, 147f
  daily caloric intake per person, 432t
  population increase in, 294t
  rapid growth following World War II, 24
  surveys in, 74–75
  urban population since 1950, 294t
  West Nile virus, 162
Alabama
  net internal migration, 263t
Alaska
  net internal migration, 264t
Algeria, 33
  impact of declining fertility on age structure, 343
  population of, 33t

Al-Qahirah (Cairo)
  population of, 307t
America. *See* Central America; North America; South America
Angola
  "hot spot" where literacy rate among women is at least 10% lower than for men, 386t
Arab Spring, 32
Argentina, 29
  meat consumption of, 428
Arizona
  net internal migration, 263t
Arkansas
  net internal migration, 263t
Armenia
  poverty rate, 398t
Asia, 278. *See also* Central Asia; East Asia; South Asia; South-Central Asia; Southeast Asia; Western Asia
  changes in life expectancy since World War II, 146, 147f
  daily caloric intake per person, 432t
  female genital mutilation, 200
  H5N1 avian influenza ("bird flu"), 162
  migration, 19
  population increase in, 294t
  population in the year 1500, 23
  rapid growth following World War II, 24
  reproductive rights, reproductive health, and the fertility transition, 201
  surveys in, 74–75
  urban population since 1950, 294t
Athens, ancient, population of, 291
Australia
  backlash against immigrants, 10

carbon dioxide emission by, 441t
  ecological footprint of, 437t
  fertility transition, 224, 225f
    secular ideas and, 197
  GNI measured in PPP, 419t
  immigrants in, 266t
  population size and growth, 39–40
Austria, 268
Aztec civilization, 27, 145

B

Babylon, population of, 291
Babylonia, early census in, 45
Bahrain, 33
  carbon dioxide emission by, 441t
  ecological footprint of, 438
  population of, 33t
Bangalore
  population of, 307t
Bangkok (Krung Thep)
  population of, 307t
Bangladesh, 23, 35–36
  birth rates lower in urban than in rural areas, 300t
  death rates lower in urban than in rural areas, 298t
  infant death rate decline since World War II, 154, 154f
  migrants from, 265, 266t
  not yet an urban-majority nation, 293
  population of, 21, 22t, 36
Beijing
  population of, 307t
Belize, 27
Benin
  "hot spot" where literacy rate among women is at least 10% lower than for men, 386t

Bogotá
    population of, 307t
Bolivia
    infant death rate decline since
        World War II, 154, 154f
Bombay (Mumbai)
    population of, 307t
Brazil, 28–29
    carbon dioxide emission by, 441t
    daily caloric intake per person, 432t
    GNI measured in PPP, 419t
    meat consumption of, 428
    number of immigrants to the
        United States, 248t
    population of, 21, 22t
    slavery in, 28–29
    Zika virus, 162
Breslau (Poland)
    life-table technique used in late
        seventeenth century, 98
Brexit, 242
Buenos Aires
    population of, 307t
Burkino Faso
    "hot spot" where literacy rate
        among women is at least 10%
        lower than for men, 386t
Burundi, 293
    "hot spot" where literacy rate
        among women is at least 10%
        lower than for men, 386t

C
Cairo (Al-Qahirah), 301–302
    population of, 307t
Calcutta (Kolkata)
    population of, 307t
California, 20, 345
    foreign-born population in, 247
    net internal migration, 264t
    San Diego County, life expectancy
        at birth in, 183–184, 184f
Canada, 19, 270–271, 273
    abortion in, 213
    carbon dioxide emission by, 441t
    census, 56t–58t, 62–64
        long form, 64
        short form, 64
    crude birth rates, 218
    Dominion of Canada, 26
    ecological footprint of, 437t
    fertility levels in, 192, 193f
    GNI measured in PPP, 419t
    Hutterites in, 192, 193f
    immigrants in, 266t
    immigration trends, 279
    improved life expectancy, 141t,
        145, 145f

    infant death rate decline since
        World War II, 154, 154f
    life expectancy always slightly
        higher than in the United
        States, 145, 145f
    market basket measure, 397
    maternal mortality ratio half the
        rate of the United States, 163
    number of immigrants to the
        United States, 248t, 249
    population size and growth, 24,
        26–27
    poverty threshold, 397
    secular ideas and the fertility tran-
        sition, 197
    sex and gender ratios, 336–337
    "Spanish influenza" deaths in,
        143–144
    Statistics Canada, 64, 73, 290
    surveys, 73
    urban place, 290
    urban revolution, 21
Caribbean
    abortion in, 213
    age transition in, 355f
    fertility transition, 224, 225f
    percentage of urban population
        living in slums, 316t
    population increase in, 294t
    poverty rate, 398t
    urban population since 1950, 294t
Central African Republic
    "hot spot" where literacy rate
        among women is at least
        10% lower than for men,
        386t
    infant death rate decline since
        World War II, 154, 154f
Central America
    last holdout of rapid population
        growth in Latin America, 24
    population size and growth,
        27–28
    Zika virus, 162
Central Asia
    poverty rate, 398t
Chad
    "hot spot" where literacy rate
        among women is at least 10%
        lower than for men, 386t
Chennai (Madras)
    population of, 307t
Chile, 29
    infant death rate decline since
        World War II, 154, 154f
China, 23, 278
    abortion in, 213, 215
    age pyramids, 347–348, 348t

    caloric intake per person, 432t
    carbon dioxide emission by,
        441t, 442
    censuses, 45, 47
        2010 census was the largest
        social investigation ever
        undertaken, 45
        children undercounted in
        census, 60, 61
    Confucius discussed the relation-
        ship between population and
        resources, 95
    demographic dividends: age tran-
        sitions at work, 347–349,
        348f, 348t
    ecological footprint of, 437t
    famine caused be selling grain to
        finance industrial growth, 16
    fertility transition, 195, 224, 225f,
        229–232, 231f
    globalization and, 9
    GNI measured in PPP, 419t
    hukou system, 304–305
    international investors, 87
    life expectancy, 148, 152
    marriage, restraints on, 112
    Marxian perspective, 112
    meat consumption of, 428–429
    migrants from, 265, 266t
        number of immigrants to the
        United States, 248t, 249
    mortality control and the environ-
        ment, 164–165
    population of, 11–12, 21, 22t, 23,
        38–39
    poverty rate, 398t
    sex and gender ratios, 336, 337f
    simulation models of past demo-
        graphic structure, 76
    smoking in, 166
    suicide decline among women
        in, 167
    Three Gorges Dam necessitated
        relocation of over a million
        people, 245
    urban transition, proximate deter-
        minants of, 303–304
    Wan xi shao (later, longer, fewer)
        campaign, 229
    water shortage in, 7
Chongqing
    population of, 307t
Ciudad de México (Mexico City)
    population of, 307t, 308
Colombian Exchange (of diseases),
    97, 142
Colorado
    net internal migration, 263t

Columbia
  birth rates lower in urban than in
    rural areas, 300t
  death rates lower in urban than in
    rural areas, 298t
  education level and fertility, 204, 204f
  number of immigrants to the
    United States, 248t
  refugees in, 280
Congo, Democratic Republic of, 22t,
    23, 35
  Ebola virus first identified in, 161
  "hot spot" where literacy rate
    among women is at least 10%
    lower than for men, 386t
  poverty rate, 398t
Congo, Republic of, 35
Connecticut
  net internal migration, 264t
Costa Rica, 27, 148
Cote d'Ivoire
  "hot spot" where literacy rate
    among women is at least 10%
    lower than for men, 386t
Cuba
  number of immigrants to the
    United States, 248t, 249

D
Delaware
  net internal migration, 263t
Delhi
  population of, 307t
Democratic Republic of Congo. *See*
    Congo, Democratic Republic of
Denmark
  early census, 46
  ecological footprint of, 437t
  fertility in, 205
    education level and, 205
Dhaka
  population of, 307t
District of Columbia
  foreign-born population in, 247
  net internal migration, 264t
Dominican Republic
  number of immigrants to the
    United States, 248t

E
East Asia
  age transition in, 355f
  crude birth rates, 218
  fertility transition, 224, 225f
  percentage of urban population
    living in slums, 316t
  population size, 37–39
    on verge of depopulation, 24
  poverty rate, 398t

Eastern Europe, 29
  abortion in, 215
  changes in life expectancy since
    World War II, 147f
  declining population in, 23
  fertility transition, 225f
East Germany, 30, 268
Ecuador
  number of immigrants to the
    United States, 248t
Egypt, 31, 33
  age-adjusted death rate (AADR), 171
  birth rates lower in urban than in
    rural areas, 300t
  death rates lower in urban than in
    rural areas, 298t
  douching in ancient times, 209
  early census in, 45
  infant death rate decline since
    World War II, 154, 154f
  King Tut died of malaria 33 centu-
    ries ago, 161
  migrants from, 265, 266t
    number of immigrants to the
      United States, 248t
  population of, 22t, 23, 33t
  poverty rate, 398t
El Salvador, 27–28, 276, 278
  number of immigrants to the
    United States, 248t
England, 46. *See also* United Kingdom
  census by William of Normandy
    (Domesday Book), 45
  city population between 1500 and
    1800, 291
  fertility transition in, 226–227,
    228f
  Malthus and neo-Malthusians,
    101–109
  Poor Laws, 105–106
  population doubled in eighteenth
    century, 98
Estonia
  carbon dioxide emission by, 441t
Ethiopia, 35
  number of immigrants to the
    United States, 248t
  population of, 22t
Europe. *See also* Eastern Europe;
    Northern Europe; Southern
    Europe; Western Europe
  abortion in, 213
  Age of Enlightenment, 13, 100
  antinatalist and pronatalist doc-
    trines during the Middle
    Ages, 95–96
  condom associated with decline in
    birth rate, 210
  crude birth rates, 218

daily caloric intake per person,
    432t
  death rate, declining, 18
  east-west migration in, 268
  European Union censuses, 47
  expansion through migration,
    19–20
  fertility transition, 201, 224, 225f,
    226–229, 228f
    secular ideas and, 197
  globalization and, 9
  Great Depression, 15, 24
  guest labor programs, 267
  immigrants
    backlash against, 10
    heading to cities, 297
    undocumented, 276–277
  life expectancy
    at end of 18th century, 141t,
      143
    improvements in, 141t
  Little Ice Age in, 143
  Mercantalism, 97–99
  migration, 19–20
  plague, last major sighting in
    Europe in 1720, in
    Marseilles, 143
  population of, 9, 13, 29–30, 294t
    on the verge of depopulating,
      24, 29
  population registers in, 46–47, 70
  poverty rate, 398t
  registration of vital events histori-
    cally done by the church, 70
  Renaissance, cultural reawakening
    in, 96–98
  reproductive rights, reproductive
    health, and the fertility tran-
    sition, 201
  segregation, residential, 322
  surveys, 74
  urban population since 1950,
    294t
  Western, changes in life expectancy
    since World War II, 147f
  World War II, 15–16, 147f
European Union
  censuses, 47
  meat consumption by, 428

F
Finland
  fertility in, 205
    education level and, 205
Florida
  foreign-born population in, 247
  net internal migration, 263t
Former Balkan states
  abortion in, 215

France, 29, 30, 128
   carbon dioxide emission by, 441t
   Condorcet saw prosperity and
      population growth as in-
      creasing hand in hand, 100
   ecological footprint of, 437t
   GNI measured in PPP, 419t
   immigrants in, 266t
   immigration to, 30
   physiocratic thought, 99
   population of, 22t

G
Gambia
   "hot spot" where literacy rate
      among women is at least 10%
      lower than for men, 386t
Gaza, 33
   population of, 33t
Georgia
   net internal migration, 263t
   poverty rate, 398t
Germany, 29–30
   anti-immigrant sentiment, 242
   carbon dioxide emission by, 441t
   censuses, 46–47
   declining population in, 23, 29
   ecological footprint of, 437t
   GNI measured in PPP, 419t
   immigrants in, 266t
   infant death rate decline since
      World War II, 154, 154f
   Marxian perspective, 107,
      110–112
   migrants from, 265, 266t
   population of, 22t, 23
   reunification of, 268
Ghana
   birth rates lower in urban than in
      rural areas, 300t
   death rates lower in urban than in
      rural areas, 298t
   infant death rate decline since
      World War II, 154, 154f
   poverty rate, 398t
Greece, 11
   Plato emphasized population
      stability over growth, 95
Guangshou (Guangdong)
   population of, 307t
Guatemala, 27–28, 276, 278
   birth rates lower in urban than in
      rural areas, 300t
   death rates lower in urban than in
      rural areas, 298t
   infant death rate decline since
      World War II, 154, 154f
   migrant caravans, 246

   number of immigrants to the
      United States, 248t
Guinea
   "hot spot" where literacy rate
      among women is at least 10%
      lower than for men, 386t
Guinea-Bissau
   "hot spot" where literacy rate
      among women is at least 10%
      lower than for men, 386t

H
Haiti
   birth rates lower in urban than in
      rural areas, 300t
   death rates lower in urban than in
      rural areas, 298t
   infant death rate decline since
      World War II, 154, 154f
   number of immigrants to the
      United States, 248t
   poverty rate, 398t
Hawaii
   foreign-born population in, 247
   net internal migration, 264t
Honduras, 27–28, 276, 278
   migrant caravans, 246
   number of immigrants to the
      United States, 248t
Hungary, 268
Hyderabad
   population of, 307t

I
Idaho
   net internal migration, 263t
Illinois
   net internal migration, 264t
India, 11, 23, 268, 278
   abortion in, 213
   birth rates lower in urban than in
      rural areas, 300t
   carbon dioxide emission by, 441t
   censuses, 47
   daily caloric intake per person, 432t
   death rates lower in urban than in
      rural areas, 298t
   demographic dividends: age transi-
      tions at work, 349–350
   ecological footprint of, 437t
   education level and fertility, 204, 204f
   GNI measured in PPP, 419t
   immigrants in, 266t
   infant death rate decline since
      World War II, 154, 154f
   international investors, 87
   Malthus on, 195
   migrants from, 265, 266t

   not yet an urban-majority nation, 293
   number of immigrants to the
      United States, 248t, 249
   population and history, 21, 22t,
      35–36
   poverty rate, 398t
   sex and gender ratios, 336
   suicide decline among women in, 167
Indiana
   net internal migration, 263t
Indian subcontinent, 23, 268
Indonesia, 35, 36–37
   carbon dioxide emission by, 441t
   daily caloric intake per person, 432t
   ecological footprint of, 437t
   GNI measured in PPP, 419t
   H5N1 avian influenza ("bird flu"), 162
   migrants from, 265, 266t
   population of, 21, 22t, 36–37
   poverty rate, 398t
   very young and old have highest
      death rates, 152f
Iowa
   net internal migration, 264t
Iran, 22t, 30, 33, 35
   carbon dioxide emission by, 441t
   GNI measured in PPP, 419t
   population of, 33t, 37
   refugees in, 280
Iraq, 33
   infant death rate decline since
      World War II, 154, 154f
   population of, 33t
Ireland, 30
   abortion in, 213
   immigration to, 30
   potato famine of late 1840s, 143
Israel, 32, 33
   creation of, 32, 268
   meat consumption of, 428
   population of, 33t
Istanbul
   population of, 307t
Italy, 29, 30
   carbon dioxide emission by, 441t
   catasto (census) in, 45
   fertility below replacement level, 30
   GNI measured in PPP, 419t
   immigrants in, 266t
   migrants from, 265, 266t
   population of, 22t, 23

J
Jakarta (Madras)
   population of, 307t
Jamaica
   number of immigrants to the
      United States, 248t

Japan, 166
  abortion in, 213
  carbon dioxide emission by, 441t
  declining population in, 23, 39
  ecological footprint of, 437t
  fertility transition, 195, 224, 225f
  globalization and, 9
  GNI measured in PPP, 419t
  improvements in life expectancy (highest in the world), 141t, 143
  infant death rate decline since World War II, 154, 154f
  population, 22t, 39
    pyramid, 338f
  urban transition, 21
    from 1800 to 2050, 292
  very young and old have highest death rates, 152f
Jordan, 32, 33
  immigrants in, 266t
  population of, 33t

K
Kansas
  net internal migration, 264t
Karachi
  population of, 307t
Kazakhstan
  carbon dioxide emission by, 441t
  immigrants in, 266t
  migrants from, 265, 266t
Kentucky
  net internal migration, 263t
Kenya, 22t, 35
Kerala (India)
  fertility below replacement level, 36
Kinki M.M.A. (Osaka)
  population of, 307t
Kinshasa
  population of, 307t
Kolkata (Calcutta)
  population of, 307t
Korea
  fertility transition, 224, 225f
  Republic of
    GNI measured in PPP, 419t
  South Korea. *See* South Korea
Krung Thep (Bangkok)
  population of, 307t
Kuwait, 33
  carbon dioxide emission by, 441t
  ecological footprint of, 438
  immigrants in, 266t
  population of, 33t

L
Lagos
  population of, 307t

Lahore
  population of, 307t
Lake Chad, 7
Latin America, 278, 283, 297
  abortion in, 213
  age transition in, 355f
  Chagas disease, 162
  fertility transition, 201, 224, 225f
  life expectancy changes since World War II, 146, 147f
  malaria, 159
  migration, 19
  percentage of urban population living in slums, 316t
  population increase in, 24, 294t
  poverty rate, 398t
  reproductive rights, reproductive health, and the fertility transition, 201
  surveys in, 74–75
  urban population since 1950, 294t
Lebanon, 33
  censuses, 48
  population of, 33t
  refugees in, 279–280
Liberia
  Ebola virus in, 161–162
Libya, 33
  population of, 33t
Lima
  population of, 307t
Liverpool, 182
London, 21, 70, 180, 291
  suburbanization, 319
London 171
Los Angeles-Long Beach-Santa Ana
  population of, 307t
Louisiana
  net internal migration, 264t
Luxembourg
  carbon dioxide emission by, 441t

M
Madras (Chennai)
  population of, 307t
Maine
  net internal migration, 263t
Mali
  birth rates lower in urban than in rural areas, 300t
  death rates lower in urban than in rural areas, 298t
  "hot spot" where literacy rate among women is at least 10% lower than for men, 386t
Manila
  population of, 307t

Maryland
  foreign-born population in, 247
  net internal migration, 264t
Massachusetts
  foreign-born population in, 247
  net internal migration, 264t
Mecca, 45
Medina, 45
MENA (Middle East and North Africa) region, 30–34
  population of, 33t
  water scarcity in, 34
Mexico
  abortion available only in Mexico City, 213
  age transition in, 350f
  carbon dioxide emission by, 441t
  census, 56t–58t, 62, 64–66
    1116 census, 65
    conteo, 65
  crude birth rates, 218
  crude death rate, 170
  demographic dividends: age transitions at work, 350f, 351
  ecological footprint of, 437t
  fertility levels in, 192, 193f
  GNI measured in PPP, 419t
  Green Revolution, 429
  infant death rate decline since World War II, 154, 154f
  life expectancy, improved, 141t, 145–146, 145f
  migrants from, 246, 265, 266t, 278
    number of immigrants to the United States, 248t, 249, 274–277
  population of, 21, 22t, 27–28
    pyramid, 338f, 339
  poverty rate, 398t
  sex and gender ratios, 336–337
  surveys in, 73–74
  Tzintzuntzan, 302–303
  "urban," definition of, 290
  urban transition, proximate determinants of, 302–303
Mexico City, 213, 310
Michigan
  net internal migration, 264t
Middle East
  abortion in, 215
  guest labor programs, 267
  MENA (Middle East and North Africa) region, 30–34
    population of, 33t
    water scarcity in, 34
  poverty rate, 398t
  West Nile virus, 162
  youth bulge, 347

Minnesota
   net internal migration, 263t
Mississippi
   net internal migration, 264t
Missouri
   net internal migration, 264t
Montana
   net internal migration, 263t
Morocco
   migrants crossing to Spain from, 276
   population of, 33t
Moscow
   population of, 307t
Mozambique
   "hot spot" where literacy rate
      among women is at least 10%
      lower than for men, 386t
Mumbai (Bombay)
   population of, 307t
Myanmar
   birth rates lower in urban than in
      rural areas, 300t
   death rates lower in urban than in
      rural areas, 298t

N
Nebraska
   net internal migration, 264t
Nepal
   "hot spot" where literacy rate
      among women is at least 10%
      lower than for men, 386t
Netherlands, 46–47
   carbon dioxide emission by, 441t
Nevada
   foreign-born population in, 247
   net internal migration, 263t
New Hampshire
   net internal migration, 263t
New Jersey
   foreign-born population in, 247
   net internal migration, 264t
New Mexico
   net internal migration, 264t
New York
   Ellis Island, 271
   foreign-born population in, 247
   net internal migration, 264t
New York City
   West Nile virus, 162
New York-Newark
   population of, 307t, 308
New Zealand
   ecological footprint of, 437t
   fertility transition, 224, 225f
   population size and growth,
      39–40
Nicaragua, 27

Niger
   crude birth rates, 218
      lower in urban than in rural
         areas, 300t
   death rates lower in urban than in
      rural areas, 298t
   fertility level in, 192, 193f
      education level and, 204, 204f
   "hot spot" where literacy rate
      among women is at least
      10% lower than for men,
      386t
   women's age at marriage, 200, 376
Nigeria, 35, 194
   birth rates lower in urban than in
      rural areas, 300t
   Boko Haram in, 35
   census-taking efforts, 47–48
   daily caloric intake per person, 432t
   death rates lower in urban than in
      rural areas, 298t
   ecological footprint of, 437t
   "hot spot" where literacy rate
      among women is at least 10%
      lower than for men, 386t
   population of, 21, 22t, 23, 338f
      predicted to be more populous
         than the United States by
         mid-century, 35
   significant numbers of polio
      victims, 148
   very young and old have highest
      death rates, 152f
   Yoruba people of, 194
North Africa
   guest labor programs, 267
   MENA (Middle East and North
      Africa) region, 30–34
   population of, 33t
   water scarcity in, 34
   poverty rate, 398t
North America
   abortion in, 213
   age transition in, 129, 355f
   daily caloric intake per person, 432t
   fertility transition, 224, 225f
   Great Depression, 15–16, 24
   increased population growth
      because of declining death
      rate, 18
   life expectancy changes since World
      War II, 146–147, 147f
   migration transition, 129
   population in, 9, 24–27, 244, 294t
      Canada, 26–27
      United States, 25–26
   urban population since 1950, 294t
   World War II, 16

North Carolina, 59
   net internal migration, 263t
North Dakota
   net internal migration, 264t
Northern Africa
   female genital mutilation, 200
   fertility transition, 224–225, 225f
   percentage of urban population
      living in slums, 316t
Northern Europe, 29
   age transition in, 354, 355f
   fertility transition in, 225f
"Northern Triangle" (Guatemala,
      Honduras, and El Salvador),
      28, 276
Norway, 30
   carbon dioxide emission by, 441t
   ecological footprint of, 437t
   infant death rate decline since
      World War II, 154, 154f
   women's age at marriage, 200

O
Oceania
   fertility transition, 224
   percentage of urban population
      living in slums, 316t
   population, 39–40, 294t
      Australia, 39–40
      New Zealand, 39–40
      Papua New Guinea, 39–40
      urban since 1950, 294t
Ohio
   net internal migration, 264t
Oklahoma
   net internal migration, 264t
Oman, 33
   carbon dioxide emission by, 441t
   population of, 33t
Oregon
   net internal migration, 263t

P
Pacific Region
   poverty rate, 398t
Pakistan, 23, 35, 36, 42, 268
   daily caloric intake per person, 432t
   "hot spot" where literacy rate
      among women is at least
      10% lower than for men,
      386t
   immigrants in, 266t
   infant death rate decline since
      World War II, 154, 154f
   migrants from, 265, 266t
   not yet an urban-majority nation, 293
   polio victims, significant numbers
      of, 148

Pakistan (*Continued*)
  population of, 21, 22t, 36
  poverty rate, 398t
  refugees in, 280
  rising age at marriage, 376
  sex ratio, 337f
Palestine, 32–33, 268
  early census in, 45
  migrants from, 265, 266t
  population of, 33t
Panama, 27
Paraguay
  infant death rate decline since
    World War II, 154, 154f
Paris
  population of, 307t
  suburbanization, 319
Pennsylvania
  net internal migration, 264t
Persian Gulf region, 269
Peru
  birth rates lower in urban than in
    rural areas, 300t
  death rates lower in urban than in
    rural areas, 298t
Philippines, 35, 37, 278
  birth rates lower in urban than in
    rural areas, 300t
  death rates lower in urban than in
    rural areas, 298t
  migrants from, 265, 266t
    to the United States, 248t
  not yet an urban-majority nation, 293
  population size and growth, 22t, 37
Plymouth Colony, 25
Poland
  crude death rate in 2018, 170
  migrants from, 265, 266t
  population of, 22t
Polynesia
  fertility transition, 224, 225f
Portugal
  fertility in, 205
    education level and, 205

Q
Qatar, 33
  carbon dioxide emission by, 441t
  ecological footprint of, 437t, 438
  population of, 33t
Quakers, American, 26
Quebec, 26–27

R
Rhode Island
  net internal migration, 264t
Rio de Janeiro
  population of, 307t

Roman Empire
  life expectancy, 142
  pronatalist doctrines of Julius and
    Augustus Caesar, 95
Romania
  migrants from, 265, 266t
Rome, ancient, 21
  census in, 45
  population of, 291
Russia
  carbon dioxide emission by, 441t
  declining population in, 23, 29
  ecological footprint of, 437t
  GNI measured in PPP, 419t
  Hutterites in, 192
  immigrants in, 266t
  impact of declining fertility on age
    structure, 343
  infant death rate decline since
    World War II, 154, 154f
  life expectancy, drop in, 30
  migrants from, 265, 266t
  pograms against Jews, 272
  population of, 21, 22t, 23
  suicide declines among men in, 167
  urban transition from 1800 to
    2050, 292

S
San Diego County
  life expectancy at birth in,
    183–184, 184f
São Paulo
  population of, 307t
Saudi Arabia, 33
  carbon dioxide emission by, 441t
  early census by Prophet
    Mohammed, 45
  GNI measured in PPP, 419t
  guest labor programs, 267
  immigrants in, 266t
  infant death rate decline since
    World War II, 154, 154f
  meat consumption by, 428
  population of, 33t
Scandinavia, 29
  increased life expectancy in, 143
Senegal
  "hot spot" where literacy rate
    among women is at least 10%
    lower than for men, 386t
Shanghai
  population of, 307t
Shenzhen
  population of, 307t
Sierra Leone
  "hot spot" where literacy rate
    among women is at least 10%
    lower than for men, 386t

Singapore
  carbon dioxide emission by, 441t
Somalia
  infant death rate decline since
    World War II, 154, 154f
South Africa
  carbon dioxide emission by, 441t
  immigrants in, 266t
  Kgatla people, mortality rate of, 194
South America
  daily caloric intake per person, 432t
  population size and growth,
    28–29
South Asia
  malaria, 159
  percentage of urban population
    living in slums, 316t
  population size and growth, 35
  poverty rate, 398t
  youth bulge, 347
South Carolina
  net internal migration, 263t
South-Central Asia
  age transition in, 355f
  fertility transition, 225f
South Dakota
  net internal migration, 264t
Southeast Asia
  percentage of urban population
    living in slums, 316t
  population size and growth, 35
Southern Europe, 29
  age transition in, 354, 355f
  declining population in, 23
  fertility transition, 225f
South Korea, 278
  carbon dioxide emission by, 441t
  crude birth rates, 218
  fertility in, 195
  meat consumption by, 428
  number of immigrants to the
    United States, 248t
South Sudan
  "hot spot" where literacy rate
    among women is at least 10%
    lower than for men, 386t
  refugees and internally displaced
    people, 279–280
"South" to "North" migration,
    20–21
Soviet Union
  allowing Jews to emigrate, 268
  Marxian perspective, 112
Spain, 30
  fertility below replacement level, 30
  GNI measured in PPP, 419t
  immigrants in, 266t
  plague, 143
  population of, 22t

Sri Lanka, 148
  not yet an urban-majority
    nation, 293
Stockholm, 297
Sub-Saharan Africa, 23, 158
  age transition in, 354, 355f
  all human life originated here, 32
  Ebola virus in, 162
  female genital mutilation, 200
  fertility transition, 224–225, 225f
  food production not keeping pace
    with population growth, 7
  "hot spots" where literacy rate
    among women is at least 10%
    lower than for men, 386t
  INDEPTH demographic surveil-
    lance system, 75
  life expectancy improvements, 141t
  malaria, 159, 161
  population
    limits on early population
      growth, 17
    percentage of urban population
      living in slums, 316–317, 316t
    size and growth, 31, 35
    in the year 1500, 23
    youth bulge, 347
  poverty rate, 398t
  transnationalism in, 283
Sweden, 30, 156
  early census, 46
  harvest failures of early 1860s, 143
Switzerland, 46
  ecological footprint of, 437t
  infant death rate decline since
    World War II, 154, 154f
Syria, 33, 34
  drought in, 446
  polio in, 148
  population of, 33t
  refugees and internally displaced
    persons, 34f, 242, 279–280
Syrian Arab Republic
  migrants from, 265, 266t

T
Taiwan
  fertility transition, 231, 231f
Tajikistan
  birth rates lower in urban than in
    rural areas, 300t
  death rates lower in urban than in
    rural areas, 298t
Tamil Nadu
  fertility below replacement level, 36
Tanzania, 22t, 35
Tennessee
  net internal migration, 263t

Texas
  foreign-born population in, 247
  net internal migration, 263t
Thailand, 22t
  carbon dioxide emission by, 441t
  GNI measured in PPP, 419t
  immigrants in, 266t
Tianjin
  population of, 307t
Togo
  "hot spot" where literacy rate
    among women is at least 10%
    lower than for men, 386t
Tokyo
  ecological footprint of, 436
  population of, 307t
  suburbanization, 319
Toronto
  population of, 308
Trinidad and Tobago
  carbon dioxide emission by, 441t
Tunisia, 33
  population of, 33t
Turkey, 22t, 31
  carbon dioxide emission by, 441t
  GNI measured in PPP, 419t
  immigrants in, 266t
  migrants from, 265, 266t
  refugees in, 279–280
Turkmenistan
  carbon dioxide emission by, 441t
Tzintzuntzeños, 302–303

U
Uganda
  refugees in, 280
  Zika virus first identified in, 162
Ukraine
  immigrants in, 266t
  migrants from, 265, 266t
United Arab Emirates, 33
  carbon dioxide emission by, 441t
  ecological footprint of, 438
  guest labor programs, 267
  immigrants in, 266t
  population of, 33t
United Kingdom, 29, 30
  carbon dioxide emission by, 441t
  ecological footprint of, 437t
  fertility transition, 226–229, 228f
  GNI measured in PPP, 419t
  immigrants to, 30, 266t
    anti-immigrant sentiment, 242
  infant death rate decline since
    World War II, 154, 154f
  life expectancy, 145
  London, 21, 70, 180, 291
  migrants from, 265, 266t

  to the United States, 248t
  population of, 22t, 23
  urban transition, 21
    from 1800 to 2050, 292
United States
  abortion in, 213
    not available to all people, 197
  African Americans
    gaps in income over time, 395f
    higher gun-related homicide
      rate, 167
    mortality rates, 181
    segregation, 320–322
    urban transition, 320–322
  age-adjusted death rate (AADR),
    171, 179
  age/sex-specific death rate
    (ASDR), 170
  age structure of legal immigrants, 344f
  age transition in, 350f, 354–357
  American Indians, 181
  birth certificate used in, 67f–68f
  carbon dioxide emission by,
    441t, 442
  census. *See* United States Census
  children in
    25% of children have at least one
      chronic health condition, 149
  cohort measures of fertility, 221
  condom associated with decline in
    birth rate, 210
  contraceptive use among
    women, 212t
  crude birth rates, 218
  daily caloric intake per person, 432t
  death, actual causes of, 168–169
    alcohol misuse, 168
    diet and activity patterns, 168
    microbial agents that could have
      been largely prevented by vac-
      cination and sanitation, 168
    motor vehicles, 169
    tobacco, 168
    toxic agents, 168
  death certificate used in, 69f
  demographic dividends: age transi-
    tions at work, 350–351, 350f
  demographic surveys, 72–73
  diversity of households, increasing,
    371–372, 371f
  ecological footprint of,
    437–438, 437t
  educational attainment over time,
    384t
  fertility transition in, 192, 193f,
    217t, 232–237, 235f
    education level and, 204, 204f
    secular ideas and, 197

United States (*Continued*)
 GNI measured in PPP, 419t
 guest labor programs, 267, 278
 healthy life expectancy (HALE), 178
 Hispanics, 181
 Hutterites in, 192, 193f
 immigration trends, 266t,
  269–278
  anti-immigrant sentiment, 10, 242
  current trends, 278
  genders of immigrants, 254, 254f
  historical background of migration and immigration laws,
   270–278, 270f
  illegal immigration in global
   context, 274–277
  percent of population that is
   foreign-born, 241f, 270f
  undocumented immigration,
   276–277
  young adults are most likely to
   be migrants, 253, 254f
 infant death rate decline since
  World War II, 154, 154f
 intercourse, limiting exposure to, 209
 life expectancy
  at end of 18th century, 141t, 143
  improved, 141t, 145, 145f
 life tables, 171, 172t–173t, 174,
  177–178
  females, 172t–173t, 177–178
  males, 175t–176t, 177–178
 maternal mortality ratio twice the
  rate of Canada, 163
 meat consumption by, 428–429
 median income by age, educational
  attainment, and marital
  status, 394f
 median net worth, 400f
 menarche, average age of, 191
 migration within, 262–265,
  263t–264t
 obesity in, 149
 occupational distributions differ
  for males and females,
  391–392, 391t
 Plymouth Colony, 25
 population, 21, 22t, 24–26
  pyramid, 338f
 poverty threshold, 397
 Quakers, 26
 race and ethnicity, 180–181,
  400–408, 405t

 racial/ethnic differences in
  number of children under
  18 living in mother-only
  families, 372, 373f
 segregation, residential, 320–322
 widening gap in family income
  between whites and blacks,
  395f, 396
 reproductive rights, reproductive
  health, and the fertility transition, 201
 sex and gender ratios, 336–337
 "Spanish influenza" deaths in,
  143–144
 suburbanization, 318–319
 suicide one of top 10 causes of
  death in males, 166
 "urban," definition of, 290
 urban transition, 21
  from 1800 to 2050, 292
 wealth distribution in, 401–404
United States Census, 48–63, 50f,
  53f, 56t–58t
 apportionment of seats in House
  of Representatives based
  upon, 52–55
 citizenship question, 51–52
 comparison of items included with
  ACS, Census of Canada, and
  Census of Mexico, 56t–58t
 content error, 62
 continuous measurement: American Community Survey, 63
 coverage error, 59–62, 60t
  African Americans and other ra-
   cial/ethnic minority groups,
   59, 60t
 differential undercount, 59, 60t
 first census (in 1790), 25
 geographically referenced data, 79t
 long form, 51
 net census undercount, 59, 60t
 people included, 58–59
 race and ethnicity questions, 49–51
 sampling error, 62–63
 short form, 51
Uruguay, 29
 infant death rate decline since
  World War II, 154, 154f
 meat consumption of, 428
Utah, 59
 net internal migration, 263t

V
Vancouver
 ecological footprint of, 436
Venezuela
 refugees from, 280
Vermont
 net internal migration, 264t
Vietnam, 35, 37, 278
 fertility in, 195
 H5N1 avian influenza ("bird flu"), 162
 meat consumption by, 428
 number of immigrants to the
  United States, 248t
 population, 22t, 37
Virginia
 net internal migration, 264t

W
Washington
 net internal migration, 263t
West Bank
 population of, 33, 33t
Western Asia
 fertility transition, 225f
 percentage of urban population
  living in slums, 316t
 rapid population growth in, 24
Western Europe, 29
 fertility transition, 225f
 improved life expectancy since
  World War II, 147
West Germany, 30, 268
West Virginia
 net internal migration, 264t
Wisconsin
 net internal migration, 264t
Wyoming
 net internal migration, 264t

Y
Yemen, 33
 population of, 33t
 poverty rate, 398t
Yoruba of Nigeria, 194

Z
Zaire
 Ebola virus first identified in, 161

SUBJECT INDEX

Note: page numbers followed by an "f" indicate figures; by a "t" indicate tables.

A

AADR (age-adjusted death rate), 170–171
Abortion, 213
  induced, 213
Abstinence, 209
Accidental or unintentional death, 166
Acculturation, 282
Achieved characteristics, 370
ACS (American Community Survey), 51, 62–63, 72
Adaptation, 282
Administrative data, 44, 71–72
Administrative records, 71
African Americans
  mortality rates, 181
  segregation, 320–322
  urban transition, 320–322
Age-adjusted death rate (AADR), 170–171
Age and sex structure, 330
Age cohorts and cohort flow, 333–335, 333f
Age differentials in mortality, 152–153, 153f
Agency for International Development, U.S. (USAID), 429
Age/sex-specific death rate (ASDR), 170
Age-specific fertility rate (ASFR), 218
Age stratification, 331–333, 332t
Age structure, reading the future from, 358–364
  backward or inverse projection, 363
  population momentum, 363–364
  population projections, 358–363
Age transition and the life course, 129–130, 329–366
  concepts of age and sex, 330–337

age cohorts and cohort flow, 333–335, 333f
age stratification, 331–333, 332t
feminization of old age, 336–337, 337f
gender and sex ratios, 335–336
demographic dividends: age transitions at work, 345–351
  China, 347–349, 348f, 348t
  India, 349–350
  measuring the age structure, 345–346
  Mexico, 350f, 351
  progression from a young to an old age structure, 346
  United States, 350–351, 350f
  youth bulge: dead end or dividend?, 346–347
demographic drivers of age transition, 338–345, 338f, 340f
  declining fertility, 342–344, 343f
  declining mortality, 340–342
  migration, 344–345, 344f
life course and population aging, 351–358, 352f
  centenarians, 358
  third age (young-old) and fourth age (old-old), 353–358
  what is old?, 352–353
overview, 329–330, 329f, 364–366
reading the future from the age structure, 358–364
  backward or inverse projection, 363
  population momentum, 363–364
  population projections, 358–363

Agricultural Revolution, 11, 425, 426–427
AIDS, 146–147, 160t, 161
Air pollution and climate change, 440–442
Alcohol misuse as the third real cause of death, 168
Al-Qaeda, 9
Alzheimer's disease, 166
Amenorrhea, 190
American Community Survey (ACS), 51, 62, 72
American Housing Survey, 73
American Indians, mortality rates among, 181
Anovulatory, 190
Anti-immigrant sentiment, 242
Antinatalist Christian doctrines, 95
Applied demography and demographic data, 43–90
  administrative data, 71–72
  applied demography, 81–87
    business planning/marketing, 83–87, 84f
    political planning, 81–82
    social planning, 82–83
  Canadian census, 56t–58t, 63–64
  careers in demographics, 87–88
  censuses, population, 44–66
  combining the census and vital statistics, 71
  historical sources, 75–76
  IPUMS: warehouse of global census data, 66
  Mexican census, 56t–58t, 64–66
  overview, 43–44, 43f, 88–90
  registration of vital events, 66–71, 67f–69f
  sample surveys, 72–75
    Canadian surveys, 73

Applied demography (*Continued*)
demographic and health
surveys, 74–75
demographic surveillance
systems, 75
European surveys, 74
Mexican surveys, 73–74
U.S. demographic surveys,
72–73
spatial demography, 76–81, 79t
GIS and the census, 80–81
mapping demographic data,
78–80
United States Census. *See* Census,
United States
Apportionment of seats in the U.S.
House of Representatives, 52
Aquaculture, 428
Aristotle, 93t
Arriaga, Eduardo, 146
Ascribed characteristics, 370
ASDR (age/sex-specific death rate), 170
ASFR (age-specific fertility rate), 218
Assimilate, 282
Asylees, 246
Aztec civilization, 27

B
Baby boom, 26–27, 84–86
Baby bust, 26–27, 84
Backward projection, 363
Banks, J.A., 227
Becker, Gary, 199
Belize, 27
Besant, Annie, 107
Billion people progression, 13–14, 14t
Bills of Mortality, 97–98
Biofuels, 7
Biological component of fertility,
189–191
Birth certificate used in United States,
67f–68f
Black Death, 12, 142
Blake, Judith, 236
Block groups, 79, 79t
Blossfeld, Hans-Peter, 378
BNANA (Build Nothing Anywhere
Near Anyone), 322–323
Boko Haram, 9, 35
Bongaarts, John, 207
Boomsters, 415
Borlaug, Norman, 431
Bradlaugh, Charles, 107
Breastfeeding, involuntary infecundity
from, 213–214
Brentano, Ludwig, 123
Brexit, 242
British North America Act of 1867, 26

Brokaw, Tom, 85
Brundtland, Gro Harlem, 448–449
Built environment, 312
Business planning/marketing,
83–87, 84f

C
Cabot, John, 25
Caesar, Julius and Augustus, 95
Caldwell, John, 148
Calendar rhythm method, 210
Calhoun, John, 314–315
Calment, Jeanne Louise, 151
Caloric intake over time, 432f
Cantillon, Richard, 123
Capitalism, 110
Cardiovascular diseases, 163
Careers in demographics, 87–88
Carlson, Elwood, 85, 334
Carrying capacity, 11, 424
Cartogram of countries of the world
by population size, 3f
CBR (crude birth rate), 216
CBSA (Core-Based Statistical Area), 305
CCFR (cumulative cohort fertility
rate), 221
CDR (crude death rate), 169–170
CEB (children ever born), 221
Census, United States, 48–63, 50f,
53f, 56t–58t
apportionment of seats in House
of Representatives based
upon, 52–55
citizenship question, 51–52
combining with vital statistics, 71
comparison of items included with
ACS, Census of Canada, and
Census of Mexico, 56t–58t
content error, 62
continuous measurement:
American Community
Survey, 63
coverage error, 59–62, 60t
first census (in 1790), 25
geographically referenced data, 79t
long form, 51
people included, 58–59
race and ethnicity questions, 49–51
sampling error, 62–63
short form, 51
Census block, 63, 79, 79t
Censuses, population, 44–66
Census metropolitan area
(CMA), 305
Census of population, 44
Census tracts, 79, 79t
Centenarians, 358
Chain migration, 258

Chamie, Joseph, 409
Charles, Enid, 116
Checks to growth, 102
Childlessness, 381–382
Children as security and labor, 195
Children ever born (CEB), 221
Child–woman ratio (CWR), 218
Chinese Exclusion Act, 271
Chlorination of water, 144
Churchill, Winston, 46
Church registers, 75
Cicero, 93t, 95
Cicourel, Aaron, 123–124
Cipolla, Carlo, 142
City systems, 308–312
cities as sustainable environments,
310–312
edge cities, 319
mega-cities, 306, 307t
Clark, Colin, 420
Climate change
air pollution and, 440–442
altering worldwide food
production, 445
CMA (census metropolitan area), 305
CNMigR (crude net migration
rate), 250
Coale, Ansley, 119, 196, 226
Co-ethics, 282
Cohabitation, 379
Cohort, 333–335, 333f
definition of, 124
measures of, 216
fertility, 221–222
size effects, in demographic transi-
tion theory, 124–125
Cohort component method, 61,
361–363
Cohort flow, 333
Columbian Exchange (of diseases),
97, 142
Combination of determinants, 383
"Commons" problem, 109
Communicable diseases, 159, 161
Components of change method of
estimating migration, 251
Components of growth method, 361
Compression of mortality, 141,
156, 156f
Conceptual model of migration decision
making, 255–257, 256f
Condorcet, Marquis de, 100, 104–105
Confucius, 93t, 95
Consequences of population growth
Malthusian perspective, 103–104,
103f
Content error, 59
United States census, 62

Continuous measurement: American Community Survey, 51, 62–63, 72
Contraceptive Prevalence Surveys, 74
Contraceptives, 209–212, 212t, 215f
emergency, 211
Copper-TE Intrauterine device (IUD), 211, 211t
Core-Based Statistical Area (CBSA), 305
Core-periphery model, 309
Coupland, Douglas, 84
Coverage error, in United States Census, 59–62, 60t
CPS (Current Population Survey), 72
Crenshaw, Edward, 347
Crowding, 313
Crude birth rate (CBR), 216
Crude death rate (CDR), 169–170
Crude net migration rate (CNMigR), 250
Crude rate of in-migration (IMigR), 250
Crude rate of out-migration (OMigR), 250
Cumulative causation, 261
Cumulative cohort fertility rate (CCFR), 221
Current Population Survey (CPS), 72
Cutler, David, 144
CWR (child–woman ratio), 218

D
DA (demographic analysis), 61
DALY (disability-adjusted life year), 178–179
Danziger, Pamela, 83
Darwin, Charles, 102, 106
Data, demographic. See Demographic perspectives and theories
Davis, Kingsley, 20, 122–124, 128
Death, accidental or unintentional, 166
Death and disease over the life cycle, 152–158
age differentials in mortality, 152–153, 153f
infant mortality, 153–155, 154f
mortality at older ages, 155–157, 156f
sex and gender differentials in mortality, 157–158
Death certificate used in United States, 69f
Declining fertility, 342–344, 343f
Declining mortality, 340–342
De facto population, 58
De jure population, 58
Delayed marriage accompanied by leaving parental nest, 376–379, 377t

"Demodystopias," 8
Demographic analysis (DA), 61
Demographic and Health Surveys (DHS), 74–75
Demographic data and applied demography, 43–90
administrative data, 71–72
applied demography, 81–87
business planning/marketing, 83–87, 84f
political planning, 81–82
social planning, 82–83
Canadian census, 56t–58t, 63–64
careers in demographics, 87–88
censuses, population, 44–66
combining the census and vital statistics, 71
data always referenced to a specific geographic area, 78
historical sources, 75–76
IPUMS: warehouse of global census data, 66
Mexican census, 56t–58t, 64–66
overview, 43–44, 43f, 88–90
registration of vital events, 66–71, 67f–69f
sample surveys, 72–75
Canadian surveys, 73
demographic and health surveys, 74–75
demographic surveillance systems, 75
European surveys, 74
Mexican surveys, 73–74
U.S. demographic surveys, 72–73
spatial demography, 76–81, 79t
GIS and the census, 80–81
mapping demographic data, 78–80
United States census. See Census, United States
Demographic dividends, 10
age transitions at work, 345–351
China, 347–349, 348f, 348t
India, 349–350
measuring the age structure, 345–346
Mexico, 350f, 351
progression from a young to an old age structure, 346
United States, 350–351, 350f
youth bulge: dead end or dividend?, 346–347
definition of, 129
key to economic development?, 423–424
Demographic metabolism, 83

Demographic overhead, 422–423
definition of, 422
Demographic perspectives and theories, 91–135
definition of demographic perspective, 92
demographic transition is really a set of transitions, 126–133, 127f
age transition, 129–130
family and household transition, 131–132
fertility transition, 127–129
health and mortality transition, 126–127
impact on local and global society, 132–133
migration transition, 130
urban transition, 130–131
demographic transition theory, 112–125
cohort size effects, 124–125
critique of, 119
description of, 115–119, 117f
Dumont, Arsène, 114–115
Durkheim, Émile, 115
Mill, John Stuart, 113–114
prelude to, 112–114
reformulation of, 119–122
theory of demographic change and response, 122–124
Malthusian perspective, 100–107
avoiding the consequences, 104–105
causes of population growth, 102–103
consequences of population growth, 103–104, 103f
critique of Malthus, 105–106
neo-Malthusians, 107–109
prelude to Malthus, 100–101
Marxian perspective, 107, 110–112
causes of population growth, 110
consequences of population growth, 110–111
critique of Marx, 111–112
over time, 93t–94t
overview, 91–93, 91f, 93t–94t, 133–135
premodern population doctrines, 95–99
second demographic transition, 117f, 125–126
Demographics, definition of, 81
Demographic surveillance systems, 75
Demographic transition, definition of, 116

Demographic transition theory, definition of, 115
Demography, applied, 43–90
  administrative data, 71–72
  applied demography, 81–87
    business planning/marketing, 83–87, 84f
    political planning, 81–82
    social planning, 82–83
  Canadian census, 56t–58t, 63–64
  careers in demographics, 87–88
  censuses, population, 44–66
  combining the census and vital statistics, 71
  historical sources, 75–76
  IPUMS: warehouse of global census data, 66
  Mexican census, 56t–58t, 64–66
  overview, 43–44, 43f, 88–90
  registration of vital events, 66–71, 67f–69f
  sample surveys, 72–75
    Canadian surveys, 73
    demographic and health surveys, 74–75
    demographic surveillance systems, 75
    European surveys, 74
    Mexican surveys, 73–74
    U.S. demographic surveys, 72–73
  spatial demography, 76–81, 79t
    GIS and Canada, 80–81
    mapping demographic data, 78–80
  United States census. See Census, United States
Demography, definition of, 5
Demography, introduction to, 3–42
  geographic distribution of world's population, 21–23, 22t
  global variation in population size and growth. See Population size and growth
  overview, 3–6, 3f, 40–42
  relationship of population to resources, 6–8
    energy, 7
    environmental degradation, 8
    food, 7
    housing and infrastructure, 7–8
    water, 7
  relationship of population to social and political dynamics, 8–10
    globalization, 9–10
    global migration, 10
    regional conflict, 8–9

  relationship of population to women's rights, 10–11
  world population growth, 11–21
    doubling, rate of, 16–17
    history of, 11–14, 12f, 14t
    how fast is the world's population growing now?, 14–16, 15f
    migration and, 19–21
    number of people who have ever lived, 18–19
    slow early growth, 17–18
    why are more recent increases so rapid?, 18
Demograpic transition, 94t
de Montellano, Bernard Ortiz, 145
Denmark
  early census, 46
  fertility in, 205
Density, definition of, 313
de Salignac de la Mothe-Fénelon, François, 46
Determinants, combination of, 383
DHS (Demographic and Health Surveys), 74–75
Diet as the second real cause of death, 168
Differential undercount, 59, 60t
  U.S. Census, 59, 60t
DIME (Dual Independent Map Encoding) files, 80
Disability-adjusted life year (DALY), 178–179
Disease and death over the life cycle, 152–158
  age differentials in mortality, 152–153, 153f
  infant mortality, 153–155, 154f
  mortality at older ages, 155–157, 156f
  sex and gender differentials in mortality, 157–158
Diseases
  communicable, 159, 161
  emerging infectious diseases, 161–162
Diversity
  growing in family structure and household composition, 371–374, 371f, 373f
Dividends, demographic. See Demographic dividends
Divorce, 382–383
Doctrine, 93
Domesday Book, 45
Domingo, Andreu, 8
Donald Trump
  anti-immigrant sentiment and the election of, 242, 246

  media show declaring immigrant "crisis," 246
Doubling, rate of, 16–17
Douching, 209–210
Drought, 444
Drucker, Peter, 83
DSE (dual-system estimation), 61
Dual Independent Map Encoding (DIME) files, 80
Dual labor market theory, 259–260
Dual-system estimation (DSE), 61
Dumont, Arsène, 94t, 114–115
Durkheim, Émile, 94t, 115
Dust Bowl, 435
Dwarf types (of grain), 429
Dystopia, 8

E
Earth's resources, use and abuse of, 416–419
  economic growth and development, 417
  measuring gross national income (GNI) and purchasing power parity, 417–419, 419f
Easterlin, Richard, 124–125, 198, 236–237
Easterlin relative cohort size hypothesis, 94t, 124
Ebola, 161–162
Ecological footprints, 436–439
  by country, 437, 439
"Ecological hoofprint," 446
Economic growth and development
  use and abuse of earth's resources, 416–417
Edge cities, 319
Education, 384–388, 384t, 386t–387t
  "hot spots" where literacy rate among women is at least 10% lower than for men, 386t
  U.S. educational attainment over time, 384t
Educational and socioeconomic differentials in mortality, 179–180
Ehrlich, Anne, 108–109
Ehrlich, Paul, 8, 108–108, 415
Electoral College votes for 2012, 2016, and 2020 elections, 43f
Emergency contraception, 211
Emerging infectious diseases, 161–162
Emigrants, 246
Empowerment of women. See Women, empowerment of
Enclave, 282

Endogenous factors, 198
Energy and population, 7
Engels, Friedrich, 107
English Poor Laws, 105–106
Enlightenment, Age of, 100
ENOE (Encuesta Nacional de
    Ocupación y Empleo;
    National Survey of Occupa-
    tion and Employment), 73–74
*Enquiry Concerning Political Justice
    and Its Influences on Morals
    and Happiness,* 100
Environment, population, and global
    sustainability, 414–455
    See also Population size and growth
    can billions more be fed, given
        our environmental issues?,
        424–431
        history of economic
            development and food,
            425–427
        moving to a more plant-based
            diet, 428–429
        our history of getting more food
            from the land, 429–431
        we are at the limit of land to
            be used for growing food,
            427–428
    demand for food is growing faster
        than the population, 423t,
        431–433
    ecological footprints, 436–439
    environmental constraints to
        growing more food,
        433–442, 441t, 442f
        air pollution and climate
            change, 440–442
        polluting the ground, 435,
            438–440
        water supply issues, 433–435
    human dimensions of environmen-
        tal change, 443–447
        assessing damage attributable to
            population growth, 443–444
        environmental disasters lead to
            death and dispersion, 444–447
        sustainable development:
            possibility or oxymoron?,
            447–450, 449t
    overview, 414–416, 414f,
        453–455
    policies aimed at slowing popula-
        tion growth, 451–452
    relation of population to economic
        development, 419–424
        are demographic dividends the
            key to economic develop-
            ment?, 423–424

does demographic overhead
    explain the relationship?,
    422–423
is population growth a stimulus
    to economic development?,
    420–422
use and abuse of earth's resources,
    416–419
    economic growth and develop-
        ment, 417
    measuring gross national
        income (GNI) and purchas-
        ing power parity, 417–419,
        419f
Environmental degradation and
    population, 8
Environmental disasters lead to death
    and dispersion, 444–447
Environmental Systems Research In-
    stitute (ESRI), 81
Essay on Population, 195, 232
*Essay on the Principle of Population
    as it affects the future im-
    provement of society; with
    remarks on the speculations
    of Mr. Godwin, M. Con-
    dorcet, and other writers,* 101
ESS (European Social Survey), 74
Ethnicity, 401
Ethnocentric, 119
European Enlightenment, 13
European expansion through
    migration, 19–20
European Fertility Project, 119–120,
    122, 126
European surveys, 74
European Union
    Brexit, 242
    censuses, 47
Exclusion, 282
Exogenous factors, 198
Expectation of life at birth, 171
Extended family, 369
Extensification of agriculture, 426
Extrapolation, 359–360
Exurbs, 322

F
Family, definition of, 369
Family and household transition,
    131–132
Family demography, definition of, 368
Family demography and life chances,
    367–413
    changing life chances, 383–410
        education, 384–388, 384t,
            386t–387t
        income, 392–396, 394f–395f

labor force participation,
    388–390
occupation, 390–392, 391t
poverty, 396–398, 398t
race and ethnicity, 401–408,
    405t
religion, 408–410
wealth, 398–400, 400f
defining, 368–375
    gender equity and empower-
        ment of women, 374–375
    growing diversity in family
        structure and household
        composition, 371–374,
        371f, 373f
overview, 367–368, 367f,
    410–413
proximal determinants of fam-
    ily and household changes,
    375–383
    childlessness, 381–382
    cohabitation, 379
    combination of determinants, 383
    delayed marriage accompanied
        by leaving parental nest,
        376–379, 377t
    divorce, 382–383
    nonmarital childbearing,
        379–381
    widowhood, 383
Family and Fertility Survey, 74
Family household, definition of, 369
Famine, 444
Farley, Reynolds, 320
Fawcett, James, 256
Fecundity, 189
Female genital mutilation (FGM), 200
Female life expectancy at birth, global
    variability in, 139f, 141t
Female singulate median age at mar-
    riage, 367f
*Feminism and Family Planning in
    Victorian England,* 227
Feminization of old age,
    336–337, 337f
Fertility
    definition of, 189
    preconditions for a decline in, 196
    proximate determinant of urban
        transition, 299–301, 300f
    regional differences in the fertility
        transition, 224–225, 225f
    three phases of (intercourse,
        conception, and gestation),
        207–208, 208t
    United States, 217t
Fertility awareness, 210
Fertility differential, 203

Fertility transition, 127–129, 187–240
  accomplishing, 223–224
  case studies, 225–237
  definition of, 188–189
  education of women important part of, 204–205, 204f
  geographic variability in, 224–225, 225f
  how can fertility be controlled?, 207–215
    contraceptives, 209–212, 212t, 215f
    induced abortion, 213
    involuntary infecundity from breastfeeding, 213–214
    proportion married: limiting exposure to intercourse, 209
    proximate determinants of fertility, 207–209, 208t
    relative importance of proximate determinants, 214–215, 215f
  how high could fertility levels be?, 189–193
    biological component, 189–191
    social component, 191–192, 193f
  ideational changes that must take place, 197–198
  measuring changes in, 215–223
    cohort measures of fertility, 221–222
    fertility intentions, 222–223
    period measures of fertility, 216–221, 217t
  motivations for lower fertility levels, 198–207
    innovation-diffusion and "cultural" perspective, 205–207
    reproductive rights, 200–202
    supply-demand framework, 198–199, 203–205, 204f
  overview, 187–188, 187f, 238–240
  preconditions for a decline in fertility, 196–197
  why was fertility high for most of human history?, 193–195
    children as security and labor, 195
    need to replenish society, 194
FGM (female genital mutilation), 200
Film optical sensing device for input to computers (FOSDIC), 80
Filtration of water, 144
Flexitarian diet, 446
Florentine catasto of 1427, 45

Fogel, Robert, 144
Food, 7
  can billions more be fed, given our environmental issues?, 424–431
    history of economic development and food, 425–427
    moving to a more plant-based diet, 428–429
    our history of getting more food from the land, 429–431
    we are at the limit of land to be used for growing food, 427–428
  demand for food is growing faster than the population, 423t, 431–433
  ecological footprints, 436–439
  environmental constraints to growing more food, 433–442, 441t, 442f
    air pollution and climate change, 440–442
    polluting the ground, 435, 438–440
    water supply issues, 433–435
Food security, 430
Forced migration, 279–281
  definition of forced migrant, 279
  refugees and internally displaced persons, 279–280
  slavery, 105280–281
Force of mortality, 169
Forward survival method of immigration estimation, 252
FOSDIC (film optical sensing device for input to computers), 80
Fourth Age, 357
Fruits of Philosophy: The Private Companion of Young Married People, 107, 209
Future, reading from the age structure, 358–364

G
Garreau, Joel, 319
Garrett, Eilidh, 227
GDP (gross domestic product), 417
GDT (Geographic Data Technology), 81
Gender and sex ratios, 335–336
  Canada, 336
  China, 336
  India, 336
  Mexico, 336
  United States, 336
Gender equity and empowerment of women, 374–375. *See also* Women, empowerment of

General fertility rate (GFR), 218
General Social Survey (GSS), 73
Generational replacement, 221
Generations and Gender Program, 74
Generation X, 26, 84
Generation Z, 85
Genesis, Book of, 93t, 95
Genetically modified seeds, 431
Genital mutilation, female (FGM), 200
Gentrification, 324
Geodemographics, 87
Geographic Data Technology (GDT), 81
Geographic distribution of world's population, 21–23, 22t
Geographic Information Science (GIScience), 77–78, 80–81, 88
Geo-referencing, 78–79
Germ theory, 144
Gerrymandering, 54
GFR (general fertility rate), 218
Global Burden of Disease project, 178
Globalization, 9–10
Global patterns of migration, 10, 265–269
  current situation, 265–267, 266t
  how did we get to this point?, 268–269
Global sustainability, population, and the environment, 414–455. *See also* Population size and growth
  can billions more be fed, given our environmental issues?, 424–431
    history of economic development and food, 425–427
    moving to a more plant-based diet, 428–429
    our history of getting more food from the land, 429–431
    we are at the limit of land to be used for growing food, 427–428
  cartogram of countries of the world by population size, 3f
  demand for food is growing faster than the population, 423t, 431–433
  ecological footprints, 436–439
  environmental constraints to growing more food, 433–442, 441t, 442f
    air pollution and climate change, 440–442
    polluting the ground, 435, 438–440
    water supply issues, 433–435

human dimensions of environmental change, 443–447
assessing damage attributable to population growth, 443–444
environmental disasters lead to death and dispersion, 444–447
sustainable development: possibility or oxymoron?, 447–450, 449t
overview, 414–416, 414f, 453–455
policies aimed at slowing population growth, 451–452
relation of population to economic development, 419–424
are demographic dividends the key to economic development?, 423–424
does demographic overhead explain the relationship?, 422–423
is population growth a stimulus to economic development?, 420–422
use and abuse of earth's resources, 416–419
economic growth and development, 417
measuring gross national income (GNI) and purchasing power parity, 417–419, 419f
Global variation in population size and growth. *See* Population size and growth
Global warming, 440
GNI (gross national income), 417
GNP (gross national product), 417
Gompertz, Benjamin, 152
Goodkind, Daniel, 60
Goodwin, William, 100, 105
Graunt, John, 97–98
"Greatest Generation," 85, 334
Great Recession, 85, 237
Greenhouse gases, 440
carbon monoxide emissions by country, 441f–442f
Green Revolution, 429–430
Griswold v. Connecticut, 234
Gross domestic product (GDP), 417
Gross migration rate (TMigR), 250
Gross national income (GNI), 417
Gross national income in purchasing power parity (GNI PPP), 418, 419f
Gross national product (GNP), 417
Gross rate of in-migration (IMigR), 250

Gross rate of out-migration (OMigR), 250
Gross reproduction rate (GRR), 220
Ground, polluting the, 435, 438–440
GSS (General Social Survey), 73
Guillard, Achille, 5, 106

H
Haines, Michael, 144
HALE (healthy life expectancy), 178
Halley, Edmund, 98
Hardin, Garrett, 107
Harrison, Harry, 8
Haub, Carl, 19
Hawley, Amos, 314
Health and mortality transition, 126–127, 139–186
causes of poor health and death, 159–169
communicable diseases, 159, 161
emerging infections diseases, 161–162
environment and morality control, 164–165
injuries, 166–167
maternal mortality, 162–163
noncommunicable diseases, 163–166
overview, 159, 160t
"real" causes of death, 167–169
top 20 causes of death in the world, 160t
changes over time, 141–149, 141t
Industrial Revolution to twentieth century, 143–146, 145f
the nutrition transition, 149
postponing death by preventing and curing disease, 147–148
Roman Empire to Industrial Revolution, 142–143
World War II as a modern turning point, 146–147, 147f
definition of, 140–141
disease and death over the life cycle, 152–158
age differentials in mortality, 152–153, 153f
infant mortality, 153–155, 154f
mortality at older ages, 155–157, 156f
sex and gender differentials in mortality, 157–158
health and mortality inequalities, 179–184
educational and socioeconomic differentials in mortality, 179–180

inequalities by race and ethnicity, 180–181
marital status and mortality, 182
neighborhood differences in mortality, 183–184, 184f
urban and rural differentials, 182–183
life span and longevity, 150–152
life span, 150–151
longevity, 151–152
measuring mortality, 169–179
age-adjusted death rates, 170–171
age/sex-specific death rates, 170
crude death rate (CDR), 169–170
disability-adjusted life years, 178–179
life table calculations, 174, 175t–176t, 177–178
life tables, 171, 172t–173t, 174
overview, 139–140, 139f, 184–186
Healthspan, 178
Healthy life expectancy (HALE), 178
Henry, Louis, 75
Heston, Charles, 8
High growth potential, 116
High-yield varieties (HYV), 429
Hispanics
mortality rates, 181
use of term "Hispanic," 20
Historical data, 44
HIV/AIDS, 146–147, 160t, 161
H1N1 virus, 143–144, 162
Hodgson, Dennis, 105
Hollerith, Herman, 80
Homeostasis, 119
Homicide, 167
for reasons beyond pure survival, unique to human beings, 166
Homo sapiens, 11
Household, definition of
Householder, 369
Housing and infrastructure, population and, 7–8
Housing unit, 369
Howe, Neil, 84
Hukou, 304–305
Human capital, 261, 370
Human dimensions of environmental change, 443–447
assessing damage attributable to population growth, 443–444
environmental disasters lead to death and dispersion, 444–447
sustainable development: possibility or oxymoron?, 447–450, 449t

Human resources, 419
Hume, David, 98, 102
Hutterites, fertility of, 192, 193f, 194
HYV (high-yield varieties), 429

I

IBM (International Business
        Machines) Corporation, 80
Ibn Khaldun, 93t, 96
ICD (International Classification of
        Diseases), 167
IDPs (internally displaced
        persons), 245
iGen, 85
Illegal immigration in global context,
        274–277
Illegal (or undocumented) immi-
        grants, 246
IMigR (crude, or gross, rate of in-
        migration), 250
Immigrants, definition of, 246
immigration laws and migration,
        270–278, 270f
Immigration trends in the United
        States, 269–278
    current trends, 278
    historical background of migration
        and immigration laws,
        270–278, 270f
    illegal immigration in global
        context, 274–277
Impact (IPAT) equation, 443
Implementing strategy, 256
Incipient decline, 116
Income, 392–396, 394f–395f
    distribution of highest per capita
        income, 414f
INDEPTH Network, 75
Induced abortion, 213
Industrial Revolution, 13, 421,
        426–427
    to twentieth century, health and
        mortality transition,
        143–146, 145f
Infant mortality rates (IMR),
        153–155, 154f
    since World War II, by country, 154f
Infectious diseases, emerging, 161–162
Injuries, 166–167
In-migrants, 246
Institutional theory, 261
Integrated Public Use Microdata
        Samples (IPUMS), 63, 66
Integration, 282
Intercensal year, 71
Intercourse, limiting exposure to, 209
Intergovernmental Panel on Climate
        Change (IPCC), 445

Intermediate variables, 207
Internally displaced persons (IDPs), 245
Internal migrants, 244, 245
Internal rural-to-urban migration,
        296–297
Internal urbanward migration, 301
International Business Machines
        (IBM) Corporation, 80
International Classification of Dis-
        eases (ICD), 167
International migration. *See*
        Migration transition
Intervening obstacles, 255–256
Intrauterine device (IUD), 211, 211t
Introduction to demography, 3–42
    geographic distribution of world's
        population, 21–23, 22t
    global variation in population size
        and growth. *See* Population
        size and growth
    overview, 3–6, 3f, 40–42
    relationship of population to
        resources, 6–8
        energy, 7
        environmental degradation, 8
        food, 7
        housing and infrastructure, 7–8
        water, 7
    relationship of population to social
        and political dynamics,
        8–10
        globalization, 9–10
        global migration, 10
        regional conflict, 8–9
    relationship of population to
        women's rights, 10–11
    world population growth, 11–21
        doubling, rate of, 16–17
        history of, 11–14, 12f, 14t
        how fast is the world's
            population growing now?,
            14–16, 15f
        migration and, 19–21
        number of people who have
            ever lived, 18–19
        slow early growth, 17–18
        why are more recent increases
            so rapid?, 18
Inverse projection, 363
IPAT (impact) equation, 443
IPCC (Intergovernmental Panel on
        Climate Change), 445
IPUMS (Integrated Public Use
        Microdata Samples), 63, 66
Islamic State, 9
Israel, 33
IUD (intrauterine device), 211, 211t
Ivanov, Serguey, 188

J
Japan
    fertility in, 195
    population size and growth, 39
Jefferson, Thomas, 105
Johnson, Robert Wood, 85
Johnson & Johnson, 85–86
Jong, Gordon De, 256
Jordan, 33

K
Kahneman, Daniel, 121
Kalleberg, Arne, 392
Keyfitz, Nathan, 18, 422
Kgatla people of South Africa, 194
King Tut, 161
Knaus, Herman, 211
Knowlton, Charles, 107, 209

L
Labor force participation, 388–390
Labour Force Survey (LFS), 73
Language as a divisive issue, 407–408
LARC (long-acting, reversible
        contraceptives), 210, 211t,
        212, 377
Laslett, Peter, 75
Leasure, J. William, 119–120
Lee, Mike, 422
Legal immigrants, 246
Lexis, Wilhelm, 334
Lexis diagram, 333–334, 333f
LFS (Labour Force Survey), 73
Libya, 33
Life and Longevity Markets
        Association, 86
Life course and the age transition,
        329–366
    concepts of age and sex, 330–337
        age cohorts and cohort flow,
            333–335, 333f
        age stratification, 331–333, 332t
        feminization of old age,
            336–337, 337f
        gender and sex ratios, 335–336
    demographic dividends: age transi-
        tions at work, 345–351
        China, 347–349, 348f, 348t
        India, 349–350
        measuring the age structure,
            345–346
        Mexico, 350f, 351
        progression from a young to an
            old age structure, 346
        United States, 350–351, 350f
        youth bulge: dead end or
            dividend?, 346–347

demographic drivers of age transition, 338–345, 338f, 340f
declining fertility, 342–344,
343f
declining mortality, 340–342
migration, 344–345, 344f
life course and population aging,
351–358, 352f
centenarians, 358
third age (young-old) and
fourth age (old-old),
353–358
what is old?, 352–353
overview, 329–330, 329f, 364–366
reading the future from the age
structure, 358–364
backward or inverse
projection, 363
population momentum,
363–364
population projections, 358–363
Life expectancy, 151, 171
Life expectancy in North America
since World War II, 147, 147f
Life span, 150–151
Life tables, 171, 172t–173t, 174,
175t–176t, 177–178
Lister, Joseph, 144
Little Ice Age in Europe, 13, 143
Lloyd, Cynthia, 188
Locke, John, 104
London Bills of Mortality, 70
Long-acting, reversible contraceptives
(LARC), 210, 211t, 212, 377
Longevity, 151–152
definition of, 150
Long-term immigrant, 246
Louix XIV, King, 63
"Lucky Few," 85, 334–335

M
Machine age, 226
"Make Room/Make Room," 8
Malaria, 159, 161
Male condom, 210, 211t, 212
Malthus, Thomas Robert, 94t, 99,
101, 195, 232, 415, 424–426
Malthusian perspective, 100–107
avoiding the consequences,
104–105
causes of population growth,
102–103
consequences of population
growth, 103–104, 103f
critique of Malthus, 105–106
neo-Malthusians, 107–109
prelude to Malthus, 100–101
Mapping demographic data, 78–80

Marital status and mortality, 182
Market basket measure, 397
Marx, Karl, 107, 118
Marxian perspective, 94t, 107,
110–112
causes of population growth, 110
consequences of population
growth, 110–111
critique of Marx, 111–112
Massey, Douglas, 121
Maternal mortality, 162–163
Maternal mortality ratio (MMR), 163
Maximum level of reproduction, 190
Mayan civilization, 27
McKeown, Thomas, 144
Mean length of generation, 221
Means of subsistence, 102
Measles, 159
Median net worth in the United
States 400f
Mega-cities, 306, 307t
Menarche, 189
Menopause, 189
Mercantilism, 93t, 97, 99
Metabolism, demographic, 83
U.S. population 1950-2050, 91f
Methane, 445
Metropolis, defining, 304–308, 307t
Metropolitan areas, 305
Metropolitan statistical area
(MSA), 305
Mexican census, 56t–58t, 64–66
1116 census, 65
conteo, 65
Mexican surveys, 73–74
Mexico Green Revolution, 429
Micropolitan areas, 305
MICS (Multiple Indicators Cluster
Surveys), 75
Migration effectiveness, 250–251
Migration evolution, 243
Migration flow, 246
Migration ratio, 251
Migration selectivity, 253
Migration stock, 246
Migration transition, 19–21, 130,
241–286
America's immigration trends,
269–278
current trends, 278
historical background of migra-
tion and immigration laws,
270–278, 270f
illegal immigration in global
context, 274–277
Canada's immigration trends, 279
defining migration, 243–249
internal migrants, 245

international migrants, 245–246
stocks versus flows,
246–249, 248t
definition of, 243
demographic driver of age transition, 344–345, 344f
European expansion, 19–20
explaining international migration,
258–259
cumulative causation, 261
dual labor market theory,
259–260
institutional theory, 261
neoclassical economics
approach, 259
network theory, 260
new household economics of
migration, 259
which theories are best?, 261
world systems theory, 260
forced migration, 279–281
refugees and internally
displaced persons, 279–280
slavery, 280–281
global patterns of migration,
265–269
current situation, 265–267, 266t
how did we get to this point?,
268–269
impact of migration on society,
281–284
measuring migration, 250–252
migration within the United States,
262–265, 263t–264t
overview, 241–243, 241f,
284–286
reasons for migration, 253–261
conceptual model of migration decision making,
255–257, 256f
migration selectivity, 253
push-pull theory, 255
selectivity by age, 253–254, 254f
selectivity by gender,
254–255
"South" to "North" migration,
20–21
urban revolution, 21
and world population growth,
19–21
Migration turnover rate, 250
Mill, John Stuart, 94t, 113–114
Millenials, 84
Miller, Grant, 144
Minnesota Population Center at the
University of Minnesota, 66
MMRM (maternal mortality
ratio), 163

Mobility, 244
Modernization theory, 117–118, 122
Mohammed
conducted a census, 45
Momentum of population growth, 363
Moral restraint, 102
Morbidity, definition of, 140
Morgan, S. Philip, 222
Mortality
definition of, 140
force of, 169
and urban transition, 297–299, 298f
Mortality and health transition,
126–127, 139–186
causes of poor health and death,
159–169
communicable diseases,
159, 161
emerging infections diseases,
161–162
injuries, 166–167
maternal mortality, 162–163
noncommunicable diseases,
163–166
overview, 159, 160t
"real" causes of death, 167–169
changes over time, 141–149, 141t
Industrial Revolution to twentieth
century, 143–146, 145f
the nutrition transition, 149
postponing death by
preventing and curing
disease, 147–148
Roman Empire to Industrial
Revolution, 142–143
World War II as a modern
turning point, 146–147, 147f
definition of, 140–141
disease and death over the life
cycle, 152–158
age differentials in mortality,
152–153, 153f
infant mortality, 153–155, 154f
mortality at older ages,
155–157, 156f
sex and gender differentials in
mortality, 157–158
health and mortality inequalities,
179–184
educational and socioeconomic
differentials in mortality,
179–180
inequalities by race and
ethnicity, 180–181
marital status and
mortality, 182
neighborhood differences in
mortality, 183–184, 184f

urban and rural differentials,
182–183
life span and longevity, 150–152
life span, 150–151
longevity, 151–152
measuring mortality, 169–179
age-adjusted death rates,
170–171
age/sex-specific death rates, 170
crude death rate (CDR),
169–170
disability-adjusted life years,
178–179
life table calculations, 174,
175t–176t, 177–178
life tables, 171, 172t–173t, 174
overview, 139–140, 139f,
184–186
Motor vehicle accidents, 169
Mover, definition of, 244
MSA (metropolitan statistical area), 305
Multiculturalism, 283
Multiple Indicators Cluster Surveys
(MICS), 75
Murdock, Steven, 88

N
National Health Interview Survey
(NHIS), 73
National Historical Geographic
Information System, 66
National Survey of Family Growth
(NSFG), 73, 189
National Survey of Occupation and
Employment (Encuesta
Nacional de Ocupación y
Empleo) (ENOE), 73–74
Natural fertility, 191
Natural increase, 25
and urban transition, 297
Natural resources, 419
Neighborhood differences in
mortality, 183–184, 184f
Neoclassical economics approach, 259
Neolithic Agrarian Revolution, 11
Neolithic Demographic Transi-
tion, 17
Neo-Malthusians, 94t, 107–109
Nepal
"hot spot" where literacy rate
among women is at least 10%
lower than for men, 386t
Net census undercount, 59, 60t
U.S. Census, 59, 60t
Net migration, 250
Net reproduction rate (NRR), 220
Network theory, 260

New household economics of
migration, 259
New Zealand
population size and growth, 39–40
NGOs (non-governmental
organizations), 451
NHIS (National Health Interview
Survey), 73
Nicaragua, 27
Nielsen Claritas, 78
NIMBY (Not in My Back Yard), 322
Noncommunicable diseases, 163–166
Nonfamily household, 369
Non-governmental organizations
(NGOs), 451
Nonmarital childbearing, 379–381
Non-Response Follow-Up (NRFU), 60
Nonsampling error, 59
"Northern Triangle" (Guatemala,
Honduras, and El Salvador), 27
Notestein, Frank, 116
NRFU (Non-Response Follow-Up), 60
NRR (net reproduction rate), 220
NSFG (National Survey of Family
Growth), 73
Nuclear family, 369
Nunn, Nathan, 13
Nutrition transition, 149

O
Obesity, 149
Occupation, 390–392, 391t
Ogino, Kyusako, 211
Old age, feminization of,
336–337, 337f
Older ages
mortality, 155–157, 156f
Old Testament of the Bible
census account, 48
OMigR (crude, or gross, rate of
out-migration), 250
Omran, Abdel, 140
On the Origin of Species, 106
Opioid crisis, 147
Opportunity costs, 199
Oral contraceptives, 210, 211t, 212
Oral rehydration therapy (ORT), 155
Orshansky, Mollie, 397
Ortho Pharmaceuticals, 86
Out-migrants, 245
Overhead, demographic, 422–423
Overshoot, 450

P
PAA (Population Association of
America), 87
Palestinians, 32
Parity progression ratio, 223

Pascal, Blaise, 242
Pasteur, Louis, 144
Penicillin, developed during World
    War II, 146
Per capita income, 416
Period data, 216
Periodic abstinence, 210
Period measures
    fertility, 216–221, 217t
Peri-urban region, 322
Petty, William, 98
Pew Research Center public opinion
    polls, 73
Physiocratic thought, 99
Physiocrats, 93t
Plague, 12–13, 97, 142–143
    last major sighting in Europe in
        1720, in Marseilles, 143
Planned obsolescence, 150
Plant-based diet, 149, 428–429
Plato, 93t, 95
Pliny (the younger), 95
Pluralism, 283
Plymouth Colony, 25
Political planning, 81–82
Polluting the ground, 435, 438–440
Population, the environment, and
        global sustainability,
        414–455. *See also* Population
        size and growth
    can billions more be fed, given
        our environmental issues?,
        424–431
        history of economic develop-
            ment and food, 425–427
        moving to a more plant-based
            diet, 428–429
        our history of getting more
            food from the land, 429–431
        we are at the limit of land to
            be used for growing food,
            427–428
    cartogram of countries of the
        world by population size, 3f
    demand for food is growing faster
        than the population, 423t,
        431–433
    ecological footprints, 436–439
    environmental constraints to grow-
        ing more food, 433–442,
        441t, 442f
        air pollution and climate
            change, 440–442
        polluting the ground, 435,
            438–440
        water supply issues, 433–435
    human dimensions of environmen-
        tal change, 443–447

assessing damage attributable to
    population growth, 443–444
environmental disasters lead
    to death and dispersion,
    444–447
sustainable development:
    possibility or oxymoron?,
    447–450, 449f
overview, 414–416, 414f, 453–455
policies aimed at slowing popula-
    tion growth, 451–452
relation of population to economic
    development, 419–424
    are demographic dividends the
        key to economic develop-
        ment?, 423–424
    does demographic overhead
        explain the relationship?,
        422–423
    is population growth a stimulus
        to economic development?,
        420–422
use and abuse of earth's resources,
    416–419
    economic growth and develop-
        ment, 417
    measuring gross national in-
        come (GNI) and purchasing
        power parity, 417–419, 419f
"Population and Development
    Review," 8
Population Association of America
    (PAA), 87
"Population Bomb," 8
Population explosion, 13
Population Explosion, The, 108–109
Population forecast, definition
    of, 359
Population (or age) pyramids, 338f,
    339, 340f, 344f
Population Reference Bureau, 19
Population registers, 44, 70
Population size and growth, 11–21,
    23–40. *See also* Population,
    the environment, and global
    sustainability
assessing damage attributable to,
    443–444
Bangladesh, 36
Central America, 27–28
doubling, rate of, 16–17
East Asia, 37–39
    China, 38–39
    Japan, 39
Europe, 29–30
history of, 11–14, 12f, 14t
how fast is the world's population
    growing now?, 14–16, 15f

India, 35–36
Indonesia, 36–37
Iran, 37
Malthusian perspective, 102–103
Marxian perspective, 110–111
Mexico, 27–28
migration and, 19–21
North Africa and Western Asia
    (Middle East and North
    Africa, MENA), 30–34
North America, 24–27, 249t
    Canada, 26–27
    United States, 25–26
number of people who have ever
    lived, 18–19
Oceania, 39–40
    Australia, 39–40
    New Zealand, 39–40
    Papua New Guinea, 39–40
overview, 21, 22t, 23–24, 24f
Pakistan, 36
Papua New Guinea, 39–40
Philippines, 37
policies aimed at slowing,
    451–452
projecting the future from the age
    structure, 363–364
relation of population to economic
    development, 419–424
    are demographic dividends the
        key to economic develop-
        ment?, 423–424
    does demographic overhead
        explain the relationship?,
        422–423
slow early growth, 17–18
South America, 28–29
South and Southeast Asia, 35
stimulus to economic develop-
    ment?, 420–422
sub-Saharan Africa, 31, 35
Vietnam, 37
why are more recent increases so
    rapid?, 18
Positive checks, 102
Postcoital contraception, 211
Postpartum infecundity, 207
Post-transitional era of
    equilibrium, 125
Potatoes, 13, 421
Potential Rating Index for Zip
    Markets (PRIZM), 77–78
Poverty, 105, 396–398, 398t
Poverty index, 397
PPP (purchasing power parity), 418
Precarious jobs, 392
Premodern population doctrines,
    95–99

Preston, Samuel, 144
Preventive checks, 102
Princeton European Fertility Project, 76
Principle of population, 101
PRIZM (Potential Rating Index for
    Zip Markets), 77–78
Procter & Gamble, 86
Pronatalist, 410
Prosperity and Parenthood, 227
Proximal determinants of family and
    household changes, 375–383
  childlessness, 381–382
  cohabitation, 379
  combination of determinants, 383
  delayed marriage accompanied
    by leaving parental nest,
    376–379, 377t
  divorce, 382–383
  nonmarital childbearing, 379–381
  widowhood, 383
Proximate determinants of fertility,
    207–209, 208t
Proximate determinants of urban
    transition, 296–304
  fertility, 299–301, 300f
  illustration from China, 303–304
  illustration from Mexico, 302–303
  internal rural-to-urban migration,
    296–297
  internal urbanward migration, 301
  mortality, 297–299, 298f
  natural increase, 297
  reclassification, 301–302
Prudential restraint, 107
Purchasing power parity (PPP), 418
Push-pull theory, 255

Q
Qinn, Nancy, 13
Quakers, American, 26
Quesnay, François, 99
Quinoa, 430–431

R
Race and ethnicity, 401–408, 405t
  inequalities and, 180–181
Racial stratification, 405
Rational choice theory (RAT), 121
Ravenstein, Ernst Georg, 255
Ready, willing, and able (RWA)
    model, 196
"Real" causes of death, 167–169
Record, R.G., 144
Rectangularization of mortality, 141,
    156, 156f
Redistricting, 52
Refugees and internally displaced
    persons, 246, 279–280

Regional conflict, 8–9
Registration of vital events, 66–71,
    67f–69f
Reher, David, 148
Reissman, Leonard, 288
Relative income hypothesis, 124
Religion, 408–410
Religiosity, 309
Religious pluralism, 408
Renaissance, 96
Reproductive rights. *See also* Women,
    empowerment of
  motivation for lower fertility lev-
    els, 200–202
Residential mobility, 249
Residential segregation, 320–322
Residual method
  for estimating immigration, 252
  for estimating migration, 251
Resources and population, 6–8. *See also*
    Global sustainability, popula-
    tion, and the environment
  energy, 7
  environmental degradation, 8
  food, 7
  housing and infrastructure,
    7–8
  water, 7
Riley, Nancy, 229
Rindfuss, Ronald, 336
Robbin, Jonathan, 77–78
Robinson, Edward G., 8
Roe v. Wade, 234
Roman Empire to Industrial Revolution
    health and mortality transition,
    142–143
Rose, Alessandra de, 378
Ruggles, Steven, 372
Rural-to-urban migration, 296–297
Russell, Bertrand, 188
RWA (ready, willing, and able)
    model, 196
Ryder, Norman, 83, 237

S
Sample surveys, 44
Sampling error, 59
  United States census, 62–63
Sanger, Margaret, 233–234
Scammon, Richard, 6
Schapera, Isaac, 194
Schofield, Roger, 148
Second demographic transition, 117f,
    125–126, 191
Secularization, 120
Seeds, genetically modified, 431
Segregation, residential, 320–322
Selectivity by age, 253–254, 254f

Selectivity by gender, 254–255
Semmelweis, Ignaz, 144
Senescence, 150
Sex and gender differentials in
    mortality, 157–158
Sex and gender ratios, 335–336
  Canada, 336
  China, 336
  India, 336
  Mexico, 336
  United States, 336
Sexual dimorphism, 158
Simon, Julian, 415, 421–422
SIPP (Survey on Income and Program
    Participation), 73
*Sketch for an Historical Picture of
    the Progress of the Human
    Mind,* 100
Slavery, 105, 280–281
Slums, 316–317, 316f
Smallpox, 148
Smith, Adam, 99
Smith, David, 218
SMSA (standard metropolitan
    statistical area), 305
Snipp, Matthew, 25
Social and political dynamics and
    population, 8–10
  globalization, 9–10
  global migration, 10
  regional conflict, 8–9
Social capillarity, 114
Social capital, 261, 370
Social component of fertility,
    191–192, 193f
Socialism, 110
Socialization process, 332
Social planning, 82–83
Social role, 332
Social status, 332
Sojourner, 244
"South" to "North" migration,
    20–21
"Soylent Green," 8
Spanish influenza, 143–144
Spatial autocorrelation, 77
Spatial demography, 76–81, 79t
  GIScience and census, 80–81
  mapping demographic data,
    78–80
Spengler, Joseph, 114
St. Augustine, 93t, 95–96
St. Thomas Aquinas, 93t
Stable population models, 340
Standard metropolitan statistical area
    (SMSA), 305
Stationary population, 340
Statistics, origin of term, 46

Statistics Canada, 64, 73, 290
Step migration, 258
Sterilization, 211, 212t
Stocks versus flows, 246–249, 248t
Stolnitz, George, 117
Strauss, William, 84
Structural mobility, 396
Suburbanization, 318–320
Suburbanize, definition of, 318
Suicide, 166–167
    unique to human beings, 166
Supply-demand framework, 198–199,
        203–205, 204f
Survey on Income and Program
        Participation (SIPP), 73
Surveys, 72–75
    Canadian surveys, 73
    demographic and health surveys,
        74–75
    demographic surveillance
        systems, 75
    European surveys, 74
    Mexican surveys, 73–74
    U.S. demographic surveys,
        72–73
Süssmilch, Johann Peter, 97–98
Sustainable development. *See* Global
        sustainability, population,
        and the environment
Synthetic cohort, 216
Szreter, Simon, 227

T
Tabulating Machine Company, 1911
Taliban, 9
Taylor, Paul, 5
TFR (total fertility rate),
        219–220, 227
Theories and perspectives,
        demographic, 91–135
    definition of demographic
        perspective, 92
    demographic transition is
        really a set of transitions,
        126–133, 127f
    age transition, 129–130
    family and household transi-
        tion, 131–132
    fertility transition, 127–129
    health and mortality transition,
        126–127
    impact on local and global
        society, 132–133
    migration transition, 130
    urban transition, 130–131
    demographic transition theory,
        112–125

cohort size effects, 124–125
critique of, 119
description of, 115–119, 117f
Dumont, Arsène, 114–115
Durkheim, Émile, 115
Mill, John Stuart, 113–114
prelude to, 112–114
reformulation of, 119–122
theory of demographic change
        and response, 122–124
Malthusian perspective, 100–107
    avoiding the consequences,
        104–105
    causes of population growth,
        102–103
    consequences of population
        growth, 103–104, 103f
    critique of Malthus, 105–106
    neo-Malthusians, 107–109
    prelude to Malthus, 100–101
Marxian perspective, 107, 110–112
    causes of population growth, 110
    consequences of population
        growth, 110–111
    critique of Marx, 111–112
over time, 93t–94t
overview, 91–93, 91f, 93t–94t,
        133–135
premodern population doctrines,
        95–99
second demographic transition,
        117f, 125–126
Theory, 93
Thinking, Fast and Slow, 121
Third Age, 357
Third age (young-old) and fourth age
        (old-old), 353–358
Thompson, Warren, 115–116
TIGER (Topologically Integrated
        Geographic Encoding and
        Referencing) files, 80–81
TMigR (gross migration rate), 250
Tobacco as the first real cause of
        death, 168
Tobler, Waldo
    First Law of Geography, 76–77
Tombstones, 75
Total fertility rate (TFR), 219–220, 227
Total migration rate (TMigR), 250
Toys R Us, 85
"Traditional" family, 372–374
Transitional growth, 116
Transition theory
    demographic transition is really a set
        of transitions, 126–133, 127f
    age transition. *See* "Age" entries
    family and household
        transition, 131–132

fertility transition. *See* Fertility
        transition
    health and mortality transition.
        See Health and Mortality
        transition
    impact on local and global
        society, 132–133
    migration transition. *See*
        Migration transition
    urban transition. *See* Urban
        transition
demographic transition theory,
        112–125
    cohort size effects, 124–125
    critique of, 119
    description of, 115–119, 117f
    Dumont, Arsène, 114–115
    Durkheim, Émile, 115
    Mill, John Stuart, 113–114
    prelude to, 112–114
    reformulation of, 119–122
    theory of demographic change
        and response, 122–124
premodern population doctrines,
        95–99
second demographic transition,
        117f, 125–126
Transnational migrant, 283
Trump, Donald
    anti-immigrant sentiment contrib-
        uting to election of, 242
    media show declaring immigrant
        "crisis," 246
    restrictions on spending money
        internationally on women's
        reproductive rights, 452
Tubal ligation, 211
Turner, Frederick Jackson, 46
Tylenol, 86
Tzintzuntzeños, 302–303

U
Ultimate Resource, The, 415
Unintentional or accidental death, 166
United Nations
    censuses, 47
    goals for sustainable development,
        449t
    Human Settlements Programme,
        316
    Statistics Division, 45
United Nations Children's Fund
        (UNICEF), 75
UNIVAC-I computer, 80
Urban agglomeration, 305
Urban and rural differentials in
        health and mortality,
        182–183

Urban crowding, 313–316
Urban hierarchy, 304–312
Urbanism concept, 314
Urban places, defining, 289–290
Urban revolution
   migration and, 21
Urban sprawl, 322–323
Urban transition, 130–131, 287–326
   definition of, 243
   historical pattern of, 291–296,
      292f–293f, 294t
   overview, 287–289, 287f, 324–326
   proximate determinants of,
      296–304
      fertility, 299–301, 300f
      illustration from China,
         303–304
      illustration from Mexico,
         302–303
      internal rural-to-urban
         migration, 296–297
      internal urbanward
         migration, 301
      mortality, 297–299, 298f
      natural increase, 297
      reclassification, 301–302
   urban evolution that accompanies,
      312–324
      gentrification, 324
      residential segregation, 320–322
      slums, 316–317, 316f
      suburbanization, 318–320
      urban crowding, 313–316
      urban sprawl, 322–323
   urban hierarchy, 304–312
      city systems, 308–312
      defining the metropolis,
         304–308, 307t
   urban places, defining, 289–290
USAID (United States Agency for
   International Development),
   429, 452

Usual residence, 58

V
Vaccinations, 144, 148
Vasectomy, 212
"Virtual census," 46
"Visible minority," 407
Vital events, registration of, 66–71,
   67f–69f
Vital statistics, 44

W
Wallace, Robert, 98, 102
Wallerstein, 122
Wan xi shao (later, longer, fewer)
   campaign, 229
Water
   chlorination of, 144
   filtration, 144
   introduction of clean water
      technology, 144
   population and, 7
   supply issues, 433–435
Wattenberg, Ben, 6
Wealth, 398–400, 400f
Wealth flow, 121
Wear and tear, 150
Wells, R.V., 76
West Nile virus, 162
Westoff, Charles, 222, 336
Widowhood, 383
William of Normandy, 45
Wirth, Louis, 314
Withdrawal, 210, 211t
Women, empowerment of, 374–375
   education
      "hot spots" where literacy rate
         among women is at least 10%
         lower than for men, 386t

      female life expectancy at birth,
         global variability in,
         139f, 141t
      female singulate median age at
         marriage, 367f
   fertility transition
      education of women important
         part of, 204–205, 204f
   relationship of population to
      women's rights, 10–11
   reproductive rights
      motivation for lower fertility
         levels, 200–202
      restrictions placed by Donald
         Trump on spending money
         internationally on women's
         reproductive rights, 452
World Fertility Survey, 74
World population. *See* Population
   size and growth
World systems theory, 260, 309
World War II
   health and mortality transition,
      146–147, 147f

X
Xenophobia, 269

Y
Yoruba of Nigeria, 194
Youth bulge: dead end or dividend?,
   346–347

Z
Zero population growth (ZPG), 340